Dear John

Congratulations on twenty years of
progress and growth of the Hoover Institution

Best regards

Myron S Scholes

07/01/2009

LES PRIX NOBEL

THE NOBEL PRIZES

1997

NOBELPRISET

The Nobel Prize

LES PRIX NOBEL

THE NOBEL PRIZES

1997

NOBEL PRIZES, PRESENTATIONS, BIOGRAPHIES, AND LECTURES

Physics

Steven Chu
Claude Cohen-Tannoudji
William D. Phillips

Chemistry

Paul D. Boyer
John E. Walker
Jens C. Skou

Physiology or Medicine

Stanley B. Prusiner

Literature

Dario Fo

Peace

International Campaign to Ban Landmines (ICBL)
Jody Williams

Prize in Economic Sciences in Memory of Alfred Nobel

Robert C. Merton
Myron S. Scholes

Almqvist & Wiksell International
Stockholm – Sweden

ISBN 91-85848-28X

Printed in Sweden by Norstedts Tryckeri AB, Stockholm 1998

CONTENTS

THE NOBEL INSTITUTIONS

THE NOBEL FOUNDATION is the organization to which has been entrusted the fortune bequeathed by Alfred Nobel in order to enable a Prize to be awarded to the most deserving person in each of the following fields: Physics, Chemistry, Physiology or Medicine, Literature, and Peace. The Foundation is the administrative body of the institutions which award the Nobel Prizes. The essential task of its Board is to administer the funds and the other property of the Foundation. The institutions responsible for awarding the Prizes elect delegates who, in turn, elect the members of the Board. One member is appointed by the Government. The electing institutions are as follows:

In Sweden:
THE ROYAL SWEDISH ACADEMY OF SCIENCES – for the Prizes in Physics and Chemistry;

THE NOBEL ASSEMBLY OF THE KAROLINSKA INSTITUTE (the full professors of the medical faculty) – for the Prize in Physiology or Medicine;

THE SWEDISH ACADEMY – for the Prize in Literature.

In Norway:
THE NORWEGIAN NOBEL COMMITTEE (five members appointed by the Norwegian Parliament) – for the Peace Prize.

The Swedish institutions set up special *Nobel Committees* which are instructed to prepare reports and to submit recommendations for the awarding of the Prizes.

In Norway, the corresponding preparatory work is entrusted by the institution that awards the Peace Prize, the Norwegian Committee, to the secretary of the committee, assisted by four experts in the fields of international relations, international law, and political history.

Prize candidates put forward by those competent under the special statutes to present proposals are studied by the respective preparatory bodies, and explanatory reports are submitted to the institutions whose task it is to award the Prizes. The institutions then make their decisions, which are irrevocable. Traditionally, all the deliberations and recommendations of the committees are secret.

In 1997, the Swedish Nobel Committees were made up by the following members:

for Physics:
BENGT NAGEL, Professor Emer. of Mathematical Physics at the Royal Institute of Technology, Stockholm, *Chairman of the Committee;* ERIK KARLSSON, Professor Emer. of Physics at Uppsala University; CECILIA JARLSKOG, Professor of Theoretical Elementary Particle Physics at Lund University; TORD CLAESON, Professor of Physics at Chalmers University of Technology, Gothenburg; MATS JONSSON, Professor of Condensed Matter Physics at Chalmers University of Technology, Gothenburg; *Secretary of the Committee:* ANDERS BÁRÁNY, Associate Professor of Theoretical Atomic Physics at Stockholm University; adjoint member: SUNE SVANBERG, Professor of Atomic Physics at Lund University.

for Chemistry:
BERTIL ANDERSSON, Professor of Biochemistry at Stockholm University, *Chairman of the Committee;* BJÖRN ROOS, Professor of Theoretical Chemistry at Lund University; LENNART EBERSON, Professor of Organic Chemistry at Lund University; TORVARD LAURENT, Professor of Medical and Physiological Chemistry at the Uppsala Biomedical Centre (BMC); BENGT NORDÉN, Professor of Physical Chemistry at Chalmers University of Technology, Gothenburg; *Secretary of the Committee:* ASTRID GRÄSLUND, Professor of Biophysics at Stockholm University; *adjoint members:* PER AHLBERG, Professor of Organic Chemistry at Gothenburg University; INGMAR GRENTHE, Professor of Inorganic Chemistry at the Royal Institute of Technology, Stockholm; ANDERS LILJAS, Professor of Molecular Biophysics at Lund University; HÅKAN WENNERSTRÖM, Professor of Theoretical Physical Chemistry at Lund University.

for Physiology or Medicine:
GÖSTA GAHRTON, Professor of Medicine, *Chairman of the Committee;* RALF PETTERSSON, Professor of Molecular Biology, *Deputy Chairman of the Committee;* STEN LINDAHL, Professor of Anaesthesiology and Intensive Care; STAFFAN NORMARK, Professor of Medical Microbiology; STEN ORRENIUS, Professor of Toxicology; *Secretary of the Committee:* NILS RINGERTZ, Professor of Medical Cell Genetics; *adjoint members:* BO ANGELIN, Professor of Clinical Metabolic Research; ANITA APERIA, Professor of Pediatrics; BERTIL DANEHOLT, Professor of Molecular Genetics; STEN GRILLNER, Professor of Physiology; HANS JÖRNVALL, Professor of Physiological Chemistry; LARS KLARESKOG, Professor of Rheumatology; RUNE TOFTGÅRD, Professor of Environmental Toxicology; KARL TRYGGVASON, Professor of Physiological Chemistry; BJÖRN VENNSTRÖM, Professor of Molecular Biology; HANS WIGZELL, Professor of Immunology.

for Literature:
KJELL ESPMARK, Professor, *Chairman of the Committee;* STURE ALLÉN, Professor, *Secretary of the Committee;* Östen Sjöstrand, Writer; LARS FORSSELL, Writer.

for the Peace Prize:

Francis Sejersted, Professor, *Chairman of the Committee;* Hanna Kvanmo, Former Member of Parliament, *Deputy Chairman of the Committee;* Gunnar Stålsett, Rector of the Practical Theological Seminar at Oslo University, and former Secretary General of the Lutheran World Federation; Sissel Rönbeck, Former Cabinet Minister and Member of Parliament; (Until November, while Rönbeck was a member of the Government, Esther Kostöl was a member of the Committee); Gunnar Berge, Former Cabinet Minister and Member of Parliament; *Secretary of the Committee:* Geir Lundestad, Professor, Director of the Norwegian Nobel Institute.

THE PRIZE-WINNERS AND CITATIONS

THE ROYAL SWEDISH ACADEMY OF SCIENCES
decided on October 15, 1997, to award the Nobel Prize in Physics jointly to

STEVEN CHU
Stanford University, Stanford, California, USA,

CLAUDE COHEN-TANNOUDJI
Collège de France and École Normale Supérieure, Paris, France, and

WILLIAM D. PHILLIPS
National Institute of Standards and Technology, Gaithersburg, Maryland, USA,

for development of methods to cool and trap atoms with laser light.

On the same day, the Academy decided to award the Nobel Prize in Chemistry with half to

PAUL D. BOYER
University of California, Los Angeles, USA, and

JOHN E. WALKER
Medical Research Council Laboratory of Molecular Biology, Cambridge, United Kingdom,

for their elucidation of the enzymatic mechanism underlaying the synthesis of adenosine triphosphate (ATP),

and half to

JENS C. SKOU
Aarhus University, Denmark,

for the first discovery of an ion-transporting enzyme, Na^+, K^+-ATPase.

THE NOBEL ASSEMBLY AT THE KAROLINSKA INSTITUTE
decided on October 6, 1997, to award the Nobel Prize in Physiology or
Medicine to

STANLEY B. PRUSINER
University of California, San Francisco, California, USA,

for his discovery of prions – a new biological principle of infection.

THE SWEDISH ACADEMY
decided on October 9, 1997, to award the Nobel Prize in Literature to

DARIO FO
Milan, Italy,

*who emulates the jesters of the Middle Ages in scourging authority and upholding the
dignity of the downtrodden.*

THE NORWEGIAN NOBEL COMMITTEE
decided on October 10, 1997, to award the Nobel Peace Prize in two equal
parts to

INTERNATIONAL CAMPAIGN TO BAN LANDMINES (ICBL), and

JODY WILLIAMS
Putney, Vermont, USA,

for their work for the banning and clearing of anti-personnel mines.

Candidates formally proposed for the various Nobel Prizes in 1997 totalled
for Physics, 290
for Chemistry, 294
for Physiology or Medicine, 199
for Literature, 208
for Peace, 129.

THE NOBEL CEREMONIES

Presentation of the Prizes in Stockholm

The Prizes in Physics, in Chemistry, in Physiology or Medicine, and in Literature, and also the Prize in Economic Sciences in Memory of Alfred Nobel, were presented to the Prize-Winners as part of a traditional programme established by the Prize-Awarding Institutions and by the Board of the Nobel Foundation. The festivities were organized by the Executive Director of the Foundation, Mr. Michael Sohlman. The ceremonies took place in the Grand Auditorium of the Concert Hall in Stockholm.

Among the guests were the year's Prize-Winners, Chu, Cohen-Tannoudji, Phillips, Boyer, Walker, Skou, Prusiner, Fo, and Merton, Scholes (Prize in Economic Sciences), and their families, and also Prize-Winners from previous years: Siegbahn (1981), Samuelsson (1982), Lederman (1988), Schawlow (1981), and Lewis (1995).

A number of members of the Government, including the Prime Minister, Mr. Göran Persson, the heads of missions and other members of the diplomatic corps honoured the ceremony with their presence. In addition to the Nobel organizations in Sweden, various academies, a number of learned and literary societies, the universities, the Nobel family, the world of arts, industry, and the press were also represented. The assembly also included high-ranking representatives of the civil service and the military.

At 4.30 p.m. His Majesty the King, Her Majesty the Queen, Her Royal Highness Crown Princess Victoria and Her Royal Highness Princess Lilian, the Dutchess of Halland, entered the hall saluted by the Royal Anthem. The ceremony then proceeded as shown in the programme reproduced on the following page.

At the end of each address delivered by the speaker responsible for introducing the prize-winning work, H.M. the King presented the Prize-Winner with the *diploma* and the *medal*.

PROGRAMME

"Kungssången"
"March in D major" KV 249 .... *Wolfgang Amadeus Mozart*
Laureates take their seats on the stage
Speech by Professor *Bengt Samuelsson*, Chairman of the Board of the Nobel
Foundation
Overture to "Die Geschöpfe des Prometeus" .... *Ludwig van Beethoven*
Presentation of the 1997 Nobel Prize in Physics to *Professor Steven Chu, Professor
Claude Cohen-Tannoudji,* and *Dr. William D. Phillips* after a speech by Professor
Bengt Nagel
Presentation of the 1997 Nobel Prize in Chemistry to *Professor Paul D. Boyer,
Dr. John E. Walker,* and *Professor Jens C. Skou* after a speech by Professor Bertil
Andersson
"La Spectre de la Rose" from Les Nuits d'Été .... *Hector Berlioz*
Soloist Charlotte Hellekant
Presentation of the Nobel Prize in Physiology or Medicine to *Professor Stanley
B. Prusiner* after a speech by Professor Ralf Pettersson
"Ging heut' morgens übers Feld" from Lieder eines fahrenden
Gesellen .... *Gustav Mahler*
Soloist Charlotte Hellekant
Presentation of the 1997 Nobel Prize in Literature to *Mr. Dario Fo* after a
speech by Professor Sture Allén
"Circus Polka for a young elephant" .... *Igor Stravinsky*
Presentation of the 1997 Sveriges Riksbank (Bank of Sweden) Prize in
Economic Sciences in Memory of Alfred Nobel to Professor *Robert C. Merton*
and *Professor Myron S. Scholes* after a speech by Professor Bertil Näslund
The Swedish National Anthem "Du gamla, Du fria"
"The Queen of Sheba's Festivity March" .... *Hugo Alfvén*
Played while the guests are leaving the auditorium

Music performed by
The Stockholm Philharmonic Orchestra
Soloist: Charlotte Hellekant, mezzosoprano
Conductor: Paavo Järvo

OPENING ADDRESS

By Professor Bengt Samuelsson, Chairman of the Board of
the Nobel Foundation.
Translation of the Swedish text.

Your Majesties, Your Royal Highnesses, Ladies and Gentlemen,

On behalf of the Nobel Foundation, I welcome you to the 1997 Prize Award
Ceremony. I would especially like to welcome this year's laureates to the
Nobel festivities in Stockholm. Along with the recipients of the Nobel Prize
for efforts to promote peace, you have helped to give the Nobel Prizes the
prestige and stature that they enjoy throughout the world. I congratulate you
for your outstanding work. You have contributed decisively to the development of your respective fields of endeavor. I am convinced that, in a historic
perspective, these advances will reflect progress in the scientific and cultural
spheres.

Alfred Nobel had a great interest in social issues. The poverty and misery
that he experienced during his formative years made a lasting impression on
him and led to a social pathos that was radical for his age. Meanwhile he had
a strong faith that technical progress in various fields would result in improved living conditions.

Scientific research constantly leads to new discoveries and new knowledge.
Advances in scientific laboratories suddenly open new opportunities in areas
that we can hardly imagine. Lasers, nuclear magnetic resonance (NMR) and
semiconductor technology are examples of advances in the field of physics
that have spawned a variety of applications in our daily lives. Their emergence
was not the product of research motivated by these later applications, but of
basic research whose simple motive was to try to understand the structure
and function of nature.

Scientists often try to justify their existence and their work by describing
the practical uses that their research may lead to. In this way, they encourage
the general public and politicians to have unrealistic expectations and to call
on scientists to solve pressing social and practical problems. This situation
often leads to misunderstandings.

The late British immunologist and Nobel laureate Peter Medawar once
said that "If politics is the art of the possible, research is surely the art of the
soluble." As this expression indicates, both basic research and applied research have their limitations. In basic research, a discovery cannot be thought
out in advance. Most of the daily work at laboratories consists of pursuing
experiments to see whether our hypotheses about how things look or work
stand up to reality. There is no scientific method for making discoveries.

In its early stages, research cannot be goal-oriented. And in explaining the limitations that actually exist, we have not been sufficiently clear. For example, there are limitations on the ability of basic scientific research to solve short-term societal problems related to better health, better environment or new energy sources. The result is unfulfilled expectations and a hesitation to vigorously stimulate basic scientific research.

Those countries or organizations that realize the importance of stimulating research of a basic nature will have the best long-range opportunities to reap the harvests of their research investments. As the will of Alfred Nobel indicates, Nobel fully understood the role of basic research and discoveries in developing techniques that eventually lead to a higher quality of life.

Discoveries always entail surprises, and at first we do not know what dangers may accompany a given discovery. Scientific knowledge is value-neutral, and ethical issues arise only when this knowledge is applied.

In their eagerness to disclose sensational news, the media often contribute to a lopsided view of research and its dangers. One recent example of journalism that has generated unnecessary concern, while casting suspicion on the good intentions of the research community, is Dolly the cloned sheep.

Dolly's entire genetic material originates from a single cell in a fully grown animal. Genetically speaking, she is a copy of this animal, just as an identical twin is a copy of his or her sibling. But that is where the similarity ends. The purpose of cloning a sheep is not to clone humans. There are already regulations and laws in the pipeline to prevent such a development. Meanwhile, however, the media have neglected to explain the useful applications of these scientific advances.

Researchers have now also cloned Polly, who has a human gene in her genetic material. By using this method, they hope to produce substances that can be used in treating diseases in humans.

Dolly exemplifies the need for a dialogue between researchers and the general public. This dialogue should be pursued with an international perspective and should lead to more effective rules for the utilization of scientific advances. Actually exploring ourselves and our surroundings by means of discoveries and development of new methods is very much in the public interest.

Literature occupied a central role in the life of Alfred Nobel. He regarded various literary forms of expression as opportunities to achieve a greater understanding of our own thoughts, lives and relationships with other people and our surroundings.

Nobel had an extensive library, which included important European literary works. Inspired by Shelley and Byron, he wrote poems in English as a young man. Toward the end of his life, he wrote the tragedy Nemesis. His best literary form of expression was probably the aphorism, where he often expressed himself drastically. One example is: "A recluse without books and ink is a dead man before he dies." This aphorism reinforces the impression that Nobel was not only interested in literature, but also dependent on it.

In his final will and testament, Nobel included a prize in literature. He stipulated that this prize should go to the person who had produced the most outstanding work "i idealisk rigtning." The meaning of the expression "idealisk" has been the object of many interpretations over the years.

During its first years, the selection of Nobel laureates in Literature was dominated by the Swedish Academy's permanent secretary, Carl David af Wirsén, who interpreted the above phrase in Nobel's will as meaning "of an idealistic tendency." This implied that the work of the laureate should be characterized "by genuine nobility, not merely in its presentation, but also in its perception and philosophy." Wirsén did not regard the Literature Prize as a mere literary award. However, Swedish novelist and playwright August Strindberg, a contemporary of Nobel and Wirsén, emphatically rejected Wirsén's reading of "idealisk" as meaning "idealistic" in the spirit of the Swedish philosopher Christopher Jacob Boström.

In his book The Nobel Prize in Literature: A Study of the Criteria behind the Choices, Academy member Kjell Espmark wrote: "Indeed, the history of the literature prize is in some ways a series of attempts to interpret an imprecisely worded will." And in an essay on the Literature Prize, Lars Gyllensten, a former permanent secretary of the Academy, declared that one must refrain from attempting a detailed analysis of the phrase in question. He added that "it suffices to say that the serious, high quality literature that can be considered for a Prize generally furthers our knowledge of mankind and the human condition and strives to enrich our lives and improve the conditions under which we live."

Sture Allén, permanent secretary of the Academy, recently analyzed the expression "idealisk" in Nobel's will from a philological standpoint. He also obtained the help of a forensic expert, because the word "idealisk" is the result of a change that Nobel made in his handwritten will. The conclusion, based on the linguistic usage of that era, is that Nobel's expression "i idealisk rigtning" means "in a direction toward an ideal" or "in an ideal-oriented direction." The delineation of this ideal is determined, in turn, by the basic criterion that applies to all the Nobel Prizes: its benefit to mankind. According to Allén, the English translation of "idealisk" should therefore be "ideal" and not "idealistic," the term used in the first official translation of the will.

Allén concluded by saying that "once an idea has been formed of how this issue appeared to Nobel, it is up to each generation to decide how the literature of the day meets his criterion. It is perhaps not evident that Nobel himself would have seen Samuel Beckett's work the way we do, to mention but one example. And seen from our perspective, it is possible that the first Nobel Laureate's name might have been different."

Today, as we award the Literature Prize and the other Prizes, it is with gratitude that we remember Alfred Nobel, his life achievements and his visionary will. This document laid the foundation for the prestige and the stimulation of advances for the benefit of mankind that the Nobel Prizes symbolize.

THE NOBEL PRIZE IN PHYSICS

Speech by Professor Bengt Nagel of the Royal Swedish Academy of Sciences. Translation of the Swedish text.

Your Majesties, Your Royal Highnesses, Ladies and Gentlemen,

The Royal Swedish Academy of Sciences has decided to award this year's Nobel Prize for Physics jointly to three physicists for "development of methods to cool and trap atoms with laser light".

The air around us consists of molecules moving back and forth with breathtaking velocities around a mean of about 500 m/s, distributed around this velocity roughly according to a bell curve, so dear to statisticians. A molecule collides with some other molecule about one billion times per second, and there are around twenty-five trillion (= million million million) molecules in each cubic centimeter. As result of this disordered rapid motion we get properties such as air pressure, the ability to transmit sound, a (fairly bad) capacity for conducting heat, etc.

If we want to study the individual or small numbers of molecules or atoms we must slow down their motion, both in order to get time to observe them, and also because the properties of our communication with them, which occurs with the help of light, are influenced by their velocity. The frequency of the light that a moving atom sends out or can absorb changes because of the Doppler effect, with which we are familiar from acoustics. We can make an analogy with an absurd opera performance–maybe something for this year's prize winner in literature–where the opera star sings her aria while moving at great velocity around the stage, colliding with and rebounding from her fellow actors. Visually this might be a spectacular performance, but acoustically it could be a disaster: the audience would think that the star didn't sing in tune. (If somebody would like to try this out, I can mention that if the singer moves with the speed of a good sprinter, the maximum variation in pitch would be half a tone interval.)

Last year's Nobel Prize in physics dealt with low temperatures, and with conventional cooling methods one might cool the atoms down to some millionths of a degree above absolute zero, which formally would correspond to velocities of some centimeters per second. The problem is that long before this temperature is reached, the atoms or molecules would have condensed into a liquid and finally a solid body. Atoms in a chorus sing different tunes from solo, and it is the solo performance we want. We must reduce the motion of the atoms while keeping them apart .

The idea of using laser light and the Doppler effect to achieve this was discussed as early as the 1970s and is based on the fact that when an atom absorbs a light particle, a photon, it receives an impulse from the absorbed photon, and if it has a velocity opposite to that of the photon, its motion is slowed down. We adjust the frequencey of the laser beam so that the photon resonates with, and hence can be absorbed only by, atoms moving in the opposite direction from that of the laser beam. – This basic idea has demanded many years of extensions and experimental developments to result in an effective cooling and trapping of atoms. An important device is the magneto-optical trap, where atoms are slowed down in an "optical molasses" consisting of three pairs of mutually opposite laser beams, and are kept trapped by a magnetic field. In the latest development, subrecoil cooling, equivalent temperatures of fractions of a millionth of a degree have been obtained.

Besides the direct importance for increasing our knowledge of the interaction between atoms and radiation which is a result of increased control of the atomic motion, one could of course ask about possible practical uses of these new advances.

The classical answer : "One day, sir, you may tax it" was given in the 1850s by Michael Faraday in reply to a question by William Gladstone, then British minister of finance–Chancellor of the Exchequer–if electricity had any practical value. Faraday's studies of electricity and magnetism laid the foundations of electrotechnology.

I cannot yet see any directly taxable object resulting from the contributions awarded this year's physics prize, but I believe it will come.

Because we can make atoms practically stand still, we can design much more precise atomic clocks; this enables us, for example, to make a more accurate position determination on earth via satellites. The awarded cooling techniques supplemented by other cooling techniques, have led to achievement of what could be called the "dream mile" of atomic physics, Bose-Einstein condensation of gases, a phenomenon predicted by Einstein more than 70 years ago. This in turn can lead to the construction of "atomic lasers", coherent intense atom beams, which among other things could be used for the construction of very small electronic components.

Professors Steven Chu and Claude Cohen-Tannoudji, Dr. William Phillips,

You have been awarded this year's Nobel Prize in Physics as leaders and representatives of the most successful groups and collaborations in the extensive work of developing methods for cooling and trapping of atoms, which has opened up a new area of control and study of atoms and atomic gases.

It is my pleasure and my privilege to convey to you the felicitations of the Royal Swedish Academy of Sciences and to ask you to step forward and receive the Prize from the hands of His Majesty the King.

THE NOBEL PRIZE IN CHEMISTRY

Speech by Professor Bertil Andersson of the Royal Swedish Academy of Sciences.
Translation of the Swedish text.

Your Majesties, Your Royal Highnesses, Ladies and Gentlemen,

Life requires energy. Our muscles require energy when we move. We need energy to think. Energy input is required for the production of new biological molecules. This year's three Nobel Laureates in Chemistry have contributed in different ways to our knowledge of how living organisms can obtain and utilize energy. Common to their discoveries is the unique adenosine triphosphate (ATP) molecule, which can store and transport energy in all organisms, whether it be a simple bacterium, a dandelion, a finch or a human being. Large quantities of ATP must be formed and consumed. Each day an adult converts a quantity of ATP roughly equivalent to his or her own body weight, and in case of physical exertion, many times more.

All energy on earth originates from the sun. Green plants can absorb sunlight and convert it into chemical energy through the process of photosynthesis, in which carbon dioxide and water form sugar, starch and other complex carbon compounds. Other organisms, such as humans and animals, are in turn dependent on these carbon compounds as sources of energy, and they burn them with the help of oxygen. That is why we breathe. Nature can thus be said to have chosen a combination of solar and coal-fired power plants for its energy supply. Although these two energy conversion systems may seem different in purely technical terms, in many respects they operate in the same way in living cells. The most important similarity is that the energy released is utilized with the help of the ATP molecule.

According to Peter Mitchell, the 1978 Nobel Laureate in Chemistry, the energy released in photosynthesis and cell respiration initiates a stream of positively charged hydrogen ions. These hydrogen ions, in turn, drive the production of ATP with the aid of a membrane-bound enzyme called ATP synthase. Two of this year's Laureates, Paul Boyer and John Walker, have studied this important enzyme and have shown that it functions in a unique way. Among other things, they have demonstrated that ATP synthase can be compared to a molecular machine, whose rotating bent axle is driven in a stepwise process by "biological electricity"–that is, the flow of hydrogen ions. Because of the asymmetry of the rotating axle, three subunits of the enzyme assume different forms and functions: a first form that binds adenosine diphosphate (or ADP) and phosphate building blocks, a second form where these two molecules are chemically combined into a new ATP molecule, and a third form where the ATP that has been formed is released. In the next twist of the axle, the three subunits switch form and thus also function with each other, and another ATP molecule can be formed, and so on. This "binding change mechanism" was put forward by Boyer in the late 1970s, but only in 1994 did his ingenious model gain general acceptance among researchers. In August of that year, Walker and his colleagues published three-dimensional images of ATP synthase that had been obtained by X-ray analysis of enzyme crystals. These X-ray images, magnified several million times, showed how an asymmetrically elongated protein molecule interacted with three other protein units that all showed mutually different forms. Walker had finally revealed the detailed blueprint of the molecular machine and shown that Boyer's theory of ATP formation was correct.

Let me now leave ATP production and instead turn to the use of ATP. In 1957, Jens Christian Skou discovered an enzyme called sodium, potassium ATPase (or Na^+,K^+-ATPase), which maintains the right ion balance in living cells. This enzyme, too, can be described with a technical analogy: It functions as a biological "pump" that transports potassium ions into a cell, while transporting sodium ions in the opposite direction out of the cell. This is a process that requires a lot of energy, and up to one third of the ATP formed in the body may be used to drive the Na^+,K^+ pump. Today, we are also aware of a number of other ion pumps, which have been discovered as a consequence of Skou's pioneering work. All these ion pumps are prerequisites for various important life functions such as transmission of nerve impulses, muscle contraction and digestion. The effects of many pharmaceuticals, such as heart and ulcer medicines, are related to the action of cellular ion pumps.

Skou's discovery clearly illustrates the unpredictability of basic research–in 1957, no one could have imagined that his somewhat odd experiments, which consisted of studying the effects of various salts on tissue from a shore crab, would be important 40 years later to industrial operations and the production of new pharmaceuticals. Research breakthroughs and their applications cannot be custom-ordered. Instead they emerge from a combination of curiosity, scientific excellence and far-sightedness.

Dr. Boyer, Dr. Skou and Dr. Walker,

I have tried to describe how your pioneering studies on the enzymology of ATP metabolism have contributed to our understanding of how living cells can store and make use of energy. Your work has revealed new principles for enzyme function, opened up new areas of chemical research as well as providing the basis for biomedical applications for the benefit of mankind. In recognition of your services to chemistry the Royal Swedish Academy of Sciences has decided to confer upon you this year's Nobel Prize for Chemistry.

On behalf of the Academy, I wish to convey to you our warmest congratulations and I now ask you to receive the Prize from the hands of His Majesty the King.

THE NOBEL PRIZE IN PHYSIOLOGY OR MEDICINE

Speech by Professor Ralf F. Pettersson of the Nobel Committee at the Karolinska Institute.
Translation of the Swedish text.

Your Majesties, Your Royal Highnesses, Ladies and Gentlemen,

This year's Nobel Prize in Physiology or Medicine has been awarded to Stanley B. Prusiner for his discovery of prions–a new biological principle of infection. What is a prion? It is a small infectious protein capable of causing fatal dementia-like diseases in man and animals. It has been known for approximately a century that infectious diseases can be caused by bacteria, viruses, fungi and parasites. All these infectious agents possess a genome, the hereditary material that provides the basis for their replication. The ability to replicate is essential for the manifestation of the diseases they cause. The most remarkable feature of prions is that they are able to replicate themselves without possessing a genome; prions lack hereditary material. Until prions were discovered, duplication without a genome was considered impossible. This discovery was unexpected and provoked controversy.

Although the existence of prions was not known until the work of Stanley Prusiner, many prion diseases have been previously documented. On Iceland, scrapie, a disease affecting sheep was first described in the 18th century. In the 1920s, the neurologists Hans Creutzfeldt and Alfons Jakob discovered a similar disease in man. During the 1950s and 60s Carleton Gajdusek studied kuru, a disease that was spread through cannibalistic rituals practised by the Fore people in New Guinea. Presently attention is focused on mad cow disease, which has affected approximately 170,000 cows in Britain. These diseases exhibit common pathologies. They are inevitably fatal due to the destruction of the brains of infected individuals. The incubation times may last for several years, during which the affected regions of the brain become gradually spongy in appearance. Gajdusek discovered that kuru and Creutzfeldt-Jakob disease could be transmitted to monkeys demonstrating that these diseases are contagious. In 1976, when Gajdusek received his Nobel Prize, the nature of the infectious agent was completely unknown. At this time, these diseases were assumed to be caused by a new unidentified virus, termed a slow or unconventional virus. During the 1970s, no significant advances regarding the nature of the agent were made, that is, not until Stanley Prusiner took on the problem.

Prusiner set out to purify the infectious agent, and after 10 years of hard work he obtained a pure preparation. To his great surprise, he found that the agent consisted only of a protein, which he named prion, a term derived from proteinaceous infectious particle. Strangely enough, he found that the protein was present in equal amounts in the brains of both diseased and healthy individuals. This discovery was confusing and it was generally concluded that Prusiner must have arrived at the wrong conclusion. How could a protein cause disease if it was present both in diseased and healthy brains? The answer to this question came when Prusiner showed that the prion protein from diseased brains had a completely different three-dimensional conformation. This led Prusiner to propose a hypothesis for how a normal protein could become a disease-causing agent by changing its conformation. The process he proposed may be compared to the transformation of Dr Jekyll to Mr Hyde–the same entity, but in two manifestations, a kind innocuous one, and a vicious lethal one. But how can a protein replicate without a genome? Stanley Prusiner suggested that the harmful prion protein could replicate by forcing the normal protein to adopt the shape of the harmful protein in a chain reaction-like process. In other words, when a harmful protein encounters a normal protein, the normal protein is converted into the harmful form. A remarkable feature of prion diseases is that they can arise in three different ways. They can occur spontaneously, or be triggered by infection, or occur as a consequence of hereditary predisposition.

The hypothesis that prions are able to replicate without a genome and to cause disease violated all conventional conceptions and during the 1980s was severely criticised. For more than 10 years, Stanley Prusiner fought an uneven battle against overwhelming opposition. Research during the 1990s has, however, rendered strong support for the correctness of Prusiner's prion hypothesis. The mystery behind scrapie, kuru, and mad cow disease has finally been unravelled. Additionally, the discovery of prions has opened up new avenues to better understand the pathogenesis of other more common dementias, such as Alzheimer's disease.

Stanley Prusiner,

Your discovery of the prions has established a novel principle of infection and opened up a new and exciting area in medical research. On behalf of the Nobel Assembly at the Karolinska Institute I wish to convey to you my warmest congratulations and I now ask you to step forward to receive your Nobel Prize from the hands of His Majesty the King.

THE NOBEL PRIZE IN LITERATURE

Speech by Professor Sture Allén of the Swedish Academy.
Translation of the Swedish text.

Your Majesties, Your Royal Highnesses, Ladies and Gentlemen,

To be a jester is, and always has been, a serious matter. Swedish mediaeval laws stipulated that it cost a man smaller fines to lay violent hands on somebody from a neighbouring county than on a man from his own part of the country; but to assault a jester, on the other hand, cost him nothing at all. If a jester is beaten up, says the thirteenth-century law concerning such people, it shall not be counted an offence. If a jester comes to bodily harm, he shall have and suffer what was given him–infamy and injury. "Let him never appeal for more justice than a thral woman lashed on her bare back."

One of Dario Fo's sources of inspiration is exactly these mediaeval jesters, unprotected by any law. According to Fo satire is what makes the most forceful impact on man. Mixing laughter and seriousness is his way of telling the truth about abuses and unrighteousness. For Alfred Nobel literary achievements were important means for fulfilling the fundamental aim of the awards, namely to confer benefit on mankind. The maintenance of human dignity is unquestionably an essential aspect of this.

Fo often refers explicitly to the mediaeval joculatores and their comedy and mysteries. In fact, a central work in his oeuvre, "Mistero buffo"–"The Comic Mysteries "–is based on old material culled from many different quarters. In the scene called "The Birth of the Jester" the crucial moment occurs when a landlord avid for more land violates the wife of the man who is breaking untilled ground. "The Marriage at Cana" is seen from the point of view of the intoxicated wine-drinker. In "The Resurrection of Lazarus" the provocative question is whether Jesus will succeed.

There are several other sources. Furthest away in time we seem to glimpse Plautus and Terence in Rome, who were of renewed interest in fifteenth century Italy. The commedia dell'arte, a creation of the sixteenth century, is of importance with its set-character parts and its oral tradition. It is also possible to catch a sly glance from Bottom the weaver and Sir Andrew Aguecheek. Impulses from our own days come from Maiakovski's epic-satirical poetry and from Brecht's didactic theatre. Incidentally, it was from Maiakovski that Fo borrowed the title "Mistero Buffo".

Another major achievement in Fo's large production is "Accidental Death of an Anarchist". The play is about the cross-examining following on the supposed accident. By and by the questioning is taken over, through a brilliantly carried out shift, by a Hamlet-like figure–il Matto–who has the kind of madness that exposes official falsehoods. All in all there are many topical allusions in Fo's plays, but the texts transcend everyday situations and are given a far wider range of application.

One cannot hold it against Fo that he is a first-rate actor. The decisive thing is that he has written plays which arouse the enthusiasm of actors and which captivate his audiences. The texts are chiselled in an interplay with the spectators and have often been given their final shape over a long time. Rapidly changing situations give impetus to the plays and shape the characters. The rhythm of the actors' lines, the witty wording and the aptitude for improvisation combine with strong intensity and artistic energy in the profoundly meaningful, steady flow of his flashes of wit. The printed texts can also give you this feeling if you give free range to your imagination. Fo's work brings to the fore the multifarious abundance of the literary field.

His independence and perspicacity have made him run great risks and right enough he has been made to experience the consequences both at home and abroad. When on one occasion he and his wife, Franca Rame, had been stopped from making an agreed-on appearance abroad, their friends and colleagues arranged a representation which they called "An Evening without Dario Fo and Franca Rame".

Looking backwards in time from Dario Fo, the ninety-fourth laureate for literature, to earlier writers given the award, it is tempting to arrest oneself at George Bernard Shaw, winner of the Prize seventy years ago. On that occasion the Swedish Academy emphasised the laureate's idealism, humanity, and stimulating satire. The two writers are no doubt different from each other, but the same evaluative words can be applied to Dario Fo.

Dear Mr. Fo,

The word dignity plays an important part in your oeuvre and is at the centre of the piece called "The Birth of the Jester". The dignity bestowed on you today may have other attributes, but it has the same core. On behalf of the Swedish Academy I congratulate you warmly on the work which has resulted in the Nobel Prize in Literature 1997 and I ask you to step forward to receive the prize from the hands of His Majesty the King.

THE NOBEL BANQUET IN STOCKHOLM

After the formal presentation of the Prizes a distinguished company gathered in the Blue Hall of the Stockholm City Hall. Among those present were: His Majesty the King and Her Majesty the Queen, Her Royal Highness Crown Princess Victoria and Her Royal Highness Princess Lilian, the Duchess of Halland.

And also:

The 1997 Prize-Winners and the previous Prize-Winners mentioned earlier.

Also present were members of the Government and of Parliament as well as heads of the diplomatic missions of the countries of the Prize-Winners and a very large number of scholars, high-ranking Swedish officials and other distinguished persons.

The Chairman of the Foundation proposed a toast to His Majesty the King. The guests rose to drink this toast. His Majesty proposed a toast to the memory of the great benefactor and philanthropist Alfred Nobel. Speeches of thanks were given by the Prize-Winners.

SPEECHES BY THE LAUREATES

Dario Fo

Io voglio fare un brindisi, anche senza bicchiere, a una grandissima regina, una vostra regina antica, che si chiamava Cristina.

Cristina è arrivata in Italia verso la seconda metà del Seicento, proprio a Roma, come hanno già detto, e conobbe il Papa, è ovvio, che era Alessandro VII. Un uomo che stava cercando di ricostruire un tessuto culturale che si era perduto proprio a Roma. Qualche anno prima c'era stato proprio il momento di punta di una reazione che era esplosa con la Controriforma. Alessandro faceva ritornare in Italia gli uomini di teatro che erano stati cacciati da questa Controriforma, e così la regina Cristina conobbe i più grandi commedianti italiani che tornavano in patria.

Amava già il teatro: con la conoscenza di questi attori, di questo teatro, si innamorò profondamente del teatro. Andando in Francia ha conosciuto Molière, e ha cominciato ad avere delle comunicazioni con lui quando è tornata in Italia. E a un certo punto Molière gli mandò una sua commedia, *Il Tartufo*. Era soltanto abbozzata.

Cristina chiese a Molière di poterla rappresentare lei in Italia, e si mise d'accordo con il Papa.

Il Papa, che era molto spiritoso disse: "Ma tu mi vuoi rovinare la reputazione con questa commedia! Questi... i cardinali mi licenziano."

Ma Molière non potè dare la commedia a Cristina perché il re la volle per sé.

Debuttò questa commedia, *Il Tartufo*, ... non era ancora finita. Era una commedia dura, che se la prendeva con ironia verso l'ipocrisia, soprattutto l'ipocrisia dei cattolici e dei parenti in particolare.

Si risolse in un disastro. Fu censurata. Fu bloccata per tre anni di seguito. Riprese per un po' di tempo e fu bloccata un'altra volta per anni ancora.

Di certo se Molière avesse dato retta a Cristina e l'avesse fatta rappresentare a Roma, nessuno si sarebbe permesso di censurarla. Cristina era protetta dal Papa, e chi poteva toccare il Papa?

Ecco, io chiedo a Voi, regina, alle principesse che sono qui stasera, se amate il teatro sostenete come Cristina sosteneva il teatro.

So...? Hai già finita la battuta? Eh? Mi ha bruciata la battuta! Non ancora, non ancora? Meglio, meglio, meglio!

Dicevo che, soprattutto quando è un teatro ironico, grottesco, dovete difenderlo, perché il teatro del ridere, è il teatro della civiltà.

E se avete delle preoccupazioni, appoggiatevi al Papa. Riuscirete senz'altro bene.

Evviva Cristina!

Even though I don't hold a glass in my hand, I'd like to raise a toast to a great Queen, a Queen of your past: Kristina.

Kristina arrived in Italy in the late 17th century. As someone already mentioned, she came to Rome and there, obviously, she got to know the Pope, Alexander VII. He was a man seeking to restore the city's ruined cultural fabric. The reaction to the Counter-Reformation had peaked a few years earlier. Alexander sought the return to Italy of the men of the theatre that had been driven away by the Counter-Reformation, and through his efforts Queen Kristina became acquainted with Italy's greatest comedians, as they returned to their homeland.

She already loved the theatre; through these actors she became enthralled with it. During a visit to France, she got to know Molière, with whom she began a correspondence on her return to Italy. At one point Molière sent her one of his comedies, *Tartuffe*. It was only a draft.

Kristina asked Molière if she could stage it in Italy, and got the consent of the Pope. The Pope, who had a great sense of humour, said: "What are you trying to do, ruin my reputation with this comedy? These . . . the cardinals will fire me."

But Molière couldn't give the play to Kristina because the King wanted it for himself.

This play, *Tartuffe*, was played for the first time . . . it wasn't completed yet. It was a vicious comedy that with great irony took to task the hypocrisy of the day, in particular the hypocrisy of the Catholics and especially as it expressed itself within the family.

It led to a disaster. It was censured. It was banned for three years in a row. It was played again for a while and then was again banned for several years.

It may be safe to assume that if Molière had given in to Kristina, and had she arranged for it to be played in Rome, no one would have dared to censure it. Kristina enjoyed the protection of the Pope, and who could touch the Pope?

So, I beg You, Queen, and you Princesses that are here this evening: if you love the theatre, give it your support, as Kristina did.

I know ...? Did you tell your joke? Eh? You've stolen my punch line! Not yet, not yet? All the better, all the better!

As I was saying, when the theatre is ironic, grotesque, it's above all then that you have to defend it, because the theatre that makes people laugh is the theatre of human reason.

And if you have any problems, seek the support of the Pope. You will no doubt succeed.

Here's to Kristina!

Translation: Paul Claesson

Stanley B. Prusiner

King Carl Gustaf, Queen Silvia, Distinguished Guests,

Tonight's awarding of the Nobel Prizes and this elegant Banquet are a grand celebration of science and culture. These events honor the vision, courage, and wisdom of Alfred Nobel, a superb scientist in his own right.

And they honor the Swedish people's uncommon sense of commitment to fulfill the enlightened wishes of Alfred Nobel–the Nobel Prizes have truly become important benchmarks in the history of science.

But the Nobel Prizes are much more than awards to scholars, they are a celebration of civilization, of mankind, and of what makes humans unique–that is their intellect from which springs creativity. I continue to be delightfully surprised by the joy, excitement, and happiness that so many of my friends and colleagues have felt when they learned of this year's Nobel Prize in Medicine; moreover, many of these friends are nonscientists who hail from many parts of our planet.

People often ask me why I persisted in doing research on a subject that was so controversial. I frequently respond by telling them that only a few scientists are granted the great fortune to pursue topics that are so new and different that only a small number of people can grasp the meaning of such discoveries initially. I am one of those genuinely lucky scientists who was handed a special opportunity to work on such a problem–that of prions.

Because our results were so novel, my colleagues and I had great difficulty convincing other scientists of the veracity of our findings and communicating to lay people the importance of work that seemed so esoteric! As more and more compelling data accumulated, many scientists became convinced. But it was the "mad cow" epidemic in Britain and the likely transmission of bovine prions to humans producing a fatal brain illness called Creutzfeldt-Jakob disease that introduced prions to the public. Yet the principles of prion biology are still so new that some scientists and most laymen, including the press, still have considerable difficulty grasping the most fundamental concepts.

Being a scientist is a special privilege: for it brings the opportunity to be creative, the passionate quest for answers to nature's most precious secrets, and the warm friendships of many valued colleagues. Collaborations extend far beyond the scientific achievements, no matter how great the accomplishments might be, the rich friendships which have no national borders are treasured even more.

Besides scientific achievement, the Nobel Prizes honor the scientific process. In science, each new result, sometimes quite surprising, heralds a step forward and allows one to discard some hypotheses, even though one or two of these might have been highly favored. No matter how new and revolutionary the findings may be, as data accumulates, even the skeptical scholars eventually become convinced except for a few who will always remain resistant. Indeed, the story of prions is truly an odyssey that has taken us from heresy to orthodoxy.

Lastly, we celebrate on the occasion of these Nobel Prizes, the triumph of science over prejudice. The wondrous tools of modern science allowed my colleagues and me to demonstrate that prions exist and that they are responsible for an entirely new principle of infection.

Tack så mycket!

Claude Cohen-Tannoudji

Vos Majestés, Vos Altesses Royales, Mesdames, Messieurs,

C'est sous le signe de la lumière que je voudrais m'adresser à vous. Depuis l'antiquité, la lumière a toujours fasciné l'esprit humain par ses multiples aspects et son caractère mystérieux. En se manifestant, tantôt comme une succession de trains d'ondes, tantôt comme un jet de corpuscules, la lumière a dévoilé pour la première fois la dualité onde-corpuscule que l'on a retrouvée ensuite dans tous les objets de la physique. Grâce à la lumière que nous recevons des étoiles et des galaxies lointaines, nous comprenons mieux la structure de l'univers qui nous entoure. Par ailleurs, c'est l'étude de la lumière émise et absorbée par les atomes qui nous a révélé les mystères de la mécanique quantique régissant la dynamique du monde microscopique, et qui a abouti à l'invention de ces sources lumineuses exceptionnelles que sont les sources laser, aux innombrables applications. Ces sources nous permettent aujourd'hui d'utiliser la lumière pour agir sur les atomes, pour les manipuler, contrôler leurs positions et leurs vitesses. Voilà encore un paradoxe étonnant de la lumière! Alors que l'impact de faisceaux laser sur la matière évoque l'idée de chaleur et de fusion, il apparaît maintenant qu'une utilisation judicieuse des interactions matière-rayonnement permet de geler les atomes à des températures proches du zéro absolu ! Il s'agit là d'un des résultats les plus importants des recherches couronnées par le Prix Nobel de cette année.

On behalf of my colleagues, Steven Chu and William Phillips, I would like to express our deep gratitude for the prestigious award which is bestowed upon us today. We see this distinction as the recognition of the work done by many: our predecessors who have introduced us to research, our young talented collaborators who have played such an important role in these discoveries, our colleagues all over the world whose contributions have been essential for building up such a research field. Winter has begun, with days becoming shorter and nights longer. Mais "c'est la nuit qu'il est beau de croire à la lumière" dit le poète Edmond Rostand. "It is during the hours of darkness that it is most glorious to believe in the light". May the light which sparkles in our eyes, may the Lucia candles which will be lighted next Saturday, fill our hearts with happiness and serenity. Let us comply with Alfred Nobel's will and dedicate this wonderful evening to the celebration of Arts, Science and Culture.

Jens C. Skou

Your Majesties, Your Royal Highnesses, Ladies and Gentlemen,

On behalf of Professor Boyer, Dr. Walker and myself, I would like to express how grateful we are for the great honour the Nobel Foundation and the Royal Swedish Academy of Sciences has bestowed upon us by awarding us the Nobel Prize in Chemistry.

It is impressive that the Nobel Foundation now for almost hundred years has been able to maintain the Nobel Prize as the most rewarding a scientist can achieve. It cannot only be due to the size of the prize, which is substantial, but also to the thoroughness behind the decisions, and because the prize ceremony is surrounded by such festivity that it attracts worldwide attention.

The Nobel Prizes and the ceremony around the awards puts focus not only on the work done by the Prize-Winners, but arouses in the public a more general interest in science, and gives us scientists a very important opportunity to tell what science is and the importance of science.

The unique prestige connected with the Prize also gives the laureates an unusual opportunity to be heard and thereby influence the public view on science and not least to influence the decision makers for the benefit of science and society.

This is perhaps the most rewarding and important aspect of the Nobel Prizes, and as far as I understand, it is also in agreement with Alfred Nobel's intentions.

Thank you for giving us this opportunity.

Robert C. Merton

Your Majesties, Your Royal Highnesses, Ladies and Gentlemen,

Myron Scholes, my colleague and dear friend of some thirty years, and I are deeply grateful to the Royal Swedish Academy of Sciences for this ultimate honour.

But for us this is also a bittersweet moment for we greatly miss our friend and collaborator, Fischer Black – especially so this special day. We are gratified that the Academy made it quite clear that, were Fischer still alive, he too would now be honoured.

Myron and I also share a wonderful array of family, friends, teachers, colleagues, and students. Among our teacher-mentors, especially two who are themselves laureates, Merton Miller for Myron, Paul Samuelson for myself. Myron wishes that his parents were alive to witness this moment, as I wish my mother were too. Happily, my father is.

And like all scientists, we too stand on the shoulders of giants, on the selective accumulation of prior knowledge. In our case, a most powerful legacy, ranging from the pioneering French mathematician, Louis Bachelier, to the all-knowing U.S. economist, Paul Samuelson.

Much has been written about the ramified effects of the options-princing model on the world's financial system. But, like other scientists, we had no practical objective. We simply found the options-pricing problem interesting. It was an engaging puzzle, a difficult challenge. And we know that just as the model helped shape the markets, the markets in turn helped shape the evolving model.

A final word: of all the many benefits conferred by the institution of the Nobel Prizes on the growth of science, not least is their according utmost recognition to still new and promising directions of inquiry, such as ours. For this too, we thank you.

PRESENTATION OF THE PRIZE IN OSLO

The Nobel Prize for Peace in 1997 was awarded to the International Campaign to Ban Landmines (ICBL) and to ICBL's coordinator Jody Williams. The presentation of the Prize took place on December 10 at a solemn ceremony in The City Hall in Oslo. Their Majesties King Harald and Queen Sonja honoured the ceremony with their presence. Representatives of the Norwegian Parliament and the Government, the heads of mission and other members of the diplomatic corps also attended the ceremony. The Nobel Foundation was represented by Professor Carl-Olof Jacobson and his wife Gunilla.

Mari Silje and Håkon Andersen Samuelsen opened the ceremony with "Passacaglia for violin and cello" by G. F. Händel/Johan Halvorsen. The chairman of the Norwegian Nobel Committee, Professor Francis Sejersted, gave a speech in honour of ICBL and Jody Williams. The 1997 laureates received the diploma and the medal. Tun Channareth accepted the medal and diploma on behalf of ICBL. Emmylou Harris sang "Abraham, Martin & John" by Nanci Griffith and Richard Noller. Jody Williams then gave her acceptance speech and Nobel Lecture. Emmylou Harris sang "Calling My Children Home" by Doyle Lawson, Charles Waller and Robert Yates. Rae McGrath gave the acceptance speech and Nobel Lecture on behalf of ICBL. Mari Silje and Håkon Andersen Samuelsen, accompanied by Knut Johannessen, concluded the ceremony with "Concert for Violin, Cello and Continuo in B-major, 2nd movement" by Antonio Vivaldi.

THE OFFICIAL ANNOUNCEMENT FROM THE NORWEGIAN NOBEL COMMITTEE:

The Norwegian Nobel Committee has decided to award the Nobel Peace Prize for 1997, in two equal parts, to the International Campaign to Ban Landmines (ICBL) and to the campaign's coordinator Jody Williams for their work for the banning and clearing of anti-personnel mines.

There are at present probably over one hundred million anti-personnel mines scattered over large areas on several continents. Such mines maim and kill indiscriminately and are a major threat to the civilian populations and to the social and economic development of the many countries affected.

The ICBL and Jody Williams started a process which in the space of a few years changed a ban on anti-personnel mines from a vision to a feasible reality. The Convention which will be signed in Ottawa in December this year is to a considerable extent a result of their important work.

There are already over 1,000 organizations, large and small, affiliated to the ICBL, making up a network through which it has been possible to express and mediate a broad wave of popular commitment in an unprecedented way. With the governments of several small and medium-sized countries taking the issue up and taking steps to deal with it, this work has grown into a convincing example of an effective policy for peace.

The Norwegian Nobel Committee wishes to express the hope that the Ottawa process will win even wider support. As a model for similar processes in the future, it could prove of decisive importance to the international effort for disarmament and peace.

THE NOBEL PRIZE FOR PEACE

Speech by Professor Francis Sejersted, Chairman of the Norwegian Nobel Committee, on the occasion of the award of the Nobel Peace Prize for 1997, Oslo, December 10, 1997.
Translation of the Norwegian text.

Your Majesties, Excellencies, Ladies and Gentlemen,

There are those among us who are unswerving in their faith that things can be done to make our world a better, safer, and more humane place, and who also, even when the tasks appear overwhelming, have the courage to tackle them. Such people deserve our admiration, and our gratitude. We are delighted and honoured to welcome some of them to the Oslo City Hall today. Our warm welcome to you, the representatives of the ICBL, the International Campaign to Ban Landmines, and to you, Jody Williams, the campaign's strongest single driving force. You have not only dared to tackle your task, but also proved that the impossible is possible. You have helped to rouse public opinion all over the world against the use of an arms technology that strikes quite randomly at the most innocent and most defenceless. And you have opened up the possibility that this wave of opinion can be channelled into political action.

We all know that the largest part of the task still lies ahead. Many nations, among them the largest, have been reluctant, at least so far, to commit themselves to not using this weapon. There is still the almost hopelessly huge and resource-consuming task of destroying the landmines–over one hundred million of them–that have been deployed. And the effort to build up opportunities for dignified lives for the many millions of innocent mine victims has only just begun. But through your self-sacrificing work, you have won support and created an organization that lead us to believe that it will be possible to reach the goal: a world completely free from anti-personnel mines. The course has been set, and the inspiration given. That is no small achievement, but a first step of very great and perhaps decisive importance. That step is what we honour you for today.

The mobilisation and focussing of broad popular involvement which we have witnessed bears promise that goes beyond the present issue. It appears to have established a pattern for how to realise political aims at the global level. The ICBL is an umbrella organization for over one thousand nongovernmental organizations, large and small, which have taken up the cause. The Norwegian Nobel Committee wishes to honour them all, and to draw attention to the impact which such broad coordination can achieve.

A second characteristic feature of this process that ought to be noted is how, in the next instance, the political level was mobilised. A week ago, in Ottawa, 121 countries signed the total ban on anti-personnel mines. Through Foreign Minister Lloyd Axworthy, the Government of Canada took the decisive initiative in that mobilisation when, in October 1996, it invited all countries to the Ottawa meeting. "Such a treaty," Axworthy said in connection with the invitation, "can be a powerful force that establishes the moral norm – that the production, use, stockpiling and transfer of anti-personnel mines is to be banned forever." The strategy adopted, in other words, was not to water the treaty down with a lot of exceptions aimed at inducing the hesitant to join in, but to convey a clear message. Though this may have frightened some countries off, it has of course, because of the overwhelming support for the process, placed the larger nations under considerable political pressure.

The problem of landmines has been on the international agenda for a long time. It was discussed in 1980, in connection with the Landmine Protocol to the Conventional Weapons Convention. It was when negotiations on the revision of that Protocol were being held in 1995–96 that frustration at the lack of progress made itself felt.

In November 1991, the Vietnam Veterans of America Foundation in Washington D.C. and Medico International in Frankfurt agreed to launch a campaign aimed at banning anti-personnel mines. When the first International Conference on Landmines was held in London in May 1993, representatives of 40 voluntary organizations attended. The following year, in Geneva, 75 organizations were represented. Today, over one thousand organizations are members of the ICBL. It was by hooking into this popular involvement that the Ottawa process came to mark a new political beginning, lifting the cause out of the backwater it had drifted into.

It is interesting to watch this initiative apparently feeding back into the United Nations and the whole system of international negotiations, and giving them new life. Effective political action is dependent on cooperation at several levels. At the national level, that is old news, first given memorable expression over 150 years ago by de Tocqueville in his famous analysis of democracy in America. Representative political bodies can not carry on politics in a vacuum. They need in some way or other to be rooted in public opinion. And public opinion must be formed and directed by the active involvement of individual members of society in society's manifold organizations or associations. These are the fundamental institutional elements of what we have learned to know as – a civil society.

The problem at the international level is that no global civil society has existed. Perhaps it is not so surprising that the UN has not always been able to be as effective as we might have wished. But in the extensive cooperation we have been registering between the multitude of nongovernmental organizations, the many national governments, and the international political system, first and foremost the UN, we may be seeing the outline of what may turn into a global civil society. We have glimpsed similar features in other connections, but hardly as clearly as in this particular case. In the bold hope this gives us for further development in the same direction, we see promising signs of a more peaceful world.

How did landmines come to be the problem that generated this kind of international concern? Weapons exist that in many ways are more terrible and pose a greater threat, nuclear weapons in particular. And is it not the case that by banning certain types of weapon, one indirectly legitimises the use of others, and thereby also legitimises war? What sort of peace policy is it just to ban certain types of weapon?

Certainly we have seen similar types of commitment, directed against nuclear weapons in particular, and the Norwegian Nobel Committee has on a number of occasions, most recently in 1995, called attention to active opposition to the build-up of nuclear arms. There is a vast difference between nuclear weapons and landmines. The former are the weapons of the rich, the latter of the poor. Yet they also have something in common. Both hit victims at a vast remove from the actual warfare. They strike mainly at civilian populations, and their effects continue for generations after the end of the armed conflict. They are weapons which cast the shadow of war also across peace. War's threat to life and limb is everywhere and never-ending. To set limits to war's repercussions for civilian populations and its impact on times of peace has always been an important aim of genuine work for peace.

At this very time, while nuclear war casts its shadow over us all – and perhaps for that very reason has remained an unrealised threat since 1945 – landmines are exploding every single day. Nearly all those killed or maimed are the poorest and most defenceless among us, and probably number some 26,000 each year. Yet the most alarming aspect of the situation may not be that total itself, but the constant threat to the much larger numbers who live in the danger zones, who do not know where they can send their children out to play, or who can only gather fuel or work in the fields at great risk to their own lives. Such people have been robbed of the opportunity to use the land to build their own societies.

The ICBL and Jody Williams' work is work for disarmament. The Norwegian Nobel Committee has frequently honoured disarmament efforts, or work for the "reduction of standing armies", to use Nobel's own words. Disarmament reduces tension and thereby the threat of war. The work of the ICBL and Jody Williams is, however, primarily aimed at what I have just mentioned: sheltering civilian populations from war. It is a humanitarian project. The Norwegian Nobel Committee's tradition of honouring humanitarian efforts goes right back to the first Peace Prize, awarded in 1901 to Henri Dunant, the founder of the Red Cross. Humanitarian work prevents war by seeking to eliminate the underlying causes of violence and war, the causes in the human mind. A humanitarian effort aims at "fraternity between nations", again to quote Nobel. It is a hand outstretched to the victims, both those who have been maimed and those in danger. It is a demonstration of care and compassion that transcends all national boundaries.

It is a paradox that what we find inside landmines is Nobel's brilliant invention, dynamite. Nobel was a profoundly moral man, and was deeply concerned about the potential of dynamite in weapons technology. At one time he developed a doctrine of deterrence. He wrote to his close friend, the peace activist Bertha von Suttner, that perhaps his factories were more effective in preventing war than her peace congresses. He can not have been completely convinced, however. When he decided to establish a peace prize, the idea probably came from Bertha von Suttner, and it was not a fear-ridden peace he wished to honour, but a peace of reconciliation and brotherhood. The inspiration from Bertha von Suttner is reflected in the special mention given in his will to the organization of peace congresses as a criterion for the award. Bertha von Suttner was to become the first woman Laureate when she was awarded the Peace Prize herself in 1905, after Nobel's death. There have not been many women among the Laureates, and no doubt there should have been more. But let us at least take credit for having made an early start. With her self-sacrificing, untiring and fruitful service to humanity and peace, Jody Williams is a worthy successor to Bertha von Suttner, who inspired the Peace Prize and brought Nobel to the realisation that peace must be rooted in the human mind.

An important step has been taken. The vast problem of landmines has effectively been placed on the international agenda. The worldwide opinion has been formed that something must be done about the problem. And the practical work of freeing the world from landmines has begun. It is in admiration, and in gratitude for their efforts to achieve that aim that we honour the ICBL and Jody Williams today with the Nobel Peace Prize for 1997. The vast and laborious task of putting an end to the production and sale of mines, destroying existing mines, and helping the victims has, however, only just begun. Let us therefore also express the hope that the process will win still greater support, so that the work can be intensified and a world without anti-personnel mines can become a reality in the foreseeable future.

THE NOBEL INSIGNIA AND THE AMOUNT OF THE PRIZE

In accordance with the statutes of the Nobel Foundation, the Prize-Winners received a diploma, a gold medal, and a document indicating the amount of the Prize. The value of each of the Prizes awarded in 1997 was 7,500,000 Swedish kronor.

The sum available for distribution among the Prize-Winners varies according to the annual net revenue of the main fund of the Nobel Foundation. In 1901, the first year in which the Prizes were awarded, each one was worth 150,000 Swedish kronor.

The diplomas presented to the laureates in Physics and in Chemistry have been designed by the artist Bengt Landin. The diploma presented to the laureate in Literature has been designed by the artist Bo Larsson. The calligraphy was designed by Annika Rücker.

The diplomas presented to the laureates in Physiology or Medicine have only the motif of the Nobel medal. Calligraphy by Susan Duvnäs.

The diplomas of the Nobel Prize for Peace, have been designed by the Norwegian artist Eva Arnesen. Calligraphy by Inger Magnus.

Steven Chu

Claude Cohen-Tannoudji

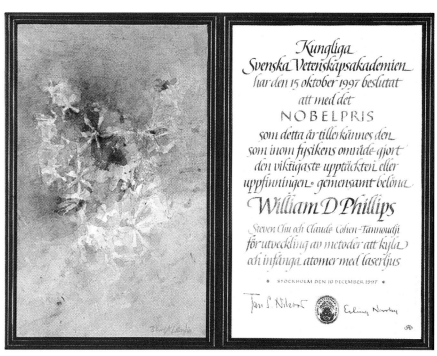

William D. Phillips

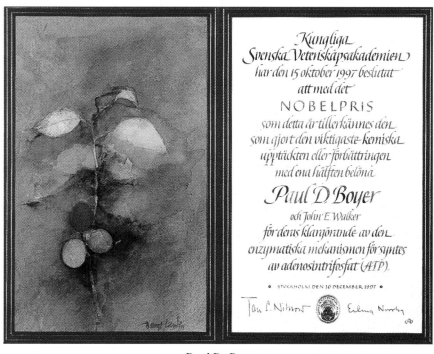

Paul D. Boyer

John E. Walker

Jens C. Skou

43

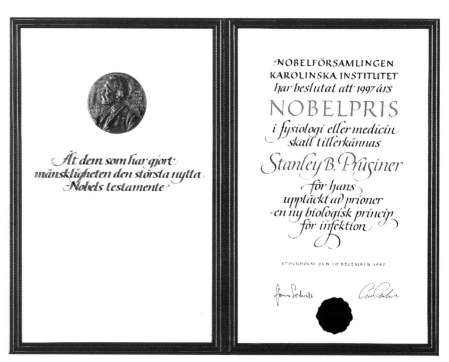

Stanley B. Prusiner

Dario Fo

International Campaign to Ban Landmines (ICBL)

Jody Williams

Robert C. Merton

Myron S. Scholes

THE NOBEL LECTURES
THE PRIZE-WINNERS
BIOGRAPHICAL NOTES

STEVEN CHU

My father, Ju Chin Chu, came to the United States in 1943 to continue his education at the Massachusetts Institute of Technology in chemical engineering, and two years later, my mother, Ching Chen Li, joined him to study economics. A generation earlier, my mother's grandfather earned his advanced degrees in civil engineering at Cornell while his brother studied physics under Perrin at the Sorbonne before they returned to China. However, when my parents married in 1945, China was in turmoil and the possibility of returning grew increasingly remote, and they decided to begin their family in the United States. My brothers and I were born as part of a typical nomadic academic career: my older brother was born in 1946 while my father was finishing at MIT, I was born in St. Louis in 1948 while my father taught at Washington University, and my younger brother completed the family in Queens shortly after my father took a position as a professor at the Brooklyn Polytechnic Institute.

In 1950, we settled in Garden City, New York, a bedroom community within commuting distance of Brooklyn Polytechnic. There were only two other Chinese families in this town of 25,000, but to our parents, the determining factor was the quality of the public school system. Education in my family was not merely emphasized, it was our raison d'être. Virtually all of our aunts and uncles had Ph.D.'s in science or engineering, and it was taken for granted that the next generation of Chu's were to follow the family tradition. When the dust had settled, my two brothers and four cousins collected three MDs, four Ph.D.s and a law degree. I could manage only a single advanced degree.

In this family of accomplished scholars, I was to become the academic black sheep. I performed adequately at school, but in comparison to my older brother, who set the record for the highest cumulative average for our high school, my performance was decidedly mediocre. I studied, but not in a particularly efficient manner. Occasionally, I would focus on a particular school project and become obsessed with, what seemed to my mother, to be trivial details instead of apportioning the time I spent on school work in a more efficient way.

I approached the bulk of my schoolwork as a chore rather than an intellectual adventure. The tedium was relieved by a few courses that seem to be qualitatively different. Geometry was the first exciting course I remember. Instead of memorizing facts, we were asked to think in clear, logical steps. Beginning from a few intuitive postulates, far reaching consequences could be derived, and I took immediately to the sport of proving theorems. I also fondly remember several of my English courses where the assigned reading often led to binges where I read many books by the same author.

Despite the importance of education in our family, my life was not completely centered around school work or recreational reading. In the summer after kindergarten, a friend introduced me to the joys of building plastic model airplanes and warships. By the fourth grade, I graduated to an erector set and spent many happy hours constructing devices of unknown purpose where the main design criterion was to maximize the number of moving parts and overall size. The living room rug was frequently littered with hundreds of metal "girders" and tiny nuts and bolts surrounding half-finished structures. An understanding mother allowed me to keep the projects going for days on end. As I grew older, my interests expanded to playing with chemistry: a friend and I experimented with homemade rockets, in part funded by money my parents gave me for lunch at school. One summer, we turned our hobby into a business as we tested our neighbors' soil for acidity and missing nutrients.

I also developed an interest in sports, and played in informal games at a nearby school yard where the neighborhood children met to play touch football, baseball, basketball and occasionally, ice hockey. In the eighth grade, I taught myself tennis by reading a book, and in the following year, I joined the school team as a "second string" substitute, a position I held for the next three years. I also taught myself how to pole vault using bamboo poles obtained from the local carpet store. I was soon able to clear 8 feet, but was not good enough to make the track team.

In my senior year, I took advanced placement physics and calculus. These two courses were taught with the same spirit as my earlier geometry course. Instead of a long list of formulas to memorize, we were presented with a few basic ideas or a set of very natural assumptions. I was also blessed by two talented and dedicated teachers.

My physics teacher, Thomas Miner was particularly gifted. To this day, I remember how he introduced the subject of physics. He told us we were going to learn how to deal with very simple questions such as how a body falls due to the acceleration of gravity. Through a combination of conjecture and observations, ideas could be cast into a theory that can be tested by experiments. The small set of questions that physics could address might seem trivial compared to humanistic concerns. Despite the modest goals of physics, knowledge gained in this way would become collected wisdom through the ultimate arbitrator – experiment.

In addition to an incredibly clear and precise introduction to the subject, Mr. Miner also encouraged ambitious laboratory projects. For the better part of my last semester at Garden City High, I constructed a physical pendulum and used it to make a "precision" measurement of gravity. The years of experience building things taught me skills that were directly applicable to the construction of the pendulum. Ironically, twenty five years later, I was to develop a refined version of this measurement using laser cooled atoms in an atomic fountain interferometer.

I applied to a number of colleges in the fall of my senior year, but because of my relatively lackluster A- average in high school, I was rejected by the Ivy

League schools, but was accepted at Rochester. By comparison, my older brother was attending Princeton, two cousins were in Harvard and a third was at Bryn Mawr. My younger brother seemed to have escaped the family pressure to excel in school by going to college without earning a high school diploma and by avoiding a career in science. (He nevertheless got a Ph.D. at the age of 21 followed by a law degree from Harvard and is now a managing partner of a major law firm.) As I prepared to go to college, I consoled myself that I would be an anonymous student, out of the shadow of my illustrious family.

The Rochester and Berkeley Years

At Rochester, I came with the same emotions as many of the entering freshman: everything was new, exciting and a bit overwhelming, but at least nobody had heard of my brothers and cousins. I enrolled in a two-year, introductory physics sequence that used *The Feynman Lectures in Physics* as the textbook. The *Lectures* were mesmerizing and inspirational. Feynman made physics seem so beautiful and his love of the subject is shown through each page. Learning to do the problem sets was another matter, and it was only years later that I began to appreciate what a magician he was at getting answers.

In my sophomore year, I became increasingly interested in mathematics and declared a major in both mathematics and physics. My math professors were particularly good, especially relative to the physics instructor I had that year. If it were not for the Feynman Lectures, I would have almost assuredly left physics. The pull towards mathematics was partly social: as a lowly undergraduate student, several math professors adopted me and I was invited to several faculty parties.

The obvious compromise between mathematics and physics was to become a theoretical physicist. My heroes were Newton, Maxwell, Einstein, up to the contemporary giants such as Feynman, Gell-Man, Yang and Lee. My courses did not stress the importance of the experimental contributions, and I was led to believe that the "smartest" students became theorists while the remainder were relegated to experimental grunts. Sadly, I had forgotten Mr. Miner's first important lesson in physics.

Hoping to become a theoretical physicist, I applied to Berkeley, Stanford, Stony Brook (Yang was there!) and Princeton. I chose to go to Berkeley and entered in the fall of 1970. At that time, the number of available jobs in physics was shrinking and prospects were especially difficult for budding young theorists. I recall the faculty admonishing us about the perils of theoretical physics: unless we were going to be as good as Feynman, we would be better off in experimental physics. To the best of my knowledge, this warning had no effect on either me or my fellow students.

After I passed the qualifying exam, I was recruited by Eugene Commins. I admired his breadth of knowledge and his teaching ability but did not yet learn of his uncanny ability to bring out the best in all of his students. He was ending a series of beta decay experiments and was casting around for a new direction of research. He was getting interested in astrophysics at the time and asked me to think about proto-star formation of a closely coupled binary pair. I had spent the summer between Rochester and Berkeley at the National Radio Astronomy Observatory trying to determine the deceleration of the universe with high red-shift radio source galaxies and was drawn to astrophysics. However, in the next two months, I avoided working on the theoretical problem he gave me and instead played in the lab.

One of my "play-experiments" was motivated by my interest in classical music. I noticed that one could hear out-of-tune notes played in a very fast run by a violinist. A simple estimate suggested that the frequency accuracy, Δv times the duration of the note, Δt did not satisfy the uncertainty relationship $\Delta v \Delta t \geq 1$. In order to test the frequency sensitivity of the ear, I connected an audio oscillator to a linear gate so that a tone burst of varying duration could be produced. I then asked my fellow graduate students to match the frequency of an arbitrarily chosen tone by adjusting the knob of another audio oscillator until the notes sounded the same. Students with the best musical ears could identify the center frequency of a tone burst that eventually sounded like a "click" with an accuracy of $\Delta v \Delta t \sim 0.1$.

By this time it was becoming obvious (even to me) that I would be much happier as an experimentalist and I told my advisor. He agreed and started me on a beta-decay experiment looking for "second-class currents", but after a year of building, we abandoned it to measure the Lamb shift in high-Z hydrogen-like ions. In 1974, Claude and Marie Bouchiat published their proposal to look for parity non-conserving effects in atomic transitions. The unified theory of weak and electromagnetic interactions suggested by Weinberg, Salam and Glashow postulated a neutral mediator of the weak force in addition to the known charged forces. Such an interaction would manifest itself as a very slight asymmetry in the absorption of left and right circularly polarized light in a magnetic dipole transition. Gene was always drawn to work that probed the most fundamental aspects of physics, and we were excited by the prospect that a table-top experiment could say something decisive about high energy physics. The experiment needed a state-of-the-art laser and my advisor knew nothing about lasers. I brashly told him not to worry; I would build it and we would be up and running in no time.

This work was tremendously exciting and the world was definitely watching us. Steven Weinberg would call my advisor every few months, hoping to hear news of a parity violating effect. Dave Jackson, a high energy theorist, and I would sometimes meet at the university swimming pool. During several of these encounters, he squinted at me and tersely asked, "Got a number yet?" The unspoken message was, "How dare you swim when there is important work to be done!"

Midway into the experiment, I told my advisor that I had suffered enough as a graduate student so he elevated me to post-doc status. Two years later, we and three graduate students published our first results. Unfortunately, we were scooped: a few months earlier, a beautiful high energy experiment at the Stanford Linear Collider had seen convincing evidence of neutral weak interactions between electrons and quarks. Nevertheless, I was offered a job as assistant professor at Berkeley in the spring of 1978.

I had spent all of my graduate and postdoctoral days at Berkeley and the faculty was concerned about inbreeding. As a solution, they hired me but also would permit me to take an immediate leave of absence before starting my own group at Berkeley. I loved Berkeley, but realized that I had a narrow view of science and saw this as a wonderful opportunity to broaden myself.

A Random Walk in Science at Bell Labs

I joined Bell Laboratories in the fall of 1978. I was one of roughly two dozen brash, young scientists that were hired within a two year period. We felt like the "Chosen Ones", with no obligation to do anything except the research we loved best. The joy and excitement of doing science permeated the halls. The cramped labs and office cubicles forced us to interact with each other and follow each others' progress. The animated discussions were common during and after seminars and at lunch and continued on the tennis courts and at parties. The atmosphere was too electric to abandon, and I never returned to Berkeley. To this day I feel guilty about it, but I think that the faculty understood my decision and have forgiven me.

Bell Labs management supplied us with funding, shielded us from extraneous bureaucracy, and urged us not to be satisfied with doing merely "good science." My department head, Peter Eisenberger, told me to spend my first six months in the library and talk to people before deciding what to do. A year later during a performance review, he chided me not to be content with anything less than "starting a new field". I responded that I would be more than happy to do that, but needed a hint as to *what* new field he had in mind.

I spent the first year at Bell writing a paper reviewing the current status of x-ray microscopy and started an experiment on energy transfer in ruby with Hyatt Gibbs and Sam McCall. I also began planning the experiment on the optical spectroscopy of positronium. Positronium, an atom made up of an electron and its anti-particle, was considered the most basic of all atoms, and a precise measurement of its energy levels was a long standing goal ever since the atom was discovered in 1950. The problem was that the atoms would annihilate into gamma rays after only 140×10^{-9} seconds, and it was impossible to produce enough of them at any given time. When I started the experiment, there were 12 published attempts to observe the optical fluorescence of the atom. People only publish failures if they have spent enough time and money so their funding agencies demand something in return.

My management thought I was ruining my career by trying an impossible experiment. After two years of no results, they strongly suggested that I abandon my quest. But I was stubborn and I had a secret weapon: his name is Allen Mills. Our strengths complemented each other beautifully, but in the end, he helped me solve the laser and metrology problems while I helped him with his positrons. We finally managed to observe a signal working with only ~4 atoms per laser pulse! Two years later and with 20 atoms per pulse, we refined our methods and obtained one of the most accurate measurements of quantum electrodynamic corrections to an atomic system.

In the fall of 1983, I became head of the Quantum Electronics Research Department and moved to another branch of Bell Labs at Holmdel, New Jersey. By then my research interests had broadened, and I was using pico-second laser techniques to look at excitons as a potential system for observing metal-insulator transitions and Anderson localization. With this apparatus, I accidentally discovered a counter-intuitive pulse-propagation effect. I was also planning to enter surface science by constructing a novel electron spectro-meter based on threshold ionization of atoms that could potentially increase the energy resolution by more than an order of magnitude.

While designing the electron spectrometer, I began talking informally with Art Ashkin, a colleague at Holmdel. Art had a dream to trap atoms with light, but the management stopped the work four years ago. An important experi-ment had demonstrated the dipole force, but the experimenters had reached an impasse. Over the next few months, I began to realize the way to hold onto atoms with light was to first get them very cold. Laser cooling was going to make possible all of Art Ashkin's dreams plus a lot more. I promptly drop-ped most of my other experiments and with Leo Holberg, my new post-doc, and my technician, Alex Cable, began our laser cooling experiment. This brings me to the beginning of our work in laser cooling and trapping of atoms and the subject of my Nobel Lecture.

Stanford and the future

Life at Bell Labs, like Mary Poppins, was "practically perfect in every way". However, in 1987, I decided to leave my cozy ivory tower. Ted Hänsch had left Stanford to become co-director of the Max Planck Institute for Quantum Optics and I was recruited to replace him. Within a few months, I also receiv-ed offers from Berkeley and Harvard, and I thought the offers were as good as they were ever going to be. My management at Bell Labs was successful in keeping me at Bell Labs for 9 years, but I wanted to be like my mentor, Gene Commins, and the urge to spawn scientific progeny was growing stronger.

Ted Geballe, a distinguished colleague of mine at Stanford who also went from Berkeley to Bell to Stanford years earlier, described our motives: "The best part of working at a university is the students. They come in fresh, enthusiastic, open to ideas, unscarred by the battles of life. They don't realize it, but they're the recipients of the best our society can offer. If a mind is ever free to be creative, that's the time. They come in believing textbooks are authoritative but eventually they figure out that textbooks and professors don't know everything, and then they start to think on their own. Then, I begin learning from them."

My students at Stanford have been extraordinary, and I have learned much from them. Much of my most important work such as fleshing out the details of polarization gradient cooling, the demonstration of the atomic fountain clock, and the development of atom interferometers and a new method of laser cooling based on Raman pulses was done at Stanford with my students as collaborators.

While still continuing in laser cooling and trapping of atoms, I have recently ventured into polymer physics and biology. In 1986, Ashkin showed that the first optical atom trap demonstrated at Bell Labs also worked on tiny glass spheres embedded in water. A year after I came to Stanford, I set about to manipulate individual DNA molecules with the so-called "optical tweezers" by attaching micron-sized polystyrene spheres to the ends of the molecule. My idea was to use two optical tweezers introduced into an optical microscope to grab the plastic handles glued to the ends of the molecule. Steve Kron, an M.D./Ph.D. student in the medical school, introduced me to molecular biology in the evenings. By 1990, we could see an image of a single, fluorescently labeled DNA molecule in real time as we stretched it out in water. My students improved upon our first attempts after they discovered our initial protocol demanded luck as a major ingredient. Using our new ability to simultaneously visualize and manipulate individual molecules of DNA, my group began to answer polymer dynamics questions that have persisted for decades. Even more thrilling, we discovered something new in the last year: identical molecules in the same initial state will choose several distinct pathways to a new equilibrium state. This "molecular individualism" was never anticipated in previous polymer dynamics theories or simulations.

I have been at Stanford for ten and a half years. The constant demands of my department and university and the ever increasing work needed to obtain funding have stolen much of my precious thinking time, and I sometimes yearn for the halcyon days of Bell Labs. Then, I think of the work my students and post-docs have done with me at Stanford and how we have grown together during this time.

THE MANIPULATION OF NEUTRAL PARTICLES

Nobel Lecture, December 8, 1997

by

STEVEN CHU

Stanford University, Departments of Physics and Applied Physics, Stanford, CA 94305-4060, USA

The written version of my lecture is a personal account of the development of laser cooling and trapping. Rather than give a balanced history of the field, I chose to present a personal glimpse of how my colleagues and I created our path of research.

I joined Bell Laboratories in the fall of 1978 after working with Eugene Commins as a graduate student and post-doc at Berkeley on a parity non-conservation experiment in atomic physics.[1] Bell Labs was a researcher's paradise. Our management supplied us with funding, shielded us from bureaucracy, and urged us to do the best science possible. The cramped labs and office cubicles forced us to rub shoulders with each other. Animated discussions frequently interrupted seminars and casual conversations in the cafeteria would sometimes mark the beginning of a new collaboration.

In my first years at Bell Labs, I wrote an internal memo on the prospects for x-ray microscopy and worked on an experiment investigating energy transfer in ruby with Hyatt Gibbs and Sam McCall as a means of studying Anderson Localization.[2, 3] This work led us to consider the possibility of Mott or Anderson transitions in other exciton systems such as GaP:N with picosecond laser techniques.[4] During this work, I accidentally discovered that picosecond pulses propagate with the group velocity, even when the velocity exceeds the speed of light or becomes negative.[5]

While I was learning about excitons and how to build picosecond lasers, I began to work with Allan Mills, the world's expert on positrons and positronium. We began to discuss the possibility of working together while I was still at Berkeley, but did not actually begin the experiment until 1979. After three long and sometimes frustrating years, a long time by Bell Labs standards, we finally succeeded in exciting and measuring the 1S–2S energy interval in positronium.[6]

MOVING TO HOLMDEL AND WARMING UP TO LASER COOLING

My entry into the field of laser cooling and trapping was stimulated by my move from Murray Hill, New Jersey, to head the Quantum Electronics Research Department at the Holmdel branch in the fall of 1983. During conversations with Art Ashkin, an office neighbor at Holmdel, I began to learn about his dream to trap atoms with light. He found an increasingly attentive listener and began to feed me copies of his reprints. That fall I was also joined by my new post-doc, Leo Hollberg. When I hired him, I had planned to construct an electron energy-loss spectrometer based on threshold ionization of a beam of atoms with a picosecond laser. We hoped to improve the energy resolution of existing spectrometers by at least an order of magnitude and then use our spectrometer to study molecular adsorbates on surfaces with optical resolution and electron sensitivity. However, Leo was trained as an atomic physicist and was also developing an interest in the possibility of manipulating atoms with light.

Leo and I spontaneously decided to drive to Massachusetts to attend a workshop on the trapping of ions and atoms organized by David Pritchard at MIT. I was ignorant of the subject and lacked the primitive intuition that is essential to add something new to a field. As an example of my profound lack of understanding, I found myself wondering about the dispersive nature of the "dipole force". The force is attractive when the frequency of light is tuned below the resonance, repulsive when tuned above the resonance, and vanishes when tuned directly on the atomic resonance. Looking back on these early fumblings, I am embarrassed by how long it took me to recognize that the effect can be explained by freshman physics. On the other hand, I was not alone in my lack of intuition. When I asked a Bell Labs colleague about this effect, he answered, "Only Jim Gordon really understands the dipole force!"

By 1980, the forces that light could exert on matter were well understood.[7] Maxwell's calculation of the momentum flux density of light,[8] and the laboratory observation of light pressure on macroscopic objects by Lebedev[9] and by Nichols and Hull[10] provided the first quantitative understanding of how light could exert forces on material objects. Einstein[11] pointed out the quantum nature of this force: an atom that absorbs a photon of energy $h\nu$ will receive a momentum impulse $h\nu/c$ along the direction of the incoming photon $\mathbf{p}_{in}$. If the atom emits a photon with momentum $\mathbf{p}_{out}$, the atom will recoil in the opposite direction. Thus the atom experiences a net momentum change $\Delta\mathbf{P}_{atom} = \mathbf{p}_{in}\text{-}\mathbf{p}_{out}$ due to this incoherent scattering process. In 1930, Frisch[12] observed the deflection of an atomic beam with light from a sodium resonance lamp where the average change in momentum was due to the scattering of one photon.

Since the scattered photon has no preferred direction, the net effect is due to the absorbed photons, resulting in scattering force, $\mathbf{F}_{scatt} = N\mathbf{p}_{in}$, where N is the number of photons scattered per second. Typical scattering rates for atoms excited by a laser tuned to a strong resonance line are on the order of 10^7 to 10^8/sec. As an example, the velocity of a sodium atom changes by 3 cm/sec per absorbed photon. The scattering force can be 10^5 times the gravitational acceleration on Earth, feeble compared to electromagnetic forces on charged particles, but stronger than any other long-range force that affect neutral particles.

There is another type of force based on the lensing (i.e. coherent scattering) of photons. A lens alters the distribution of momentum of a light field, and by Newton's third law, the lens must experience a reaction force equal and opposite to the rate of momentum change of the light field. For example, a positive lens will be drawn towards regions of high light intensity as shown in Fig. 1.[13] In the case of an atom the amount of lensing is calculated by adding the amplitude of the incident light field with the dipole field generated by the atomic electrons driven by the incident field.

Figure 1. A photograph of a 10 μm glass sphere trapped in water with green light from an argon laser coming from above. The picture is a fluorescence image taken using a green blocking, red transmitting filter. The exiting (refracted) rays show a notable decrease in beam angles relative to the incident rays. The increased forward momentum of the light results in an upward force on the glass bead needed to balance the downward scattering force. The stria in the forward-scattered light is a common Mie-scattering ring pattern. (Courtesy A. Ashkin).

This reaction force is also called the "dipole force". The oscillating electric field $\mathbf{E}$ of the light induces a dipole moment $\mathbf{p}$ on the particle. If the induced dipole moment is in phase with $\mathbf{E}$, the interaction energy $-\mathbf{p}\cdot\mathbf{E}$ is lower in high field regions. If the induced dipole moment is out of phase with the driving field, the particle's energy is increased in the electric field and the particle will feel a force ejecting it out of the field. If we model the atom or particle as a damped harmonic oscillator, the sign change of the dipole force is easy to understand. An oscillator driven below its natural resonant frequency responds in phase with the driving field, while an oscillator driven above its natural frequency oscillates out of phase with the driving force. Exactly on resonance, the oscillator is 90 degrees out of phase and $\mathbf{p}\cdot\mathbf{E} = 0$.

The dipole force was first discussed by Askar'yan[14] in connection with plasmas as well as neutral atoms. The possibility of trapping atoms with this force was considered by Letokhov,[15] who suggested that atoms might be confined along one dimension in the nodes or antinodes of a standing wave of light tuned far from an atomic transition. In 1970, Arthur Ashkin had succeeded in trapping micron-sized particles with a pair of opposing, focused beams of laser light, as shown in Fig. 2. Confinement along the axial direction was due to the scattering force: a displacement towards either of the focal points of the light would result in an imbalance of scattered light that would push the particle back to the center of the trap. Along the radial direction, the out-wardly directed scattering force could be overcome by the attractive dipole force. In the following years, other stable particle trapping geometries were demonstrated by Ashkin,[16] and in 1978, he proposed the first three-dimensional traps for atoms.[17] In the same year, with John Bjorkholm and Richard Freeman, he demonstrated the dipole force by focusing an atomic beam using a focused laser beam.[18]

Focused laser beams

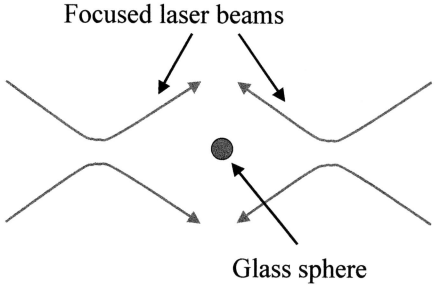

Glass sphere

Figure 2. A schematic diagram of the first particle trap used by Ashkin. Confinement in the axial direction is due to an imbalance of the scattering forces between the left and right propagating beams. Confinement in the radial direction results from the induced dipole force which must overcome the outwardly directed scattering force.

Despite this progress, experimental work at Bell labs stopped a year later because of two major obstacles. First, the trapping forces generated by intense focused laser beams are feeble. Atoms at room temperature would have an average energy $\frac{3}{2}k_BT \sim \frac{1}{2}mv^2$, orders of magnitude greater than could be confined by the proposed traps. A cold source of atoms with sufficiently high flux did not exist and a trap with large volume was needed to maximize the number of atoms that could be trapped. Second, the relatively large-volume optical trap made from opposing light beams was found to have serious heating problems. An atom could absorb a photon from one beam and be stimulated back to the initial state by a photon from the opposing beam. In this process, it would receive two photon impulses in the same direction. However, the same atom could have been excited and stimulated by the two beams in the reverse order, resulting in a net impulse in the other direction. Since the order of absorption and stimulated emission is random, this process would increase the random velocity of the atom and they would quickly heat and boil out of the trap. This heating effect was rigorously calculated by Jim Gordon with Ashkin for a two-level atom.[19]

TAKING THE PLUNGE INTO THE COLD

My first idea to solve the trap loading problem was modest at best, but it got me to think seriously about trapping atoms. I proposed to make a cold source of atoms by depositing sodium atoms into a rare-gas matrix of neon.[20] By heating the cryogenic surface supporting this matrix of atoms with a pulsed laser, I thought it should be possible to "puff" the neon and sodium atoms into a vapor with a temperature of a few tens of Kelvin. Once a vapor, a reasonable fraction of the sodium would become isolated atoms and the puffed source would contain the full Maxwell-Boltzmann distribution of atoms, including the very slowest atoms. In a conventional atomic beam, the slowest atoms are knocked out of the way by faster moving atoms overtaking them. In a puffed source, the surface could be quickly heated and cooled so that there would be no fast atoms coming from behind. An added advantage was that the source would turn off quickly and completely so that the detection of even a few trapped atoms would be possible.

Soon after my passage from interested bystander to participant, I realized that the route to trapping was through laser cooling with counter-propagating beams of light. If the laser beams were tuned below the atomic resonance, a moving atom would Doppler-shift the beam opposing its motion closer to resonance and shift the beam co-propagating with the motion away from resonance. Thus, after averaging over many impulses of momentum from both beams, the atom would experience a net force opposing its motion. In the limit where the atoms were moving slowly enough so that the difference in the absorption due to the Doppler effect was linearly proportional to the velocity, this force would result in viscous damping, $\mathbf{F} = -\alpha\mathbf{v}$. This elegant idea was proposed by Hänsch and Schawlow in 1975.[21] A related cooling scheme was proposed by Wineland and Itano in the same year.[22]

An estimate of the equilibrium temperature is obtained by equating the cooling rate in the absence of heating with the heating rate in the absence of cooling,

$$dW_{heating}/dt = dW_{cooling}/dt = -\mathbf{F}\cdot\mathbf{v}.$$

The heating rate is due to the random kicks an atom receives by randomly scattering photons from counter-propagating beams that surround the atoms.[23, 19] The momentum grows as a random walk in momentum space so the average random momentum p would increase as

$$\frac{dW_{heating}}{dt} = \frac{d}{dt}(\frac{p^2}{2M}) = \frac{N(p_r)^2}{2M}$$

where p_r is the momentum recoil due to each photon and N is the number of photon kicks per second. By equating the heating rate to the cooling rate, one can calculate an equilibrium temperature as a function of the laser intensity, the linewidth of the transition, and the detuning of the laser from resonance. The minimum equilibrium temperature $k_B T_{min} = \hbar\Gamma/2$, where Γ is the linewidth of the transition, was predicted to occur at low intensities and a detuning $\Delta v = \Gamma/2$ where the Doppler shift asymmetry was a maximum. In the limit of low intensity, all of the laser beams would act independently and the heating complications that would result from stimulated transitions between opposing laser beams could be ignored.

Not only would the light cool the atoms, it would also confine them. The laser cooling scheme was analogous to the Brownian motion of a dust particle immersed in water. The particle experiences a viscous drag force and the confinement time in a region of space could be estimated based on another result in elementary physics: the mean square displacement $\langle x^2 \rangle$ after a time Δt described by a random walk, $\langle x^2 \rangle = 2Dt$, where the diffusion constant is given by the Einstein relation $D = k_B T/\alpha$. For atoms moving with velocities $\mathbf{v}$ such that $\mathbf{k} \cdot \mathbf{v} < \Gamma$, the force would act as a viscous damping force $\mathbf{F} = -\alpha\mathbf{v}$. By surrounding the atoms with six beams propagating along the $\pm$ x, y and z directions, we could construct a sea of photons that would act like an exceptionally viscous fluid: an "optical molasses".[24] If the light intensity was kept low, the atoms would quickly cool to temperatures approaching T_{min}. Once cooled, they would remain confined in a centimeter region of space for times as long as a fraction of a second.

At this point, Leo and I shelved our plans to build the electron spectrometer and devoted our energies to making the optical molasses work. We rapidly constructed the puffing source of sodium needed to load the optical molasses. To simplify matters, we began with a pellet of sodium heated at room temperature. Rather than deal with the complications of a rare gas matrix, Leo and I decided to increase the number of cold atoms by slowing atoms from the puff source before attempting the optical molasses experiment. There were several early experiments that slowed atomic beams with laser light,[25] but sodium atoms had to be slowed to velocities on the order of 200–300 cm/sec (essentially stopped!) before an atom trap could be loaded. Two groups achieved this milestone in late 1984: a group at the National Bureau of Standards in Gaithersburg, Maryland, led by Bill Phillips using a tapered magnetic field[26] and another NBS group in Boulder, Colorado, led by Jan Hall.[27] We decided to copy the technique of Ertmer, et al.,[27] and use an electro-optic generator to produce a frequency-shifted sideband. The frequency-shifted light is directed against the atoms coming off the sodium surface, and as the atoms slow down, the frequency is changed in order to keep the light in resonance with the Doppler shifting atoms.

Leo was better at electronics than I and assumed the responsibility of the radio-frequency part of the project while I set out to build a wideband, transmission line electro-optic modulator. One of the advantages of working at Bell Laboratories was that one could often find a needed expert consultant within the Labs. Much of the electro-optic modulator development was pioneered at the Labs in Holmdel in the 1960s and we were still the leaders of the field in 1983. I learned about making electro-optic modulators by reading *the* book written by a colleague, Ivan Kaminow.[28] I enlisted Larry Buhl to cut and polish the $LiTaO_3$ crystal for the modulator. Rod Alferness taught me about microwave impedance matching and provided the SMA "launchers" needed to match Leo's electronics with my parallel-plate transmission line modulator. One month after we decided to precool the atoms with a frequency-swept laser beam, we had a functioning, wideband gigahertz electro-optic modulator and driver and could begin to precool the atoms from our puffing source.

In the early spring of 1984, Leo and I started with a completely bare optical table, no vacuum chamber, and no modulator. Later that spring, John Bjorkholm, who had previously demonstrated the dipole force by focusing an atomic beam, joined our experiment. In the early summer, I recruited Alex Cable, a fresh graduate from Rutgers. Officially he was hired as my "technician": unofficially, he became a super-graduate student. In less than one year, we submitted our optical molasses paper.[29, 30] The two papers reporting the stopping of atomic beams [26, 27] were published one month earlier.

The apparatus we built to demonstrate optical molasses is shown in Figs. 3a and 3b. We had an ultra-high-vacuum chamber, but did not want to be hampered by long bake-out times to achieve good vacuum. Instead, we built a cryo-shield painted with Aquadag, a graphite-based substance. When cooled

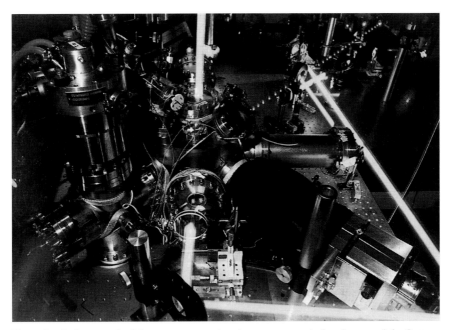

Figure 3 a. A photograph of the apparatus used to demonstrate optical molasses and the first optical trap for atoms. The photograph is a double exposure made by photographing the apparatus under normal lighting conditions and then photographing the laser beams by moving a white card along the beam path in a darkened room. The 10 Hz pulsed laser used to evaporate the sodium pellet (doubled YAG at 532nm) appears as dots of light.

Figure 3 b. Art Ashkin and the author in front of the apparatus in 1986, shortly after the first optical trapping experiment was completed.

to liquid-nitrogen temperatures, the shield became a very effective sorption pump: we could open the vacuum chamber one day and be running by the next day. Fast turnaround time has always been important to me. Mistakes are unavoidable, so I wanted an apparatus that would allow mistakes to be corrected as rapidly as possible.

The first signals of atoms confined in optical molasses showed confinement times of a few tens of milliseconds, but shortly afterwards we improved the storage time by over an order of magnitude. Surprisingly, it took us a week after achieving molasses to look inside the vacuum can with our eyes instead of with a photomultiplier tube. When we finally did, we were rewarded with the sight shown in Fig. 4.

In this early work, the laser beams were aligned to be as closely counter-propagating as we could manage. A year later, we stumbled onto a misalignment configuration that produced another order of magnitude increase in the storage time. This so-called "super-molasses" alignment of our beams also created a compression of the atoms into a region of space on the order of 2 mm diameter from an initial spread of 1 cm. We were never able to understand this phenomena and after a number of attempts, published a brief summary of these results in conference proceedings.[31]

In our first molasses work, we realized that the traditional method of measuring the temperature by measuring the Doppler broadening of an atomic resonance line would not work for the low temperatures we hoped to achieve. Instead we introduced a time-of-flight technique to directly measure the vel-

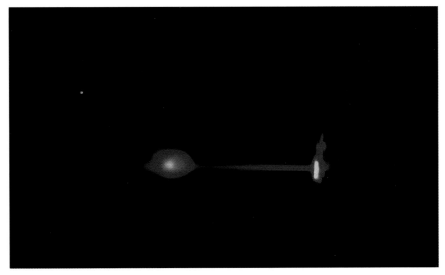

Figure 4. A photograph of sodium atoms confined in optical molasses experiment. The atoms were pre-cooled by a counterpropagating laser before entering the region of six crossed laser beams.

ocity distribution of the atoms. After allowing the atoms in the molasses to come to equilibrium, we turned off the light for a variable amount of time. The fast atoms escaped ballistically during this time while the slower atoms were recaptured by the molasses. Our first measurements showed a temperature of 185μK, slightly lower than the minimum temperature allowed by the theory of Doppler cooling. We then made the cardinal mistake of experimental physics: instead of listening to Nature, we were overly influenced by theoretical expectations. By including a fudge factor to account for the way atoms filled the molasses region, we were able to bring our measurement into accord with our expectations.

ON TO OPTICAL TRAPPING

Once we demonstrated optical molasses, we began to explore ways to achieve our original goal of optically trapping atoms. As a point of reference, Bill Phillips and his collaborators had reported the magnetic trapping of sodium atoms[32] two weeks before our optical molasses paper came out. Although the 1/e storage of the molasses confinement in our first experiment was a respectable τ~0.36 sec, optical molasses does not provide a restoring force that would push the atoms to the center of the trap.

Despite the fact that we were in possession of a great source of cold atoms, the path to trapping was not yet clear to us for a number of reasons: (*i*) Optical traps based strictly on the scattering force seemed to be ruled out because of a no-trapping theorem referred to as the "Optical Earnshaw Theorem". This theorem was published in response to earlier proposals to make atom traps based on the scattering force.[33, 34] (*ii*) We believed a trap

68

based on an opposing-beam geometry was not viable because of the severe stimulated heating effects. (*iii*) Finally, we ruled out a single focused laser beam because of the tiny trapping volume. We were wrong on all counts.

Immediately after the molasses experiment, we tried to implement a large-volume ac light trap suggested by Ashkin.[35] Our attempt failed, and after a few months, we began to cast around for other alternatives. One possibility was another type of ac trap we proposed at a conference talk in December of 1984,[36] but we wanted something simpler. Sometime in the winter of 1986, during one of our brainstorming sessions on what to do next, John Bjork-holm tried to resurrect the single focused beam trap first proposed in Ashkin's 1978 paper.[17] I promptly rejected the idea because of the small trapping volume. A ~1-watt laser focused to produce a ~5-mK-deep trap would have a trapping volume of ~10^{-7}cm^3. Since the density of atoms in our optical molasses was 10^6 atoms/cm^3, we would capture fewer than one atom in a trap surrounded by 10^6 atoms in molasses. A day or two after convincing the group that a trap based on a focused laser beam would not work, I realized that many more atoms would be captured by the trap than my original estimate. An atom close to the trap might not be immediately captured, but it would have repeated opportunities to fall into the trap during its random walk in optical molasses.

The trap worked. We could actually see the random walk loading with our own eyes. A tiny dot of light grew in brightness as more atoms fell into the trap. During the first days of trapping success, I ran up and down the halls, pulling people into our lab to share in the excitement. My director, Chuck Shank, showed polite enthusiasm, but I was not sure he actually picked out the signal from the reflections in the vacuum can windows and the surrounding fluorescence. Art Ashkin came down with the flu shortly after our initial success. He confessed to me later that he began to have doubts: as he lay in bed with a fever; he wasn't sure whether the fever caused him to imagine we had a working trap.

We tried to image the tiny speck of light onto an apertured photomultiplier tube, but the slightest misalignment would include too much light from the surrounding molasses. It was a frustrating experience not to be able to produce a repeatable signal on a photomultiplier tube if we could actually see the atoms with our eyes. Then it dawned on me: if we could see the signal with our eyes, we could record it with a sensitive video camera and then analyze the video tape! A local RCA representative, tickled by the experiment, loaned us a silicon-intensified video camera. Our trapping paper included a photo of our trapped atoms, the first color picture published in Physical Review Letters.[37]

As we began the atom trapping, Art decided to trap micron-sized particles of glass in a single focused beam as a "proof of principle" for the atom trap. Instead of an atom in optical molasses, he substituted a silica (glass) sphere embedded in water. A micron-sized sphere is far more polarizable than an atom and Ashkin felt that it could be trapped at room temperature if the intensity gradient in the axial direction that would draw the glass bead into the focus of the light could overcome the scattering force pushing the particle out of the trap. This more macroscopic version of the optical tweezers trap was demonstrated quickly and gave us more confidence that the atom trap might work.[38] At that time, none of us realized how this simple "toy experiment" was going to flower.

Shortly after we demonstrated the optical trap, I hired Mara Prentiss as a new permanent staff member in my department. She began to work on the super-molasses riddle with us when I got a phone call from Dave Pritchard at MIT. He told me he and his student, Eric Raab, had been working on a scattering-force trap that would circumvent the Optical Earnshaw Theorem.[33] This theorem states that a scattering-force trap is impossible provided the scattering force $\mathbf{F}_{scatt}$ is proportional to the laser intensity $\mathbf{I}$. The proof was straight forward: $\nabla\cdot\mathbf{F}_{scatt} = 0$ since any region in empty space must have the net intensity flux inward equal to the flux outward. Thus there cannot be a region in space where all force lines $\mathbf{F}_{scatt}$ point inward to a stable trapping point. Pritchard, Carl Wieman, and their colleagues had noted that the assumption $\mathbf{F}_{scatt} \propto \mathbf{I}$ need not be true.[39] They went on to suggest possible combinations of external magnetic or electric fields that could be used to create a stable optical trap.

Raab had had difficulties in getting a scattering-force trap to work at MIT and, as a last attempt before giving up, they asked if we were interested in collaborating with them on this work. The basic idea is illustrated in Fig. 5 for the case of an atom with F = 1 in the ground state and F = 2 in the excited state, where F is the total angular momentum quantum number. A weak spherical quadrupole trap magnetic field would split the Zeeman sublevels of a multilevel atom illuminated by counterpropagating circularly polarized laser beams. Due to the slight Zeeman-shift, an atom to the right of the trap center optically pump predominantly into the m_F = -1 state. Once in this state, the large difference in the scattering rates for σ^- light and σ^+ light causes the atom to experience a net scattering force towards the trap center. Atoms to the left of center would scatter more photons from the σ^+ beam. Since the laser beams remain tuned below all of the Zeeman split resonance lines, optical molasses cooling would still be occurring. The generalization to three dimensions is straightforward.

All we needed to do, was insert a pair of modest magnetic-field coils into our apparatus to test this idea. I wound some refrigeration tubing for the magnetic-field coils, but had to tear myself away to honor a previous commitment to help set up a muonium spectroscopy experiment with Allan Mills, Ken Nagamine and collaborators.[40] A few days later, the molasses was running again, and I received a call at the muon facility in Japan from Alex, his voice trembling with excitement. The trap worked spectacularly well and the atom cloud was blindingly bright compared to our dipole trap. Instead of the measly 1000 atoms we had in our first trap, they were getting 10^7 to 10^8 atoms.[41]

The basic idea for the trap was due to Jean Dalibard, a protégé of Claude Cohen-Tannoudji. His idea was stimulated by a talk given by Dave Pritchard on how the Earnshaw theorem could be circumvented. I called Jean in Paris

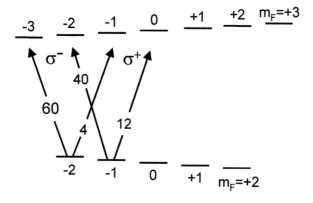

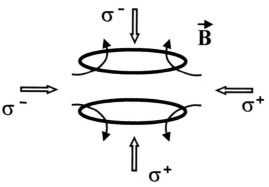

Figure 5. The magneto-optic trap for atoms with an F = 2 ground state and a F = 3 excited state. The slight energy level shifts of the Zeeman sub-levels cause symmetry to be broken and the atoms to optically pump predominantly into either the $m_F = +2$ or $m_F = -2$ state for **B**<0 or **B**>0. Once in the optically pumped states, the atoms are pushed towards the **B** = 0 region due to the large difference in relative strengths of the transition rates. The relative transition rates for σ^+ and σ^- light for the $m_F = -2$ and -1 states are shown.

to convince him that his name should go on the paper we were writing. Jean is both brilliant and modest, and felt it would be inappropriate to be a co-author since he did not do any of the work.[42]

The magneto-optic trap (commonly referred to as the MOT) immediately seized the attention of the growing community of coolers and trappers. Carl Wieman's group showed that atoms could be directly loaded from a tenuous vapor without the intermediate step of slowing an atomic beam.[43] By increasing the size of the laser beams used in the trap, Kurt Gibble and I showed that as many as $\sim 4 \times 10^{10}$ atoms could be trapped.[44] Wolfgang Ketterle, Pritchard, et al.[45] showed that the density of atoms in the MOT could be increased significantly by causing atoms to scatter less light in the central portion of the trap by blocking the repumping beam in that region of space. Stimulated by their shadowing idea, my collaborators and I at Stanford showed that by simply turning off the repumping light at the end stage of molasses dramatically increases the density of low-temperature atoms in the MOT.[46]

Figure 5 b. A photograph of atoms confined in a magneto-optic trap. The line of fluorescence below the ball of trapped atoms is due to the atomic beam used to load the trap.

The invention and development of the MOT exemplifies how the field of laser cooling and trapping grew out of the combined ideas and cooperation of an international set of scientists. For this reason, I find it especially fitting that the magneto-optic trap is the starting point of most experiments using laser-cooled atoms.

OPTICAL MOLASSES REVISITED

In the winter of 1987, I decided to leave the "ivory tower" of Bell Labs and accept an offer to become a professor at Stanford. When I left Bell Labs, we had just demonstrated the magneto-optic trap and it was clear the trap would provide an ideal starting point for a number of experiments. I arrived at Stanford in the fall of 1987, not knowing how long it would take to build a new research team.[47] Bill Phillips and Claude Cohen-Tannoudji were assembling powerful teams of scientists that could not be duplicated at Stanford. Dave Pritchard had been cultivating a powerful group at MIT. Other "home run hitters" in atomic physics such as Carl Wieman and Alain Aspect had just entered the field. Meanwhile, I had to start over again, writing proposals and meeting with prospective graduate students. If I had thought carefully about starting a new lab in the face of this competition, I might not have moved.

As with many aspects of my career, I may not have made the smart move, but I made a lucky move. From 1988 to 1993, I entered into the most productive time in my scientific career to date. My first three graduate students were Mark Kasevich, Dave Weiss, and Mike Fee. I also had two post-docs, Yaakov Shevy and Erling Riis who joined my group my first year at Stanford.

By January of 1988, Dave and Yaakov had a magneto-optic trap going in the original chamber we used to demonstrate optical molasses and the dipole trap. The plan was to improve the optical trapping techniques and then use the new laser cooling and trapping technology to explore new physics that could be accessed with cold atoms.

Another chamber was being assembled by Mark and Erling with the intent of studying the "quantum reflection" of atoms from cold surfaces. While I was at Bell Labs, Allan Mills and Phil Platzman began to get me interested in studying quantum reflection with ultracold atoms. The problem can be simply posed as follows: consider an atom with a long de Broglie wavelength λ incident on an idealized, short-range, *attractive* potential. In general there is a transmitted wave and reflected wave, but in the limit where λ is much greater than the length scale of the potential, one gets the counterintuitive result that the probability of reflection goes to unity. A real surface potential has a power-law attraction of the form $1/z^n$ and has no length scale. An atom near a surface will experience an attractive van der Waals force with a $1/z^3$ potential and, further away, the attractive potential would become $1/z^4$ due to "retarded potential" effects first discussed by Casimir. There are also subtleties to the problem when inelastic scattering channels are included. This problem had attracted the attention of a considerable number of theorists and experimentalists.

My plan of research was soon tossed out the window by a discovery that sent shock waves through the laser cooling community. By 1987, other groups began to produce optical molasses in their labs and measured atom temperatures near the expected limit,[48, 49] but in the spring of 1988, Bill Phillips and co-workers reported that sodium atoms in optical molasses could be cooled to temperatures far below the limit predicted by theory.[50] The NIST group reported the temperature of sodium atoms cooled in optical molasses to be 43 ± 20 μK and that the temperature did not follow the frequency dependence predicted by theory. The result was so surprising, they performed three different time-of-flight methods to confirm their result. Within a few months, three separate groups led by Wieman, Cohen-Tannoudji, and myself verified that sodium and cesium atoms in optical molasses could be cooled well below the Doppler limit.

As with many big "surprises", there were earlier hints that something was amiss. My group had been discussing the "super-molasses" problem at conferences since 1986. At a laser spectroscopy conference in Åre, Sweden in 1987, the NIST group reported molasses lifetimes with a very different frequency dependence from the one predicted by the simple formula $\langle x^2 \rangle = 2D\tau/\alpha^2$ that we published in our first molasses paper.[51] This group also found that the trap was more stable to beam imbalance than had been expected. In our collective euphoria over cooling and trapping atoms, the research community had not performed the basic tests to measure the properties of optical molasses, and I was the most guilty.

At the end of June, 1988, Claude and I attended a conference on spin-polarized quantum systems in Torino, Italy and gave a summary of the new surprises in laser cooling known at that time.[52] After our talks, Claude and I had lunch and compared the findings in our labs. The theory that predicted the minimum temperature for two-level atoms was beyond reproach. We felt the lower temperatures must be due to the fact that the atoms we were playing with were *real* atoms with Zeeman sub-levels and hyperfine splittings. Our hunch was that the cooling mechanism probably had something to do with the Zeeman sub-level structure and not the hyperfine structure, since cesium (Δv_{hfs} = 9.19 GHz) and sodium (Δv_{hfs} = 1.77 GHz) were both cooled to temperatures corresponding to an rms velocity on the order 4 to 5 times the recoil velocity, $v_{recoil} = \hbar k/M$ and $k = 2\pi/\lambda$. By then we also knew that the magnetic field had to be reduced to below 0.05 Gauss to achieve the best cooling.

After the conference, Claude returned to Paris while I was scheduled to give several more talks in Europe. My next stop was Munich, where I told Ted Hänsch that I thought it had to be an optical pumping effect. My knowledge of optical pumping was rudimentary, so I spent half a day in the local physics library reading about the subject. I was getting increasingly discouraged when I came across an article that referred to "Cohen-Tannoudji states". It was beginning to dawn on me that Claude and Jean were better positioned to figure out this puzzle.

After Munich, I went to Pisa where I gave a talk about our positronium and muonium spectroscopy work.[53, 54, 55] There, I finally realized how molasses was cooling the atoms. The idea was stimulated by a intuitive remark made by one of the speakers during his talk, "...the atomic polarization responds in the direction of the driving light field..." The comment reminded me of a ball-and-stick model of an atom as an electron (cloud) tethered by a weakly damped harmonic force to a heavy nucleus. I realized the cooling was due to a combination of optical pumping, light shifts, and the fact that the polarization in optical molasses changed at different points in space. A linearly polarized laser field drives the atomic cloud up and down, while a circularly polarized field drives the cloud in a circle. In optical molasses, the x, y, and z-directed beams all have mutually perpendicular linear polarizations and the polarization of the light field varies from place to place. As a simple example, consider a one-dimensional case where two opposing light beams have mutually perpendicular linear polarizations as shown in Fig. 6. The electron cloud wants to rotate with an elliptical helicity that is dependent on the atom's position in space.

Another effect to consider is the ac Stark (light) shift. In the presence of light, the energy levels of an atom are shifted, and the amount of the shift is proportional to the coupling strength of the light. Suppose an atom with angular momentum F = 2 is in σ^+ light tuned below resonance. It will optically pump into the m_F = +2 state and its internal energy in the field will be lowered as shown in Fig. 6 c. If it then moves into a region in space where the light is σ^-, the transition probability is very weak and consequently the ac Stark shift is small. For sodium the m_F = +2 energy is lowered 15 times more in σ^+ light than in σ^- light. Hence, the atom gains internal energy by moving into the σ^- region. This increase in internal energy must come at the expen-

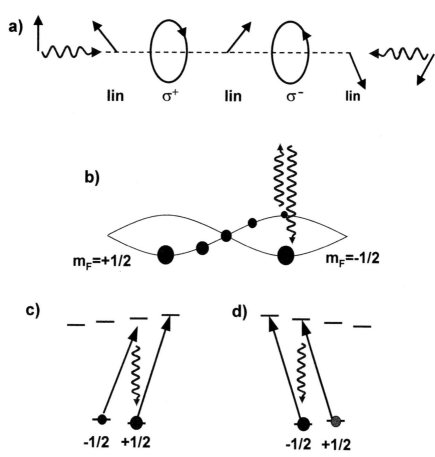

Figure 6. Polarization gradient cooling for an atom with an $F = 1/2$ ground state and an $F = 3/2$ excited state. a) The interference of two linearly polarized beams of light with orthogonal polarizations creates a field of varying elliptical polarization as shown. Under weak excitation, the atom spends most of its time in the ground states. b) The energy of the $m_F = \pm 1/2$ ground states as a function of position in the laser field is shown. c) An atom in a σ^+-field will optically pump mostly into the $m_F = +1/2$ ground state, the lower internal energy state. d) If the atom moves into a region of space where the light is σ^-, its internal energy increases due to the decreased light shift (AC Stark shift) of the $m_F = +1/2$ state in that field. The atom slows down as it goes up a potential hill created by the energy level shift. As the atom nears the top of the hill, it begins to optically pump to the $m_F = -1/2$ state, putting the atom into the lowest energy state again. Laser cooling by repeated climbing of potential hills has been dubbed "Sisyphus cooling" after the character in the Greek myth condemned forever to roll a boulder up a hill.

se of its kinetic energy. The final point is that the atom in the new region in space will optically pump into the $m_F = -2$ state (Fig. 6 d). Thus the atom will find itself again in a low-energy state due to the optical pumping process. The ensemble of atoms loses energy, since the spontaneously emitted photons are slightly blue-shifted with respect to the incident photons.

Cooling in polarization gradients is related to a cooling mechanism that occurs for two-level atoms in the presence of two counter-propagating laser beams. In the low-intensity limit, the force is described by our intuitive notion of scattering from two independent beams of light, as first discussed by

Hänsch and Schawlow. [21] However, at high intensities, the force reverses sign so that one obtains a cooling force for positive detuning. This cooling force has been treated by Gordon and Ashkin for all levels of intensity in the low velocity limit,[19] and by Minogin and Serimaa in the high-intensity limit for all velocities.[56] A physical interpretation of the cooling force in the high-intensity limit based on the dressed-atom description was given by Dalibard and Cohen-Tannoudji.[57] In their treatment, the atom gains internal energy at the expense of kinetic energy as it moves in the standing-wave light field. The gain in internal energy is dissipated by spontaneous emission, which is more likely to occur when the atom is at the maximum internal energy. When the atom makes a transition, it will find itself most often at the bottom of the dressed-state potential hills. Following Albert Camus, Jean and Claude again revived *Le Mythe de Sisyphe* by naming this form of cooling after the character in Greek mythology, Sisyphus, who was condemned eternally roll a boulder up a hill.

The name "optical molasses" takes on a more profound meaning with this new form of cooling. Originally, I conceived of the name thinking of a viscous fluid associated with cold temperatures: "slow as molasses in January". With this new understanding, we now know that cooling in optical molasses has two parts: at high speeds, the atom feels a viscous drag force, but at lower speeds where the Doppler shift becomes negligible, the optical pumping effect takes over. An atom sees itself walking in a swamp of molasses, with each planted foot sinking down into a lower energy state. The next step requires energy to lift the other foot up and out of the swamp, and with each sinking step, energy is drained from the atom.

The Pisa conference ended on Friday, and on Sunday, I went to Paris to attend the International Conference on Atomic Physics. That Sunday afternoon, Jean and I met and compared notes. It was immediately obvious that the cooling models that Jean and Claude and I concocted were the same. Jean, already scheduled to give a talk at the conference, gave a summary of their model.[58] I was generously given a "post-post-deadline" slot in order to give my account of the new cooling mechanism.[59]

Detailed accounts of laser cooling in light fields with polarization gradients followed a year later in a special issue of JOSA B dedicated to cooling and trapping. Dalibard and Cohen-Tannoudji provided an elegant quantum mechanical treatment of simple model systems.[60] They discussed two different types of cooling, depending on whether the counter-propagating light beams were comprised of mutually perpendicular linear polarizations or opposing σ^+ -σ^- beams. Their approach allowed them to derive the cooling force and diffusion of momentum (heating) as a function of experimental parameters such as detuning, atomic linewidth, optical pumping time, etc., that could be experimentally tested.

My graduate students and I presented our version of the Sisyphus cooling mechanism in the same issue.[61] In order to obtain quantitative calculations that we could compare to our experimental results, we chose to calculate the cooling forces using the optical Bloch equations generalized for the sodium F

= 2 ground state → F = 3 excited state transition. We derived the steady-state cooling forces as a function of atomic velocity for the same two simple polarization configurations, but for sodium atoms instead of a model system. However, we also showed considered by Dalibard and Cohen-Tannoudji that steady-state forces *cannot* be used to estimate the velocity distribution and that the transient response of the atom in molasses with polarization gradients was significant.[62] A weak point of our paper was that we made *ad hoc* assumptions in our treatment of the diffusion of momentum, and the predicted Monte Carlo calculations of the velocity distributions were sensitive to the details of these assumptions. Since that time, more rigorous quantum Monte Carlo methods have been developed.

In a companion experimental paper,[63] we measured non-thermal velocity distributions of atoms cooled in the laser fields treated in our theory paper. We also measured the velocity distributions of atoms cooled in σ^+–σ^+ light.[64] Under these conditions, sodium atoms will optically pump into an effective two-level system consisting of the $3S_{1/2}$, F = 2, m_F = +2 and $3P_{3/2}$, F = 3, m_F = +3 states. This arrangement allowed us finally to verify the predicted frequency dependence of the temperature for a two-level atom, three years after the first demonstration of Doppler cooling. In the course of those experiments, Dave Weiss discovered a magnetic-field-induced cooling[63] that could be explained in terms of Sisyphus-like effects and optical pumping.[61] This cooling mechanism was explored in further detail by Hal Metcalf and collaborators.[65]

The NIST discovery of sub-Doppler temperatures showed that the limiting temperature based on the Doppler effect was not actually a limit. What is the fundamental limit to laser cooling? One might think that the limit would be the recoil limit $k_B T \sim (p_r)^2/2M$, since the last photon spontaneously emitted from an atom results in a random velocity of this magnitude. However, even this barrier can be circumvented. For example, an ion tightly held in a trap can use the mass of the trap to absorb the recoil momentum. The so-called sideband cooling scheme proposed by Dehmelt and Wineland[66] and demonstrated by Wineland and collaborators[67] can in principle cool an ion so that the fractional occupancy of two states separated by an energy ΔE can have an effective temperature T_{eff} less than the recoil temperature, where T_{eff} is defined by $e^{-\Delta E/kT}$.

For free atoms, it is still possible to cool an ensemble of atoms so that their velocity spread is less than photon recoil velocity by using velocity-selection techniques. The Ecolé Normale group devised a clever velocity-selection scheme based on a process they named "velocity selective coherent population trapping".[68] In their first work, metastable helium atoms were cooled along one dimension of an atomic beam to a transverse (one-dimensional) temperature of 2 µK, a factor of 2 below the single photon recoil temperature. The effective temperature of the velocity-selected atoms decreases roughly as the square root of the time that the velocity-selection light is on, so much colder temperatures may be achieved for longer cooling times. In subsequent experiments, they used atoms precooled in optical molasses and achieved much colder temperatures in two and three dimensions.[69] An important point to emphasize is that this method has no strict cooling limit: the longer the cooling time, the smaller the spread in velocity. However, there is a trade-off between the final temperature and the number of atoms cooled to this temperature since the atom finds it harder to randomly walk into a progressively smaller section of velocity space. Eventually, the velocity-selective cooling becomes velocity "selection" in the sense that the number of atoms in the velocity-selected state begins to decrease.

APPLICATIONS OF LASER COOLING AND TRAPPING

During the time we were studying polarization gradient cooling, my group of 3 students and one post-doc at Stanford began to apply the newly developed cooling and trapping techniques, but even those plans were soon abandoned.

After the completion of the studies of polarization gradient optical molasses cooling, Erling Riis, Dave Weiss and Kam Moler constructed a two-dimensional version of the magneto-optic trap where sodium atoms from a slowed atomic beam were collected, cooled in all three dimensions and compressed radially before being allowed to exit the trap in the axial direction.[70] This "optical funnel" increased the phase space density of an atomic beam by five orders of magnitude. Another five orders of magnitude are possible with a cesium beam and proper launching of the atoms in a field with moving polarization gradients. Ertmer and colleagues developed a two-dimensional compression and cooling scheme with the magneto-optic trap.[71] These two experiments demonstrated the ease with which laser cooling can be used to "focus" an atomic beam without the limitations imposed by the "brightness theorem" in optics.

In our other vacuum chamber, Mark Kasevich and Erling Riis were given the task of producing an atomic fountain as a first step in the quantum reflection experiment. That was to be Mark's thesis. The idea was to launch the atoms upwards in an atomic fountain with a slight horizontal velocity. When the atoms reached their zenith, they would strike a vertically oriented surface. As they were setting up this experiment, I asked them to do the first of a number of "quickie experiments". "Quickies" were fast diversions I promised would only take a few weeks, and the first detour was to use the atomic fountain to do some precision spectroscopy.

In the early 1950s, Zacharias attempted to make an "atomic fountain" by directing a beam of atoms upwards. Although most of the atoms would crash into the top of the vacuum chamber, the very slowest atoms in the Maxwell distribution were expected to follow a ballistic trajectory and return to the launching position due to gravity. The goal of Zacharias' experiment was to excite the atoms in the fountain with Ramsey's separated oscillatory field technique, the method used in the cesium atomic clock.[72] Atoms initially in state $|1\rangle$ would enter a microwave cavity on the way up and become excited into a superposition of two quantum states $|1\rangle$ and $|2\rangle$. While in that superposition state, the relative phases of the two states would precess with a frequency $\hbar\omega = E_1 - E_2$. When the atoms passed through the microwave cavity on the way down, they would again be irradiated by the microwave field. If the microwave generator were tuned exactly to the atomic frequency ω, the second pulse would excite the atoms completely into the state $|2\rangle$. If the microwave source were π radians (half a cycle) out of phase with the atoms, they would be returned to state $|1\rangle$ by the second pulse. For a time Δt separating the two excitation pulses, the oscillation "linewidth" $\Delta\omega_{rf}$ of this transition satisfies $\Delta\omega_{rf}\Delta t = \pi$.

This behavior is a manifestation of the Heisenberg uncertainty principle: the uncertainty ΔE in the measurement of an energy interval times the quantum measurement time Δt must be greater than Planck's constant $\Delta E\Delta t\geq\hbar$. An atomic fountain would increase the measurement time by more than two orders of magnitude as compared to conventional atomic clocks with horizontally moving thermal beams. Zacharias hoped to measure the gravitational redshift predicted by Einstein: identical clocks placed at different heights in a gravitational field will be frequency shifted with respect to each other. The atom fountain clock, during its trajectory, would record less time than the stationary microwave source driving the microwave cavity.

Unfortunately, Zacharias' experiment failed. The slowest atoms in the Maxwell-Boltzmann distribution were scattered by faster atoms overtaking them from behind and never returned to the microwave cavity. The failure was notable in several respects. The graduate student and post-doc working on the project still got good jobs, and the idea remained in the consciousness of the physics community.[73] With our source of laser cooled atoms, it was a simple matter for us to construct an atomic fountain.[74] Atoms were first collected in a magneto-optic trap and then launched upwards by pushing from below with another laser beam. At the top of the ballistic trajectory, we irradiated the atoms with two microwave pulses separated by 0.25 seconds, yielding a linewidth of 2 Hz. Ralph DeVoe at the IBM Almaden Research center joined our experiment and provided needed assistance in microwave technology. With our demonstration atomic fountain, we measured the sodium ground-state hyperfine splitting to an accuracy of one part in 10^9.

After the theory of polarization-gradient cooling was developed, we realized that there was a much better way to launch the atoms. By pushing with a single laser beam from below, we would heat up the atoms due to the random recoil kicks from the scattered photons. However, by changing the frequency of the molasses beams so that the polarization gradients would be in a frame of reference moving relative to the laboratory frame, the atoms would cool to polarization-gradient temperatures in the moving frame. The atoms could be launched with precise velocities and with no increase in temperature.[75]

André Clairon and collaborators constructed the first cesium atomic fountain.[76] Kurt Gibble and I analyzed the potential accuracy of an atomic fountain frequency standard and suggested that the phase shifts due to collisions might be a limiting factor to the ultimate accuracy of such a clock.[77] We then constructed an atomic fountain frequency source that surpassed the short term stability of the primary Cs references maintained by standards laboratories.[78] In that work, we also measured the frequency shift due to ultracold collisions in the fountain, a systematic effect which may be the limiting factor of a cesium clock. The group led by Clairon has recently improved upon our short-term stability. More important, they achieved an accuracy estimated to be $\Delta v/v \leq 2 \times 10^{-15}$, limited by the stability of their hydrogen maser reference.[79] Such a clock started at the birth of the universe would be off by less than four minutes today, ~15 billion years later.

The next "quickie" to follow the atomic fountain was the demonstration of normal incidence reflection of atoms from an evanescent wave. Balykin, *et al.*[80] deflected an atomic beam by a small angle with an evanescent sheet of light extending out from a glass prism. If the light is tuned above the atomic resonance, the induced dipole **p** will be out of phase with the driving field. The atom with energy $-\mathbf{p} \cdot \mathbf{E}$ is then repelled from the light by the dipole force. The demonstration of normal incidence reflection with laser-cooled atoms was a necessary first step towards the search for quantum reflection. With our slow atoms, we wanted to demonstrate an "atomic trampoline" trap by bouncing atoms from a curved surface of light created by internally reflecting a laser beam from a plano-concave lens. Unfortunately, the lens we used produced a considerable amount of scattered light, and the haze of light "levitated" the atoms and prevented us from seeing bouncing atoms. Mark ordered a good quality lens and we settled for bouncing atoms from the dove-prism surface[81] with the intent of completing the work when the lens arrived. We never used the lens he ordered because of another exciting detour in our research. A few years later, a trampoline trap was demonstrated by Cohen-Tannoudji's group.[82] The evolution of gravito-optic atom traps is summarized in Fig. 7.

While waiting for the delivery of our lens, we began to think about the next stage of the quantum reflection experiment. The velocity spread of the atoms in the horizontal direction would be determined by a collimating slit, but I was unhappy with this plan. The quantum reflection experiment would require exquisitely cold atoms with a velocity spread corresponding to an effective temperature of a small fraction of a micro-kelvin. Given the finite size of our atoms confined in the MOT, very narrow collimating slits would reduce the flux of atoms to distressingly low levels. Ultimately, collimating slits would cause the atoms to diffract.

While flying home from a talk, the solution to the velocity-selection problem came to me. Instead of using collimating slits, we could perform the velocity selection with the Doppler effect. Usually, the Doppler sensitivity is limited by the linewidth of the optical transition. However, if we induced a two-photon transition between two ground states with lasers beams at frequencies v_1 and v_2, there is no linewidth associated with an excited state. If the frequency of v_2 is generated by an electro-optic modulator so that $v_2 = v_1 + v_{rf}$, the frequency jitter of the excitation laser would not enter since the transition would depend on the frequency difference $v_2 - v_1 = v_{rf}$. The linewidth Δv would be limited by the transition time Δt it took to induce the two-photon transition, and our atomic fountain would give us lots of time. Despite the fact that the resonance would depend on the frequency *difference*, the

Balykin, Letokhov, Ovchinnikov
and Sidorov (1987)

Kasevich, Weiss and Chu (1989)

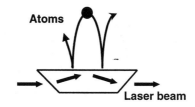

Aminoff, *et al.,* (1993)

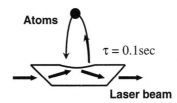

H.J. Lee, *et al.,* (1996)

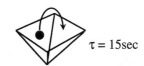

Inverted pyramid trap from 4
sheets of light.

Figure 7. Some of the highlights in the development of the reflection of atoms from optical sheets of light tuned to the blue side of the atomic resonance. Since the atoms spend a considerable amount of time in free fall, blue de-tuned optical traps allow fairly efficient cooling with stimulated Raman pulses. Over 3×10^6 sodium atoms have been Raman cooled to the recoil temperature at densities of 2×10^{11} atoms/cm^3 in an inverted pyramid trap.

Doppler sensitivity would depend on the frequency *sum* if the two laser beams were counter-propagating. This idea would allow us to achieve Doppler sensitivity equivalent to an ultraviolet transition, but with the frequency control of the microwave domain, and it would be easy. In a proof of principle experiment, we created an ensemble of atoms with a velocity spread of 270 μm/sec corresponding to an effective 1-dimensional "temperature" of 24 picokelvin and a de Broglie wavelength of 51 μm.[83] We also used the Doppler sensitivity to measure velocity distributions with sub-nanokelvin resolution.

By 1990, we were aware of several groups trying to construct atom interferometers based on the diffraction of atoms by mechanical slits or diffraction gratings, and their efforts stimulated us to think about different approaches to atom interferometry. We knew there is a one-to-one correspondence between the Doppler sensitivity and the recoil an atom experiences when it makes an optical transition. With a two-photon Raman transition with counter-propagating beams of light, the recoil is $\Delta p = \hbar k_{eff}$, where $k_{eff} = (k_1 + k_2)$, and it is this recoil effect that allowed us to design a new type of atom interferometer.

If an atom with momentum p and in state $|1\rangle$, described by the combined quantum state $|1,p\rangle$, is excited by a so-called "$\pi/2$" pulse of coherent light, the atom is driven into an equal superposition of two states $|1,p\rangle$ and $|2,p+\hbar k_{eff}\rangle$. After a time Δt, the two wave packets will have separated by a distance $(\hbar k_{eff}/M)\Delta t$. Excitation by a π pulse induces the part of the atom in state $|1,p\rangle$ to make the transition $|1,p\rangle \rightarrow |2,p+\hbar k_{eff}\rangle$ and the part of the atom in $|2,p+\hbar k_{eff}\rangle$ to make the transition $|2,p+\hbar k_{eff}\rangle \rightarrow |1,p\rangle$. After another interval Δt, the two parts of the atom come back together and a second $\pi/2$ pulse with the appropriate phase shift with respect to the atomic phase can put the atom into either of the states $|1,p\rangle$ or $|2,p+\hbar k_{eff}\rangle$. This type of atom interferometer is the atomic analog of an optical Mach-Zender interferometer and is closely related to an atom interferometer first discussed by Bordé.[84] In collaboration with the PTB group led by Helmcke, Bordé used this atom interferometer to detect rotations.[85]

By January of 1991, shortly after we began seeing interference fringes, we heard that the Konstanz group led by Jürgen Mlynek[86] had demonstrated a Young's double slit version atom interferometer and that the MIT group, led by Dave Pritchard[87] had succeeded in making a grating interferometer. Instead of using atoms in a thermal beam, we based our interferometer on an atomic fountain of laser-cooled atoms. We knew we had a potentially exquisite measuring device because of the long measurement time and wanted to use our atom interferometer to measure something before we submitted a paper.

As we began to think of what we could easily measure with our interferometer, Mark made a fortuitous discovery: the atom interferometer showed a phase shift that scaled as Δt^2, the delay time between the $\pi/2$ and π pulses, and correctly identified that this phase shift was due to the acceleration of the atoms due to gravity. An atom accelerating will experience a Doppler shift with respect to the lasers in a laboratory frame of reference propagating in the direction of **g**. Even though the laser beams were propagating in the nominally horizontal direction, the few milliradian "misalignment" created enough of phase shift to be easily observable.

Our analysis of this phase shift based on Feynman's path-integral approach to quantum mechanics was outlined in the first demonstration of our atom interferometer[88] and expanded in our subsequent publications.[89, 90, 91, 92] Storey and Cohen-Tannoudji have published an excellent tutorial paper on this approach as well.[93] Consider a laser beam propagating parallel to the direction of gravity, as shown in Fig 8. The phase shift of the atom has two parts: (*i*) a free-evolution term $e^{iS_{Cl}/\hbar}$, where

$$S_{Cl} = \int_r^L dt$$

is the action evaluated along the classical trajectory r, and (*ii*), a phase term due to the atom interacting with the light. The evaluation of the integrals for both paths shows that the free-evolution part contributes no net phase shift between the two arms of the interferometer. The part of the phase shift due to the light/atom interaction is calculated by using the fact that an atom that makes a transition $|1,p\rangle \rightarrow |2,p+\hbar k\rangle$ acquires a phase factor $e^{-i(k_L z - \omega t)}$, where z is the vertical position of the atom and $k_L = k_1 + k_2$ is the effective k vector of the light. A transition $|2,p+\hbar k\rangle \rightarrow |1,p\rangle$ adds a phase factor $e^{+i(k_L z - \omega t)}$. If the atom does not make a transition, the phase factor due to the light is unity. If k_L is parallel to g, the part of the atom in the upper path will have a total phase $\phi_{upper} = k_L \cdot (z_A - z_B)$ read into the atom by the light. The part of the atom in the lower path will have a given phase angle $\phi_{lower} = k_L \cdot (z_{B'} - z_C)$. In the absence of gravity, $z_A - z_B = z_{B'} - z_C$, and there is no net phase shift between the two paths. However, with gravity, $z_B - z_A = g\Delta t^2/2$, while $z_{B'} - z_C = 3g\Delta t^2/2$. Thus the net phase shift is $\Delta\phi = k_L g\Delta t^2$. Notice that the acceleration is measured in the

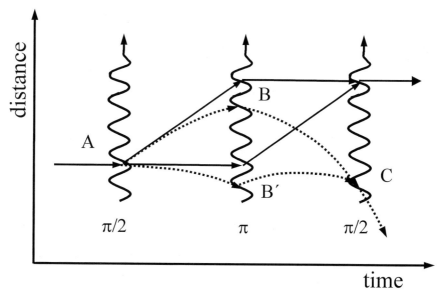

Figure 8. An atom interferometer based on optical pulses of light. The phase of the optical field is read into the atom during a transition from one state to another. In the absence of gravity (solid lines), the part of the atom moving along the upper path from the first $\pi/2$ pulse to the π pulse will experience 3 cycles of phase less than the part of the atom that moves along the lower path. The lower path experiences an identical loss of phase during the time between the π pulse and the second $\pi/2$ pulse. If the excitation frequency is exactly on resonance, the atom will be returned back to the initial state. With gravity (dotted lines), the phase loss of the upper path is more than the phase loss of the lower path since $z_C - z_{B'}$ is greater than $z_B - z_A$. Thus, by measuring displacements during a time Δt in terms of a phase difference, we can measure velocity changes due to g or photon recoil effects (Fig. 9) in the time domain.

time domain: we record the change in phase $\Delta\phi = k_L \Delta z$ that occurs after a time Δt.

The phase shift of the interferometer is measured by considering the relative phase between the atomic phase of the two parts of the atom and the phase of the light at position C. If the light is in phase with the atom, the second $\pi/2$ pulse will cause the atom to return to state $|1,p\rangle$. If it is π out of phase, the atom will be put into state $|2,p+\hbar k\rangle$. Thus the phase shift is measured in terms of the relative populations of these two states.

For the long interferometer times Δt that are obtainable in an atomic fountain, the phase shift can be enormous. For $\Delta t = 0.2$ seconds, over 4×10^6 cycles of phase difference accumulate between the two paths of the interferometer. In our first atom interferometer paper, we demonstrated a resolution in g of $\Delta g/g = 10^{-6}$, and with improved vibration isolation, achieved a resolution of $\Delta g/g<3\times10^{-8}$.[89] With a number of refinements, including the use of an actively stabilized vibration isolation system,[94] we have been able maintain the full fringe contrast for times up to $\Delta t = 0.2$ seconds and have improved the resolution to one part in 10^{-10}.[92]

Soon after the completion of our first atom interferometer measurements, Mark Kasevich thought of a way to cool atoms with stimulated Raman transitions.[95] Since the linewidth of a Raman transition is governed by the time to make the transition, we had a method of addressing a very narrow velocity slice of atoms within an ensemble already cooled by polarization-gradient cooling. Atoms are initially optically pumped into a particular hyperfine state $|1\rangle$. A Raman transition $|1\rangle \rightarrow |2\rangle$ is used to push a small subset of them towards v = 0. By changing the frequency difference v_1-v_2 for each successive pulse, different groups of atoms in the velocity distribution can be pushed towards $v = 0$, analogous to the "frequency chirp" cooling methods used to slow atomic beams. A critical difference is that Raman pulses permit much higher-resolution Doppler selectivity. After each Raman pulse, a pulse is used to optically pump the atom back into $|1\rangle$. During this process, the atom will spontaneously emit one or more photons and can remain near $v = 0$. The tuning of the optical pulses are adjusted so that an atom that scatters into a velocity state near $v = 0$ will have a low probability of further excitation. This method of cooling is analogous to coherent population trapping except that the walk in velocity space is directed towards $v = 0$. In our first demonstration of this cooling process, sodium atoms were cooled to less than $0.1T_{recoil}$ in one dimension, with an 8-fold increase in the number of atoms near $v = 0$. In later work, we extended this cooling technique to two and three dimensions.[96]

This cooling technique has also been shown to work in an optical dipole trap. We were stimulated to return to dipole traps by Phillips' group[97] and by Dan Heinzen's group,[98] who demonstrated dipole traps tuned very far from resonance. In this type of trap, the heating due to the scattering of trapping light is greatly reduced. A nondissipative dipole trap turns out to be useful in a number of applications. In traps formed by sheets of blue detuned light (a successor to the trampoline traps), we showed that atomic coherences can be preserved for 4 seconds despite hundreds of bounces.[99] We also demonstrated evaporative cooling in a red detuned dipole trap made from two crossed beams of light.[100, 101] Atoms can be Raman cooled in both red and blue detuned dipole traps.[102, 46] In our most recent work, over 10^6 atoms have been Raman cooled in a blue-detuned dipole trap to less than T_{recoil}. This is a factor of ~300 below what is needed for Bose condensation, but a factor of 400 improvement over the "dark-spot" magneto-optic trap phase space densities. Unfortunately, a heating process prevented us from evaporatively cooling to achieve Bose condensation with an optical trap. Recently, Wolfgang Ketterle and collaborators have loaded an optical dipole trap with a Bose condensate created in a magnetic trap.[103] With this trap they have been able to find the Feshbach resonances[104] calculated for sodium[105] in which the s-wave scattering length changes sign. Since this resonance is only one gauss wide, a non-magnetic trap makes its detection much easier. Optical traps could also be used to hold Bose condensates in magnetic-field-insensitive states for precision atom interferometry.

Our ability to measure small velocity changes with stimulated Raman transitions suggested another application of atom interferometry. If an atom absorbs a photon of momentum $p_\gamma = h\nu/c$, it will receive an impulse $\Delta p = M\Delta v$. Thus $h/M = c\Delta v/\nu$, and since Δv can be measured as a frequency shift, the possibility of making a precision measurement of h/M dropped into our lap. After realizing this opportunity, I called Barry Taylor at NIST and asked if this measurement with an independent measurement of Planck's constant could put the world on an atomic mass standard. He replied that the first application of a precise h/M measurement would be a better determination of the fine-structure constant α, since α can be expressed as

$$\alpha^2 = (2R_\infty/c)(m_p/m_e)(M_{atom}/m_p)(h/M_{atom}).$$

All of the quantities[106] in the above relation can be measured precisely in terms of frequencies or frequency shifts.

Dave Weiss' thesis project was changed to measure h/M with our newly acquired Doppler sensitivity. The interferometer geometry he chose was previously demonstrated as an extension of the Ramsey technique into the optical domain.[84] If two sets of $\pi/2$ pulses are used, two interferometers are created with displaced endpoints as shown in Fig. 9. The displacement is measured in terms of a phase difference in the relative populations of the two interferometers, analogous to the way we measured the acceleration of gravity. This displacement was increased by sandwiching a number of π pulses in between the two pairs of $\pi/2$ pulses. With Brent Young, Dave Weiss obtained a resolution of roughly a part in 10^7 in h/M_{Cs}.[107, 108] In that work, systematic effects were observed at the 10^6 level, but rather than spending significant time to understand those effects, we decided to develop a new atom interferometer method with a vertical geometry to measure h/M.

Instead of using impulses of momentum arising from off-resonant Raman pulses, I wanted to use an adiabatic transfer method demonstrated by Klaus Bergmann and collaborators.[109] The beauty of an adiabatic transfer method

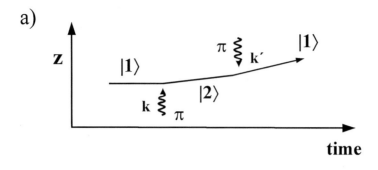

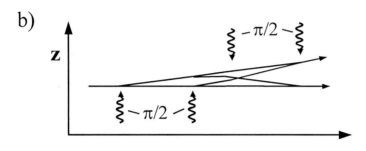

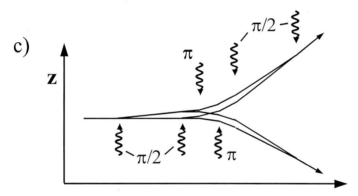

Figure 9 a. The basic method for measuring the recoil velocity requires two counterpropagating pulses of light. Because of energy and momentum conservation, the excitation light must satisfy $\hbar\omega - \hbar\omega_{12} = \mathbf{k} \cdot \mathbf{v} \pm (\hbar k)^2/2m$, where v is the velocity of the atom relative to the k-vector of the light and the sign depends on whether the initial state is higher or lower in energy than the final state. An atom at rest in ground state $|1\rangle$ is excited by a π pulse at frequency $\omega = \omega_{12} + \hbar k^2/2m$. The atom, recoiling with velocity $v = \hbar k/m$ in state $|2\rangle$ is returned back to $|1\rangle$ with a counter-propagating photon $\omega' = \omega_{12} - \hbar kk'/m + \hbar k^2/2m$. The two resonances are shifted relative to each other by $\Delta\omega = \omega' - \omega = \hbar(k+k')^2/2m$.

Figure 9 b. In order to increase the resolution without sacrificing counting rate, two sets of counterpropagating $\pi/2$ pulses are used instead of two π pulses. Thus, we are naturally led to use two atom interferometers whose end points are separated in space due to the photon recoil effect. Since the measurement is based on the relative separation of two similar atom interferometers, there are a number of "common mode" subtractions that add to the inherent accuracy of the experiment.

Figure 9 c. To further increase the resolution of the measurement, we sandwich many π pulses, each pulse coming from alternate directions. Only 2 π pulses are shown in the figure, but up to 60 π pulses are used in the actual experiment, where each π pulse separates the two interferometers by a velocity of $4\hbar k/m$.

86

is that it is insensitive to the small changes in experimental parameters such as intensity and frequency that adversely affect off-resonant π pulses. In addition, we showed that the ac Stark shift, a potentially troublesome systematic effect when using off-resonant Raman transitions, is absent when using adiabatic transfer in a strictly three level system.[110]

Consider an atom with two ground states and one excited state as shown in Fig 10 a. Bergmann *et al.* showed that the rediagonalized atom/light system will always have a "dark" eigenstate, not connected to the excited state. Suppose, for simplicity, that the amplitudes $A_1 = \langle e|H_{EM}|g_1\rangle$ and $A_2 = \langle e|H_{EM}|g_2\rangle$ are equal, where H_{EM} is the Hamiltonian describing the light/atom interaction. An atom initially in state $|g_1\rangle$ is in the dark state provided only ω_2 light is on. If we then slowly increase the intensity of ω_1 light until the beams have equal intensities, the dark state will adiabatically evolve into $\frac{1}{\sqrt{2}}[|g_1\rangle-|g_2\rangle]$. If we then turn down the intensity of ω_2 while leaving ω_1 on, the atom will evolve into state $|g_2\rangle$. Thus we can move the atom from state $|g_1\rangle$ to state $|g_2\rangle$ without ever going through the excited state.

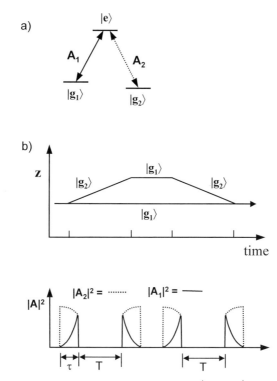

Figure. 10 a. An atomic system consisting of ground states $|g_1\rangle$ and $|g_2\rangle$ and an excited state $|e\rangle$ connected by amplitudes A_1 and A_2.

Fig. 10 b. In this space-time diagram of our adiabatic interferometer, the first interaction transfers the atom from $|g_1\rangle$ to the superposition state $(1/\sqrt{2})(|g_1\rangle+|g_2\rangle)$. In the second region, both frequencies are turned on simultaneously, projecting the atomic state $|\Psi(T+\tau)\rangle$ onto the dark superposition state $|\Psi(T+\tau)\rangle_D$ evaluated at the start of the pulse. This state is then adiabatically evolved into $|g_1\rangle$ by the light profiles shown in the second interaction region. To complete the interferometer, the sequence is repeated for adiabatic transfers with k_{eff} in the opposite direction as in Fig 9. Atom paths that do not contribute to the interference signal are not shown.

The work of Bergmann prompted Marte, Zoller and Hall[111] to suggest that this transfer process could also be used to induce a momentum change on an atom. Groups led by Mara Prentiss[112] and Bill Phillips[113] soon demonstrated the mechanical effect of this transition. In these experiments, the time-delayed light pulses were generated by having the atoms intersect spatially displaced laser beams. With atoms moving slowly in an atomic fountain, we could independently vary the intensity of each beam with acousto-optic modulators. This freedom allowed us to construct an atom interferometer using the adiabatic transfer method.[114] At different interaction points, differently shaped pulses are required, as shown in Fig. 10. For example, the first "adiabatic" beamsplitters require that ω_2 turn on first, but both ω_1 and ω_2 turn off in unison, while the second interaction point has both ω_1 and ω_2 turn on together and then ω_1 turn off first. With an adiabatic transfer interferometer, we are able to separate the two atom interferometers by up to ~250$\hbar$k units of momentum without significant degradation of signal.

Currently, our atom interferometric method of measuring h/M_{Cs} has a resolution of ~2 parts in 10^{-9} (1 ppb in α), corresponding to a velocity resolution less than $1/30$ of an atom diameter/second. In terms of Doppler spectroscopy, this precision corresponds to a resolution in a Doppler shift of less than 100 µHz out of ~10^{15} Hz. We have been looking for systematic effects for the past five months and there are a few remaining tests to perform before publishing a value for h/M. The other measurements needed to determine α, such as the mass ratios m_e/m_p and m_p/M_{Cs}, and the frequency of the Cs D_1 line will be measured to a precision of better than one part in 10^{-9} in the near future. Curiously, some of the most accurate methods of determining are direct applications of three Nobel Prizes: the Josephson effect (56 ppb), the quantized Hall effect (24 ppb) and the equating of the ion-trap measurement of the electron magnetic moment with the QED calculation (4.2 ppb).[115]

OTHER APPLICATIONS IN ATOMIC PHYSICS

The topics I have discussed above are a small, personally skewed sampling of the many applications of the new technology of laser cooling and atom trapping. These techniques have already been used in nonlinear optics and quantum optics experiments. Laser-cooled atoms have spawned a cottage industry in the study of ultracold collisions. Atom traps offer the hope that radioactive species can be used for more precise studies of parity nonconservation effects due to the weak interactions and more sensitive searches for a breakdown of time-reversal invariance.

A particularly spectacular use of cold-atom technology has been the demonstration of Bose condensation in a dilute gas by Eric Cornell, Carl Weiman and collaborators,[116] and later by teams led by Wolfgang Ketterle[117] and Randy Hulet.[118] The production of this new state of matter opens exciting opportunities to study collective effects in a quantum gas with powerful diagnostic methods in laser spectroscopy. The increase in phase-space density of Bose condensed atoms will also generate new applications, just as the phase-space density increase due to laser cooling and trapping started a number of new areas of research.

APPLICATIONS IN BIOLOGY AND POLYMER SCIENCE

In 1986, the world was excited about atom trapping. During this time, Art Ashkin began to use optical tweezers to trap micron-sized particles. While experimenting with colloidal tobacco mosaic viruses,[119] he noticed tiny, translucent objects in his sample. Rushing into my lab, he excitedly proclaimed that he had "discovered *Life*". I went into his lab, half thinking that the excitement of the last few years had finally gotten the better of him. In his lab was a microscope objective focusing an argon laser beam into a petri dish of water. Off to the side was an old Edmund Scientific microscope. Squinting into the microscope, I saw my eye lashes. Squinting harder, I occasionally saw some translucent objects. Many of these objects were "floaters", debris in my vitreous humor that could be moved by blinking my eyes. Art assured me that there were *other* objects there that would not move when I blinked my eyes. Sure enough, there were objects in the water that could be trapped and would swim away if the light were turned off. Art had discovered bugs in his apparatus, but these were *real* bugs, bacteria that had eventually grown in his sample beads and water.

His discovery was quickly followed by the demonstration that infrared light focused to megawatts/cm^2 could be used to trap live e-coli bacteria and yeast for hours without damage.[120] Other work included the internal cell manipulation of plant cells, protozoa, and stretching of viscoelastic cytoplasm.[121] Steve Block and Howard Berg soon adapted the optical tweezers technique to study the mechanical properties of the flagella motor,[122] and Michael Burns and collaborators used the tweezers to manipulate live sperm.[123] Objects on the molecular scale could also be manipulated with optical tweezers. Block *et al.* sprinkled a low-density coverage of kinesin motor molecules onto a sphere and placed the sphere on a microtubule. When the kinesin was activated with ATP, the force and displacement generated by a single kinesin molecule could be measured.[124] Related experiments on the molecular motor actin/myosin associated with skeletal muscles have also been performed by Jeff Finer, Bob Simmons and Jim Spudich[125] using an active feedback optical tweezers developed in my lab.[126] Steve Kron and I developed a method to hold and simultaneously view a single molecule of DNA by attaching polystyrene handles to the ends of the molecule.[127, 128] These early experiments introduced an important tool for biologists, at both the cellular and the molecular level. The applications of this tool in biology have exploded and may eventually overtake the activity in atomic physics.[129]

My original goal in developing methods to manipulate DNA was to study, in real time, the motion of enzymes moving on the molecule. However, once we began to play with the molecules, we noticed that a stretched molecule of DNA would spring back like a rubber band when the extensional force was turned off, as shown in Fig 11. The "springiness" of the molecule is due to

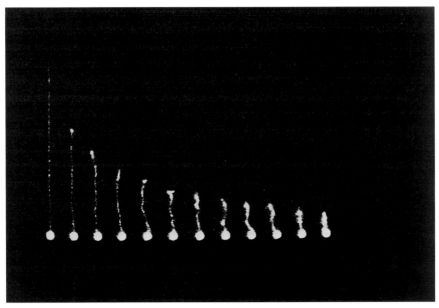

Fig. 11a: A series of video images showing the relaxation of a single molecule "rubber band" of DNA initially stretched by flowing fluid past the molecule. The DNA is stained with approximately one dye molecule for every 5 base-pairs and visualized in an optical microscope.[132]

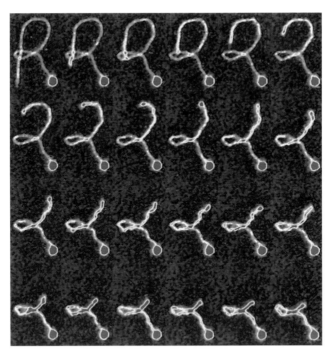

Fig. 11b: The relaxation of a stained DNA molecule in an entangled solution of unstained DNA. The molecule, initially pulled through the polymer solution with an optical tweezers, is seen to relax along a path defined by its contour. This work graphically shows that polymers in an entangled solution exhibit "tube-like" motion.[131] This result and a separate measurement of the diffusion of the DNA in a similar polymer solution[134] verifies de Gennes' reptation theory used to explain a general scaling feature of viscoelastic materials.

90

entropy considerations: the configurations of a flexible polymer are enumerated by counting the possible ways of taking a random walk of a large, but finite number of steps. A stretched molecule is in an unlikely configuration, and the system will move towards the much more likely equilibrium configuration of a random coil. Our accidental observation of a single-molecule rubber band created yet another detour: DNA from a lambda-phage virus is large enough to visualize and manipulate, and yet small enough so that the basic equations of motion describing a polymer are still valid. We stumbled onto a new way of addressing long-standing questions in polymer dynamics and began a program in polymer physics that is continuing today.[130, 131, 132, 133, 134, 135, 136, 137]

CLOSING REMARKS

The techniques I have discussed, to borrow an advertising slogan of AT&T, have enabled us to "reach out and touch" atoms and other neutral particles in powerful new ways. Laser beams can now reach into a vacuum chamber, capture and cool atoms to micro-kelvin temperatures, and toss them upwards in an atomic fountain. With this technique, a new generation of atomic clocks is being developed. Atoms quantum mechanically split apart and brought back together in an interferometer have given us inertial sensors of exquisite precision and will allow us to measure fundamental constants with unprecedented accuracy. Atom trapping and cooling methods allow us to Bose-condense a gas of atoms. With this condensate, we have begun to examine many-body effects in a totally new regime. The condensates are beginning to provide a still brighter source of atoms which we can exploit. Laser traps allow us to hold onto living cells and organelles within cells without puncturing the cell membrane. Single molecules of DNA are being used to study fundamental questions in polymer dynamics. The force and displacement generated by a dynesin molecule as it burns *one* ATP molecule can now be measured. This proliferation of applications into physics, chemistry, biology and medicine has occurred in less than a decade and is continuing, and we will no doubt see further applications of this new-found control over matter.

In 1985, when my colleagues and I first demonstrated optical molasses, I never foresaw the wealth of applications that would follow in just a few years. Instead of working with a clear vision of the future, I followed my nose, head close to the ground where the scent is strongest.

All of my contributions cited in this lecture were the result of working with the numerous gifted collaborators mentioned in this lecture. Without them, I would have done far less.

On a larger scale, the field of cooling and trapping was built out of the interwoven contributions of many researchers. Just as my associates and I were inspired by the work of others, our worldwide colleagues have already added immensely to our contributions. I consider this Nobel Prize to be the recognition of our collective endeavors. As scientists, we hope that others take note of what we have done and use our work to go in directions we never imagined. In this way, we continue to add to the collective scientific legacy.

REFERENCES

1. R. Conti, P. Bucksbaum, S. Chu, E. Commins, and L. Hunter, Phys. Rev. Lett. **42,** 343 (1979). See also, S. Chu, E. Commins, and R. Conti, Phys. Lett. **60A,** 96 (1977).
2. S. Chu, H.M. Gibbs, S.L. McCall, and A. Passner), Phys. Rev. Lett. **45,** 1715 (1980).
3. S. Chu, H.M. Gibbs, and S.L. McCall, Phys. Rev. B **24,** 7162 (1981).
4. P. Hu, S. Chu, and H.M. Gibbs, in *Picosecond Phenomena II*, eds. R.M. Hochstrasser, W. Kaiser and C.V. Shank (Springer-Verlag, 1980), p. 308.
5. S. Chu and S. Wong, Phys. Rev. Lett. **48,** 738 (1982); Also, see Comments, Phys. Rev. Lett. **49,** 1293 (1982).
6. S. Chu and A.P. Mills, Phys. Rev. Lett. **48,** 1333 (1982); S. Chu, A.P. Mills, Jr. and J.L. Hall, Phys. Rev. Lett. **52,** 1689 (1984).
7. A more complete account of this early history can be found in *Light Pressure on Atoms*, V.G. Minogin and V.S. Letokhov, (Gordon Breach Science, New York, 1987).
8. J.C. Maxwell, *A Treatise on Electricity and Magnetism*, 3rd ed. (1897), Reprint by Dover Publications, New York, (1954).
9. P. Lebedev, Ann. Phys., Leipzig, **6,** 433 (1901).
10. E.F. Nichols and G.F. Hull, Phys. Rev. **17,** 26 (1903), ibid. p 91.
11. A. Einstein, Phys. Z. **18,** 121 (1917). English translation in *Sources of Quantum mechanics*, ed. B.L. Waeerden (North-Holland, Amsterdam, 1967), pp. 63–78.
12. O.R. Frisch, Zs. Phys. **86,** 42 (1933) pp. 63–78.
13. Detailed calculation of lensing in the Mie scattering range (where the wavelength of the light is less than the diameter of the particle) can be found in a number of publications. See, for example, A. Ashkin, Biophys. J. **61,** 569 (1992).
14. G.A. Askar'yan, Zh. Eskp. Teor. Fiz. **42,** 1567 (1962).
15. V.S. Letokhov, Pis'ma Zh. Eskp. Teor. Fiz. 7, 348 (1968).
16. A. Ashkin, Science **210,** 1081 (1980).
17. A. Ashkin, Phys. Rev. Lett. **40,** 729 (1978).
18. J.E. Bjorkholm, R.R. Freeman, A. Ashkin and D.B. Pearson, Phys. Rev. Lett. **41,** 1361 (1978).
19. J.P. Gordon and A. Ashkin, Phys. Rev. A **21,** 1606 (1980).
20. S. Chu, AT&T Internal Memo, 11311-840509-12TM (1984).
21. T.W. Hänsch and A.L. Schawlow, Opt. Commun. **13,** 68 (1975).
22. D.J. Wineland and W.M. Itano, Bull. Am. Phys. Soc. **20,** 637 (1975).
23. D.J. Wineland and W.M. Itano, Phys. Rev. A **20,** 1521 (1979).
24. I wanted our paper to be titled "Demonstration of Optical Molasses". John Bjorkholm was a purist and felt that the phrase was specialized jargon at its worst. We compromised and omitted the phrase from the title but introduced it in the text of the paper.
25. For a comprehensive discussion of the work up to 1985, see W.D. Phillips, J.V. Prodan and H.J. Metcalf, J. Opt. Soc. Am. B **2,** 1751 (1985).
26. J. Prodan, A. Migdall, W.D. Phillips, I. So, H. Metcalf, and J. Dalibard., Phys. Rev. Lett. **54,** 992 (1985).
27. W. Ertmer, R. Blatt, J.L. Hall, and M. Zhu, Phys. Rev. Lett. **54,** 996 (1985).
28. I.P. Kaminow, *An Introduction to Electro-optic Devices*, (Academic Press, New York, 1974), pp 228–233.
29. S. Chu, L. Hollberg, J.E. Bjorkholm, A. Cable and A. Ashkin, Phys. Rev. Lett. **55,** 48 (1985).
30. The components of the experiment were assembled from parts of previous experiments: the cw dye laser needed for the optical molasses and the pulsed YAG laser

were previously used in a dye laser oscillator/amplifier system in a positronium spectroscopy experiment. A surplus vacuum chamber in a development section of Bell Laboratories became our molasses chamber.

31. S. Chu, M.G. Prentiss, A. Cable, and J.E. Bjorkholm, in *Laser Spectroscopy VII*, W. Persson and S. Svanberg, eds., (Springer-Verlag, Berlin, 1988) pp 64–67; Y. Shevy, D.S. Weiss, and S. Chu, in *Spin Polarized Systems*, ed. S. Stringari (World Scientific, Singapore, 1989), pp 287–294.

32. A. L. Migdall, J.V. Prodan, W.D. Phillips, T.H. Bergeman, and H.J. Metcalf, Phys. Rev. Lett. **54**, 2596 (1985).

33. A. Ashkin and J.P. Gordon, Opt. Lett., **8** 511 (1983).

34. A summary of this theorem and other "no trapping" theorems can be found in: S. Chu, in *Laser Manipulations of Atoms and Ions,* Proceedings of the International School of Physics "Enrico Fermi", course CXVIII, eds. E. Arimondo, W.D. Phillips, and F. Strumia (North-Holland, Amsterdam, 1992) pp 239–288.

35. A. Ashkin, Opt. Lett. **9,** 454 (1984).

36. S. Chu, J.E. Bjorkholm, A. Ashkin, L. Hollberg, and A. Cable, *Methods of Laser Spectroscopy,* eds. Y. Prior, A. Ben-Reuven, and M. Rosenbluh, (Plenum, New York 1985), pp. 41–50. The conference proceedings gave a snapshot of our thinking in December of 1985.

37. S. Chu, J.E. Bjorkholm, A. Ashkin, and A. Cable, Phys. Rev. Lett. **57**, 314 (1986).

38. A. Ashkin, J.M. Dziedzic, J.E. Bjorkholm, and S. Chu, Opt. Lett. **11**, 288 (1986).

39. D.E. Pritchard, E.L. Raab, V.S. Bagnato, C.E. Weiman, and R.N. Watts, Phys. Rev. Lett. **57**, 310 (1986).

40. Allan Mills had persuaded me to participate in a muonium spectroscopy experiment and I had been working on that experiment in parallel with the laser cooling and trapping work since 1985.

41. E.L. Raab, M. Prentiss, A. Cable, S. Chu, and D.E. Pritchard, Phys. Rev. Lett. **59**, 2631 (1987).

42. I gave a brief history of these events in reference 34. See also D. Pritchard and W. Ketterle, in *Laser Manipulations of Atoms and Ions*, Proceedings of the International School of Physics "Enrico Fermi", course CXVIII, eds. E. Arimondo, W.D. Phillips, and F. Strumia (North-Holland, Amsterdam, 1992) pp 473–496.

43. C. Monroe, W. Swann, H. Robinson, and C.E. Wieman, Phys. Rev. Lett. **65**, 1571 (1990). Raab and Pritchard had tried to get the scattering force trap to work at MIT by trying to capture the atoms directly from vapor, but the vapor pressure turned out to be too high for efficient capture.

44. K. Gibble, S. Kasapi and S. Chu, Opt. Lett. **17**, 526 (1992).

45. W. Ketterle, K. Davis, M. Joffe, A. Martin and D. Pritchard, Phys. Rev. Lett. **70**, 2253 (1993).

46. H.J. Lee, C.S. Adams, M. Kasevich and S. Chu, Phys. Rev. Lett. **76**, 2658 (1996).

47. I tried to persuade Alex Cable to come with me and become my first graduate student. By this time he was blossoming into a first rate researcher and I knew he would do well as a graduate at Stanford. He turned down my offer and a year later resigned from Bell Labs. While he was my technician, he had started a company making optical mounts. His company, "Thor Labs" is now a major supplier of optical components.

48. D. Sesko, C. Fan and C. Weiman, J. Opt. Soc. Am. B **5**, 1225 (1988).

49. W.D. Phillips, private communication.

50. P. Lett, R.N. Watts, C. Westbrook, and W.D. Phillips, Phys. Rev. Lett. **61**, 169 (1988).

51. P. Gould, P. Lett. and W. Phillips, in *Laser Spectroscopy VIII,* eds. W. Person and S. Svanberg (Springer-Verlag, Berlin, 1987) p 64.

52. Y. Shevy, D. Weiss and S. Chu, in *Spin Polarized Quantum Systems,* ed S. Stingari, (World Scientific, Singapore, 1989), pp. 287–294.

53. S. Chu, in *The Hydrogen Atom;* eds. G.F. Bassani, M. Inguscio, and T.W. Hänsch, (Springer-Verlag,1989), p 144.

54. M.S. Fee, A.P. Mills, S. Chu, E.D. Shaw, K. Danzmann, R.J. Chichester, D.M. Zuckerman, Phys. Rev. Lett. **70,** 1397 (1993); M.S. Fee, S. Chu, A.P. Mills, E.D. Shaw, K. Danzmann, R.J. Chichester, D.M. Zuckerman, Phys. Rev. A **48,** 192 (1993).

55. S. Chu, A.P. Mills, Jr., A.G. Yodh, K. Nagamine, H. Miyake, and T. Kuga, Phys. Rev. Lett. **60,** 101 (1988).

56. V.G. Minogin and O.T. Serimaa, Opt. Commun. **30,** 373 (1979). Also see V.G. Minogin Opt. Commun. **37,** 442 (1981).

57. J. Dalibard and C. Cohen-Tannoudji, J. Opt Soc. Am. B **2,** 1707 (1985).

58. J. Dalibard, C. Solomon, A. Aspect, E. Arimondo, R. Kasier, N. Vansteenkiste, and C. Cohen-Tannoudji, in *Atomic Physics 11,* eds. S. Haroche, J.C. Gay and G. Grynberg, (World Scientific, Singapore, 1989) pp. 199–214.

59. S. Chu, D. Weiss, Y. Shevy and P. Ungar, in *Atomic Physics 11,* eds. S. Haroche, J.C. Gay and G. Grynberg, (World Scientific, Singapore, 1989) pp 636–638.

60. J. Dalibard and C. Cohen-Tannoudji, J. Opt. Soc. Am. B **6,** 2023 (1989).

61. P.J. Ungar, D.S. Weiss, E. Riis, and S. Chu, J. Opt. Soc. Am. B **6,** 2058 (1989).

62. See Fig. 13 of ref. 60.

63. D.S. Weiss, E. Riis, Y. Shevy, P.J. Ungar and S. Chu, J. Opt. Soc. Am. B **6,** 2072 (1989).

64. We showed in Y. Shevy, D.S. Weiss, P.J. Ungar and S. Chu, Phys. Rev. Lett. 62, 1118, (1988) that a linear force vs. velocity dependence $\mathbf{F}(\upsilon) = -\alpha\upsilon$ would result in a Maxwell-Boltzmann distribution.

65. S-Q. Shang, B. Sheehy, P. van der Straten and H. Metcalf, Phys. Rev. Lett. **65,** 317 (1990).

66. See, for example, H. Dehmelt, Science **247,** 539, (1990).

67. F. Diedrich, J. C. Berquist, W. Itano, and D.J. Wineland, Phys. Rev. Lett. **62,** 403 (1989).

68. A. Aspect, E. Arimondo, R. Kaiser, N. Vansteenkiste, and C. Cohen-Tannoudji, Phys. Rev. Lett. **621,** 826 (1988); see also J. Opt. Soc. B **6,** 2112, (1989) by the same authors.

69. J. Lawall, S. Kulin, B. Saubamea, N. Bigelow, M. Leduc, and C. Cohen-Tannoudji, Phys. Rev. Lett. **75,** 4194 (1995).

70. E. Riis, D.S. Weiss, K.A. Moler, and S. Chu, Phys. Rev. Lett. **64,** 1658 (1990).

71. J. Nellessen, J. Werner and W. Ertmer, Opt. Commun. **78,** 300 (1990).

72. See, for example N.F. Ramsey, *Molecular Beams* (Oxford University Press, Oxford, 1956).

73. See, for example, A. De Marchi, G.D. Rovera and A. Premoli, Metrologia 20, 37 (1984). I had heard of this attempt while still a graduate student at Berkeley. We discussed the advantages of a cesium fountain atomic clock in K. Gibble and S. Chu, Metrologia **29,** 201, (1992).

74. M.A. Kasevich, E. Riis, S. Chu, and R.G. DeVoe, Phys. Rev. Lett. **63,** 612 (1989).

75. D.S. Weiss, E. Riis, M. Kasevich, K.A. Moler, and S. Chu, in *Light Induced Kinetic Effects on Atoms, Ions, and Molecules,* eds. L. Moi, S. Gozzini, C. Gabbanini, E. Arimondo, F. Strumia, (ETS Editrice, Pisa 1991) pp. 35–44.

76. A. Clarion, C. Salomon, S. Guellati and W.D. Phillips, Europhys. Lett. **16,** 165 (1991).

77. K. Gibble and S. Chu, Metrologia **29,** 201, (1992).

78. K. Gibble and S. Chu, Phys. Rev. Lett. **70,** 1771 (1993).

79. S. Ghezali, Ph. Laurent, S.N. Lea and A. Clairon, Europhys. Lett. **36,** 25 (1996).

80. V.I. Balykin, V.S. Letokhov, Yu.B. Ovchinnikov and A.I. Sidorov, Phys. Rev. Lett. **60,** 2137 (1988).

81. M.A. Kasevich, D.S. Weiss, and S. Chu, Opt. Lett., **15,** 667 (1990).

82. C.G. Aminoff, A.M. Steane, P. Bouyer, P. Desbiolles, J. Dalibard and C. Cohen-Tannoudji. Phys. Rev. Lett. **71,** 3083 (1993).

83. M. Kasevich, D. Weiss, E. Riis, K. Moler, S. Kasapi and S. Chu, Phys. Rev. Lett. **66,** 2297 (1991).

84. Ch. Bordé, Phys. Lett. A **140,** 10 (1989).

85. F. Riehle, Th. Kisters, A. Witte, S. Helmcke and Ch. Borde, Phys. Rev. Lett. **67,** 177 (1991).
86. O. Carnal and J. Mlynek, Phys. Rev. Lett. **66,** 2689 (1991).
87. D. Keith, C. Eksstrom, O. Turchette and D. Pritchard, Phys. Rev. Lett. **66,** 2693 (1991).
88. M. Kasevich and S. Chu, Phys. Rev. Lett. **67,** 181 (1991).
89. M. Kasevich and S. Chu, Applied Physics B **54,** 321 (1992).
90. K. Moler, D.S. Weiss, M. Kasevich, and S. Chu, Phys. Rev. A **45,** 342 (1991).
91. B. Young, M. Kasevich and S. Chu, in *Atom Interferometry,* ed. P. Berman (Academic Press, New York, 1997) pp 363–406.
92. A. Peters, K.Y. Chung, B. Young, J. Hensley and S. Chu, Philosophical Trans. A **355,** 2223 (1997).
93. P. Storey and C. Cohen-Tannoudji, J. Phys. **4,** 1999 (1994).
94. J. Hensley, A. Peters and S. Chu, Review of Scientific Instruments, in press (1998).
95. M. Kasevich and S. Chu, Phys. Rev. Lett. **69,** 1741 (1992).
96. N. Davidson, H.J. Lee, M. Kasevich, and S. Chu, Phys. Rev. Lett. **72,** 3158 (1994).
97. S. Rolston, C. Gerz, K. Helmerson, P.S. Jessen, P.D. Lett, W.D. Phillips, R.J.C. Spreeuw and C.I. Westbrook, Proc. SPIE **1726,** 205 (1992).
98. J.D. Miller, R. Cline, D. Heinzen, Phys. Rev. A**47,** R4567 (1993).
99. N. Davidson, H.J. Lee, C.S. Adams, M. Kasevich and S. Chu, Phys. Rev. Lett. **74,** 1311 (1995).
100. C.S. Adams, H.J. Lee, N. Davidson, M. Kasevich, and S. Chu, Phys. Rev. Lett. **74,** 3577 (1995).
101. Improved results are reported in H.J. Lee, C.S. Adams, N. Davidson, B. Young, M. Weitz, M. Kasevich, and S. Chu, in *Atomic Physics 14,* eds. C. Weiman and D. Wineland (AIP, New York) 1995, pp. 258–278.
102. M. Kasevich, H.J. Lee, C.A. Adams and S. Chu, in *Laser Spectroscopy 12,* eds. M. Inguscio, M. Allegrini, A. Sasso (World Scientific, Singapore, 1996) pp. 13–16.
103. D.M. Stamper-Kurn, M.R. Andrews, A.P. Chikkatur, S. Inouye, H.-J. Meisner, J. Strenger and W. Ketterle, Phys. Rev. Lett. **80,** 2072 (1998).
104. H. Feshbach, Ann. Phys. (NY) **19,** 287 (1962).
105. A.J. Moerdijk, B.J. Verhaar and A. Axelsson, Phys. Rev. A **51,** 4852 (1995).
106. The speed of light c is now a defined quantity. "2" is also known well.
107. D.S. Weiss, B.C. Young, and S. Chu, Phys. Rev. Lett. **70,** 2706 (1993).
108. D.S. Weiss, B.C. Young and S. Chu, Applied Physics B **59,** 217–256 (1994).
109. U. Gaubatz, P. Rudecker, M. Becker, S. Schiemann, M. Kültz, and K. Bergmann, Chem. Phys. Lett. **149,** 463 (1988).
110. M. Weitz, B. Young and S. Chu, Phys. Rev. A **50,** 2438 (1994).
111. P. Marte, P. Zoller and J.L. Hall, Phys. Rev. A **44,** R4118 (1991).
112. J. Lawall and M. Prentiss, Phys. Rev. Lett. **72,** 993 (1994).
113. L.S. Goldner, C. Gerz, R.J.C. Spreew, S.L. Rolstom, C.I. Westbrook, W. Phillips, P. Marte and P. Zoller, Phys. Rev. Lett. **72,** 997 (1994).
114. M. Weitz, B.C. Young, and S. Chu, Phys. Rev. Lett. **73,** 2563 (1994).
115. For a review of the current status of α, see T. Kinoshita, Rep. Prog. Phys. **59,** 1459 (1966).
116. M.H. Anderson, J.R. Ensher, M.R. Matthews, C.E. Wieman and E.A. Cornell, Science **269,** 198 (1995).
117. K.B. Davis, M-O Mewes, M. R. Anderson, N.J. van Druten, D.S. Durfee, D.M. Kurn and W. Ketterle, Phys. Rev. Lett. **75,** 3969 (1995).
118. C.C. Bradley, C.A. Sackett and R.G. Hulet, Phys. Rev. Lett. **78,** 985 (1997).
119. A. Ashkin and J.M. Dziedzic, Science **235,** 1517 (1987).
120. A. Ashkin, J.M. Dziedzic and T. Yamane, Nature (London) **330,** 769 (1987).
121. A. Ashkin and J.M. Dziedzic, Science **253,** 1517 (1987); Proc. Natl. Acad. Sci. USA **86,** 7914 (1989).
122. S. Block, D.F. Blair and H.C. Berg, Nature **338,** 514 (1989).

123. Y. Tadir, W. Wright, O. Vafa, T. Ord, R. Asch and M. Burns, Fertil. Steril. **52,** 870 (1989).

124. S. Block, L. Goldstein, and B. Schnapp, Nature **348,** 348 (1990); also see K. Svoboda and S. Block, Cell **77,** 773 (1994) and references contained within.

125. J.T. Finer, R.M. Simmons, J.A. Spudich, Nature **368,** 113 (1994).

126. H.M. Warrick, R.M. Simmons, J.F. Finer, T.Q.P. Uyeda, S. Chu, and J.A. Spudich, chapter 1 in *Methods in Cell Biology,* **39,** Academic, New York (1993) pp. 1–21; R.M. Simmons, J.T. Finer, S. Chu and J.A. Spudich, Biophys. J. **70,** 1813–1822 (1996).

127. S. Chu and S. Kron, Int. Quantum Electronics Conf. Tech Digest, (Optical Soc. of Am., Washington DC, 1990) p 202; M. Kasevich, K. Moler, E. Riis, E. Sunderman, D. Weiss, and S. Chu, *Atomic Physics 12,* eds. J.C. Zorn and R.R. Lewis, (Am. Inst. of Physics, New York 1990), pp. 47–57.

128. S. Chu, Science, **253,** 861, (1991).

129. Much of the activity has been reviewed by A. Ashkin, Proc. Natl. Acad. Sci. USA **94,** 4853 (1997).

130. Preliminary results were reported in S. Chu, Science, **253,** 861, (1991)

131. T. Perkins, D.E. Smith and S. Chu, Science **64,** 819 (1994).

132. T.T. Perkins, S.R. Quake, D.E. Smith and S. Chu, Science **264,** 822 (1994).

133. T.T. Perkins, D.E. Smith, R.G. Larson, and S. Chu, Science **268,** 83 (1994).

134. D.E. Smith, T.T. Perkins and S. Chu, Phys. Rev. Lett. **75,** 4146 (1995).

135. D.E. Smith, T.T. Perkins and S. Chu, Macromolecules **29,** 1372 (1996).

136 S.R. Quake and S. Chu, Nature, **388,** 151 (1997).

137. T.T. Perkins, D.E. Smith and S. Chu, Science **276,** 2016 (1997).

Claude Cohen-Tannoudji

CLAUDE N. COHEN-TANNOUDJI

I was born on April 1, 1933 in Constantine, Algeria, which was then part of France. My family, originally from Tangiers, settled in Tunisia and then in Algeria in the 16th century after having fled Spain during the Inquisition. In fact, our name, Cohen-Tannoudji, means simply the Cohen family from Tangiers. The Algerian Jews obtained the French citizenship in 1870 after Algeria became a French colony in 1830.

My parents lived a modest life and their main concern was the education of their children. My father was a self-taught man but had a great intellectual curiosity, not only for biblical and talmudic texts, but also for philosophy, psychoanalysis and history. He passed on to me his taste for studies, for discussion, for debate, and he taught me what I regard as being the fundamental features of the Jewish tradition–studying, learning and sharing knowledge with others.

As a child, I was very lucky to escape the tragic events which marked this century. The arrival of the Americans in Algeria, in November of 1942, saved us from the nazi persecutions that were spreading throughout Europe at the time. I completed my primary and secondary school education in Algiers. And I was also lucky enough to finish high school in very good conditions and to leave Algiers for Paris, in 1953, before the war in Algeria and the stormy period that preceded the independence.

I came to Paris because I was admitted to the Ecole Normale Supérieure. This French "grande école", founded during the French Revolution about 200 years ago, selects the top high school students who do well in the selective final examination. The four years at this school, from 1953 to 1957, were indeed a unique experience for me. During the first year, I attended a series of fascinating lectures in mathematics given by Henri Cartan and Laurent Schwartz, in physics by Alfred Kastler. Initially, I was more interested in mathematics but Kastler's lectures were so stimulating, and his personality so attractive, that I ended up changing to physics.

In 1955, when I joined Kastler's group to do my "diploma" work, the group was very small. One of Kastler's first students, Jean Brossel, who had returned four years before from M.I.T. where he had done research work with Francis Bitter, was supervising the thesis work of Jacques Emile Blamont and Jacques Michel Winter.

We were a small group, but the enthusiasm for research was exceptional and we worked hard. Brossel and Kastler were in the lab nearly day and night, even on weekends. We had endless discussions on how to interpret our experimental results. At the time, the equipment was rather poor and we did what we could without computers, recorders and signal averagers. We measured resonance curves point by point with a galvanometer, each curve five times, and then averaged by hand. We were, somehow, able to get nice curves and exciting results. I think that what I learned during that period was essential for my subsequent research work and key personalities such as Alfred Kastler and Jean Brossel certainly had a significant role in it.

We were going together, once a week, to attend the new lectures given in Saclay by Albert Messiah on quantum mechanics, by Anatole Abragam on NMR and by Claude Bloch on nuclear physics. I can still remember the stimulating atmosphere of these lectures.

During the summer of 1955, I also spent two months at the famous Les Houches summer school in the Alps. This school has contributed largely to the development of theoretical physics in France. At that time, the school offered an intense training in modern physics with about six lectures a day, for two months, and the lecturers were J. Schwinger, N. Ramsey, G. Uhlenbeck, W. Pauli, A. Abragam, A. Messiah, C. Bloch... to mention a few.

After finishing my "diploma" studies, I still had to get through the final examination "Agrégation" before leaving Ecole Normale as a student. The "Agrégation" is a competitive examination for teaching posts in high schools. The preparation consists of theoretical and experimental courses as well as some pedagogical training. You give a lecture attended by other students and a professor and after, there is a moment of general debate and constructive criticism in view of perfecting your lecture. Kastler, I remember, participated in the pedagogical training and he taught us how to organize and present our lecture.

Well, about this time I met Jacqueline who became my wife in 1958. She has shared with me all the difficult and happy times of life. She has been able to pursue her own career as a high school physics and chemistry teacher, to raise our three children Alain, Joëlle and Michel, to be part of the daily life of a researcher which can sometimes be very difficult and demanding. We have had, as many, our share of family tragedy and losing our oldest son Alain was a great misfortune to us all. Alain died in 1993, of a long illness, at the age of 34.

After the "Agrégation", I left the Ecole Normale and did my military service which was very long (28 months) because of the Algeria war. I was, though, assigned part of the time to a scientific department supervised by Jacques Emile Blamont. We were studying the upper atmosphere with rockets releasing sodium clouds at the sunset. By looking at the fluorescence light re-emitted by the sodium atoms excited by the sunlight, it was possible to measure the variations with the altitude of various parameters such as the wind velocity or the temperature.

Then, in the beginning of 1960, I came back to the laboratory to do a Ph.D. under the supervision of Alfred Kastler and Jean Brossel with a research post at the CNRS (French National Center for Scientific Research). The lab had by then been expanded. Bernard Cagnac was finishing his thesis on the optical pumping of the odd isotopes of mercury and I was trying, with

Jean-Pierre Barrat, to derive a master equation for the optical pumping cycle and to understand the physics of the off-diagonal elements of the density matrix (the so-called atomic "coherences"). Our calculations predicted the existence of "light shifts" for the various Zeeman sublevels, a curious phenomenon we did not expect at all. I decided to try to see this effect. Cagnac left me his experimental set up during Christmas vacations and I remember getting the first experimental evidence on Christmas Eve of 1960. I was very excited and both Kastler and Brossel were very happy indeed. Kastler called the effect the "Lamp shift", since it is produced by the light coming from a discharge lamp. Nowadays, it is called light shift or a.c. Stark shift. I built a new experimental set up to check in detail several other predictions of our calculations, especially the conservation of Zeeman coherences during the optical pumping cycle. I submitted my Ph.D. in December of 1962. The members of the committee were Jean Brossel, Pierre Jacquinot, Alfred Kastler and Jacques Yvon.

Shortly after my Ph.D. Alfred Kastler urged me to accept a teaching position at the University of Paris. I followed his advice and started to teach at the undergraduate level. At about this time, there was a new reform in the University system : the so-called "troisième cycle" that consisted of teaching a graduate level with a flexible program. Jean Brossel asked me to teach quantum mechanics. He was teaching atomic physics, Alfred Kastler and Jacques Yvon statistical physics, Pierre Aigrain and Pierre-Gilles de Gennes solid state physics.

We had the best students of the Ecole Normale attending these lectures, so I set up a small group where every year a new student would join in and do a post-graduate thesis or a Ph.D. In 1967, I was asked to teach quantum mechanics at a lower level (second cycle). The book "Quantum Mechanics" originated from this teaching experience and was done in collaboration with Franck Laloë and Bernard Diu.

Understanding atom-photon interactions in the high intensity limit where perturbative treatments are no longer valid was one of the main goals of our research group. This led us to develop a new approach to these problems where one considers the "atom + photons" system as a global isolated system described by a time-independent Hamiltonian having true energy levels. We called such a system the "dressed atom". Although the quantum description of the electromagnetic field used in such an approach is not essential to interpret most physical effects encountered in atomic physics, it turned out that the dressed atom approach was very useful in providing new physical insights into atom-photon interactions. New physical effects, which were difficult to predict by standard semiclassical methods, were appearing clearly in the energy diagram of the dressed atom when examining how this energy diagram changes when the number of photons increases. We first introduced the dressed atom approach in the radio-frequency range while Nicole Polonsky, Serge Haroche, Jacques Dupont-Roc, Claire Landré, Gilbert Grynberg, Maryvonne Ledourneuf, Claude Fabre were working on their thesis. One of the new effects which were predicted and observed was the modification, and even the cancellation of the Landé factor of an atomic level by interaction with an intense, high frequency radio-frequency field. This effect presents some analogy with the g–2 anomaly of the electron spin except that it has the opposite sign: the g-factor of the atomic level is reduced by virtual absorption and re-emission of RF photons whereas the g-factor of the electron spin is enhanced by radiative corrections.

We devoted a lot of efforts to the interpretation of this change of sign and this led us, years later (with Jacques Dupont-Roc and Jean Dalibard), to propose new physical pictures involving the respective contributions of vacuum fluctuations and radiation reaction. And while this was going on, we had some very stimulating discussions with Victor Weisskopf who has always been interested in the physical interpretation of the g–2 anomaly.

The dressed atom approach has also been very useful in the optical domain. Spontaneous emission plays an important role as a damping mechanism and as a source of fluorescence photons. Serge Reynaud and I applied this approach to the interpretation of resonance fluorescence in intense resonant laser beams. New physical pictures were given for the Mollow triplet and for the absorption spectrum of a weak probe beam, with the prediction and the observation of new Doppler free lines resulting from a compensation of the Doppler effect by velocity dependent light shifts. The picture of the dressed atom radiative cascade also provided new insights into photon correlations and photon antibunching. New types of time correlations between the photons emitted in the two sidebands of the Mollow triplet were predicted in this way and observed experimentally at the Institut d'Optique in Orsay, in collaboration with Alain Aspect.

An important event in my scientific life has been my appointment as a Professor at the Collège de France in 1973. The Collège de France is a very special institution created in 1530, by King François I, to counterbalance the influence of the Sorbonne which was, at that time, too scholastic and where only latin and theology were taught. The first appointed by the King were 3 lecturers in Hebrew, 2 in Greek and 1 in Mathematics. This institution survived all revolutions and remains, to this day, reputed for its flexibility. Today there are 52 professors in all subjects, and lectures are open to all, for there is no registration and no degrees given. We professors are free to choose the topics of our lectures. The only rule is that these lectures must change and deal with different topics every year, which is very difficult and demanding. It is, however, very stimulating because this urges one to broaden one's knowledge, to explore new fields and to challenge oneself. No doubt that without such an effort I would not have started many of the research lines that have been explored by my research group. I am very grateful to Anatole Abragam who is at the origin of my appointment at the Collège de France. Part of this teaching experience incited the two books on quantum electrodynamics and quantum optics written with Jacques Dupont-Roc and Gilbert Grynberg.

In the early 1980s, I chose to lecture on radiative forces, a field which was very new at that time. I was also trying with Serge Reynaud, Christian Tanguy and Jean Dalibard to apply the dressed atom approach to the interpretation of atomic motion in a laser wave. New ideas were emerging from such an analysis related to, in particular, the interpretation of the mean value, the fluctuations and the velocity dependence of dipole forces in terms of spatial gradients of dressed state energies and of spontaneous transitions between these dressed states.

When in 1984 I was given the possibility to appoint someone to the position of Associate Director for my laboratory, at the Collège de France, I offered the post to Alain Aspect and then invited him to join me in forming, with Jean Dalibard, a new experimental group on laser cooling and trapping. A year later, Christophe Salomon who came back from a postdoctoral stay in JILA with Jan Hall, decided to join our group. This was a new very exciting scientific period for us. We began to investigate a new cooling mechanism suggested by the dressed atom approach and that resulted from correlations between the spatial modulations of the dressed state energies in a high intensity laser standing wave and the spatial modulations of the spontaneous rates between the dressed states. As a result of these correlations, the moving atom is running up potential hills more frequently than down. We first called such a scheme "stimulated blue molasses" because it appears for a blue detuning of the cooling lasers, contrary to what happens for Doppler molasses which require a red detuning. In fact, this new scheme was the first high intensity version of what is called now "Sisyphus cooling", a denomination that we introduced in 1986. We also observed, shortly after, the channeling of atoms at the nodes or antinodes of a standing wave. This was the first demonstration of laser confinement of neutral atoms in optical-wavelength-size regions.

A few years later, in 1988, when sub-Doppler temperatures were observed by Bill Phillips, who had been collaborating with us, we were prepared with our background in optical pumping, light shifts and dressed atoms, to find the explanation of such anomalous low temperatures. In fact, they were resulting from yet another (low intensity) version of Sisyphus cooling. Similar conclusions were reached by Steve Chu and his colleagues. At the same time, we were exploring, with Alain Aspect and Ennio Arimondo, the possibility of applying coherent population trapping to laser cooling. By making such a quantum interference effect velocity selective, we were able to demonstrate a new cooling scheme with no lower limit, which can notably cool atoms below the recoil limit corresponding to the recoil kinetic energy of an atom absorbing or emitting a single photon. These exciting developments opened the microKelvin and even the nanoKelvin range to laser cooling, and they allowed several new applications to be explored with success.

These applications will not be described here since they are the subject of the Nobel Lecture which follows this presentation. The purpose here was merely to give an idea of my scientific itinerary and to express my gratitude to all those who have helped me live such a great adventure: my family, my teachers, my students and my fellow colleagues all over the world.

I dedicate my Nobel Lecture to the memory of my son Alain.

MANIPULATING ATOMS WITH PHOTONS

Nobel Lecture, December 8, 1997

by

Claude N. Cohen-Tannoudji

Collège de France et Laboratoire Kastler Brossel* de l'Ecole Normale
Supérieure, 24 rue Lhomond, 75231 Paris Cedex 05, France

Electromagnetic interactions play a central role in low energy physics. They
are responsible for the cohesion of atoms and molecules and they are at the
origin of the emission and absorption of light by such systems. This light is
not only a source of information on the structure of atoms. It can also be
used to act on atoms, to manipulate them, to control their various degrees of
freedom. With the development of laser sources, this research field has considerably expanded during the last few years. Methods have been developed
to trap atoms and to cool them to very low temperatures. This has opened the
way to a wealth of new investigations and applications.

Two types of degrees of freedom can be considered for an atom: the internal degrees of freedom, such as the electronic configuration or the spin
polarization, in the center of mass system; the external degrees of freedom,
which are essentially the position and the momentum of the center of mass.
The manipulation of internal degrees of freedom goes back to optical pumping [1], which uses resonant exchanges of angular momentum between
atoms and circularly polarized light for polarizing the spins of these atoms.
These experiments predate the use of lasers in atomic physics. The manipulation of external degrees of freedom uses the concept of radiative forces resulting from the exchanges of linear momentum between atoms and light.
Radiative forces exerted by the light coming from the sun were already invoked by J. Kepler to explain the tails of the comets. Although they are very
small when one uses ordinary light sources, these forces were also investigated experimentally in the beginning of this century by P. Lebedev, E. F.
Nichols and G. F. Hull, R. Frisch. For a historical survey of this research field,
we refer the reader to review papers [2, 3, 4, 5] which also include a discussion of early theoretical work dealing with these problems by the groups of
A. P. Kazantsev, V. S. Letokhov, in Russia, A. Ashkin at Bell Labs, S. Stenholm
in Helsinki.

It turns out that there is a strong interplay between the dynamics of internal and external degrees of freedom. This is at the origin of efficient laser
cooling mechanisms, such as "Sisyphus cooling" or "Velocity Selective Cohe-

---

* Laboratoire Kastler Brossel is a Laboratoire associé au CNRS et à l'Université Pierre et Marie
Curie.

rent Population Trapping", which were discovered at the end of the 80's (for a historical survey of these developments, see for example [6]). These mechanisms have allowed laser cooling to overcome important fundamental limits, such as the Doppler limit and the single photon recoil limit, and to reach the microKelvin, and even the nanoKelvin range. We devote a large part of this paper (sections 2 and 3) to the discussion of these mechanisms and to the description of a few applications investigated by our group in Paris (section 4). There is a certain continuity between these recent developments in the field of laser cooling and trapping and early theoretical and experimental work performed in the 60's and the 70's, dealing with internal degrees of freedom. We illustrate this continuity by presenting in section 1 a brief survey of various physical processes, and by interpreting them in terms of two parameters, the radiative broadening and the light shift of the atomic ground state.

1. BRIEF REVIEW OF PHYSICAL PROCESSES

To classify the basic physical processes which are used for manipulating atoms by light, it is useful to distinguish two large categories of effects: dissipative (or absorptive) effects on the one hand, reactive (or dispersive) effects on the other hand. This partition is relevant for both internal and external degrees of freedom.

1.1 EXISTENCE OF TWO TYPES OF EFFECTS IN ATOM-PHOTON INTERACTIONS

Consider first a light beam with frequency ω_L propagating through a medium consisting of atoms with resonance frequency ω_A. The index of refraction describing this propagation has an imaginary part and a real part which are associated with two types of physical processes. The incident photons can be absorbed, more precisely scattered in all directions. The corresponding attenuation of the light beam is maximum at resonance. It is described by the imaginary part of the index of refraction which varies with $\omega_L-\omega_A$ as a Lorentz absorption curve. We will call such an effect a dissipative (or absorptive) effect. The speed of propagation of light is also modified. The corresponding dispersion is described by the real part n of the index of refraction whose difference from 1, $n-1$, varies with $\omega_L-\omega_A$ as a Lorentz dispersion curve. We will call such an effect a reactive (or dispersive) effect.

Dissipative effects and reactive effects also appear for the atoms, as a result of their interaction with photons. They correspond to a broadening and to a shift of the atomic energy levels, respectively. Such effects already appear when the atom interacts with the quantized radiation field in the vacuum state. It is well known that atomic excited states get a natural width Γ, which is also the rate at which a photon is spontaneously emitted from such states. Atomic energy levels are also shifted as a result of virtual emissions and reabsorptions of photons by the atom. Such a radiative correction is simply the Lamb shift [7].

Similar effects are associated with the interaction with an incident light beam. Atomic ground states get a radiative broadening Γ', which is also the rate at which photons are absorbed by the atom, or more precisely scattered from the incident beam. Atomic energy levels are also shifted as a result of virtual absorptions and reemissions of the incident photons by the atom. Such energy displacements $\hbar\Delta'$ are called light shifts, or ac Stark shifts [8, 9].

In view of their importance for the following discussions, we give now a brief derivation of the expressions of Γ' and Δ', using the so-called dressed-atom approach to atom-photon interactions (see for example [10], chapter VI). In the absence of coupling, the two dressed states $|g, N\rangle$ (atom in the ground state g in the presence of N photons) and $|e, N–1\rangle$ (atom in the excited state e in the presence of $N–1$ photons) are separated by a splitting $\hbar\delta$, where $\delta = \omega_L - \omega_A$ is the detuning between the light frequency ω_L and the atomic frequency ω_A. The atom-light interaction Hamiltonian V_{AL} couples these two states because the atom in g can absorb one photon and jump to e. The corresponding matrix element of V_{AL} can be written as $\hbar\Omega/2$, where the so-called Rabi frequency Ω is proportional to the transition dipole moment and to $\sqrt{N}$. Under the effect of such a coupling, the two states repel each other, and the state $|g, N\rangle$ is shifted by an amount $\hbar\Delta'$, which is the light shift of g. The contamination of $|g, N\rangle$ by the unstable state $|e, N–1\rangle$ (having a width Γ) also confers to the ground state a width Γ'. In the limit where $\Omega \ll \Gamma$ or $|\delta|$, a simple perturbative calculation gives:

$$\Gamma' = \Omega^2 \frac{\Gamma}{\Gamma^2 + 4\delta^2} \tag{1}$$

$$\Delta' = \Omega^2 \frac{\delta}{\Gamma^2 + 4\delta^2} \tag{2}$$

Both Γ' and Δ' are proportional to $\Omega^2 \propto N$, i.e. to the light intensity. They vary with the detuning $\delta = \omega_L - \omega_A$ as Lorentz absorption and dispersion curves, respectively, which justifies the denominations absorptive and dispersive used for these two types of effects. For large detunings ($|\delta| \gg \Gamma$), Γ' varies as $1/\delta^2$ and becomes negligible compared to Δ' which varies as $1/\delta$. On the other hand, for small detunings, ($|\delta| \ll \Gamma$), Γ' is much larger than Δ'. In the high intensity limit, when Ω is large compared to Γ and $|\delta|$, the two dressed states resulting from the coupling are the symmetric and antisymmetric linear combinations of $|g, N\rangle$ and $|e, N–1\rangle$. Their splitting is $\hbar\Omega$ and they share the instability Γ of e in equal parts, so that $\Gamma' = \Gamma/2$. One can explain in this way various physical effects such as the Rabi flopping or the Autler-Townes splittings of the spectral lines connecting e or g to a third level [11].

1.2 MANIPULATION OF INTERNAL DEGREES OF FREEDOM
1.2.1 Optical pumping

Optical pumping is one of the first examples of manipulation of atoms by light [1]. It uses resonant excitation of atoms by circularly polarized light for transferring to the atoms part of the angular momentum carried by the light beam. It is based on the fact that different Zeeman sublevels in the atomic ground state have in general different absorption rates for incoming polarized light. For example, for a $J_g = 1/2 \leftrightarrow J_e = 1/2$ transition, only atoms in the sublevel $M_g = -1/2$ can absorb σ^+-polarized light. They are excited in the sublevel $M_e = +1/2$ of e from which they can fall back in the sublevel $M_g = +1/2$ by spontaneous emission of a π-polarized photon. They then remain trapped in this state because no further σ^+-transition can take place. It is possible in this way to obtain high degrees of spin orientation in atomic ground states.

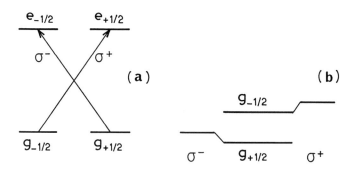

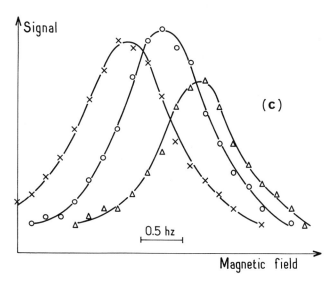

Figure 1. Experimental observation of light shifts (from reference [12]). For a $J_g = 1/2 \leftrightarrow J_e = 1/2$ transition (a), a σ^+-polarized non-resonant excitation shifts only the sublevel $g_{-1/2}$ (right part of b), whereas a σ^--polarized excitation shifts only the sublevel $g_{+1/2}$ (left part of b). The detuning δ is positive and very large compared to the Zeeman splittings in e and g. The Zeeman splitting in the ground state is thus increased in the first case, decreased in the second one. (c) magnetic resonance signal versus magnetic field, in units of the corresponding Larmor frequency. The central curve (circles) is the resonance curve in the absence of light shift. When the non-resonant light beam is introduced, either σ^+-polarized (crosses) or σ^--polarized (triangles) the magnetic resonance curve is light shifted in opposite directions.

1.2.2 *Light shifts*

Optical pumping is a dissipative effect because it is associated with resonant absorption of photons by the atom. Non-resonant optical excitation produces light shifts of the ground state Zeeman sublevels. Because of the polarization selection rules, light shifts depend on the polarization of the exciting light and vary in general from one Zeeman sublevel to another. Consider for example a $J_g = 1/2 \leftrightarrow J_e = 1/2$ transition (Fig.1a). A σ^+-polarized excitation shifts only the Zeeman sublevel $M_g = -1/2$, whereas a σ^--polarized excitation shifts only the sublevel $M_g = +1/2$ (Fig.1b). Magnetic resonance curves in the ground state g which are very narrow because the relaxation time in g can be very long, are thus light shifted by a polarized non-resonant excitation, and the sign of this shift changes when one changes the polarization of the light beam from σ^+ to σ^-. It is in this way that light shifts were first observed [12]. Fig.1c gives an example of experimental results obtained by exciting the transition 6^1S_0, $F = 1/2 \leftrightarrow 6^3P_1$, $F = 1/2$ of ^{199}Hg atoms by the non-resonant light coming from a lamp filled with another isotope (^{201}Hg).

Light shifts can be considered from different points of view. First, they can be interpreted as a radiative correction, due to the interaction of the atom with an incident field rather than with the vacuum field. This is why Alfred Kastler called them "Lamp shifts". Secondly, they introduce perturbations to high precision measurements using optical methods, which must be taken into account before extracting spectroscopic data from these measurements. Finally, because of their variation from one sublevel to another, the effect of light shifts can be described in terms of fictitious magnetic or electric fields [13]. This explains why the light shifts produced by a non-resonant laser standing wave are being more and more frequently used to produce spatial modulations of the Zeeman splittings in the ground state on an optical wavelength scale. This would not be easily achieved with spatially varying real magnetic fields. We will see in section 2 interesting applications of such a situation.

1.3 *MANIPULATION OF EXTERNAL DEGREES OF FREEDOM*

1.3.1 *The two types of radiative forces*

There are two types of radiative forces, associated with dissipative and reactive effects respectively.

Dissipative forces, also called radiation pressure forces or scattering forces, are associated with the transfer of linear momentum from the incident light beam to the atom in resonant scattering processes. They are proportional to the scattering rate Γ'. Consider for example an atom in a laser plane wave with wave vector **k**. Because photons are scattered with equal probabilities in two opposite directions, the mean momentum transferred to the atom in an absorption-spontaneous emission cycle is equal to the momentum $\hbar\mathbf{k}$ of the absorbed photon. The mean rate of momentum transfer, *i.e.* the mean force, is thus equal to $\hbar\mathbf{k}\Gamma'$. Since Γ' saturates to $\Gamma/2$ at high intensity (see section 1.1), the radiation pressure force saturates to $\hbar\mathbf{k}\Gamma/2$. The corresponding acceleration (or deceleration) which can be communicated to an atom with mass M, is equal to $a_{max} = \hbar k\Gamma/2M = v_R/2\tau$, where $v_R = \hbar k/M$ is the recoil velocity of the atom absorbing or emitting a single photon, and $\tau = 1/\Gamma$ is the radiative lifetime of the excited state. For sodium atoms, $v_R = 3 \times 10^{-2}$ m/s and $\tau = 1.6 \times 10^{-8}$ s, so that a_{max} can reach values as large as 10^6 m/s^2, *i.e.* $10^5 g$ where g is the acceleration due to gravity. With such a force, one can stop a thermal atomic beam in a distance of the order of one meter, provided that one compensates for the Doppler shift of the decelerating atom, by using for example a spatially varying Zeeman shift [14, 15] or a chirped laser frequency [16].

Dispersive forces, also called dipole forces or gradient forces [2, 3, 17], can be interpreted in terms of position dependent light shifts $\hbar\Delta'(\mathbf{r})$ due to a spatially varying light intensity [18]. Consider for example a laser beam well detuned from resonance, so that one can neglect Γ' (no scattering process). The atom thus remains in the ground state and the light shift $\hbar\Delta'(\mathbf{r})$ of this state plays the role of a potential energy, giving rise to a force which is equal and opposite to its gradient : $\mathbf{F} = -\nabla[\hbar\Delta'(\mathbf{r})]$. Such a force can also be interpreted as resulting from a redistribution of photons between the various plane waves forming the laser wave in absorption-stimulated emission cycles. If the detuning is not large enough to allow Γ' to be neglected, spontaneous transitions occur between dressed states having opposite gradients, so that the instantaneous force oscillates back and forth between two opposite values in a random way. Such a dressed atom picture provides a simple interpretation of the mean value and of the fluctuations of dipole forces [19].

1.3.2 *Applications of dissipative forces – Doppler cooling and magneto-optical traps*

We have already mentioned in the previous subsection the possibility of decelerating an atomic beam by the radiation pressure force of a laser plane wave. Interesting effects can also be obtained by combining the effects of two counterpropagating laser waves.

A first example is Doppler cooling, first suggested for neutral atoms by T. W. Hänsch and A.L. Schawlow [20] and, independently for trapped ions, by D. Wineland and H. Dehmelt [21]. This cooling process results from a Doppler induced imbalance between two opposite radiation pressure forces. The two counterpropagating laser waves have the same (weak) intensity and the same frequency and they are slightly detuned to the red of the atomic frequency ($\omega_L < \omega_A$). For an atom at rest, the two radiation pressure forces exactly balance each other and the net force is equal to zero. For a moving atom, the apparent frequencies of the two laser waves are Doppler shifted. The counterpropagating wave gets closer to resonance and exerts a stronger radiation pressure force than the copropagating wave which gets farther from resonance. The net force is thus opposite to the atomic velocity v and can be written for small v as $F = -\alpha v$ where α is a friction coefficient. By using three pairs of counterpropagating laser waves along three orthogonal directions, one can damp the atomic velocity in a very short time, on the order of a few microseconds, achieving what is called an "optical molasses" [22].

The Doppler friction responsible for the cooling is necessarily accompanied by fluctuations due to the fluorescence photons which are spontaneously emitted in random directions and at random times. These photons communicate to the atom a random recoil momentum $\hbar k$, responsible for a momentum diffusion described by a diffusion coefficient D [3, 18, 25]. As in usual Brownian motion, competition between friction and diffusion usually leads to a steady-state, with an equilibrium temperature proportional to D/α. The theory of Doppler cooling [23, 24, 25] predicts that the equilibrium temperature obtained with such a scheme is always larger than a certain limit T_D, called the Doppler limit, and given by $k_B T_D = \hbar \Gamma / 2$ where Γ is the natural width of the excited state and k_B the Boltzmann constant. This limit, which is reached for $\delta = \omega_L - \omega_A = -\Gamma/2$, is, for alkali atoms, on the order of 100 μK. In fact, when the measurements became precise enough, it appeared that the temperature in optical molasses was much lower than expected [26]. This indicates that other laser cooling mechanisms, more powerful than Doppler cooling, are operating. We will come back to this point in section 2.

The imbalance between two opposite radiation pressure forces can be also made position dependent though a spatially dependent Zeeman shift produced by a magnetic field gradient. In a one-dimensional configuration, first suggested by J. Dalibard in 1986, the two counterpropagating waves, which are detuned to the red ($\omega_L < \omega_A$) and which have opposite circular polarizations are in resonance with the atom at different places. This results in a restoring force towards the point where the magnetic field vanishes. Furthermore the non zero value of the detuning provides a Doppler cooling. In fact, such a scheme can be extended to three dimensions and leads to a robust, large and deep trap called "magneto-optical trap" or "MOT" [27]. It combines trapping and cooling, it has a large velocity capture range and it can be used for trapping atoms in a small cell filled with a low pressure vapour [28].

1.3.3 *Applications of dispersive forces : laser traps and atomic mirrors*
When the detuning is negative ($\omega_L - \omega_A < 0$), light shifts are negative. If the laser beam is focussed, the focal zone where the intensity is maximum appears as a minimum of potential energy, forming a potential well where sufficiently cold atoms can be trapped. This is a laser trap. Laser traps using a single focussed laser beam [29] or two crossed focussed laser beams [30, 31] have been realized. Early proposals [32] were considering trapping atoms at the antinodes or nodes of a non resonant laser standing wave. Channeling of atoms in a laser standing wave has been observed experimentally [33].

If the detuning is positive, light shifts are positive and can thus be used to produce potential barriers. For example an evanescent blue detuned wave at the surface of a piece of glass can prevent slow atoms impinging on the glass surface from touching the wall, making them bounce off a "carpet of light" [34]. This is the principle of mirrors for atoms. Plane atomic mirrors [35, 36] have been realized as well as concave mirrors [37].

2. SUB-DOPPLER COOLING

In the previous section, we discussed separately the manipulation of internal and external degrees of freedom, and we have described physical mechanisms involving only one type of physical effect, either dispersive or dissipative. In fact, there exist cooling mechanisms resulting from an interplay between spin and external degrees of freedom, and between dispersive and dissipative effects. We discuss in this section one of them, the so-called "Sisyphus cooling" or "polarization-gradient cooling" mechanism [38, 39] (see also [19]), which leads to temperatures much lower than Doppler cooling. One can understand in this way the sub-Doppler temperatures observed in optical molasses and mentioned above in section 1.3.2.

2.1 *SISYPHUS EFFECT*

Most atoms, in particular alkali atoms, have a Zeeman structure in the ground state. Since the detuning used in laser cooling experiments is not too large compared to Γ, both differential light shifts and optical pumping transitions exist for the various ground state Zeeman sublevels. Furthermore, the laser polarization varies in general in space so that light shifts and optical pumping rates are position-dependent. We show now, with a simple one-dimensional example, how the combination of these various effects can lead to a very efficient cooling mechanism.

Consider the laser configuration of Fig.2a, consisting of two counterpropagating plane waves along the z-axis, with orthogonal linear polarizations and with the same frequency and the same intensity. Because the phase shift between the two waves increases linearly with z, the polarization of the total field changes from σ^+ to σ^- and vice versa every $\lambda/4$. In between, it is elliptical or linear.

Consider now the simple case where the atomic ground state has an angular momentum $J_g = 1/2$. As shown in subsection (1.2), the two Zeeman sublevels $M_g = \pm 1/2$ undergo different light shifts, depending on the laser polarization, so that the Zeeman degeneracy in zero magnetic field is removed. This gives the energy diagram of Fig.2b showing spatial modulations of the Zeeman splitting between the two sublevels with a period $\lambda/2$.

If the detuning δ is not too large compared to Γ, there are also real absorptions of photons by the atom followed by spontaneous emission, which give rise to optical pumping transfers between the two sublevels, whose direction depends on the polarization: $M_g = -1/2 \rightarrow M_g = +1/2$ for a σ^+ polarization, $M_g = +1/2 \rightarrow M_g = -1/2$ for a σ^- polarization. Here also, the spatial modulation of the laser polarization results in a spatial modulation of the optical pumping rates with a period $\lambda/2$ (vertical arrows of Fig.2b).

The two spatial modulations of light shifts and optical pumping rates are of course correlated because they are due to the same cause, the spatial modulation of the light polarization. These correlations clearly appear in Fig.2b. With the proper sign of the detuning, optical pumping always transfers atoms from the higher Zeeman sublevel to the lower one. Suppose now that the

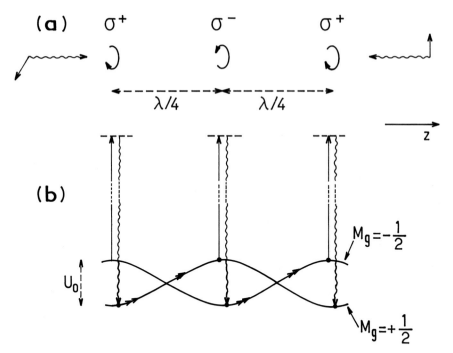

Figure 2. Sisyphus cooling. Laser configuration formed by two counterpropagating plane waves along the z-axis with orthogonal linear polarizations (a). The polarization of the resulting electric field is spatially modulated with a period $\lambda/2$. Every $\lambda/4$, it changes from σ^+ to σ^- and vice versa. For an atom with two ground state Zeeman sublevels $M_g = \pm 1/2$, the spatial modulation of the laser polarization results in correlated spatial modulations of the light shifts of these two sublevels and of the optical pumping rates between them (b). Because of these correlations, a moving atom runs up potential hills more frequently than down (double arrows of b).

atom is moving to the right, starting from the bottom of a valley, for example in the state $M_g = +1/2$ at a place where the polarization is σ^+. Because of the finite value of the optical pumping time, there is a time lag between internal and external variables and the atom can climb up the potential hill before absorbing a photon and reach the top of the hill where it has the maximum probability to be optically pumped in the other sublevel, i.e. in the bottom of a valley, and so on (double arrows of Fig.2b). Like Sisyphus in the Greek mythology, who was always rolling a stone up the slope, the atom is running up potential hills more frequently than down. When it climbs a potential hill, its kinetic energy is transformed into potential energy. Dissipation then occurs by light, since the spontaneously emitted photon has an energy higher than the absorbed laser photon (anti-Stokes Raman processes of Fig.2b). After each Sisyphus cycle, the total energy E of the atom decreases by an amount of the order of U_0, where U_0 is the depth of the optical potential wells of Fig.2b, until E becomes smaller than U_0, in which case the atom remains trapped in the potential wells.

The previous discussion shows that Sisyphus cooling leads to temperatures T_{Sis} such that $k_B T_{\text{Sis}} \simeq U_0$. According to Eq. (2), the light shift U_0 is proportional to $\hbar\Omega^2/\delta$ when $4|\delta| > \Gamma$. Such a dependence of T_{Sis} on the Rabi frequency Ω and on the detuning δ has been checked experimentally with cesium atoms [40]. Fig.3 presents the variations of the measured temperature T with the dimensionless parameter $\Omega^2/\Gamma|\delta|$. Measurements of T versus intensity for different values of δ show that T depends linearly, for low enough intensities, on a single parameter which is the light shift of the ground state Zeeman sub-levels.

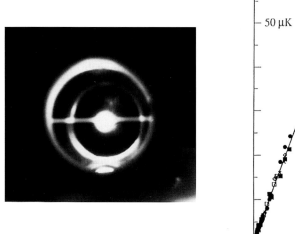
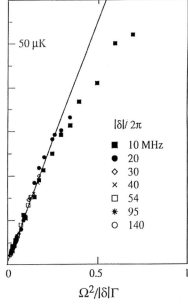

Figure 3. Temperature measurements in cesium optical molasses (from reference [40]). The left part of the figure shows the fluorescence light emitted by the molasses observed through a window of the vacuum chamber. The horizontal bright line is the fluorescence light emitted by the atomic beam which feeds the molasses and which is slowed down by a frequency chirped laser beam. Right part of the figure : temperature of the atoms measured by a time of flight technique versus the dimensionless parameter $\Omega^2/|\delta|\Gamma$ proportional to the light shift (Ω is the optical Rabi frequency, δ the detuning and Γ the natural width of the excited state).

2.2 THE LIMITS OF SISYPHUS COOLING

At low intensity, the light shift $U_0 \propto \hbar\Omega^2/\delta$ is much smaller than $\hbar\Gamma$. This explains why Sisyphus cooling leads to temperatures much lower than those achievable with Doppler cooling. One cannot however decrease indefinitely the laser intensity. The previous discussion ignores the recoil due to the spontaneously emitted photons which increases the kinetic energy of the atom by an amount on the order of E_R, where

$$E_R = \hbar^2 k^2/2M \qquad (3)$$

is the recoil energy of an atom absorbing or emitting a single photon. When U_0 becomes on the order or smaller than E_R, the cooling due to Sisyphus cooling becomes weaker than the heating due to the recoil, and Sisyphus cooling no longer works. This shows that the lowest temperatures which can be achieved with such a scheme are on the order of a few E_R/k_B. This result is confirmed by a full quantum theory of Sisyphus cooling [41, 42] and is in good agreement with experimental results. The minimum temperature in Fig.3 is on the order of $10E_R/k_B$.

2.3 OPTICAL LATTICES

For the optimal conditions of Sisyphus cooling, atoms become so cold that they get trapped in the quantum vibrational levels of a potential well (see Fig.3b). More precisely, one must consider energy bands in this periodic structure [43]. Experimental observation of such a quantization of atomic motion

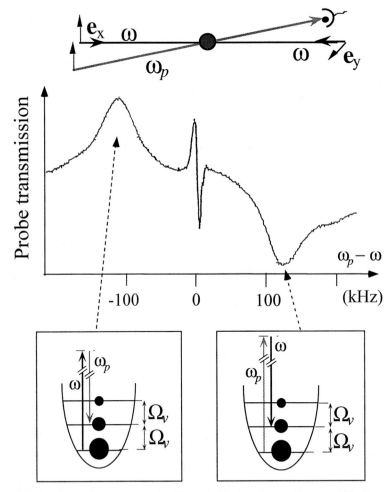

Figure 4. Probe absorption spectrum of a 1-D optical lattice (from reference [44]). The upper part of the figure shows the two counterpropagating laser beams with frequency ω and orthogonal linear polarizations forming the 1D-optical lattice, and the probe beam with frequency ω_p whose absorption is measured by a detector. The lower part of the figure shows the probe transmission versus $\omega_p - \omega$. The two lateral resonances corresponding to amplification or absorption of the probe are due to stimulated Raman processes between vibrational levels of the atoms trapped in the light field (see the two insets). The central narrow structure is a Rayleigh line due to the antiferromagnetic spatial order of the atoms.

in an optical potential was first achieved in one dimension [44] [45]. Atoms are trapped in a spatial periodic array of potential wells, called a "1D-optical lattice", with an antiferromagnetic order, since two adjacent potential wells correspond to opposite spin polarizations. 2D and 3D optical lattices have been realized subsequently (see the review papers [46] [47]).

3. SUBRECOIL LASER COOLING

3.1 *THE SINGLE PHOTON RECOIL LIMIT. HOW TO CIRCUMVENT IT*

In most laser cooling schemes, fluorescence cycles never cease. Since the random recoil $\hbar k$ communicated to the atom by the spontaneously emitted photons cannot be controlled, it seems impossible to reduce the atomic momentum spread δp below a value corresponding to the photon momentum $\hbar k$. Condition $\delta p = \hbar k$ defines the "single photon recoil limit". It is usual in laser cooling to define an effective temperature T in terms of the half-width δp (at $1/\sqrt{e}$) of the momentum distribution by $k_B T/2 = \delta p^2/2M$. In the temperature scale, condition $\delta p = \hbar k$ defines a "recoil temperature" T_R by:

$$\frac{k_B T_R}{2} = \frac{\hbar^2 k^2}{2M} = E_R \qquad (4)$$

The value of T_R ranges from a few hundred nanoKelvin for alkalis to a few microKelvin for helium.

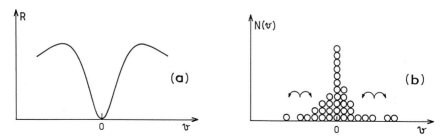

Figure 5. Subrecoil laser cooling. The random walk of the atom in velocity space is supposed to be characterized by a jump rate R which vanishes for $v = 0$ (a). As a result of this inhomogeneous random walk, atoms which fall in a small interval around $v = 0$ remain trapped there for a long time, on the order of $[R(v)]^{-1}$, and accumulate (b).

It is in fact possible to circumvent this limit and to reach temperatures T lower than T_R, a regime which is called "subrecoil" laser cooling. The basic idea is to create a situation where the photon absorption rate Γ', which is also the jump rate R of the atomic random walk in velocity space, depends on the atomic velocity $v = p/M$ and vanishes for $v = 0$ (Fig.5a). Consider then an atom with $v = 0$. For such an atom, the absorption of light is quenched. Consequently, there is no spontaneous reemission and no associated random recoil. One protects in this way ultracold atoms (with $v \approx 0$) from the "bad" effects of the light. On the other hand, atoms with $v \neq 0$ can absorb and reemit light. In such absorption-spontaneous emission cycles, their velocities change in a random way and the corresponding random walk in v-space can transfer atoms from the $v \neq 0$ absorbing states into the $v \simeq 0$ dark states where they remain trapped and accumulate (see Fig. 5b). This reminds us of what happens in a Kundt's tube where sand grains vibrate in an acoustic standing wave and accumulate at the nodes of this wave where they no longer move. Note however that the random walk takes place in velocity space for the situation considered in Fig. 5b, whereas it takes place in position space in a Kundt's tube.

Up to now, two subrecoil cooling schemes have been proposed and demonstrated. In the first one, called "Velocity Selective Coherent Population Trapping" (VSCPT), the vanishing of $R(v)$ for $v = 0$ is achieved by using destructive quantum interference between different absorption amplitudes [48]. The second one, called Raman cooling, uses appropriate sequences of stimulated Raman and optical pumping pulses for tailoring the appropriate shape of $R(v)$ [49].

3.2 BRIEF SURVEY OF VSCPT

We first recall the principle of the quenching of absorption by "coherent population trapping", an effect which was discovered and studied in 1976 [50, 51]. Consider the 3-level system of Fig.6, with two ground state sublevels g_1 and g_2 and one excited sublevel e_0, driven by two laser fields with frequencies ω_{L1} and ω_{L2}, exciting the transitions $g_1 \leftrightarrow e_0$ and $g_2 \leftrightarrow e_0$, respectively. Let $\hbar\Delta$ be the detuning from resonance for the stimulated Raman process consisting of the absorption of one ω_{L1} photon and the stimulated emission of one ω_{L2} photon, the atom going from g_1 to g_2. One observes that the fluorescence

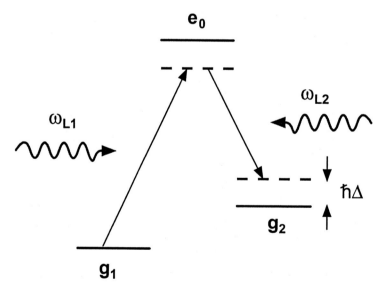

Figure 6. Coherent population trapping. A three-level atom g_1, g_2, e_0 is driven by two laser fields with frequences ω_{L1} and ω_{L2} exciting the transitions $g_1 \leftrightarrow e_0$ and $g_2 \leftrightarrow e_0$, respectively. $\hbar\Delta$ is the detuning from resonance for the stimulated Raman process induced between g_1 and g_2 by the two laser fields ω_{L1} and ω_{L2}. When $\Delta = 0$, atoms are optically pumped in a linear superposition of g_1 and g_2 which no longer absorbs light because of a destructive interference between the two absorption amplitudes $g_1 \rightarrow e_0$ and $g_2 \rightarrow e_0$.

rate R vanishes for $\Delta = 0$. Plotted versus Δ, the variations of R are similar to those of Fig.5a with v replaced by Δ. The interpretation of this effect is that atoms are optically pumped into a linear superposition of g_1 and g_2 which is not coupled to e_0 because of a destructive interference between the two absorption amplitudes $g_1 \rightarrow e_0$ and $g_2 \rightarrow e_0$.

The basic idea of VSCPT is to use the Doppler effect for making the detuning Δ of the stimulated Raman process of Fig.6 proportional to the atomic velocity v. The quenching of absorption by coherent population trapping is thus made velocity dependent and one achieves the situation of Fig. 5.a. This is obtained by taking the two laser waves ω_{L1} and ω_{L2} counterpropagating along the z-axis and by choosing their frequencies in such a way that $\Delta = 0$ for an atom at rest. Then, for an atom moving with a velocity v along the z-axis, the opposite Doppler shifts of the two laser waves result in a Raman detuning $\Delta = (k_1 + k_2)\, v$ proportional to v.

A more quantitative analysis of the cooling process [52] shows that the dark state, for which $R = 0$, is a linear superposition of two states which differ not only by the internal state (g_1 or g_2) but also by the momentum along the z-axis:

$$|\psi_D\rangle = c_1 \,|g_1, -\hbar k_1\rangle + c_2 \,|g_2, +\hbar k_2\rangle \qquad (5)$$

This is due to the fact that g_1 and g_2 must be associated with different momenta, $-\hbar k_1$ and $+\hbar k_2$, in order to be coupled to the same excited state $|e_0, p = 0\rangle$ by absorption of photons with different momenta $+\hbar k_1$ and $-\hbar k_2$. Furthermore, when $\Delta = 0$, the state (5) is a stationary state of the total atom + laser photons system. As a result of the cooling by VSCPT, the atomic momentum distribution thus exhibits two sharp peaks, centered at $-\hbar k_1$ and

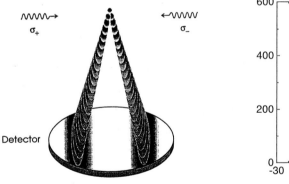 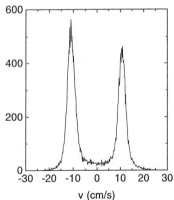

Figure 7. One-dimensional VSCPT experiment. The left part of the figure shows the experimental scheme. The cloud of precooled trapped atoms is released while the two counterpropagating VSCPT beams with orthogonal circular polarizations are applied during a time $\theta = 1$ms. The atoms then fall freely and their positions are detected 6.5 cm below on a microchannel plate. The double band pattern is a signature of the 1D cooling process which accumulates the atoms in a state which is a linear superposition of two different momenta. The right part of the figure gives the velocity distribution of the atoms detected by the microchannel plate. The width δv of the two peaks is clearly smaller than their separation $2v_R$ where $v_R = 9.2$ cm/s is the recoil velocity. This is a clear signature of subrecoil cooling.

$+\hbar k_2$, with a width δp which tends to zero when the interaction time Θ tends to infinity.

The first VSCPT experiment [48] was performed on the 2^3S_1 metastable state of helium atoms. The two lower states g_1 and g_2 were the $M = -1$ and $M = +1$ Zeeman sublevels of the 2^3S_1 metastable state, e_0 was the $M = 0$ Zeeman sublevel of the excited 2^3P_1 state. The two counterpropagating laser waves had the same frequency $\omega_{L1} = \omega_{L2} = \omega_L$ and opposite circular polarizations. The two peaks of the momentum distribution were centered at $\pm\hbar k$, with a width corresponding to $T \simeq T_R/2$. The interaction time was then increased by starting from a cloud of trapped precooled helium atoms instead of using an atomic beam as in the first experiment [53]. This led to much lower temperatures (see Fig.7). Very recently, temperatures as low as $T_R/800$ have been observed [54].

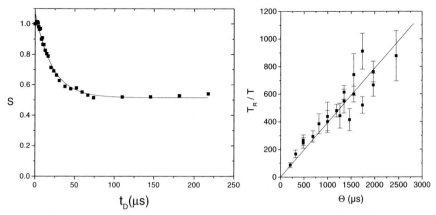

Figure 8. Measurement of the spatial correlation function of atoms cooled by VSCPT (from reference [54]). After a cooling period of duration θ, the two VSCPT beams are switched off during a dark period of duration t_D. The two coherent wave packets into which atoms are pumped fly apart with a relative velocity $2v_R$ and get separated by a distance $a = 2v_R t_D$. Reapplying the two VSCPT beams during a short probe pulse, one measures a signal S which can be shown to be equal to $[1 + G(a)]/2$ where $G(a)$ is the spatial overlap between the two identical wave packets separated by a. From $G(a)$, which is the spatial correlation function of each wave packet, one determines the atomic momentum distribution which is the Fourier transform of $G(a)$. The left part of the figure gives S versus a. The right part of the figure gives T_R/T versus the cooling time θ, where T_R is the recoil temperature and T the temperature of the cooled atoms determined from the width of $G(a)$. The straight line is a linear fit in agreement with the theoretical predictions of Lévy statistics. The lowest temperature, on the order of $T_R/800$, is equal to 5 nK.

In fact, it is not easy to measure such low temperatures by the usual time of flight techniques, because the resolution is then limited by the spatial extent of the initial atomic cloud. A new method has been developed [54] which consists of measuring directly the spatial correlation function of the atoms $G(a) = \int_{-\infty}^{+\infty} dz \phi^*(z + a) \phi(z)$, where $\phi(z)$ is the wave function of the atomic wave packet. This correlation function, which describes the degree of spatial coherence between two points separated by a distance a, is simply the Fourier transform of the momentum distribution $|\phi(p)|^2$. This method is analogous to Fourier spectroscopy in optics, where a narrow spectral line $I(\omega)$ is more easily inferred from the correlation function of the emitted electric field $G(\tau)$

118

$= \int_{-\infty}^{+\infty} dt E^*(t + \tau)E(t)$, which is the Fourier transform of $I(\omega)$. Experimentally, the measurement of $G(a)$ is achieved by letting the two coherent VSCPT wave packets fly apart with a relative velocity $2v_R = 2\hbar k/m$ during a dark period t_D, during which the VSCPT beams are switched off. During this dark period, the two wave packets get separated by a distance a $= 2v_R t_D$, and one then measures with a probe pulse a signal proportional to their overlap. Fig.8a shows the variations with t_D of such a signal S (which is in fact equal to $[1 + G(a)]/2$). From such a curve, one deduces a temperature $T \simeq T_R/625$, corresponding to $\delta p \simeq \hbar k/25$. Fig.8b shows the variations of T_R/T with the VSCPT interaction time θ. As predicted by theory (see next subsection), T_R/T varies linearly with θ and can reach values as large as 800.

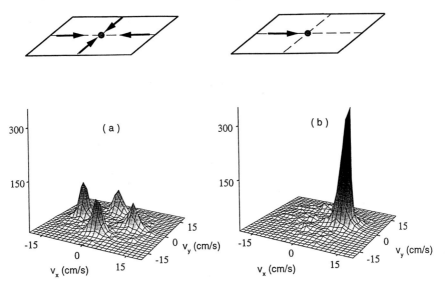

Figure 9. Two-dimensional VSCPT experiment (from reference [58]). The experimental scheme is the same as in Fig. 7, but one uses now four VSCPT beams in a horizontal plane and atoms are pumped into a linear superposition of four different momentum states giving rise to four peaks in the two-dimensional velocity distribution (a). When three of the four VSCPT laser beams are adiabatically switched off, the whole atomic population is transferred into a single wave packet (b).

VSCPT has been extended to two [55] and three [56] dimensions. For a $J_g = 1 \leftrightarrow J_e = 1$ transition, it has been shown [57] that there is a dark state which is described by the same vector field as the laser field. More precisely, if the laser field is formed by a linear superposition of N plane waves with wave vectors $\mathbf{k}_i$ ($i = 1,2,...N$) having the same modulus k, one finds that atoms are cooled in a coherent superposition of N wave packets with mean momenta $\hbar\mathbf{k}_i$ and with a momentum spread δp which becomes smaller and smaller as the interaction time θ increases. Furthermore, because of the isomorphism between the de Broglie dark state and the laser field, one can adiabatically change the laser configuration and transfer the whole atomic population into a single wave packet or two coherent wave packets chosen at will [58]. Fig. 9 shows an example of such a coherent manipulation of atomic wave packets in two dimensions. In Fig.9a, one sees the transverse velocity distribution associated with the four wave packets obtained with two pairs of counterpropagating laser waves along the x and y-axis in a horizontal plane; Fig.9b shows the single wave packet into which the whole atomic population is transferred by switching off adiabatically three of the four VSCPT beams. Similar results have been obtained in three dimensions.

3.3 SUBRECOIL LASER COOLING AND LÉVY STATISTICS

Quantum Monte Carlo simulations using the delay function [59, 60] have provided new physical insight into subrecoil laser cooling [61]. Fig.10 shows for example the random evolution of the momentum p of an atom in a 1D-VSCPT experiment. Each vertical discontinuity corresponds to a spontaneous emission process during which p changes in a random way. Between two successive jumps, p remains constant. It clearly appears that the random walk of the atom in velocity space is anomalous and dominated by a few rare events whose duration is a significant fraction of the total interaction time. A simple analysis shows that the distribution $P(\tau)$ of the trapping times τ in a small trapping zone near $v = 0$ is a broad distribution which falls as a power-law in the wings. These wings decrease so slowly that the average value $\langle \tau \rangle$ of τ (or the variance) can diverge. In such cases, the central limit theorem (CLT) can obviously no longer be used for studying the distribution of the total trapping time after N entries in the trapping zone separated by N exits.

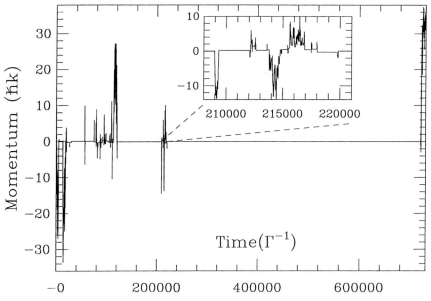

Figure 10. Monte Carlo wave function simulation of one-dimensional VSCPT (from reference [61]). Momentum p characterizing the cooled atoms versus time. Each vertical discontinuity corresponds to a spontaneous emission jump during which p changes in a random way. Between two successive jumps, p remains constant. The inset shows a zoomed part of the sequence.

120

It is possible to extend the CLT to broad distributions with power-law wings [62, 63]. We have applied the corresponding statistics, called "Lévy statistics", to subrecoil cooling and shown that one can obtain in this way a better understanding of the physical processes as well as quantitative analytical predictions for the asymptotic properties of the cooled atoms in the limit when the interaction time θ tends to infinity [61, 64]. For example, one predicts in this way that the temperature decreases as $1/\theta$ when $\theta \to \infty$, and that the wings of the momentum distribution decrease as $1/p^2$, which shows that the shape of the momentum distribution is closer to a Lorentzian than a Gaussian. This is in agreement with the experimental observations represented in Fig.8. (The fit in Fig.8a is an exponential, which is the Fourier transform of a Lorentzian).

One important feature revealed by this theoretical analysis is the non-ergodicity of the cooling process. Regardless of the interaction time θ, there are always atomic evolution times (trapping times in the small zone of Fig.5a around $v = 0$) which can be longer than θ. Another advantage of such a new approach is that it allows the parameters of the cooling lasers to be optimized for given experimental conditions. For example, by using different shapes for the laser pulses used in one-dimensional subrecoil Raman cooling, it has been possible to reach for Cesium atoms temperatures as low as 3 nK [65].

4. A FEW EXAMPLES OF APPLICATIONS

The possibility of trapping atoms and cooling them at very low temperatures, where their velocity can be as low as a few mm/s, has opened the way to a wealth of applications. Ultracold atoms can be observed during much longer times, which is important for high resolution spectroscopy and frequency standards. They also have very long de Broglie wavelengths, which has given rise to new research fields, such as atom optics, atom interferometry and Bose-Einstein condensation of dilute gases. It is impossible to discuss here all these developments. We refer the reader to recent reviews such as [5]. We will just describe in this section a few examples of applications which have been recently investigated by our group in Paris.

4.1 CESIUM ATOMIC CLOCKS
Cesium atoms cooled by Sisyphus cooling have an effective temperature on the order of 1 μK, corresponding to a r.m.s. velocity of 1 cm/s. This allows them to spend a longer time T in an observation zone where a microwave field induces resonant transitions between the two hyperfine levels g_1 and g_2 of the ground state. Increasing T decreases the width $\Delta v \sim 1/T$ of the microwave resonance line whose frequency is used to define the unit of time. The stability of atomic clocks can thus be considerably improved by using ultracold atoms [66. 67].

In usual atomic clocks, atoms from a thermal cesium beam cross two microwave cavities fed by the same oscillator. The average velocity of the atoms is several hundred m/s, the distance between the two cavities is on the

121

order of 1 m. The microwave resonance between g_1 and g_2 is monitored and is used to lock the frequency of the oscillator to the center of the atomic line. The narrower the resonance line, the more stable the atomic clock. In fact, the microwave resonance line exhibits Ramsey interference fringes whose width Δv is determined by the time of flight T of the atoms from one cavity to another. For the longest devices, T, which can be considered as the observation time, can reach 10 ms, leading to values of $\Delta v \sim 1/T$ on the order of 100 Hz.

Much narrower Ramsey fringes, with sub-Hertz linewidths can be obtained in the so-called "Zacharias atomic fountain" [68]. Atoms are captured in a magneto-optical trap and laser cooled before being launched upwards by a laser pulse through a microwave cavity. Because of gravity they are decelerated, they return and fall back, passing a second time through the cavity. Atoms therefore experience two coherent microwave pulses, when they pass through the cavity, the first time on their way up, the second time on their way down. The time interval between the two pulses can now be on the order of 1 sec, *i.e.* about two orders of magnitude longer than with usual clocks. Atomic fountains have been realized for sodium [69] and cesium [70]. A short-term relative frequency stability of $1.3 \times 10^{-13} \tau^{-1/2}$, where τ is the integration time, has been recently measured for a one meter high Cesium fountain [71, 72]. For $\tau = 10^4 s$, $\Delta v/v \sim 1.3 \times 10^{-15}$ and for $\tau = 3 \times 10^4 s$, $\Delta v/v \sim 8 \times 10^{-16}$ has been measured. In fact such a stability is most likely limited by the Hydrogen maser which is used as a reference source and the real stability, which could be more precisely determined by beating the signals of two fountain clocks, is expected to reach $\Delta v/v \sim 10^{-16}$ for a one day integration time. In addition to the stability, another very important property of a frequency standard is its accuracy. Because of the very low velocities in a fountain device, many systematic shifts are strongly reduced and can be evaluated with great precision. With an accuracy of 2×10^{-15}, the BNM-LPTF fountain is presently the most accurate primary standard [73]. A factor 10 improvement in this accuracy is expected in the near future.

To increase the observation time beyond one second, a possible solution consists of building a clock for operation in a reduced gravity environment. Such a microgravity clock has been recently tested in a jet plane making parabolic flights. A resonance signal with a width of 7 Hz has been recorded in a $10^{-2}g$ environment. This width is twice narrower than that produced on earth in the same apparatus. This clock prototype (see Fig.11) is a compact and transportable device which can be also used on earth for high precision frequency comparison.

Atomic clocks working with ultracold atoms could not only provide an improvement of positioning systems such as the GPS. They could be also used for fundamental studies. For example, one could build two fountains clocks, one with cesium and one with rubidium, in order to measure with a high accuracy the ratio between the hyperfine frequencies of these two atoms. Because of relativistic corrections, the hyperfine splitting is a function of $Z\alpha$ where α is the fine structure constant and Z is the atomic number [74]. Since Z is not the same for cesium and rubidium, the ratio of the two hyperfine

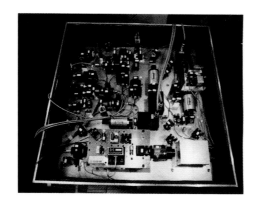

Figure 11. The microgravity clock prototype. The left part is the 60 cm × 60 cm × 15 cm optical bench containing the diode laser sources and the various optical components. The right part is the clock itself (about one meter long) containing the optical molasses, the microwave cavity and the detection region.

structures depends on α. By making several measurements of this ratio over long periods of time, one could check Dirac's suggestion concerning a possible variation of α with time. The present upper limit for $\dot{\alpha}/\alpha$ in laboratory tests [74] could be improved by two orders of magnitude.

Another interesting test would be to measure with a higher accuracy the gravitational red shift and the gravitational delay of an electromagnetic wave passing near a large mass (Shapiro effect [75]).

4.2 GRAVITATIONAL CAVITIES FOR NEUTRAL ATOMS

We have already mentioned in section 1.3 the possibility of making atomic mirrors for atoms by using blue detuned evanescent waves at the surface of a piece of glass. Concave mirrors (Fig.12a) are particularly interesting because the transverse atomic motion is then stable if atoms are released from a point located below the focus of the mirror. It has been possible in this way to observe several successive bounces of the atoms (Fig.12b) and such a system can be considered as a "trampoline for atoms" [37]. In such an experiment, it is a good approximation to consider atoms as classical particles bouncing off a concave mirror. In a quantum mechanical description of the experiment, one must consider the reflection of the atomic de Broglie waves by the mirror. Standing de Broglie waves can then be introduced for such a "gravitational cavity", which are quite analogous to the light standing waves for a Fabry-Perot cavity [76]. By modulating at frequency $\Omega/2\pi$ the intensity of the evanescent wave which forms the atomic mirror, one can produce the equivalent of a vibrating mirror for de Broglie waves. The reflected waves thus have a modulated Doppler shift. The corresponding frequency modulation of these waves has been recently demonstrated [77] by measuring the energy change ΔE of the bouncing atom, which is found to be equal to $n\hbar\Omega$, where $n = 0, \pm 1, \pm 2, ...$ (Figs.12c and d). The discrete nature of this energy spectrum is a pure quantum effect. For classical particles bouncing off a vibrating mirror, ΔE would vary continuously in a certain range.

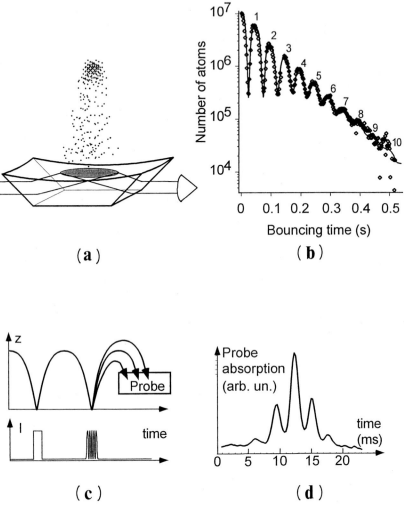

Figure 12. Gravitational cavity for neutral atoms (from references [37] and [77]). Trampoline for atoms (a) – Atoms released from a magneto-optical trap bounce off a concave mirror formed by a blue detuned evanescent wave at the surface of a curved glass prism. Number of atoms at the initial position of the trap versus time after the trap has been switched off (b). Ten successive bounces are visible in the figure. Principle of the experiment demonstrating the frequency modulation of de Broglie waves (c). The upper trace gives the atomic trajectories (vertical position z versus time). The lower trace gives the time dependence of the intensity I of the evanescent wave. The first pulse is used for making a velocity selection. The second pulse is modulated in intensity. This produces a vibrating mirror giving rise to a frequency modulated reflected de Broglie wave which consists in a carrier and sidebands at the modulation frequency. The energy spectrum of the reflected particles is thus discrete so that the trajectories of the reflected particles form a discrete set. This effect is detected by looking at the time dependence of the absorption of a probe beam located above the prism (d).

4.3 *BLOCH OSCILLATIONS*

In the subrecoil regime where δp becomes smaller than $\hbar k$, the atomic coherence length $h/\delta p$ becomes larger than the optical wavelength $\lambda = h/\hbar k = 2\pi/k$ of the lasers used to cool the atom. Consider then such an ultracold atom in the periodic light shift potential produced by a non resonant laser standing wave. The atomic de Broglie wave is delocalized over several periods of the periodic potential, which means that one can prepare in this way quasi-Bloch states. By chirping the frequency of the two counterpropagating laser waves forming the standing wave, one can produce an accelerated standing wave. In the rest frame of this wave, atoms thus feel a constant inertial force in addition to the periodic potential. They are accelerated and the de Broglie wavelength $\lambda_{dB} = h/M\langle v \rangle$ decreases. When $\lambda_{dB} = \lambda_{Laser}$, the de Broglie wave is Bragg-reflected by the periodic optical potential. Instead of increasing linearly with time, the mean velocity $\langle v \rangle$ of the atoms oscillates back and forth. Such Bloch oscillations, which are a textbook effect of solid-state physics, are more easily observed with ultracold atoms than with electrons in condensed matter because the Bloch period can be much shorter than the relaxation time for the coherence of de Broglie waves (in condensed matter, the relaxation processes due to collisions are very strong). Fig.13 shows an example of Bloch oscillations [78] observed on cesium atoms cooled by the improved subrecoil Raman cooling technique described in [65].

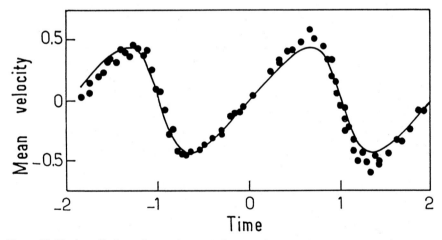

Figure 13. Bloch oscillations of atoms in a periodic optical potential (from reference [78]. Mean velocity (in units of the recoil velocity) versus time (in units of half the Bloch period) for ultracold cesium atoms moving in a periodic optical potential and submitted in addition to a constant force.

5. CONCLUSION

We have described in this paper a few physical mechanisms allowing one to manipulate neutral atoms with laser light. Several of these mechanisms can be simply interpreted in terms of resonant exchanges of energy, angular and linear momentum between atoms and photons. A few of them, among the most efficient ones, result from a new way of combining well known physical effects such as optical pumping, light shifts, coherent population trapping. We have given two examples of such cooling mechanisms, Sisyphus cooling and subrecoil cooling, which allow atoms to be cooled in the microKelvin and nanoKelvin ranges. A few possible applications of ultracold atoms have been also reviewed. They take advantage of the long interaction times and long de Broglie wavelengths which are now available with laser cooling and trapping techniques.

One can reasonably expect that further progress in this field will be made in the near future and that new applications will be found. Concerning fundamental problems, two directions of research at least look promising. First, a better control of "pure" situations involving a small number of atoms in well-defined states exhibiting quantum features such as very long spatial coherence lengths or entanglement. In that perspective, atomic, molecular and optical physics will continue to play an important role by providing a "testing bench" for improving our understanding of quantum phenomena. A second interesting direction is the investigation of new systems, such as Bose condensates involving a macroscopic number of atoms in the same quantum state. One can reasonably hope that new types of coherent atomic sources (sometimes called "atom lasers") will be realized, opening the way to interesting new possibilities.

It is clear finally that all the developments which have occurred in the field of laser cooling and trapping are strengthening the connections which can be established between atomic physics and other branches of physics, such as condensed matter or statistical physics. The use of Lévy statistics for analyzing subrecoil cooling is an example of such a fruitful dialogue. The interdisciplinary character of the present researches on the properties of Bose condensates is also a clear sign of the increase of these exchanges.

REFERENCES

[1]   A. Kastler, J. Phys. Rad. **11,** 255 (1950).

[2]   A. Ashkin, Science, **210,** 1081 (1980).

[3]   V.S. Letokhov and V.G. Minogin, Phys.Reports, **73,** 1 (1981).

[4]   S. Stenholm, Rev.Mod.Phys. **58,** 699 (1986).

[5]   C.S. Adams and E. Riis, Prog. Quant. Electr. **21,** 1 (1997).

[6]   C. Cohen-Tannoudji and W. Phillips, Physics Today **43,** No 10, 33 (1990).

[7]   W. Heitler, "The quantum theory of radiation", 3rd ed. (Clarendon Press, Oxford, 1954).

[8]   J-P. Barrat and C.Cohen-Tannoudji, J.Phys.Rad. **22,** 329 and 443 (1961).

[9]   C.Cohen-Tannoudji , Ann. Phys. Paris **7,** 423 and 469 (1962).

[10] C. Cohen-Tannoudji, J. Dupont-Roc and G. Grynberg, "Atom-photon interactions– Basic processes and applications", (Wiley, New York, 1992).

[11] S.H. Autler and C.H. Townes, Phys.Rev. **100,** 703 (1955).

[12] C. Cohen-Tannoudji, C.R.Acad.Sci.(Fr) **252,** 394 (1961).

[13] C. Cohen-Tannoudji and J. Dupont-Roc, Phys.Rev. **A5,** 968 (1972).

[14] W.D.Phillips and H.Metcalf, Phys.Rev.Lett. **48,** 596 (1982).

[15] J.V.Prodan, W.D.Phillips and H.Metcalf, Phys.Rev.Lett. **49,** 1149 (1982).

[16] W. Ertmer, R. Blatt, J.L. Hall and M. Zhu, Phys.Rev.Lett. **54,** 996 (1985).

[17] G.A. Askarian, Zh.Eksp.Teor.Fiz. **42,** 1567 (1962) [Sov.Phys.JETP, 15, 1088 (1962)].

[18] C. Cohen-Tannoudji, "Atomic motion in laser light", in "Fundamental systems in quantum optics", J. Dalibard, J.-M. Raimond, and J. Zinn-Justin eds, Les Houches session LIII (1990), (North-Holland, Amsterdam 1992) p.1.

[19] J. Dalibard and C. Cohen-Tannoudji, J.Opt.Soc.Am. **B2,** 1707 (1985).

[20] T.W. Hänsch and A.L. Schawlow, Opt. Commun. **13,** 68 (1975).

[21] D.Wineland and H.Dehmelt, Bull.Am.Phys.Soc. **20,** 637 (1975).

[22] S. Chu, L. Hollberg, J.E. Bjorkholm, A. Cable and A. Ashkin, Phys. Rev. Lett. **55,** 48 (1985).

[23] V.S. Letokhov, V.G. Minogin and B.D. Pavlik, Zh.Eksp.Teor.Fiz. **72,** 1328 (1977) [Sov.Phys.JETP, **45,** 698 (1977)].

[24] D.J. Wineland and W. Itano, Phys.Rev. **A20,** 1521 (1979).

[25] J.P. Gordon and A. Ashkin, Phys.Rev. **A21,** 1606 (1980).

[26] P.D. Lett, R.N. Watts, C.I. Westbrook, W. Phillips, P.L. Gould and H.J. Metcalf, Phys. Rev. Lett. **61,** 169 (1988).

[27] E.L. Raab, M. Prentiss, A. Cable, S. Chu and D.E. Pritchard, Phys.Rev.Lett. **59,** 2631 (1987).

[28] C. Monroe, W. Swann, H. Robinson and C.E. Wieman, Phys.Rev.Lett. **65,** 1571 (1990).

[29] S. Chu, J.E. Bjorkholm, A. Ashkin and A. Cable, Phys.Rev.Lett. **57,** 314 (1986).

[30] C.S. Adams, H.J. Lee, N. Davidson, M. Kasevich and S. Chu, Phys. Rev. Lett. **74,** 3577 (1995).

[31] A. Kuhn, H. Perrin, W. Hänsel and C. Salomon, OSA TOPS on Ultracold Atoms and BEC, 1996, Vol. 7, p.58, Keith Burnett (ed.), (Optical Society of America, 1997).

[32] V.S. Letokhov, Pis'ma.Eksp.Teor.Fiz. **7,** 348 (1968) [JETP Lett., **7,** 272 (1968)].

[33] C. Salomon, J. Dalibard, A. Aspect, H. Metcalf and C. Cohen-Tannoudji, Phys. Rev. Lett. **59,** 1659 (1987).

[34] R.J. Cook and R.K. Hill, Opt. Commun. **43,** 258 (1982)

[35] V.I. Balykin, V.S. Letokhov, Yu. B. Ovchinnikov and A.I. Sidorov, Phys. Rev. Lett. **60,** 2137 (1988).

[36] M.A. Kasevich, D.S. Weiss and S. Chu, Opt. Lett. **15,** 607 (1990).

[37] C.G. Aminoff, A.M. Steane, P. Bouyer, P. Desbiolles, J. Dalibard and C. Cohen-Tannoudji, Phys. Rev. Lett. **71,** 3083 (1993).

[38] J. Dalibard and C. Cohen-Tannoudji, J. Opt. Soc. Am. **B6,** 2023 (1989).

[39] P.J. Ungar, D.S. Weiss, E. Riis and S. Chu, JOSA **B6,** 2058 (1989).

[40] C. Salomon, J. Dalibard, W. Phillips, A. Clairon and S. Guellati, Europhys. Lett. **12,** 683 (1990).

[41] Y. Castin, These de doctorat, Paris (1991).

[42] Y. Castin and K. Mølmer, Phys. Rev. Lett. **74,** 3772 (1995).

[43] Y. Castin and J. Dalibard, Europhys.Lett. **14,** 761 (1991).

[44] P. Verkerk, B. Lounis, C. Salomon, C. Cohen-Tannoudji, J.-Y. Courtois and G. Grynberg, Phys. Rev. Lett. **68,** 3861 (1992).

[45] P.S. Jessen, C. Gerz, P.D. Lett, W.D. Phillips, S.L. Rolston, R.J.C. Spreeuw and C.I. Westbrook, Phys. Rev. Lett. **69,** 49 (1992).

[46] G. Grynberg and C. Triché, in Proceedings of the International School of Physics "Enrico Fermi", Course CXXXI, A. Aspect, W. Barletta and R. Bonifacio (Eds), p.243, IOS Press, Amsterdam (1996); A. Hemmerich, M. Weidemüller and T.W. Hänsch, same Proceedings, p.503.

[47] P.S. Jessen and I.H. Deutsch, in Advances in Atomic, Molecular and Optical Physics, **37,** 95 (1996), ed. by B. Bederson and H. Walther.

[48] A. Aspect, E. Arimondo, R. Kaiser, N. Vansteenkiste, and C. Cohen-Tannoudji, Phys. Rev. Lett. **61,** 826 (1988).

[49] M. Kasevich and S. Chu, Phys. Rev. Lett. **69,** 1741 (1992).

[50] Alzetta G., Gozzini A., Moi L., Orriols G., Il Nuovo Cimento **36B,** 5 (1976).

[51] Arimondo E., Orriols G., Lett. Nuovo Cimento **17,** 333 (1976).

[52]   A. Aspect, E. Arimondo, R. Kaiser, N. Vansteenkiste, and C. Cohen-Tannoudji, J. Opt. Soc. Am. **B6**, 2112 (1989).

[53]   F. Bardou, B. Saubamea, J. Lawall, K. Shimizu, O. Emile, C. Westbrook, A. Aspect, C. Cohen-Tannoudji, C. R. Acad. Sci. Paris **318**, 877-885 (1994).

[54]   B. Saubamea, T.W. Hijmans, S. Kulin, E. Rasel, E. Peik, M. Leduc and C. Cohen-Tannoudji, Phys.Rev.Lett. **79**, 3146 (1997).

[55]   J. Lawall, F. Bardou, B. Saubamea, K. Shimizu, M. Leduc, A. Aspect and C. Cohen-Tannoudji, Phys. Rev. Lett. **73**, 1915 (1994).

[56]   J. Lawall, S. Kulin, B. Saubamea, N. Bigelow, M. Leduc and C. Cohen-Tannoudji, Phys. Rev. Lett. **75**, 4194 (1995).

[57]   M.A. Ol'shanii and V.G. Minogin, Opt. Commun. **89**, 393 (1992).

[58]   S. Kulin, B. Saubamea, E. Peik, J. Lawall, T.W. Hijmans, M. Leduc and C .Cohen-Tannoudji, Phys. Rev. Lett. **78**, 4185 (1997).

[59]   C. Cohen-Tannoudji and J. Dalibard, Europhys. Lett. **1**, 441 (1986).

[60]   P. Zoller, M. Marte and D.F. Walls, Phys. Rev. **A35**, 198 (1987).

[61]   F. Bardou, J.-P Bouchaud, O. Emile, A. Aspect and C. Cohen-Tannoudji, Phys. Rev. Lett. **72**, 203 (1994).

[62]   B.V. Gnedenko and A.N. Kolmogorov, "Limit distributions for sum of independent random variables" (Addison Wesley, Reading, MA, 1954).

[63]   J.P. Bouchaud and A. Georges, Phys. Rep. **195**, 127 (1990).

[64]   F. Bardou, Ph. D. Thesis, University of Paris XI, Orsay (1995).

[65]   J. Reichel, F. Bardou, M. Ben Dahan, E. Peik, S. Rand, C. Salomon and C. Cohen-Tannoudji, Phys. Rev. Lett. **75**, 4575 (1995).

[66]   K. Gibble and S. Chu, Metrologia, **29**, 201 (1992).

[67]   S.N. Lea, A. Clairon, C. Salomon, P. Laurent, B. Lounis, J. Reichel, A. Nadir, and G. Santarelli, Physica Scripta **T51**, 78 (1994).

[68]   J. Zacharias, Phys.Rev. **94**, 751 (1954). See also : N. Ramsey, Molecular Beams, Oxford University Press, Oxford, 1956.

[69]   M. Kasevich, E. Riis, S. Chu and R. de Voe, Phys. Rev. Lett. **63**, 612 (1989).

[70]   A. Clairon, C. Salomon, S. Guellati and W.D. Phillips, Europhys. Lett. **16**, 165 (1991).

[71]   S. Ghezali, Ph. Laurent, S.N. Lea and A. Clairon, Europhys. Lett. **36**, 25 (1996).

[72]   S. Ghezali, Thèse de doctorat, Paris (1997).

[73]   E. Simon, P. Laurent, C. Mandache and A. Clairon, Proceedings of EFTF 1997, Neuchatel, Switzerland.

[74]   J. Prestage, R. Tjoelker and L. Maleki, Phys. Rev. Lett. **74**, 3511 (1995).

[75]   I.I.Shapiro, Phys. Rev. Lett. **13**, 789 (1964).

[76]   H. Wallis, J. Dalibard and C. Cohen-Tannoudji, Appl. Phys. **B54**, 407 (1992).

[77]   A. Steane, P. Szriftgiser, P. Desbiolles and J. Dalibard, Phys. Rev. Lett. **74**, 4972 (1995).

[78]   M. Ben Dahan, E. Peik, J. Reichel, Y. Castin and C. Salomon, Phys. Rev. Lett. **76**, 4508 (1996).

William D. Phillips

WILLIAM D. PHILLIPS

I was born on 5 November 1948 in Wilkes-Barre, Pennsylvania, just across the river from the town of Kingston, where my parents lived with my one and a half year old sister, Maxine. My parents had come to this small Pennsylvania town from places and backgrounds that were far apart and yet quite similar.

My mother, Mary Catherine Savino (later, Savine), was born in the southern Italian village of Ripacandida in 1913. Among her earliest memories are riding into her grandfather's vineyards in a horse-drawn cart. Her father emigrated to the US and brought the family to Altoona, Pennsylvania in 1920. Her new American schoolmates teased her for her inability to speak English and taunted her as a "Wop" for her Italian heritage. She resolved to excel, and so she did, graduating near the top of her class from Altoona High School.

My father, William (Bill) Cornelius Phillips, was born in Juniata, a community on the edge of Altoona, in 1907. His father was a carpenter and his mother operated a boarding house to augment the family income. His grandfather was a barrel-maker, who would demonstrate the quality of his product by jumping onto the finished barrel in front of the customer. Dad could trace his heritage to ancestors from Wales who fought in the American Revolution.

My father and mother were each the first in their families to go to college, each attending Juniata College, a small school in Huntingdon, Pennsylvania, founded and strongly influenced by the pacifist Church of the Brethren. My father and mother graduated from Juniata in 1930 and 1936, respectively, but never met until a Juniata professor who knew them both suggested to my father that he might call a young Juniata alumna and ask her out. This Italian Catholic young woman and this Welsh-American Methodist young man met, fell in love, got married, earned Masters degrees and became professional social workers in the hard coal country of Pennsylvania.

I grew up surrounded by family and friends, church and school, and physical and mental activity. I clearly remember the value my parents placed on reading and education. My parents read to us and encouraged us to read. As soon as I could read for myself, walking across town to the library became a regular activity. Almost as far back as I can remember, I was interested in science. I assembled a collection of bottles of household substances as my "chemistry set" and examined almost anything I could find with the microscope my parents gave me. Although they had no particular knowledge or special interest in science, they supported mine. Science was only one of the passions of my childhood, along with fishing, baseball, bike riding and tree climbing. But as time went on, Erector sets, microscopes, and chemistry sets captured more of my attention than baseball bats, fishing rods, and football helmets. In 1956, my family moved from Kingston to Butler, near Pittsburgh. I remember that during that time I decided that science was going to be my life work, and sometime during the late 1950s, I came to appreciate, in a very incomplete and naive way, the simplicity and beauty of physics.

My brother Tom was born in 1957–a concrete confirmation, my sister and I believed, of the power of prayer. We had been praying for a sibling, unaware that our parents could decide, and *had* decided, that two children were enough. Apparently our prayers were effective. The result was a thrill and a blessing for all of us. Another blessing was my being placed into an experimental "accelerated" class. There, dedicated and concerned teachers taught us things that were not part of the ordinary elementary school curriculum, like French and advanced mathematics. When my family moved to Camp Hill, near Harrisburg, in 1959, interested teachers continued to provide me with advanced instruction, and when I entered the 7th grade of Camp Hill High School in 1960, it was in another accelerated program.

During this time, I had a laboratory in the basement of our family home. Ignorant and heedless of the dangers of asbestos, electricity, and ultraviolet light, I spent many hours experimenting with fire, explosives, rockets and carbon arcs. But life was not all science. I ran for the track team and played for the tennis team at school. During the summer, I spent all day either on the tennis courts or in the community swimming pool, and considered the advantages of life as a tennis bum.

While my parents were not directly involved in my scientific interests, they tolerated my experiments, even when the circuit breakers all tripped because of my overloads. They were always encouraging, and there was never any lack of intellectual stimulation. Dinner table conversations included discussions of politics, history, sociology, and current events. We children were heard and respected, but we had to compete for the privilege of expressing our opinions. In these discussions our parents transmitted important values about respect for other people, for their cultures, their ethnic backgrounds, their faith and beliefs, even when very different from our own. We learned concern for others who were less fortunate than we were. These values were supported and strengthened by a maturing religious faith.

In high school, I enjoyed and profited from well-taught science and math classes, but in retrospect, I can see that the classes that emphasized language and writing skills were just as important for the development of my scientific career as were science and math. I certainly feel that my high school involvement in debating competitions helped me later to give better scientific talks, that the classes in writing style helped me to write better papers, and the study of French greatly enhanced the tremendously fruitful collaboration I was to have with Claude Cohen-Tannoudji's research group.

The summer after my junior year in high school, I worked at the University of Delaware doing sputtering experiments. It was a great experience and I learned an important truth from Jim Comas, the graduate student who supervised me. "An experimental physicist," he told me, "is someone who gets paid for working at his hobby."

Another important part of my high school experience was meeting Jane Van Wynen. Her family had moved from Maine when we were in ninth grade, but we largely ignored each other until our senior year when, during a school trip to the New York World's Fair during it's closing days in 1965, I became suddenly aware of her considerable charms. She was not so immediately convinced that I had any charms of interest to her, but my natural tenacity paid off, and we started dating.

In the fall of 1966 I started my studies at Juniata College, as my mother and father, my Aunt Betty, and my sister had before me, and as my younger brother, Tom would later. Juniata had a foreign language requirement, which could be satisfied by studying two years of a language or by passing a test. I passed the test in French, whereupon the chairman of the French department, who knew my sister, a French major in her senior year, suggested that I enroll in an advanced French literature class. Being a naive freshman, I did. The professor lectured in French, we read classic French literature and wrote our exams in French–not what I was used to in high school! I got a "C" on my first test and realized that college was not going to be as easy as high school. I finished the course with an "A", and learned an important lesson: I would have to work hard at Juniata.

Physics with calculus was a challenge as well, but a true joy. Ray Pfrogner, who taught that first course, revealed a beauty and a unity in physics and mathematics that, until then, I had lacked the tools to appreciate. Some evenings he invited us students to showings of films of Richard Feynman's classic public lectures on "The Character of Physical Law." These events included popcorn that Pfrogner popped himself. Feynman's breezy yet incisive style on occasional evenings and Pfrogner's clear expositions every other morning fueled my passion for physics.

My passion for Jane was also increasing during this time, fueled by daily letters, weekly phone calls and infrequent visits to her school, Penn State University. It is a passion that has matured and deepened but remained undiminished over the years. Our separation during our college years meant that I did not have a highly active social life, leaving lots of time for physics.

During my first year at Juniata, Wilfred Norris, the Physics Department chairman, invited me to start on the laboratory course normally taken by third-year students–a series of classic physics experiments, which I did under his supervision. Later, I started doing serious research under Norris's direction, rebuilding an X-band electron spin resonance (ESR) spectrometer and trying to resolve discrepancies in the literature about ESR linewidths.

In my senior year I spent a semester doing ESR at Argonne National Laboratories, working with Juan McMillan and Ted Halpern. There, I experienced full-time research, performed by a team of professionals who would discuss what the important problems were, decide what to do, how to do it, and then go into the lab and do it. I loved it!

Back at Juniata for my final semester, I was applying to graduate schools.

First on my list was Princeton–because I had heard its graduate program was superb and because a visitor to Juniata had told me that a physics student from my school would never be accepted to Princeton! I *was* accepted, but a visit to Princeton left me unconvinced that I wanted to go there. From the lobby of the Princeton physics building, I called Dan Kleppner at the Massachusetts Institute of Technology (MIT).

Dan had seen my application to MIT, including my experience in magnetic resonance, and had invited me to visit his group and consider working on a hydrogen maser experiment. So I visited MIT (and Harvard for good measure); I was struck by the pleasant camaraderie, and the friendly yet electric atmosphere that Dan had created in his group. That emotional reaction, and Jane's desire to return to New England, more than any purely scientific considerations, made me decide to go to MIT. I never regretted that decision, or any of the other decisions I made afterwards based on considerations of the heart.

During a hectic several weeks in 1970, Jane and I graduated from our respective colleges, married, honeymooned and moved to Boston. At MIT I started working with Fred Walther on the high-field hydrogen maser, another X-band magnetic resonance spectrometer. I learned how to do electronics, machining, plumbing and vacuum–all skills I have found essential in experimental research. I also learned from Dan, and from the others in his group, a way of thinking about physics intuitively, and a way of inquiring about a problem that has shaped the way I approach physics to this day. The style of open and lively discussion of physics problems that I found in Dan's group is one that I have tried to emulate in my own group at NIST. I also try to follow the principle Dan taught by example: that one can do physics at the frontiers, competing with the best in the world, and do it with openness, humanity and cooperation.

For my thesis research I measured the magnetic moment of the proton in H_2O. Through this project I met others in the community of precision measurements and fundamental constants–in particular, Barry Taylor and Ed Williams at the National Bureau of Standards. By the time I completed that measurement (which is, at least for the moment, still the best of its kind), tunable dye lasers had become commercially available and had found their way into our lab. I decided that I should learn more about these new toys and, with Dan's encouragement, embarked on an experiment to study the collisions of laser-excited atoms. I finally wrote up both experiments for my thesis and defended it in 1976.

I accepted a Chaim Weizmann fellowship to work on projects of my own choosing at MIT for another two years. During that time, I continued to work on collisions with Dave Pritchard and Jim Kinsey; I also started work on Bose-Einstein condensation (BEC) in spin-polarized hydrogen with Dan and Tom Greytak. We were filled with optimism in the early days of that experiment, but today, 22 years later, BEC of hydrogen is still "just around the corner." Nevertheless, the innovations achieved by that group, long after I left, along with the developments in laser cooling recognized by this year's Nobel Prize, were crucial in showing the way to the eventual success of BEC in alkali vapors.

At the party celebrating my thesis in 1976, Dan Kleppner said it was fortunate that I had done the second experiment, using lasers, because otherwise I would probably have ended up going to the National Bureau of Standards (NBS). In 1978 I accepted a position at NBS (later renamed the National Institute of Standards and Technology–NIST) in Barry Taylor's division, working with Ed Williams and Tom Olsen on precision measurements of the proton gyromagnetic ratio and of the Absolute Ampere. These were exciting projects, but my experience with lasers and atomic physics had also earned me the opportunity to devote part of my time to exploring ways of improving measurement capabilities using those tools. I used that opportunity to pursue laser cooling, and the story of how that went is told in the accompanying Nobel Lecture.

In 1979, shortly after Jane and I moved to Gaithersburg, we joined Fairhaven United Methodist Church. We had not been regular church-goers during our years at MIT, but Ed and Jean Williams invited us to Fairhaven and there we found a congregation whose ethnic and racial diversity offered an irresistible richness of worship experience. Later that year, our first daughter, Catherine, now known as Caitlin, was born. In 1981 Christine was born. Our children have been an unending source of blessing, adventure and challenge. Their arrival, at a time when both Jane and I were trying to establish ourselves in new jobs, required a delicate balancing of work, home, and church life. Somehow, our faith and our youthful energy got us through that period.

At NBS, with some borrowed equipment and some extra money that Barry Taylor, in his inimitable fashion, obtained from somewhere, I got started with laser cooling. Support from the Office of Naval Research allowed Hal Metcalf to spend time at NBS in those early days. I had worked with Hal a little at MIT, and I knew that his unbounded enthusiasm and his effervescent creativity were priceless qualities. My collaborating with Hal on laser cooling was the first and one of the most important among many valuable interactions with colleagues who came to NIST, or whom I met elsewhere. I have mentioned many of these in my Lecture, and I want to emphasize again how much they have contributed to the development of laser cooling, and particularly, how important the senior group members, Kris Helmerson, Paul Lett, Steve Rolston, and Chris Westbrook, have been. I also want to recall the words of Bengt Nagel in his formal remarks to Steve Chu, Claude Cohen-Tannoudji and myself on 10 December 1997 in Stockholm. He said that we were being recognized as leaders and *representatives* of our groups. The three of us feel very strongly that this Prize honors all of those wonderful colleagues who contributed so much to the development of laser cooling.

Since the announcement of the award of the 1997 Nobel Prize in Physics, I have been honored to receive greetings and congratulations from colleagues and friends all over the world, as well as from many people whom I did not know. One such greeting came, not to me but to my children, from Susan Hench Bowis. She had read newspaper accounts of the announcement and recalled to my teenage daughters that she had been 17 when in 1950 her father, Philip Hench, had been awarded the Nobel Prize in Physiology or Medicine. He had been far from home at the time of the announcement, as I had been, and, like Caitlin, Susan Hench had been away at school. Transatlantic telephone calls were not common in those days, and so when she eventually made contact and congratulated her father, it was by cable. He cabled back to her, "Prouder of you, my darling, than of any prize." Surely the Nobel Prize is the highest award a scientist could hope to receive, and I have received it with a sense of awe that I am in the company of those who have received it before. But no prize can compare in importance to the family and friends I count as my greatest treasures.

LASER COOLING AND TRAPPING OF NEUTRAL ATOMS

Nobel Lecture, December 8, 1997

by

WILLIAM D. PHILLIPS

National Institute of Standards and Technology, Physics Laboratory, Atomic Physics Division, Gaithersburg, MD 20899, USA

INTRODUCTION

In 1978, while I was a postdoctoral fellow at MIT, I read a paper [1] by Art Ashkin in which he described how one might slow down an atomic beam of sodium using the radiation pressure of a laser beam tuned to an atomic resonance. After being slowed, the atoms would be captured in a trap consisting of focused laser beams, with the atomic motion being damped until the temperature of the atoms reached the microkelvin range. That paper was my first introduction to laser cooling, although the idea of laser cooling (the reduction of random thermal velocities using radiative forces) had been proposed three years earlier in independent papers by Hänsch and Schawlow [2] and Wineland and Dehmelt [3]. Although the treatment in Ashkin's paper was necessarily over-simplified, it provided one of the important inspirations for what I tried to accomplish for about the next decade. Another inspiration appeared later that same year: Wineland, Drullinger and Walls published the first laser cooling experiment [4], in which they cooled a cloud of Mg ions held in a Penning trap. At essentially the same time, Neuhauser, Hohenstatt, Toschek and Dehmelt [5] also reported laser cooling of trapped Ba$^+$ ions.

Those laser cooling experiments of 1978 were a dramatic demonstration of the mechanical effects of light, but such effects have a much longer history. The understanding that electromagnetic radiation exerts a force became quantitative only with Maxwell's theory of electromagnetism, even though such a force had been conjectured much earlier, partly in response to the observation that comet tails point away from the sun. It was not until the turn of the century, however, that experiments by Lebedev [6] and Nichols and Hull [7, 8] gave a laboratory demonstration and quantitative measurement of radiation pressure on macroscopic objects. In 1933, Frisch [9] made the first demonstration of light pressure on atoms, deflecting an atomic sodium beam with resonance radiation from a lamp. With the advent of the laser, Ashkin [10] recognized the potential of intense, narrow-band light for manipulating atoms and in 1972 the first "modern" experiments demonstrated the deflection of atomic beams with lasers [11, 12]. All of this set the stage for the laser cooling proposals of 1975 and for the demonstrations in 1978 with ions.

Comet tails, deflection of atomic beams and the laser cooling proposed in

1975 are all manifestation of the radiative force that Ashkin has called the "scattering force," because it results when light strikes an object and is scattered in random directions. Another radiative force, the dipole force, can be thought of as arising from the interaction between an induced dipole moment and the gradient of the incident light field. The dipole force was recognized at least as early as 1962 by Askar'yan [13], and in 1968, Letokhov [14] proposed using it to trap atoms–even before the idea of laser cooling! The trap proposed by Ashkin in 1978 [1] relied on this "dipole" or "gradient" force as well. Nevertheless, in 1978, laser cooling, the reduction of random velocities, was understood to involve only the scattering force. Laser trapping, confinement in a potential created by light, which was still only a dream, involved both dipole and scattering forces. Within 10 years, however, the dipole force was seen to have a major impact on laser cooling as well.

Without understanding very much about what difficulties lay in store for me, or even appreciating the exciting possibilities of what one might do with laser cooled atoms, I decided to try to do for neutral atoms what the groups in Boulder and Heidelberg had done for ions: trap them and cool them. There was, however, a significant difficulty: we could not first trap and then cool neutral atoms. Ion traps were deep enough to easily trap ions having temperatures well above room temperature, but none of the proposed neutral atom traps had depths of more than a few kelvin. Significant cooling was required before trapping would be possible, as Ashkin had outlined in his paper [1], and it was with this idea that I began.

Before describing the first experiments on the deceleration of atomic beams, let me digress slightly and discuss why laser cooling is so exciting and why it has attracted so much attention in the scientific community: When one studies atoms in a gas, they are typically moving very rapidly. The molecules and atoms in air at room temperature are moving with speeds on the order of 300 m/s, the speed of sound. This thermal velocity can be reduced by refrigerating the gas, with the velocity varying as the square root of the temperature, but even at 77 K, the temperature at which N_2 condenses into a liquid, the nitrogen molecules are moving at about 150 m/s. At 4 K, the condensation temperature of helium, the He atoms have 90 m/s speeds. At temperatures for which atomic thermal velocities would be below 1 m/s, any gas in equilibrium (other than spin-polarized atomic hydrogen) would be condensed, with a vapor pressure so low that essentially no atoms would be in the gas phase. As a result, all studies of free atoms were done with fast atoms. The high speed of the atoms makes measurements difficult. The Doppler shift and the relativistic time dilation cause displacement and broadening of the spectral lines of thermal atoms, which have a wide spread of velocities. Furthermore, the high atomic velocities limit the observation time (and thus the spectral resolution) in any reasonably-sized apparatus. Atoms at 300 m/s pass through a meter-long apparatus in just 3 ms. These effects are a major limitation, for example, to the performance of conventional atomic clocks.

The desire to reduce motional effects in spectroscopy and atomic clocks was and remains a major motivation for the cooling of both neutral atoms

138

and ions. In addition, some remarkable new phenomena appear when atoms are sufficiently cold. The wave, or quantum nature of particles with momentum p becomes apparent only when the deBroglie wavelength, given by $\lambda_{dB} = h/p$, becomes large, on the order of relevant distance scales like the atom-atom interaction distances, atom-atom separations, or the scale of confinement. Laser cooled atoms have allowed studies of collisions and of quantum collective behavior in regimes hitherto unattainable. Among the new phenomena seen with neutral atoms is Bose-Einstein condensation of an atomic gas [15, 16], which has been hailed as a new state of matter, and is already becoming a major new field of investigation. Equally impressive and exciting are the quantum phenomena seen with trapped ions, for example, quantum jumps [17–19], Schrödinger cats [20], and quantum logic gates [21].

LASER COOLING OF ATOMIC BEAMS

In 1978 I had only vague notions about the excitement that lay ahead with laser cooled atoms, but I concluded that slowing down an atomic beam was the first step. The atomic beam was to be slowed using the transfer of momentum that occurs when an atom absorbs a photon. Fig. 1 shows the basic

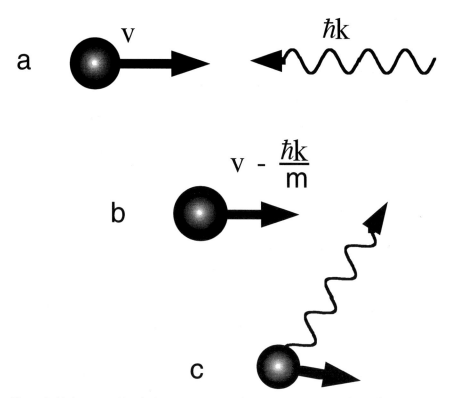

Figure 1. (a) An atom with velocity v encounters a photon with momentum $\hbar k = h/\lambda$; (b) after absorbing the photon, the atom is slowed by $\hbar k/m$; (c) after re-radiation in a random direction, on average the atom is slower than in 1a.

process underlying the "scattering force" that results. An atomic beam with velocity v is irradiated by an opposing laser beam. For each photon that a ground-state atom absorbs, it is slowed by $v_{rec} = \hbar k/m$ ($k = 2\pi/\lambda$ where λ is the wavelength of the light). In order to absorb again the atom must return to the ground state by emitting a photon. Photons are emitted in random directions, but with a symmetric average distribution, so their contribution to the atom's momentum averages to zero. The randomness results in a "heating" of the atom, discussed below.

For sodium atoms interacting with the familiar yellow resonance light, v_{rec} = 3 cm/s, while a typical beam velocity is about 10^5 cm/s, so the absorption-emission process must occur about 3×10^4 times to bring the Na atom to rest. In principle, an atom could radiate and absorb photons at half the radiative decay rate of the excited state (a 2-level atom in steady state can spend at most half of its time in the excited state). For Na, this implies that a photon could be radiated every 32 ns on average, bringing the atoms to rest in about 1 ms. Two problems, optical pumping and Doppler shifts, can prevent this from happening. I had an early indication of the difficulty of decelerating an atomic beam shortly after reading Ashkin's 1978 paper. I was then working with a sodium atomic beam at MIT, using tunable dye lasers to study the collisional properties of optically excited sodium. I tuned a laser to be resonant with the Na transition from $3S_{1/2} \rightarrow 3P_{3/2}$, the D2 line, and directed its beam opposite to the atomic beam. I saw that the atoms near the beam source were fluorescing brightly as they absorbed the laser light, while further away from the source, the atoms were relatively dim. The problem, I concluded, was optical pumping, illustrated in Fig. 2.

Sodium is not a two-level atom, but has two ground hyperfine levels (F = 1 and F = 2 in Fig. 2), each of which consists of several, normally degenerate,

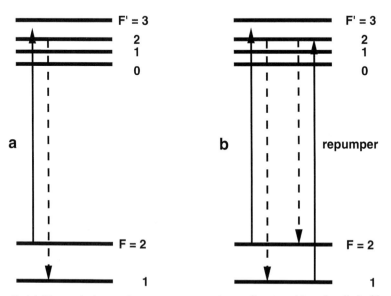

Figure 2. (a) The optical pumping process preventing cycling transitions in alkalis like Na; (b) Use of a repumping laser to allow many absorption-emission cycles.

states. Laser excitation out of one of the hyperfine levels to the excited state can result in the atom radiating to the other hyperfine level. This optical pumping essentially shuts off the absorption of laser light, because the linewidths of the transition and of the laser are much smaller than the separation between the ground state hyperfine components. Even for atoms excited on the $3S_{1/2}$ (F = 2) → $3P_{3/2}$ (F' = 3) transition, where the only allowed decay channel is to F = 2, off-resonant excitation of F' = 2 (the linewidth of the transition is 10 MHz, while the separation between F' = 2 and F' = 3 is 60 MHz) leads to optical pumping into F = 1 after only about a hundred absorptions. This optical pumping made the atoms "dark" to my laser after they traveled only a short distance from the source.

An obvious solution (Fig. 2b) is to use a second laser frequency, called a re-pumper, to excite the atoms out of the "wrong" (F = 1) hyperfine state so that they can decay to the "right" state (F = 2) where they can continue to cool. Given the repumper, another problem becomes apparent: the Doppler shift. In order for the laser light to be resonantly absorbed by a counterpropagating atom moving with velocity v, the frequency ω of the light must be lower by kv than the resonant frequency for an atom at rest. As the atom repeatedly absorbs photons, slowing down as desired, the Doppler shift changes and the atom goes out of resonance with the light. The natural linewidth $\Gamma/2\pi$ of the optical transition in Na is 10 MHz (full width at half maximum). A change in velocity of 6 m/s gives a Doppler shift this large, so after absorbing only 200 photons, the atom is far enough off resonance that the rate of absorption is significantly reduced. The result is that only atoms with the "proper" velocity to be resonant with the laser are slowed, and they are only slowed by a small amount.

Nevertheless, this process of atoms being slowed and pushed out of resonance results in a cooling or narrowing of the velocity distribution. In an atomic beam, there is typically a wide spread of velocities around $v_{th} = 3k_B T/m$. Those atoms with the proper velocity will absorb rapidly and decelerate. Those that are too fast will absorb more slowly, then more rapidly as they come into resonance, and finally more slowly as they continue to decelerate. Atoms that are too slow to begin with will absorb little and decelerate little. Thus atoms from a range of velocities around the resonant velocity are pushed into a narrower range centered on a lower velocity. This process was studied theoretically by Minogin [22] and in 1981, at Moscow's Institute for Spectroscopy, was used in the first experiment clearly demonstrating laser cooling of neutral atoms [23].

Fig. 3 shows the velocity distribution after such cooling of an atomic beam. The data was taken in our laboratory, but is equivalent to what had been done in Moscow. The characteristic of this kind of beam cooling is that only a small part of the total velocity distribution (the part near resonance with the laser beam) is slowed by only a small amount (until the atoms are no longer resonant). The narrow peak, while it represents true cooling in that its velocity distribution is narrow, consists of rather fast atoms.

One solution to this problem had already been outlined in 1976 by Letok-

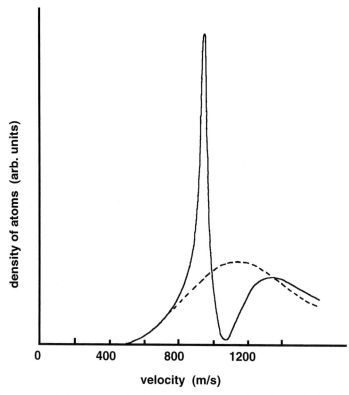

Figure. 3. Cooling an atomic beam with a fixed frequency laser. The dotted curve is the velocity distribution before cooling, and the solid curve is after cooling. Atoms from a narrow velocity range are transferred to a slightly narrower range centered on a lower velocity.

hov, Minogin and Pavlik [24] They suggested a general method of changing the frequency (chirping) of the cooling laser so as to interact with all the atoms in a wide distribution and to stay in resonance with the atoms as they are cooled. The Moscow group applied the technique to decelerating an atomic beam [25] but without clear success [26]. (Later, in 1983, John Prodan and I obtained the first clear deceleration and cooling of an atomic beam with this "chirp-cooling" technique [27–30]. Those first attempts failed to bring the atoms to rest, something that was finally achieved by Ertmer, Blatt, Hall and Zhu [31].) The chirp-cooling technique is now one of the two standard methods for decelerating beams. The other is "Zeeman cooling."

By late 1978, I had moved to the National Bureau of Standards (NBS), later named the National Institute of Standards and Technology (NIST), in Gaithersburg. I was considering how to slow an atomic beam, realizing that the optical pumping and Doppler shift problems would both need to be addressed. I understood how things would work using the Moscow chirp-cooling technique and a repumper. I also considered using a broadband laser, so that there would be light in resonance with the atoms, regardless of their velocity. (This idea was refined by Hoffnagle [32] and demonstrated by Hall's group [33]). Finally I considered that instead of changing the frequency of the laser to stay in resonance with the atoms (chirping), one could use a magnetic field to change the energy level separation in the atoms so as to keep them in resonance with the fixed-frequency laser (Zeeman cooling). All of these ideas for cooling an atomic beam, along with various schemes for avoiding optical pumping, were contained in a proposal [34] that I submitted to the Office of Naval Research in 1979. Around this time Hal Metcalf, from the State University of New York at Stony Brook, joined me in Gaithersburg and we began to consider what would be the best way to proceed. Hal contended that all the methods looked reasonable, but we should work on the Zeeman cooler because it would be the most fun! Not only was Hal right about the fun we would have, but his suggestion led us to develop a technique with particularly advantageous properties. The idea is illustrated in Fig. 4.

The atomic beam source directs atoms, which have a wide range of velocities, along the axis (z-direction) of a tapered solenoid. This magnet has more windings at its entrance end, near the source, so the field is higher at that end. The laser is tuned so that, given the field-induced Zeeman shift and the velocity-induced Doppler shift of the atomic transition frequency, atoms with velocity v_o are resonant with the laser when they reach the point where the field is maximum. Those atoms then absorb light and begin to slow down. As their velocity changes, their Doppler shift changes, but is compensated by the change in Zeeman shift as the atoms move to a point where the field is weaker. At this point, atoms with initial velocities slightly lower than v_o come into resonance and begin to slow down. The process continues with the initially fast atoms decelerating and staying in resonance while initially slower atoms come into resonance and begin to be slowed as they move further down the solenoid. Eventually all the atoms with velocities lower than v_o are brought to a final velocity that depends on the details of the magnetic field and laser tuning.

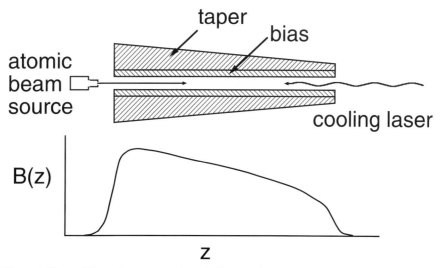

Figure 4. Upper: Schematic representation of a Zeeman slower. Lower: Variation of the axial field with position.

The first tapered solenoids that Hal Metcalf and I used for Zeeman cooling of atomic beams had only a few sections of windings and had to be cooled with air blown by fans or with wet towels wrapped around the coils. Shortly after our initial success in getting some substantial deceleration, we were joined by my first post-doc, John Prodan. We developed more sophisticated solenoids, wound with wires in many layers of different lengths, so as to produce a smoothly varying field that would allow the atoms to slow down to a stop while remaining in resonance with the cooling laser.

These later solenoids were cooled with water flowing over the coils. To improve the heat transfer, we filled the spaces between the wires with various heat-conducting substances. One was a white silicone grease that we put onto the wires with our hands as we wound the coil on a lathe. The grease was about the same color and consistency as the diaper rash ointment I was then using on my baby daughters, so there was a period of time when, whether at home or at work, I seemed to be up to my elbows in white grease.

The grease-covered, water-cooled solenoids had the annoying habit of burning out as electrolytic action attacked the wires during operation. Sometimes it seemed that we no sooner obtained some data than the solenoid would burn out and we were winding a new one.

On the bright side, the frequent burn-outs provided the opportunity for refinement and redesign. Soon we were potting the coils in a black, rubbery resin. While it was supposed to be impervious to water, it did not have good adhesion properties (except to clothing and human flesh) and the solenoids continued to burn out. Eventually, an epoxy coating sealed the solenoid against the water that allowed the electrolysis, and in more recent times we replaced water with a fluorocarbon liquid that does not conduct electricity or support electrolysis. Along the way to a reliable solenoid, we learned how to slow and stop atoms efficiently [27, 35–41].

The velocity distribution after deceleration is measured in a detection region some distance from the exit end of the solenoid. Here a separate detection laser beam produces fluorescence from atoms having the correct velocity to be resonant. By scanning the frequency of the detection laser, we were able to determine the velocity distribution in the atomic beam. Observations with the detection laser were made just after turning off the cooling laser, so as to avoid any difficulties with having both lasers on at the same time. Fig. 5 shows the velocity distribution resulting from Zeeman cooling: a large fraction of the initial distribution has been swept down into a narrow final velocity group.

One of the advantages of the Zeeman cooling technique is the ease with which the optical pumping problem is avoided. Because the atoms are always in a strong axial magnetic field (that is the reason for the "bias" windings in Fig. 4), there is a well-defined axis of quantization that allowed us to make use of the selection rules for radiative transitions and to avoid the undesirable optical pumping. Figure 6 shows the energy levels of Na in a magnetic field. Atoms in the $3S_{1/2}$ ($m_F = 2$) state, irradiated with circularly polarized σ^+ light, must increase their m_F by one unit, and so can go only to the $3P_{3/2}$ ($m_{F'} = 3$)

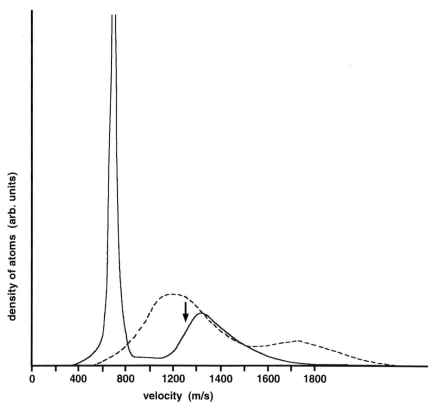

Figure 5. Velocity distribution before (dashed) and after (solid) Zeeman cooling. The arrow indicates the highest velocity resonant with the slowing laser. (The extra bump at 1700 m/s is from F = 1 atoms, which are optically pumped into F = 2 during the cooling process)

state. This state in turn can decay only to $3S_{1/2}$ ($m_F = 2$), and the excitation process can be repeated indefinitely. Of course, the circular polarization is not perfect, so other excitations are possible, and these may lead to decay to other states. Fortunately, in a high magnetic field, such transitions are highly unlikely [35] : either they involve a change in the nuclear spin projection m_I, which is forbidden in the high field limit, or they are far from resonance. These features, combined with high purity of the circular polarization, allowed us to achieve, without a "wrong transition," the 3×10^4 excitations required to stop the atoms. Furthermore, the circular polarization produced some "good" optical pumping: atoms not initially in the $3S_{1/2}$ ($m_F = 2$) state were pumped into this state, the "stretched" state of maximum projection of angular momentum, as they absorbed the angular momentum of the light. These various aspects of optical selection rules and optical pumping allowed the process of Zeeman cooling to be very efficient, decelerating a large fraction of the atoms in the beam.

In 1983 we discussed a number of these aspects of laser deceleration, including our early chirp-cooling results, at a two-day workshop on "Laser-Cooled and Trapped Atoms" held at NBS in Gaithersburg [42]. I view this as

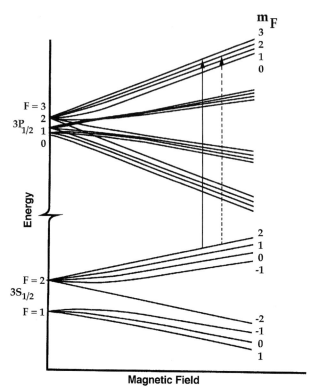

Figure 6. Energy levels of Na in a magnetic field. The cycling transition used for laser cooling is shown as a solid arrow, and one of the nearly forbidden excitation channels leading to undesirable optical pumping is shown dashed.

an important meeting in that it and its proceedings stimulated interest in laser cooling . In early 1984, Stig Stenholm, then of the University of Helsinki, organized an international meeting on laser cooling in Tvärminne, a remote peninsula in Finland. Fig. 7 shows the small group attending (I was the photographer), and in that group, only some of the participants were even active in laser cooling at the time. Among these were Stig Stenholm (who had done pioneering work in the theory of laser cooling and the mechanical effects of light on atoms [43–51]) along with some of his young colleagues; Victor Balykin and Vladimir Minogin from the Moscow group; and Claude Cohen-Tannoudji and Jean Dalibard from Ecole Normale Supérieure (ENS) in Paris, who had begun working on the theory of laser cooling and trapping. Also present were Jürgen Mlynek and Wolfgang Ertmer, both of whom now lead major research groups pursuing laser cooling and atom optics. At that time, however, only our group and the Moscow group had published any experiments on cooling of neutral atoms.

Much of the discussion at the Tvärminne meeting involved the techniques of beam deceleration and the problems with optical pumping. I took a light-hearted attitude toward our trials and tribulations with optical pumping, often joking that any unexplained features in our data could certainly be attributed to optical pumping. Of course, at the Ecole Normale, optical pump-

146

Figure 7. Stig Stenholm's "First International Conference on Laser Cooling" in Tvärminne, March 1984. Back row, left to right: Juha Javanainen, Markus Lindberg, Stig Stenholm, Matti Kaivola, Nis Bjerre, (unidentified), Erling Riis, Rainer Salomaa, Vladimir Minogin. Front row: Jürgen Mlynek, Angela Guzmann, Peter Jungner, Wolfgang Ertmer, Birger Ståhlberg, Olli Serimaa, Jean Dalibard, Claude Cohen-Tannoudji, Victor Balykin.

ing had a long and distinguished history. Having been pioneered by Alfred Kastler and Jean Brossel, optical pumping had been the backbone of many experiments in the Laboratoire de Spectroscopie Hertzienne (now the Laboratoire Kastler-Brossel). After one discussion in which I had joked about optical pumping, Jean Dalibard privately mentioned to me, "You know, Bill, at the Ecole Normale, optical pumping is not a joke." His gentle note of caution calmed me down a bit, but it turned out to be strangely prophetic as well. As we saw a few years later, optical pumping had an important, beautiful, and totally unanticipated role to play in laser cooling, and it was surely no joke.

STOPPING ATOMS

As successful as Zeeman cooling had been in producing large numbers of decelerated atoms as in Fig. 5, we had not actually observed the atoms at rest, nor had we trapped them. In fact, I recall a conversation with Steve Chu that took place during the International Conference on Laser Spectroscopy in Interlaken in 1983 in which I had presented our results on beam deceleration [27]. Steve was working on positronium spectroscopy but was wondering whether there still might be something interesting to be done with laser cooling of neutral atoms. I offered the opinion that there was still plenty to do, and in particular, that trapping of atoms was still an unrealized goal. It wasn't long before each of us achieved that goal, in very different ways.

Our approach was to first get some stopped atoms. The problem had been that, in a sense, Zeeman cooling worked too well. By adjusting the laser frequency and magnetic field, we could, up to a point, choose the final velocity of the atoms that had undergone laser deceleration. Unfortunately, if we chose too small a velocity, no slow atoms at all appeared in the detection region. Once brought below a certain velocity, about 200 m/s, the atoms always continued to absorb enough light while traveling from the solenoid to the detection region so as to stop before reaching the detector. By shutting off the cooling laser beam and delaying observation until the slow atoms arrived in the observation region, we were able to detect atoms as slow as 40 m/s with a spread of 10 m/s, corresponding to a temperature (in the atoms' rest frame) of 70 mK [36].

The next step was to get these atoms to come to rest in our observation region. We were joined by Alan Migdall, a new post-doc, Jean Dalibard, who was visiting from ENS, and Ivan So, Hal Metcalf's student. We decided that we needed to proceed as before, shutting off the cooling light, allowing the slow atoms to drift into the observation region, but then to apply a short pulse of additional cooling light to bring the atoms to rest. The sequence of laser pulses required to do this–a long pulse of several milliseconds for doing the initial deceleration, followed by a delay and then another pulse of a few hundred microseconds, followed by another delay before detection–was provided by a rotating wheel with a series of openings corresponding to the places where the laser was to be on. Today we accomplish such pulse sequences with acousto-optic modulators under computer control, but in those days it required careful construction and balancing of a rapidly rotating wheel.

The result of this sequence of laser pulses was that we had atoms at rest in our observation region with a velocity spread corresponding to <100 mK [52]. Just following our 1985 paper reporting this in Physical Review Letters was a report of the successful stopping of atoms by the chirp-cooling method in Jan Hall's group [31]. At last there were atoms slow enough to be trapped, and we decided to concentrate first on magnetostatic trapping.

MAGNETIC TRAPPING OF ATOMS

The idea for magnetic traps had first appeared in the literature as early as 1960 [53–55], although Wolfgang Paul had discussed them in lectures at the University of Bonn in the mid-1950s, as a natural extension of ideas about magnetic focusing of atomic beams [56–58]. Magnetic trapping had come to our attention particularly because of the successful trapping of cold neutrons [59]. We later learned that in unpublished experiments in Paul's laboratory, there were indications of confining sodium in a magnetic trap [60].

148

The idea of magnetic trapping is that in a magnetic field, an atom with a magnetic moment will have quantum states whose magnetic or Zeeman energy increases with increasing field and states whose energy decreases, depending on the orientation of the moment compared to the field. The increasing-energy states, or low-field-seekers, can be trapped in a magnetic field configuration having a point where the magnitude of the field is a relative minimum. (No dc field can have a relative maximum in free space [61], so high-field-seekers cannot be trapped.) The requirement for stable trapping, besides the kinetic energy of the atom being low enough, is that the magnetic moment move adiabatically in the field. That is, the orientation of the magnetic moment with respect to the field should not change.

We considered some of the published designs for trapping neutrons, including the spherical hexapole [62], a design comprising three current loops, but we found them less than ideal. Instead we decided upon a simpler design, with two loops, which we called a spherical quadrupole. The trap, its magnetic field lines and equipotentials are shown in Fig. 8. Although we thought that we had discovered an original trap design, we later learned that Wolfgang Paul had considered this many years ago, but had not given it much attention because atoms were not harmonically bound in such a trap. In fact, the potential for such a trap is linear in the displacement from the center and has a cusp there.

With a team consisting of Alan Migdall, John Prodan, Hal Metcalf and myself, and with the theoretical support of Tom Bergeman, we succeeded in trapping atoms in the apparatus shown in Fig. 9 [63]. As in the experiments that stopped atoms, we start with Zeeman slowing, decelerating the atoms to 100 m/s in the solenoid. The slowing laser beam is then extinguished, allowing the atoms to proceed unhindered for 4 ms to the magnetic trap. At this point, only one of the two trap coils has current; it produces a magnetic field that brings the atoms into resonance with the cooling laser when it is turned on again for 400 ms, bringing the atoms to rest. Once the atoms are stopped, the other coil is energized, producing the field shown in Fig. 8, and the trap is sprung. The atoms are held in the trap until released, or until collisions with the room-temperature background gas molecules in the imperfect vacuum knock them out. After the desired trapping time, we turn off the magnetic field, and turn on a probe laser, so as to see how many atoms remain in the trap. By varying the frequency of this probe on successive repetitions of the process, we could determine the velocity distribution of the atoms, via their Doppler shifts.

The depth of our trap was about 17 mK (25 mT), corresponding to Na atoms with a velocity of 3.5 m/s. In the absence of trapping fields, atoms that fast would escape from the region of the trap coils in a few milliseconds. Fig. 10 shows a section of chart paper with spectra of the atoms remaining after 35 ms of trapping time. If the trap had not been working, we would have seen essentially nothing after that length of time, but the signal, noisy as it was, was unmistakable. It went away when the trap was off, and it went away when we did not provide the second pulse of cooling light that stops the atoms before

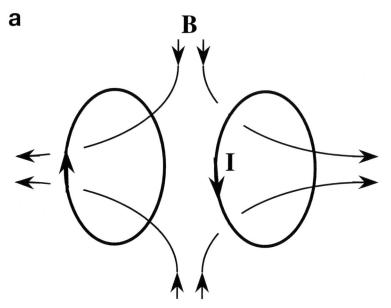

Figure 8. (a) Spherical quadrupole trap with lines of B-field.

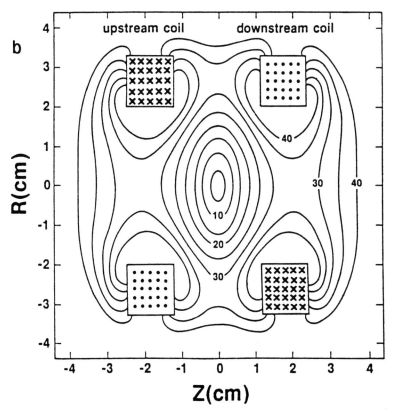

Figure 8. (b) Equipotentials of our trap (equal field magnitudes in millitesla), in a plane containing the symmetry (z) axis.

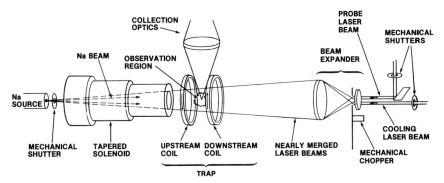

Figure 9: Schematic of the apparatus used to magnetically trap atoms.

trapping them. This was just the signature we were looking for, and Hal Metcalf expressed his characteristic elation at good results with his exuberant "WAHOO!!" at the top of the chart.

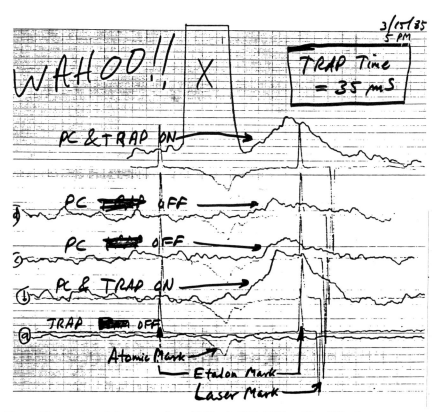

Figure 10. A section of chart paper from 15 March 1985. "PC" and "no PC" refer to presence or absence of the "post-cooling" pulse that brings the atoms to rest in the trapping region.

As the evening went on, we were able to improve the signal, but we found that the atoms did not stay very long in the trap, a feature we found a bit frustrating. Finally, late in the evening we decided to go out and get some fast food, talk about what was happening and attack the problem afresh. When we returned a little later that night, the signal had improved and we were able to trap atoms for much longer times. We soon realized that during our supper break the magnetic trap had cooled down, and stopped outgassing, so the vacuum just in the vicinity of the trap improved considerably. With this insight we knew to let the magnet cool off from time to time, and we were able to take a lot of useful data. We continued taking data until around 5:00 am, and it was probably close to 6:00 am when my wife Jane found Hal and me in our kitchen, eating ice cream as she prepared to leave for work. Her dismay at the lateness of our return and our choice of nourishment at that hour was partially assuaged by Hal's assurance that we had accomplished something pretty important that night.

Figure 11a presents the sequence of spectra taken after various trapping times, showing the decrease in signal as atoms are knocked out of the trap by collisions with the background gas molecules. Figure 11b shows that the loss of atoms from the trap is exponential, as expected, with a lifetime of a bit less than one second, in a vacuum of a few times 10^{-6} pascals. A point taken when the vacuum was allowed to get worse illustrates that poor vacuum made the signal decay faster. In more recent times, we and others have achieved much longer trapping times, mainly because of an improved vacuum. We now observe magnetic trap lifetimes of one minute or longer in our laboratory.

Since our demonstration [63] of magnetic trapping of atoms in 1985, many different kinds of magnetic atom traps have been used. At MIT, Dave Pritchard's group trapped [64] and cooled [65] Na atoms in a linear quadrupole magnetic field with an axial bias field, similar to the trap first discussed by Ioffe and collaborators [66] in 1962, and later by others [67, 68]. Similar traps were used by the Kleppner-Greytak group to trap [69] and evaporative-

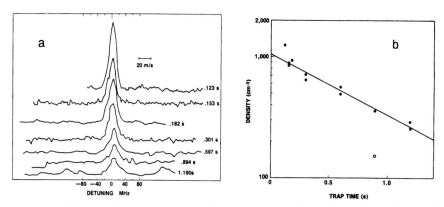

Figure 11. (a) Spectra of atoms remaining in the magnetic trap after various times; (b) Decay of number of trapped atoms with time. The open point was taken at twice the background pressure of the other points.

ly cool [70] atomic hydrogen, and by Walraven's group to trap [71] and laser-cool hydrogen [72]. The Ioffe trap has the advantage of having a non-zero magnetic field at the equilibrium point, in contrast to the spherical quadrupole, in which the field is zero at the equilibrium point. The zero field allows the magnetic moment of the atom to flip (often called Majorana flopping), so that the atom is in an untrapped spin state. While this problem did not cause difficulties in our 1985 demonstration, for colder atoms, which spend more time near the trap center, it can be a quite severe loss mechanism [73, 74]. In 1995, modifications to the simple quadrupole trap solved the problem of spins flips near the trap center, and allowed the achievement of Bose-Einstein condensation [15, 16].

OPTICAL MOLASSES

At the same time that we were doing the first magnetic trap experiments in Gaithersburg, the team at Bell Labs, led by Steve Chu, was working on a different and extremely important feature of laser cooling. After a beautiful demonstration in 1978 of the use of optical forces to focus an atomic beam [75], the Bell Labs team had made some preliminary attempts to decelerate an atom beam, and then moved on to other things. Encouraged by the beam deceleration experiments in Gaithersburg and in Boulder, Steve Chu reassembled much of that team and set out to demonstrate the kind of laser cooling suggested in 1975 by Hänsch and Schawlow [2]. (The physical principles behind the Hänsch and Schawlow proposal are, of course, identical to those expressed in the 1975 Wineland and Dehmelt laser cooling proposal [3]. These principles had already led to the laser cooling of trapped ions [4, 5]. The foci of Refs. [2, 3], however, has associated Hänsch and Schawlow with neutral atoms and Wineland and Dehmelt with ions.) In fact, the same physical principle of Doppler cooling results in the compression of the velocity distribution associated with laser deceleration of an atomic beam (see sections 2 and 3 of [76]). Nevertheless, in 1985, laser cooling of a gas of neutral atoms at rest, as proposed in [2] had yet to be demonstrated.

The idea behind the Hänsch and Schawlow proposal is illustrated in Fig. 12. A gas of atoms, represented here in one dimension, is irradiated from both sides by laser beams tuned slightly below the atomic resonance frequency. An atom moving toward the left sees that the laser beam opposing its motion is Doppler shifted toward the atomic resonance frequency. It sees that the laser beam directed along its motion is Doppler shifted further from its resonance. The atom therefore absorbs more strongly from the laser beam that opposes its motion, and it slows down. The same thing happens to an atom moving to the right, so all atoms are slowed by this arrangement of laser beams. With pairs of laser beams added along the other coordinate axes, one obtains cooling in three dimensions. Because of the role of the Doppler effect in the process, this is now called Doppler cooling.

Later treatments [4, 5, 43, 46, 77–79] recognized that this cooling process leads to a temperature whose lower limit is on the order of $\hbar\Gamma$, where Γ is the

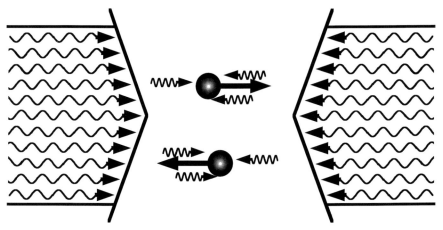

Figure 12. Doppler cooling in one dimension.

rate of spontaneous emission of the excited state (Γ^{-1} is the excited state life-time). The temperature results from an equilibrium between laser cooling and the heating process arising from the random nature of both the absorption and emission of photons. The random addition to the average momentum transfer produces a random walk of the atomic momentum and an increase in the mean square atomic momentum. This heating is countered by the cooling force F opposing atomic motion. The force is proportional to the atomic velocity, as the Doppler shift is proportional to velocity. In this, the cooling force is similar to the friction force experienced by a body moving in a viscous fluid. The rate at which energy is removed by cooling is $F \cdot v$, which is proportional to v^2, so the cooling rate is proportional to the kinetic energy. By contrast the heating rate, proportional to the total photon scattering rate, is independent of atomic kinetic energy for low velocities. As a result, the heating and cooling come to equilibrium at a certain value of the average kinetic energy. This defines the temperature for Doppler cooling, which is

$$m <v_i^2> = k_B T = \frac{\hbar \Gamma}{4} \left(\frac{\Gamma}{2\delta} + \frac{2\delta}{\Gamma} \right) \qquad (1)$$

where δ is the angular frequency of the detuning of the lasers from atomic resonance and v_i is the velocity along some axis. This expression is valid for 3D Doppler cooling in the limit of low intensity and when the recoil energy $\hbar^2 k^2/2m \ll \hbar \Gamma$. Interestingly, the equilibrium velocity distribution for Doppler cooling is the Maxwell-Boltzmann distribution. This follows from the fact that the Fokker-Planck equation describing the damping and heating in laser cooling is identical in form to the equation that describes collisional equilibrium of a gas [51]. Numerical simulations of real cases, where the recoil energy does not vanish, show that the distribution is still very close to Maxwellian [80]. The minimum value of this temperature called the Doppler cooling limit, occurring when $\delta = -\Gamma/2$, is

$$k_B T_{Dopp} = \frac{\hbar \Gamma}{2}. \qquad (2)$$

154

The first rigorous derivation of the cooling limit appears to be by Letokhov, Minogin and Pavilik [77] (although the reader should note that Eq. (32) is incorrectly identified with the rms velocity). Wineland and Itano [78] give derivations for a number of different situations involving trapped and free atoms and include the case where the recoil energy is not small but the atoms are in collisional equilibrium.

The Doppler cooling limit for sodium atoms cooled on the resonance transition at 589 nm where $\Gamma/2\pi = 10$ MHz, is 240 μK, and corresponds to an rms velocity of 30 cm/s along a given axis. The limits for other atoms and ions are similar, and such low temperatures were quite appealing. Before 1985, however, these limiting temperatures had not been obtained in either ions or neutral atoms.

A feature of laser cooling not appreciated in the first treatments was the fact that the spatial motion of atoms in any reasonably sized sample would be diffusive. For example, a simple calculation [80] shows that a sodium atom cooled to the Doppler limit has a "mean free path" (the mean distance it moves before its initial velocity is damped out and the atom is moving with a different, random velocity) of only 20 μm, while the size of the laser beams doing the cooling might easily be one centimeter. Thus, the atom undergoes diffusive, Brownian-like motion, and the time for a laser cooled atom to escape from the region where it is being cooled is much longer than the ballistic transit time across that region. This means that an atom is effectively "stuck" in the laser beams that cool it. This stickiness, and the similarity of laser cooling to viscous friction, prompted the Bell Labs group [81] to name the intersecting laser beams "optical molasses." At NBS [41], we independently used the term "molasses" to describe the cooling configuration, and the name "stuck." Note that an optical molasses is not a trap. There is no restoring force keeping the atoms in the molasses, only a viscous inhibition of their escape.

Using the techniques for chirp cooling an atomic beam developed at NBS-JILA [31] and a novel pulsed beam source, Chu's team at Bell Labs succeeded in loading cold sodium atoms into an optical molasses [81]. They observed the expected long "lifetime" (the time required for the atoms to diffuse out of the laser beams) of the molasses, and they developed a method, now called "release-and-recapture," for measuring the temperature of the atoms. The method is illustrated in Fig. 13. First, the atoms are captured and stored in the molasses, where for short periods of time they are essentially immobile due to the strong damping of atomic motion (13a). Then, the molasses laser beams are switched off, allowing the atoms to move ballistically away from the region to which they had originally been viscously confined (13b). Finally the laser beams are again turned on, recapturing the atoms that remain in the intersection (molasses) region (13c). From the fraction of atoms remaining after various periods of ballistic expansion one can determine the velocity distribution and therefore the temperature of the atoms at the time of release. The measured temperature at Bell Labs was 240^{+200}_{-60} μK [82]. The large uncertainty is due to the sensitive dependence of the analysis on the size and density distribution of atoms in the molasses, but the result was satis-fyingly consistent with the predicted Doppler cooling limit.

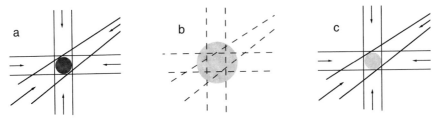

Figure 13. Release-and-recapture method for temperature measurement.

By the end of 1986, Phil Gould and Paul Lett had joined our group and we had achieved optical molasses in our laboratory at NBS, loading the molasses directly from a decelerated beam. (Today it is also routine to load atoms directly into a magneto-optical trap (MOT) [83] from an uncooled vapor [84, 85], and then into molasses.) We repeated the release-and-recapture tem-perature measurements, found them to be compatible with the reported measurements of the Bell Labs group, and we proceeded with other experi-ments. In particular, with Paul Julienne, Helen Thorsheim and John Wiener, we made a 2-focus laser trap and used it to perform the first measurements of a specific collision process (associative ionization) with laser cooled atoms [86]. (Earlier, Steve Chu and his colleagues had used optical molasses to load a single-focus laser trap–the first demonstration of an optical trap for atoms [87].) In a sense, our collision experiment represented a sort of closure for me because it realized the 2-focus trap proposed in Ashkin's 1978 paper, the paper that had started me thinking about laser cooling and trapping. It also was an important starting point for our group, because it began a new and highly productive line of research into cold collisions, producing some truly surprising and important results [88–94]. In another sense, though, that ex-periment was a detour from the road that was leading us to a new understan-ding of optical molasses and of how laser cooling worked.

SUB-DOPPLER LASER COOLING

During 1987 Gould, Lett and I investigated the behavior of optical molasses in more detail. Because the temperature was hard to measure and its meas-urement uncertainty was large, we concentrated instead on the molasses life-time, the time for the atoms to diffuse out of the intersecting laser beams. We had calculated, on the basis of the Doppler cooling theory, how the lifetime would vary as a function of the laser frequency detuning and the laser inten-sity. We also calculated how the lifetime should change when we introduced a deliberate imbalance between the two beams of a counter-propagating pair. Now we wanted to compare experimental results with our calculations. The results took us somewhat by surprise.

Fig. 14 shows our measurements [80] of the molasses lifetime as a function

156

of laser frequency along with the predicted behavior according to the Doppler cooling theory. The 1-D theory did not quantitatively reproduce the observed 3-D diffusion times, but that was expected. The surprise was the qualitative differences: the experimental lifetime peaked at a laser detuning above 3 linewidths, while the theory predicted a peak below one linewidth. We did not know how to reconcile this difficulty, and the results for the drift induced by beam imbalance were also in strong disagreement with the Doppler theory. In our 1987 paper, we described our failed attempts to bring the Doppler cooling theory into agreement with our data and ended saying [95] : "It remains to consider whether the multiple levels and sublevels of Na, multiple laser frequencies, or a consideration of the detailed motion of the atoms in 3-D can explain the surprising behavior of optical molasses." This was pure guesswork, of course, but it turned out to have an element of truth, as we shall see below.

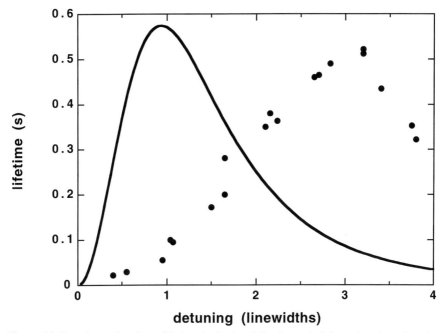

Figure. 14. Experimental molasses lifetime (points) and the theoretical decay time (curve) vs. detuning of molasses laser from resonance.

Having seen such a clear discrepancy between the Doppler cooling theory and the experimental results, with no resolution in sight, we, as experimentalists, decided to take more data. Paul Lett argued that we should measure the temperature again, this time as a function of the detuning, to see if it, too, would exhibit behavior different from that predicted by the theory. We felt, however, that the release-and-recapture method, given the large uncertainty associated with it in the past, would be unsuitable. Hal Metcalf suggested a different approach, illustrated in Fig. 15.

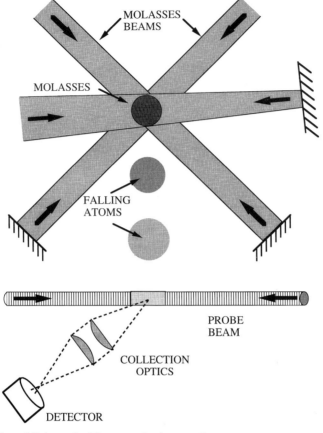

Figure 15. Time-of-flight method for measuring laser cooling temperatures.

In this time-of-flight (TOF) method, the atoms are first captured by the optical molasses, then released by switching off the molasses laser beams. The atom cloud expands ballistically, according to the distribution of atomic velocities. When atoms encounter the probe laser beam, they fluoresce, and the time distribution of fluorescence gives the time-of-flight distribution for atoms arriving at the probe. From this the temperature can be deduced. Now, with a team that included Paul Lett, Rich Watts, Chris Westbrook, Phil Gould, as well as Hal Metcalf and myself, we implemented the TOF temperature measurement. In our experiment, the probe was placed as close as 1 cm from the center of the molasses, which had a radius of about 4.5 mm. At the lowest expected temperature, the Doppler cooling limit of 240 μK for Na atoms, a significant fraction of the atoms would have been able to reach the probe, even with the probe above the molasses. For reasons of convenience, we did put the probe beam above the molasses, but we saw no fluorescence from atoms reaching the probe after the molasses was turned off. We spent a considerable time testing the detection system to be sure that everything was working properly. We deliberately "squirted" the atoms to the probe beam by heating them with a pair of laser beams in the horizontal plane, and verified that such heated atoms reached the probe and produced the expected time-of-flight signal.

Finally, we put the probe *under* the molasses. When we did, we immediately saw the TOF signals, but were reluctant to accept the conclusion that the atoms were colder than the Doppler cooling theory predicted, until we had completed a detailed modeling of the TOF signals. Figure 16 shows a typical TOF distribution for one of the colder observed temperatures, along with the model predictions. The conclusion was inescapable: Our atoms had a temperature of about 40 μK, much colder than the Doppler cooling limit of 240 μK. They had had insufficient kinetic energy to reach the probe when it

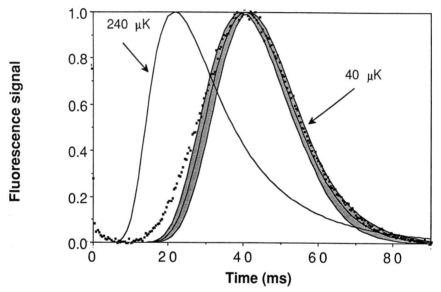

Figure. 16. The experimental TOF distribution (points) and the predicted distribution curves for 40 μK and 240 μK (the predicted lower limit of Doppler cooling). The band around the 40 μK curve reflects the uncertainty in the measurement of the geometry of the molasses and probe.

was placed above the molasses. As clear as this was, we were apprehensive. The theory of the Doppler limit was simple and compelling. In the limit of low intensity, one could derive the Doppler limit with a few lines of calculations (see for example, Ref. [80]); the most complete theory for cooling a two-level atom [96] did not predict a cooling limit any lower. Of course, everyone recognized that sodium was not a two-level atom, but it had seemed unlikely that it made any significant difference (our speculation in Ref. [95] notwithstanding). At low laser intensity the temperature depends on the laser detuning and the linewidth of the transition. Since the linewidth is identical for all possible transitions in the Na D2 manifold, and since the cooling transition ($3S_{1/2}$ (F = 2) $\rightarrow$ $3P_{3/2}$ (F = 3)) was well separated from nearby transitions, and all the Zeeman levels were degenerate, it seemed reasonable that the multilevel structure was unimportant in determining the cooling limit.

As it turned out, this was completely wrong. At the time, however, the

Doppler limit seemed to be on firm theoretical ground, and we were hesitant to claim that it was violated experimentally. Therefore, we sought to confirm our experimental results with other temperature measurement methods. One of these was to refine the "release and recapture" method described above. The large uncertainties in the earlier measurements [81] arose mainly from uncertainties in the size of the molasses and the recapture volume. We addressed that problem by sharply aperturing the molasses laser beams so the molasses and recapture volumes were well defined. We also found that it was essential to include the effect of gravity in the analysis (as we had done already for the TOF method). Because released atoms fall, the failure to recapture atoms could be interpreted as a higher temperature if gravity is not taken into account.

Another method was the "fountain" technique. Here we exploited our initial failure to observe a TOF signal with the probe above the molasses. By adjusting the height of the probe, we could measure how high the atoms could go before falling back under the influence of gravity. Essentially, this allowed us to measure the atoms' kinetic energy in terms of their gravitational potential energy, a principle very different from the TOF method. Finally, we used the "shower" method. This determined how far the atoms spread in the horizontal direction as they fell following release from the molasses. For this, we measured the fluorescence from atoms reaching the horizontal probe laser beam at different positions along that beam. From this transverse position distribution, we could get the transverse velocity distribution and therefore the temperature.

(The detailed modeling of the signals expected from the various temperature measurement methods was an essential element in establishing that the atomic temperature was well below the Doppler limit. Rich Watts, who had come to us from Hal Metcalf's lab and had done his doctoral dissertation with Carl Wieman, played a leading role in this modeling. Earlier, with Wieman, he had introduced the use of diode lasers in laser cooling. With Metcalf, he was the first to laser cool rubidium, the element with which Bose-Einstein condensation was first achieved. He was a pioneer of laser cooling and continued a distinguished scientific career at NIST after completing his postdoctoral studies in our group. Rich died in 1996 at the age of 39, and is greatly missed.)

While none of the additional methods proved to be as accurate as the TOF technique (which became a standard tool for studying laser cooling temperatures), each of them showed the temperature to be significantly below the Doppler limit. Sub-Doppler temperatures were not the only surprising results we obtained. We also (as Paul Lett had originally suggested) measured the temperature as a function of the detuning from resonance of the molasses laser. Figure 17 shows the results, along with the prediction of the Doppler cooling theory. The dependence of the temperature on detuning is strikingly different from the Doppler theory prediction, and recalls the discrepancy evident in Fig. 14. Our preliminary study indicated that the temperature did not depend on the laser intensity (although later measurements [80, 97, 98] showed that the temperature actually had a linear dependence on intensity). We observed that the temperature depended on the polarization of the molasses laser beams, and was highly sensitive to the ambient magnetic field. Changing the field by 0.2 mT increased the temperature from 40 μK to 120 μK when the laser was detuned 20 MHz from resonance (later experiments [80] showed even greater effects). This field dependence was particularly surprising, considering that transitions were being Zeeman shifted on the order of 14 MHz/mT, so the Zeeman shifts were much less than either the detuning or the 10 MHz transition linewidth.

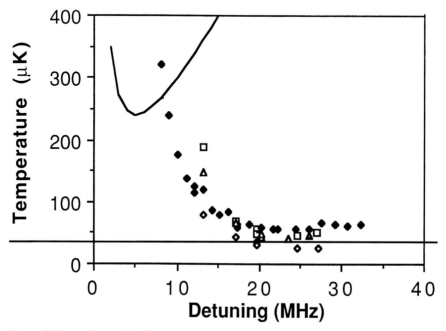

Figure 17. Dependence of molasses temperature on laser detuning (points) compared to the prediction of Doppler cooling theory (curve). The different symbols represent different molasses-to-probe separations.

Armed with these remarkable results, in the early spring of 1988 we sent a draft of the paper [99] describing our measurements to a number of experimental and theoretical groups working on laser cooling. I also traveled to a few of the leading laser cooling labs to describe the experiments in person and discuss them. Many of our colleagues were skeptical, as well they might have been, considering how surprising the results were. In the laboratories of Claude Cohen-Tannoudji and of Steve Chu, however, the response was: "Let's go into the lab and find out if it is true." Indeed, they soon confirmed sub-Doppler temperatures with their own measurements and they began to work on an understanding of how such low temperatures could come about. What emerged from these studies was a new concept of how laser cooling works, an understanding that is quite different from the original Hänsch-Schawlow and Wineland-Dehmelt picture.

During the spring and summer of 1988 our group was in close contact with Jean Dalibard and Claude Cohen-Tannoudji as they worked out the new theory of laser cooling and we continued our experiments. Their thinking centered on the multilevel character of the sodium atom, since the derivation of the Doppler limit was rigorous for a two-level atom. The sensitivity of temperature to magnetic field and to laser polarization suggested that the Zeeman sublevels were important, and this proved to be the case. Steve Chu (now at Stanford) and his colleagues followed a similar course, but the physical image that Dalibard and Cohen-Tannoudji developed has dominated the thinking about multi-level laser cooling. It involves a combination of multilevel atoms, polarization gradients, light shifts and optical pumping. How these work together to produce laser cooling is illustrated in simple form in Fig. 18, but the reader should see the Nobel Lectures of Cohen-Tannoudji and Chu along with the more detailed papers [100–103]

Figure 18a shows a 1-D set of counterpropagating beams with equal intensity and orthogonal, linear polarizations. The interference of these beams produces a standing wave whose polarization varies on a sub-wavelength distance scale. At points in space where the linear polarizations of the two beams are in phase with each other, the resultant polarization is linear, with an axis that bisects the polarization axes of the two individual beams. Where the phases are in quadrature, the resultant polarization is circular and at other places the polarization is elliptical. An atom in such a standing wave experiences a fortunate combination of light shifts and optical pumping processes.

Because of the differing Clebsch-Gordan coefficients governing the strength of coupling between the various ground and excited sublevels of the atom, the light shifts of the different sublevels are different, and they change with polarization (and therefore with position). Fig. 18b shows the sinusoidal variation of the ground-state energy levels (reflecting the varying light shifts or dipole forces) of a hypothetical $J_g = 1/2 \rightarrow J_e = 3/2$ atomic system. Now imagine an atom to be at rest at a place where the polarization is circular σ^- as at $z = \lambda/8$ in Fig. 18a. As the atom absorbs light with negative angular momentum and radiates back to the ground states, it will eventually be optically pumped into the $m_g = -1/2$ ground state, and simply cycle between this state and the excited $m_e = -3/2$ state. For low enough intensity and large enough detuning we can ignore the time the atom spends in the excited state and consider only the motion of the atom on the ground state potential. In the $m_g = -1/2$ state, the atom is in the lower energy level at $z = \lambda/8$, as shown in Fig. 18b. As the atom moves, it climbs the potential hill of the $m_g = -1/2$ state, but as it nears the top of the hill at $z = 3\lambda/8$, the polarization of the light becomes σ^+ and the optical pumping process tends to excite the atom in such a way that it decays to the $m_g = +1/2$ state. In the $m_g = +1/2$ state, the atom is now again at the bottom of a hill, and it again must climb, losing kinetic energy, as it moves. The continual climbing of hills recalls the Greek myth of Sisyphus, so this process, by which the atom rapidly slows down while passing through the polarization gradient, is called Sisyphus cooling. Dalibard and Cohen-Tannoudji had already described another kind of Sisyphus cooling, for 2-level

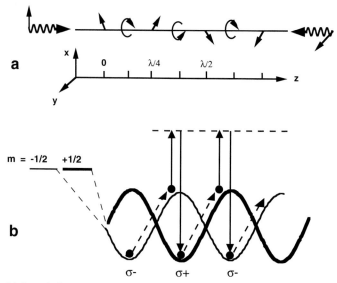

Figure 18. (a) Interfering, counterpropagating beams having orthogonal, linear polarizations create a polarization gradient. (b) The different Zeeman sublevels are shifted differently in light fields with different polarizations; optical pumping tends to put atomic population on the lowest energy level, but non-adiabatic motion results in "Sisyphus" cooling.

atoms [104] so the mechanism and the name were already familiar. In both kinds of Sisyphus cooling, the radiated photons, in comparison with the absorbed photons, have an excess energy equal to the light shift. By contrast, in Doppler cooling, the energy excess comes from the Doppler shift.

The details of this theory were still being worked out in the summer of 1988, the time of the International Conference on Atomic Physics, held that year in Paris. The sessions included talks about the experiments on sub-Doppler cooling and the new ideas to explain them. Beyond that, I had lively discussions with Dalibard and Cohen-Tannoudji about the new theory. One insight that emerged from those discussions was an understanding of why we had observed such high sensitivity of temperature to magnetic field: It was not the size of the Zeeman shift compared to the linewidth or the detuning that was important. Rather, when the Zeeman shift was comparable to the much smaller (≈ 1 MHz) light shifts and optical pumping rates, the cooling mechanism, which depended on these phenomena, would be disturbed. We now suggested a crucial test: the effect of the magnetic field should be reduced if the light intensity were higher. From Paris, I telephoned back to the lab in Gaithersburg and urged my colleagues to perform the appropriate measurements.

The results were as we had hoped. Figure 19 shows temperature as a function of magnetic field for two different light intensities. At magnetic fields greater than 100 μT (1 gauss), the temperature was lower for higher light intensity, a reversal of the usual linear dependence of temperature and intensity [80, 98]. We considered this to be an important early confirmation of the qualitative correctness of the new theory, confirming the central role played

163

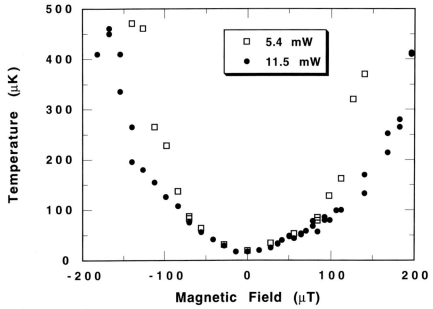

Figure 19. Temperature vs. magnetic field in a 3D optical molasses. Observation of lower temperature at higher intensity when the magnetic field was high provided an early confirmation of the new theory of sub-Doppler cooling.

by the light shift and the magnetic sublevels in the cooling mechanism. Joined by Steve Rolston and Carol Tanner we (Paul Lett, Rich Watts, Chris Westbrook and myself) carried out additional studies of the behavior of optical molasses, providing qualitative comparisons with the predictions of the new theory. Our 1989 paper [80], "Optical Molasses" summarized these results and contrasted the predictions of Doppler cooling with the new theory. Steve Chu's group also published additional measurements at the same time [105]. Other, even more detailed measurements in Paris [98] (where I was very privileged to spend the academic year of 1989–1990) left little doubt about the correctness of the new picture of laser cooling. In those experiments we cooled Cs atoms to 2.5 μK. It was a truly exciting time, when the developments in the theory and the experiments were pushing each other to better understanding and lower temperatures. Around this time, Jan Hall (whose pioneering work in chirp-cooling [31] had done so much to launch the explosive activity a few years before) commented that being in the field of laser cooling was an experience akin to being in Paris at the time of the Impressionists. Figure 20 symbolizes the truth of that comment.

OPTICAL LATTICES

In 1989 we began a different kind of measurement on laser cooled atoms, a measurement that was to lead us to a new and highly fruitful field of research. We had always been a bit concerned that all of our temperature measurements gave us information about the velocity distribution of atoms *after* their

164

Figure 20. Hal Metcalf, Claude Cohen-Tannoudji and the author on the famous bridge in Monet's garden at Giverny, ca. 1990.

release from the optical molasses and we wanted a way to measure the temperature *in situ*. Phil Gould suggested that we measure the spectrum of the light emitted from the atoms while they were being cooled. For continuous, single frequency irradiation at low intensity and large detuning, most of the fluorescence light scattered from the atoms should be "elastically" scattered, rather than belonging to the "Mollow triplet" of high-intensity resonance fluorescence [106]. This elastically scattered light will be Doppler shifted by the moving atoms and its spectrum should show a Doppler broadening characteristic of the temperature of the atomic sample. The spectrum will also contain the frequency fluctuations of the laser itself, but these are relatively slow for a dye laser, so Gould suggested a heterodyne method of detection, where the fluorescent light is mixed on a photodiode with local oscillator light derived from the molasses laser, producing a beat signal that is free of the laser frequency fluctuations.

The experiment was not easy, and it worked mainly because of the skill and perseverance of Chris Westbrook. An example of the surprising spectrum we obtained [107] is shown in Fig. 21. The broad pedestal corresponded well to

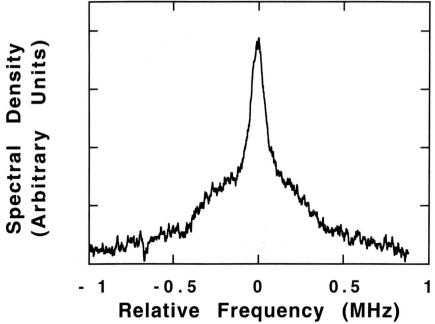

Figure 21. Heterodyne spectrum of fluorescence from Na atoms in optical molasses. The broad component corresponds to a temperature of 84 µK, which compares well with the temperature of 87 µK measured by TOF. The narrow component indicates a sub-wavelength localization of the atoms.

what we expected from the time-of-flight temperature measurement on a similar optical molasses, but the narrow central peak was a puzzle. After rejecting such wild possibilities as the achievement of Bose-Einstein condensation (Fig. 21 looks remarkably similar to velocity distributions in partially Bose-condensed atomic gases) we realized that the answer was quite simple: we were seeing line-narrowing from the Lamb-Dicke effect [108] of atoms localized to less than a wavelength of light. Atoms were being trapped by the dipole force in periodically spaced potential wells like those of Fig. 18b. We knew from both theory and experiments that the thermal energy of the atoms was less than the light shifts producing the potential wells, so it was quite reasonable that the atoms should be trapped. Confined within a region much less than a wavelength of light, the emitted spectrum shows a suppression of the Doppler width, the Lamb-Dicke effect, which is equivalent to the Mössbauer effect. This measurement [107] marked the start of our interest in what are now called optical lattices: spatially periodic patterns of light-shift-induced potential wells in which atoms are trapped and well localized. It also represents a realization of the 1968 proposal of Letokhov [14] to reduce the Doppler width by trapping atoms in a standing wave.

Joined by Poul Jessen, who was doing his Ph.D. research in our lab, we refined the heterodyne technique and measured the spectrum of Rb atoms in a 1-D laser field like that of Figure 18a. Figure 22 shows the results [109], which display well-resolved sidebands around a central, elastic peak. The si-

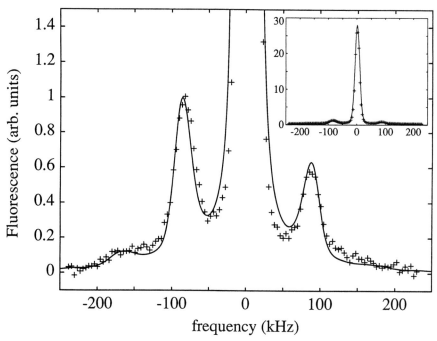

Figure 22. Vertical expansion of the spectrum emitted by Rb atoms in a 1-D optical lattice. The crosses are the data of ref. [109]; the curve is a first-principles calculation of the spectrum [110]. The calculation has no adjustable parameters other than an instrumental broadening. Inset: unexpanded spectrum.

debands are separated from the elastic peak by the frequency of vibration of atoms in the 1-D potential wells. The sideband spectrum can be interpreted as spontaneous Raman scattering, both Stokes and anti-Stokes, involving transitions that begin on a given quantized vibrational level for an atom bound in the optical potential and end on a higher vibrational level (the lower sideband), the same level (elastic peak) or a lower level (the higher sideband). We did not see sidebands in the earlier experiment in a 3D, 6-beam optical molasses [107] at least in part because of the lack of phase stability among the laser beams [111]. We have seen well-resolved sidebands in a 3D, 4-beam lattice [112].

The spectrum of Fig. 22 gives much information about the trapping of atoms in the potential wells. The ratio of sideband intensity to elastic peak intensity gives the degree of localization, the ratio of the two sideband intensities gives the temperature, and the spacing of the sidebands gives the potential well depth. Similar, but in many respects complementary, information can be obtained from the absorption spectrum of such an optical lattice, as illustrated by the experiments performed earlier in Paris [113]. The spectrum of Fig. 22 can be calculated from first principles [110] and the comparison of the experimental and theoretical spectra shown provides one of the most detailed confirmations of our ability to predict theoretically the behavior of laser cooled atoms.

In our laboratory, we have continued our studies of optical lattices, using adiabatic expansion to achieve temperatures as low as 700 nK [114], applying Bragg scattering to study the dynamics of atomic motion [115–118], and extending heterodyne spectral measurements to 3-D [112]. The Paris group has also continued to perform a wide range of experiments on optical lattices [119–122], as have a number of other groups all over the world.

The optical lattice work has emphasized that a typical atom is quite well localized within its potential well, implying a physical picture rather different from the Sisyphus cooling of Fig. 18, where atoms move from one well to the next. Although numerical calculations give results in excellent agreement with experiment in the case of lattice-trapped atoms, a physical picture with the simplicity and power of the original Sisyphus picture has not yet emerged. Nevertheless, the simplicity of the experimental behavior makes one think that such a picture should exist and remains to be found. The work of Refs. [123, 124] may point the way to such an understanding.

CONCLUSION

I have told only a part of the story of laser cooling and trapping at NIST in Gaithersburg, and I have left out most of the work that has been done in other laboratories throughout the world. I have told this story from my personal vantage point as an experimentalist in Gaithersburg, as I saw it unfold. The reader will get a much more complete picture by also reading the Nobel Lectures of Steve Chu and Claude Cohen-Tannoudji. For the work in my lab, I have tried to follow the thread that leads from laser deceleration and cooling of atomic beams [30, 35, 36, 52] to magnetic trapping [63], the discovery of sub-Doppler cooling [80, 99], and the beginnings of optical lattice studies [107, 109]. Topics such as later studies of lattices, led by Steve Rolston, and collisions of cold atoms, led by Paul Lett, have only been mentioned, and other areas such as the optical tweezer work [125, 126] led by Kris Helmerson have been left out completely.

The story of laser cooling and trapping is still rapidly unfolding, and one of the most active areas of progress is in applications. These include "practical" applications like atomic clocks, atom interferometers, atom lithography, and optical tweezers, as well as "scientific" applications such as collision studies, atomic parity non-conservation, and Bose-Einstein condensation (BEC). (The latter is a particularly beautiful and exciting outgrowth of laser cooling and trapping. Since the 1997 Nobel festivities, our laboratory has joined the growing number of groups having achieved BEC, as shown in Fig. 23.) Most of these applications were completely unanticipated when laser cooling started, and many would have been impossible without the unexpected occurrence of sub-Doppler cooling.

Laser cooling and trapping has from its beginnings been motivated by a blend of practical applications and basic curiosity. When I started doing laser cooling, I had firmly in mind that I wanted to make better atomic clocks. On the other hand, the discovery of sub-Doppler cooling came out of a desire to

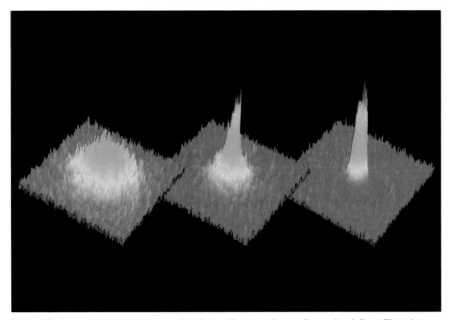

Figure 23. One of the most recent applications of laser-cooling and trapping is Bose-Einstein condensation in an atomic vapor. The figure shows a series of representations of the 2D velocity distribution of a gas of Na atoms at different stages of evaporative cooling through the BEC transition. The velocity distribution changes from a broad thermal one (left) to include a narrow, condensate peak (middle), and finally to be nearly pure condensate (right). The data were obtained in our laboratory in February of 1998, by L. Deng, E. Hagley, K. Helmerson, M. Kozuma, R. Lutwak, Y. Ovchinnikov, S. Rolston, J. Wen and the author. Our procedure was similar to that used in the first such observation of BEC, in Rb, at NIST/JILA in 1995 [15].

understand better the basic nature of the cooling process. Nevertheless, without sub-Doppler cooling, the present generation of atomic fountain clocks would not have been possible.

I hesitate to predict where the field of laser cooling and trapping will be even a few years from now. Such predictions have often been wrong in the past, and usually too pessimistic. But I firmly believe that progress, both in practical applications and in basic understanding, will be best achieved through research driven by both aims.

ACKNOWLEDGMENTS

I owe a great debt to all of the researchers in the many laboratories around the world who have contributed so much to the field of laser cooling and trapping of neutral atoms. Their friendly competition and generous sharing of understanding and insights has inspired me and educated me in an invaluable way. Very special thanks go to those researchers with whom I have been privileged to work here in Gaithersburg: to Hal Metcalf, who was part of the laser cooling experiments from the start, through most of the work described in this paper; to postdocs John Prodan, Alan Migdall, Phil Gould, Chris Westbrook, and Rich Watts, whose work led our group to the discovery of sub-Doppler cooling, and who moved on to distinguished careers elsewhere; to Paul Lett, Steve Rolston, and Kris Helmerson who also were pivotal figures in the development of laser cooling and trapping in Gaithersburg, who have formed the nucleus of the present Laser Cooling and Trapping Group (and who have graciously provided considerable help in the preparation of this manuscript); and to all the other postdocs, visitors and students who have so enriched our studies here. To all of these, I am thankful, not only for scientific riches but for shared friendship.

I know that I share with Claude Cohen-Tannoudji and with Steve Chu the firm belief that the 1997 Nobel Prize in Physics honors not only the three of us, but all those other researchers in this field who have made laser cooling and trapping such a rewarding and exciting subject.

I want to thank NIST for providing and sustaining the intellectual environment and the resources that have nurtured a new field of research and allowed it to grow from a few rudimentary ideas into a major branch of modern physics. I also thank the U.S. Office of Naval Research, which provided crucial support when I and my ideas were unproven, and which continues to provide invaluable support and encouragement.

There are many others, friends, family and teachers who have been of great importance. I thank especially my wife and daughters who have supported and encouraged me and provided that emotional and spiritual grounding that makes achievement worthwhile. Finally, I thank God for providing such a wonderful and intriguing world for us to explore, for allowing me to have the pleasure of learning some new things about it, and for allowing me to do so in the company of such good friends and colleagues.

REFERENCES

1. A. Ashkin, "Trapping of atoms by resonance radiation pressure," Phys. Rev. Lett. **40**, 729 (1978).
2. T. Hänsch and A. Schawlow, "Cooling of gases by laser radiation," Opt. Commun. **13**, 68 (1975).
3. D. Wineland and H. Dehmelt, "Proposed 10^{14} $\Delta\nu < \nu$ laser fluorescence spectroscopy on Tl$^+$ mono-ion oscillator III," Bull. Am. Phys. Soc. **20**, 637 (1975).
4. D. Wineland, R. Drullinger and F. Walls, "Radiation-pressure cooling of bound resonant absorbers," Phys. Rev. Lett. **40**, 1639 (1978).
5. W. Neuhauser, M. Hohenstatt, P. Toschek and H. Dehmelt, "Optical-sideband cooling of visible atom cloud confined in parabolic well," Phys. Rev. Lett. **41**, 233 (1978).
6. P. Lebedev, "Untersuchungen über die Druckkräfte des Lichtes," Ann. Phys. **6**, 433 (1901).
7. E. F. Nichols and G. F. Hull, "A Preliminary communication on the pressure of heat and light radiation," Phys. Rev. **13**, 307 (1901).
8. E. F. Nichols and G. F. Hull, "The pressure due to radiation," Phys. Rev. **17**, 26 (1903).
9. R. Frisch, "Experimenteller Nachweis des Einstenschen Strahlungsrückstosses," Z. Phys. **86**, 42 (1933).
10. A. Ashkin, "Atomic-beam deflection by resonance-radiation pressure," Phys. Rev. Lett. **25**, 1321 (1970).

11. R. Schieder, H. Walther and L. Wöste, "Atomic beam deflection by the light of a tunable dye laser," Opt. Commun. **5**, 337 (1972).

12. J.-L. Picqué and J.-L. Vialle, "Atomic-beam deflection and broadening by recoils due to photon absorption or emission," Opt. Commun. **5**, 402 (1972).

13. G. A. Askar'yan, "Effects of the gradient of a strong electromagnetic beam on electrons and atoms," Sov. Phys. JETP **15**, 1088 (1962).

14. V. Letokhov, "Narrowing of the Doppler width in a standing light wave," [Pisma Zh. Eksp. Teor. Fiz. **7**, 348 (1968)] JETP Lett. **7**, 272 (1968).

15. M. H. Anderson, J. R. Ensher, M. R. Matthews, C. E. Wieman and E. A. Cornell, "Observation of Bose-Einstein Condensation in a Dilute Atomic Vapor Below 200 Nanokelvin," Science **269**, 198 (1995).

16. K. B. Davis, M.-O. Mewes, M. R. Andrews, N. J. van Druten, D. S. Durfee, D. M. Kurn and W. Ketterle, "Bose-Einstein condensation in a gas of sodium atoms," Phys. Rev. Lett. **75**, 3969 (1995).

17. W. Nagourney, J. Sandberg and H. Dehmelt, "Shelved optical electron amplifier: observation of quantum jumps," Phys. Rev. Lett. **56**, 2797 (1986).

18. T. Sauter, W. Neuhauser, R. Blatt and P. Toschek, "Observation of quantum jumps," Phys. Rev. Lett. **57**, 1696 (1986).

19. J. C. Bergquist, R. G. Hulet, Wayne M. Itano and D. J. Wineland, "Observation of quantum jumps in a single atom," Phys. Rev. Lett. **57**, 1699 (1986).

20. C. Monroe, D. M. Meekhof, B. E. King and D. J. Wineland, "A "Schrödinger Cat" superposition state of an atom," Science **272**, 1131 (1996).

21. C. Monroe, D. M. Meekhof, B. E. King, W. M. Itano and D. J. Wineland, "Demonstration of a fundamental quantum logic gate," Phys. Rev. Lett. **75**, 4714 (1995).

22. V. G. Minogin, "Deceleration and monochromatization of atomic beams by radiation pressure," Opt. Commun. **34**, 265 (1980).

23. S. Andreev, V. Balykin, V. Letokhov and V. Minogin, "Radiative slowing and reduction of the energy spread of a beam of sodium atoms to 1.5K in an oppositely directed laser beam," [Pis'ma Zh. Eksp. Teor. Fiz. **34** 463 (1981)] JETP Lett. **34**, 442 (1981).

24. V. Letokhov, V. Minogin and B. Pavlik, "Cooling and trapping of atoms and molecules by a resonant laser field," Opt. Comm. **19**, 72 (1976).

25. V. Balykin, V. Letokhov and V. Mushin, "Observation of the cooling of free sodium atoms in a resonance laser field with a scanning frequency," [Pis'ma Zh. Eksp. Teor. Fiz. **29**, 614 (1979)] JETP Lett. **29**, 560 (1979).

26. V. Balykin, "Cyclic interaction of Na atoms with circularly polarized laser radiation," Opt. Comm. **33**, 31 (1980).

27. W. Phillips, J. Prodan and H. Metcalf, "Laser Cooling of Free Neutral Atoms in an Atomic Beam", in *Laser Spectroscopy VI*, H. Weber, W. Luthy, Ed. (Springer-Verlag, Berlin, 1983) p. 162.

28. W. D. Phillips and J. V. Prodan, "Chirping the Light - Fantastic?", in *Laser-cooled and Trapped Atoms*, W. D. Phillips, Ed. (Natl. Bur. Stand., Wash. DC, 1983), vol. Spec. Publ. 653, p. 137.

29. J. V. Prodan and W. D. Phillips, "Chirping the Light- Fantastic? Recent NBS Atom Cooling Experiments," Prog. Quant. Electr. **8**, 231 (1984).

30. W. D. Phillips and J. V. Prodan, "Cooling atoms with a frequency chirped laser", in *Coherence and Quantum Optics V*, L. Mandel, E. Wolf, Ed. (Plenum, New York, 1984) p. 15.

31. W. Ertmer, R. Blatt, J. Hall and M. Zhu, "Laser manipulation of atomic beam velocities: Demonstration of stopped atoms and velocity reversal," Phys. Rev. Lett. **54**, 996 (1985).

32. J. Hoffnagle, "Proposal for continuous white-light cooling of an atom beam," Opt. Lett. **13**, 102 (1988).

33. M. Zhu, C. W. Oates and J. L. Hall, "Continuous high-flux monovelocity atomic beam based on a broadband laser-cooling technique," Phys. Rev. Lett. **67**, 46 (1991).

34. W. D. Phillips, Proposal to the Office of Naval Research from the National Bureau of Standards, Laser cooling and trapping of neutral atoms (1979).

35. W. Phillips and H. Metcalf, "Laser deceleration of an atomic beam," Phys. Rev. Lett. **48**, 596 (1982).

36. J. Prodan, W. Phillips and H. Metcalf, "Laser production of a very slow monoenergetic atomic beam," Phys. Rev. Lett. **49**, 1149 (1982).

37. W. D. Phillips, J. V. Prodan and H. J. Metcalf, "Neutral Atomic Beam Cooling Experiments at NBS", in *Laser-cooled and Trapped Atoms*, W. D. Phillips, Ed. (Natl. Bur. Stand., Wash. DC, 1983), vol. Spec. Publ. 653, p. 1.

38. W. D. Phillips, J. V. Prodan and H. J. Metcalf, "Laser-cooled Atomic Beams", in *Atomic Physics IX*, R. S. Van Dyck, E. N. Fortson, Ed. (World Scientific, Singapore, 1984) p. 338.

39. W. D. Phillips, J. V. Prodan and H. J. Metcalf, "Neutral Atomic Beam Cooling Experiments at NBS," Prog. Quant. Electr. **8**, 119 (1984).

40. H. Metcalf and W. D. Phillips, "Laser Cooling of Atomic Beams," Comments At. Mol. Phys. **16**, 79 (1985).

41. W. D. Phillips, J. Prodan and H. Metcalf, "Laser cooling and electromagnetic trapping of neutral atoms," J. Opt. Soc. Am. B **2**, 1751 (1985).

42. W. D. Phillips, Ed., *Laser-Cooled and Trapped Atoms* , Natl. Bur. Stand. (U. S.), Spec. Publ. 653 (1993).

43. S. Stenholm, "Theoretical foundations of laser spectroscopy," Phys. Rep. **43**, 151 (1978).

44. S. Stenholm, "Redistribution of molecular velocities by optical processes," Appl. Phys. **15**, 287 (1978).

45. J. Javanainen and S. Stenholm, "Broad band resonant light pressure I: Basic equations," Appl. Phys. **21**, 35 (1980).

46. J. Javanainen and S. Stenholm, "Broad band resonant light pressure II: Cooling of gases," Appl. Phys. **21**, 163 (1980).

47. J. Javanainen and S. Stenholm, "Laser cooling of trapped particles I: The heavy particle limit," Appl. Phys. **21**, 283 (1980).

48. J. Javanainen and S. Stenholm, "Laser cooling of trapped particles II: The fast particle limit," Appl. Phys. **24**, 71 (1981).

49. J. Javanainen and S. Stenholm, "Laser cooling of trapped particles III: The Lamb-Dicke limit," Appl. Phys. **24**, 151 (1981).

50. S. Stenholm, "Dynamics of trapped particle cooling in the Lamb-Dicke limit," J. Opt. Soc. Am. B **2**, 1743 (1985).

51. S. Stenholm, "The semiclassical theory of laser cooling," Rev. Mod. Phys. **58**, 699 (1986).

52. J. Prodan, A. Migdall, W. D. Phillips, I. So, H. Metcalf and J. Dalibard, "Stopping atoms with laser light," Phys. Rev. Lett. **54**, 992 (1985).

53. C. V. Heer, "A low temperature atomic beam oscillator", in *Quantum Electronics*, C. H. Townes, Ed. (Columbia University Press, New York, 1960) p. 17.

54. V. V. Vladimirskii, "Magnetic mirror, channels and bottles for cold neutrons," Sov. Phys. JETP [Zh. Eksp. Teor. Fiz **39**, 1062 (1960)] **12**, 740 (1961).

55. C. V. Heer, "Feasibility of containment of quantum magnetic dipoles," Rev. Sci. Instrum. **34**, 532 (1963).

56. R. Vauthier, "Dispositif de focalisation pour particules électriquement neutres," C. R. Acad. Sci. (Paris) **228**, 1113 (1949).

57. H. Friedburg and W. Paul, "Optische Abbildung mit neutralen Atomen," Naturwissenschaften **38**, 159 (1951).

58. H. Friedburg, "Optische Abbildung mit neutralen Atomen," Z. Phys. **130**, 493 (1951).

59. K.-J. Kugler, W. Paul and U. Trinks, "A magnetic storage ring for neutrons," Phys. Lett. **72B**, 422 (1978).

60. B. Martin, thesis, Universität Bonn, Report No. Bonn-IR-75-8 (1975)

61. W. Wing, "On neutral particle trapping in quasistatic electromagnetic fields," Prog. Quant. Electr. **8**, 181 (1984).
62. R. Golub and J. Pendlebury, "Ultra-cold neutrons," Rep. Prog. Phys. **42**, 439 (1979).
63. A. Migdall, J. Prodan, W. Phillips, T. Bergeman and H. Metcalf, "First observation of magnetically trapped neutral atoms," Phys. Rev. Lett. **54**, 2596 (1985).
64. V. Bagnato, G. Lafyatis, A. Martin, E. Raab, R. Ahmad-Bitar and D. E. Pritchard, "Continuous slowing and trapping of neutral atoms," Phys. Rev. Lett. **58**, 2194 (1987).
65. K. Helmerson, A. Martin and D. Pritchard, "Laser cooling of magnetically trapped neutral atoms," J. Opt. Soc. Am. B **9**, 1988 (1992).
66. Y. V. Gott, M. S. Ioffe and V. G. Telkovsky, "Some new results on confining of plasmas in a magnetic trap", in *Nuclear Fusion*, Ed. (International Atomic Energy Agency, Vienna, 1962) p. 1045.
67. D. E. Pritchard, "Cooling neutral atoms in a magnetic trap for precision spectroscopy," Phys. Rev. Lett. **51**, 1336 (1983).
68. T. Bergeman, G. Erez and H. J. Metcalf, "Magnetostatic trapping fields for neutral atoms," Phys. Rev. A **35**, 1535 (1987).
69. H. F. Hess, G. P. Kochanski, J. M. Doyle, N. Masuhara, Daniel Kleppner and T. J. Greytak, "Magnetic Trapping of Spin-Polarized Atomic Hydrogen," Phys. Rev. Lett. **59**, 672 (1987).
70. N. Masuhara, J. M. Doyle, J. C. Sandberg, D. Kleppner, T. J. Greytak, H. F. Hess and G. P. Kochanski, "Evaporative cooling of spin-polarized atomic hydrogen," Phys. Rev. Lett. **61**, 935 (1988).
71. R. van Roijen, J. J. Berkhout, S. Jaakkol and J. T. M. Walraven, "Experiments with atomic hydrogen in a magnetic trapping field," Phys. Rev. Lett. **61**, 931 (1988).
72. I. D. Setija, H. G. C. Werij, O. J. Luiten, M. W. Reynolds, T. W. Hijmans and J. T. M. Walraven, "Optical Cooling of Atomic Hydrogen in a Magnetic Trap," Phy. Rev. Lett. **70**, 2257 (1994).
73. W. Petrich, M. H. Anderson, J. R. Ensher and E. A. Cornell, "Stable, Tightly Confining Magnetic Trap for Evaporative Cooling of Neutral Atoms," Phys. Rev. Lett. **74**, 3352 (1995).
74. K. B. Davis, M.-O. Mewes, M. A. Joffe, M. R. Andrews and W. Ketterle, "Evaporative cooling of sodium atoms," Phys. Rev. Lett. **74**, 5202 (1995).
75. J. Bjorkholm, R. Freeman, A. Ashkin and D. Pearson, "Observation of focusing of neutral atoms by the dipole forces of resonance-radiation pressure," Phys. Rev. Lett. **41**, 1361 (1978).
76. W. D. Phillips, "Laser cooling and trapping of neutral atoms", in *Laser Manipulation of Atoms and Ions (Proceedings of the International School of Physics "Enrico Fermi", Course CXVIII)*, E. Arimondo, W. Phillips, F. Strumia, Ed. (North Holland, Amsterdam, 1992) p. 289.
77. V. S. Letokhov, V. G. Minogin and B. D. Pavlik, "Cooling and capture of atoms and molecules by a resonant light field," Sov. Phys. JETP **45**, 698 (1977).
78. D. Wineland and W. Itano, "Laser cooling of atoms," Phys. Rev. A **20**, 1521 (1979).
79. J. Javanainen, "Light-pressure cooling of trapped ions in three dimensions," Appl. Phys. **23**, 175 (1980).
80. P. D. Lett, W. D. Phillips, S. L. Rolston, C. E. Tanner, R. N. Watts and C. I. Westbrook, "Optical molasses," J. Opt. Soc. Am. B **6**, 2084 (1989).
81. S. Chu, L. Hollberg, J. Bjorkholm, A. Cable and A. Ashkin, "Three-dimensional viscous confinement and cooling of atoms by resonance radiation pressure," Phys. Rev. Lett. **55**, 48 (1985).
82. The high temperature observed in this experiment has since been ascribed to the presence of a stray magnetic field from an ion pump. S. Chu, personal communication, (1997).
83. E. Raab, M. Prentiss, A. Cable, S. Chu and D. Pritchard, "Trapping of neutral sodium atoms with radiation pressure," Phys. Rev. Lett. **59**, 2631 (1987).

84. C. Monroe, W. Swann, H. Robinson and C. Wieman, "Very cold trapped atoms in a vapor cell," Phys. Rev. Lett. **65**, 1571 (1990).

85. A. Cable, M. Prentiss and N. P. Bigelow, "Observations of sodium atoms in a magnetic molasses trap loaded by a continuous uncooled source," Opt. Lett. **15**, 507 (1990).

86. P. L. Gould, P. D. Lett, P. S. Julienne, W. D. Phillips, H. R. Thorsheim and J. Weiner, "Observation of associative ionization of ultracold laser-trapped sodium atoms," Phys. Rev. Lett. **60**, 788 (1988).

87. S. Chu, J. Bjorkholm, A. Ashkin and A. Cable, "Experimental observation of optically trapped atoms," Phys. Rev. Lett. **57**, 314 (1986).

88. P. D. Lett, P. S. Jessen, W. D. Phillips, S. L. Rolston, C. I. Westbrook and P. L. Gould, "Laser modification of ultracold collisions: Experiment," Phys. Rev. Lett. **67**, 2139 (1991).

89. P. D. Lett, K. Helmerson, W. D. Phillips, L. P. Ratliff, S. L. Rolston and M. E. Wagshul, "Spectroscopy of Na_2 by photoassociation of ultracold Na," Phys. Rev. Lett. **71**, 2200 (1993).

90. L. P. Ratliff, M. E. Wagshul, P. D. Lett, S. L. Rolston and W. D. Phillips, "Photoassociative Spectroscopy of 1_g, 0_u^+ and 0_g^- States of Na_2," J. Chem. Phys. **101**, 2638 (1994).

91. P. D. Lett, P. S. Julienne and W. D. Phillips, "Photoassociative Spectroscopy of Laser-Cooled Atoms," Annu. Rev. Phys. Chem. **46**, 423 (1995).

92. K. Jones, P. Julienne, P. Lett, W. Phillips, E. Tiesinga and C. Williams, "Measurement of the atomic Na(3P) lifetime and of retardation in the interaction between two atoms bound in a molecule," Europhys. Lett. **35**, 85 (1996).

93. E. Tiesinga, C. J. Williams, P. S. Julienne, K. M. Jones, P. D. Lett and W. D. Phillips, "A spectroscopic determination of scattering lengths for sodium atom collisions," J. Res. Natl. Inst. Stand. Technol. **101**, 505 (1996).

94. M. Walhout, U. Sterr, C. Orzel, M. Hoogerland and S. L. Rolston, "Optical Control of Ultracold Collisions in Metastable Xenon," Phys. Rev. Lett. **74**, 506 (1995).

95. P. L. Gould, P. D. Lett and W. D. Phillips, "New Measurements with Optical Molasses", in *Laser Spectroscopy VIII*, W. Persson, S. Svanberg, Ed. (Springer-Verlag, Berlin, 1987) p. 64.

96. J. P. Gordon and A. Ashkin, "Motion of atoms in a radiation field," Phys. Rev. A **21**, 1606 (1980).

97. W. D. Phillips, C. I. Westbrook, P. D. Lett, R. N. Watts, P. L. Gould and H. J. Metcalf, "Observation of atoms laser-cooled below the Doppler limit", in *Atomic Physics 11*, S. Haroche, J. C. Gay, G. Grynberg, Ed. (World Scientific, Singapore, 1989) p. 633.

98. C. Salomon, J. Dalibard, W. D. Phillips, A. Clairon and S. Guellati, "Laser cooling of cesium atoms below 3 microkelvin," Europhys. Lett. **12**, 683 (1990).

99. P. D. Lett, R. N. Watts, C. I. Westbrook, W. D. Phillips, P. L. Gould and H. J. Metcalf, "Observation of atoms laser cooled below the Doppler limit," Phys. Rev. Lett. **61**, 169 (1988).

100. J. Dalibard and C. Cohen-Tannoudji, "Laser cooling below the Doppler limit by polarization gradients: simple theoretical models," J. Opt. Soc. Am. B **6**, 2023 (1989).

101. P. J. Ungar, D. S. Weiss, E. Riis and S. Chu, "Optical molasses and multilevel atoms: theory," J. Opt. Soc. Am. B **6**, 2058 (1989).

102. C. Cohen-Tannoudji and W. D. Phillips, Physics Today **43**, 33 (1990).

103. C. Cohen-Tannoudji, "Atomic Motion in Laser Light", in *Fundamental Systems in Quantum Optics*, J. Dalibard, J.-M. Raimond, J. Zinn-Justin, Ed. (North Holland, Amsterdam, 1992) p. 1.

104. J. Dalibard and C. Cohen-Tannoudji, "Dressed-atom approach to atomic motion in laser light: the dipole force revisited," J. Opt. Soc. Am. B **2**, 1707 (1985).

105. D. S. Weiss, E. Riis, Y. Shevy, P. J. Ungar and S. Chu, "Optical molasses and multilevel atoms: experiment," J. Opt. Soc. Am. B **6**, 2072 (1989).

106. B. R. Mollow, "Power spectrum of light scattered by two-level systems," Phys. Rev. **188**, 1969 (1969).

107. C. I. Westbrook, R. N. Watts, C. E. Tanner, S. L. Rolston, W. D. Phillips, P. D. Lett and P. L. Gould, "Localization of atoms in a three dimensional standing wave of light," Phys. Rev. Lett. **65**, 33 (1990).

108. R. H. Dicke, "The effect of collisions upon the Doppler width of spectral lines," Phys. Rev. **89**, 472 (1953).

109. P. S. Jessen, C. Gerz, P. D. Lett, W. D. Phillips, S. L. Rolston, R. J. C. Spreeuw and C. I. Westbrook, "Observation of quantized motion of Rb atoms in an optical field," Phys. Rev. Lett. **69**, 49 (1992).

110. P. Marte, R. Dum, R. Taïeb, P. Lett and P. Zoller, "Wave function calculation of the fluorescence spectrum of 1-D optical molasses," Phys. Rev. Lett. **71**, 1335 (1993).

111. G. Grynberg, B. Lounis, P. Verkerk, J.-Y. Courtois and C. Salomon, "Quantized motion of cold cesium atoms in two- and three-dimensional optical potentials," Phys. Rev. Lett. **70**, 2249 (1993).

112. M. Gatzke, G. Birkl, P. S. Jessen, A. Kastberg, S. L. Rolston and W. D. Phillips, "Temperature and localization of atoms in 3D optical lattices," Phys. Rev. A **55**, R3987 (1997).

113. P. Verkerk, B. Lounis, C. Salomon, C. Cohen-Tannoudji, J.-Y. Courtois and G. Grynberg, "Dynamics and Spatial Order of Cold Cesium Atoms in a Periodic Optical Potential," Phys. Rev. Lett. **68**, 3861 (1992).

114. A. Kastberg, W. D. Phillips, S. L. Rolston, R. J. C. Spreeuw and P. S. Jessen, "Adiabatic cooling of cesium to 700 nK in an optical lattice," Phys. Rev. Lett. **74**, 1542 (1995).

115. G. Birkl, M. Gatzke, I. H. Deutsch, S. L. Rolston and W. D. Phillips, "Bragg Scattering from Atoms in Optical Lattices," Phys. Rev. Lett. **75**, 2823 (1995).

116. G. Raithel, G. Birkl, A. Kastberg, W. D. Phillips and S. L. Rolston, "Cooling and localization dynamics in optical lattices," Phys. Rev. Lett. **78**, 630 (1997).

117. G. Raithel, G. Birkl, W. D. Phillips and S. L. Rolston, "Compression and parametric driving of atoms in optical lattices," Phys. Rev. Lett. **78**, 2928 (1997).

118. W. D. Phillips, "Quantum motion of atoms confined in an optical lattice," Materials Science and Engineering B **48**, 13 (1997).

119. B. Lounis, P. Verkerk, J.-Y. Courtois, C. Salomon and G. Grynberg, "Quantized atomic motion in 1D cesium molasses with magnetic field," Europhys. Lett. **21**, 13 (1993).

120. D. R. Meacher, D. Boiron, H. Metcalf, C. Salomon and G. Grynberg, "Method for velocimetry of cold atoms," Phys. Rev. **A50**, R1992 (1994).

121. P. Verkerk, D. R. Meacher, A. B. Coates, J.-Y. Courtois, S. Guibal, B. Lounis, C. Salomon and G. Grynberg, "Designing Optical Lattices: an Investigation with Cesium Atoms," Europhys. Lett. **26**, 171 (1994).

122. D. R. Meacher, S. Guibal, C. Mennerat, J.-Y. Courtois, K. I. Pestas and G. Grynberg, "Paramagnetism in a cesium lattice," Phys. Rev. Lett. **74**, 1958 (1995).

123. Y. Castin, Doctoral Dissertation, Ecole Normale Supérieure (1992) (See section IV 3 e).

124. Y. Castin, K. Berg-Sorensen, J. Dalibard and K. Mølmer, "Two-dimensional Sisyphus cooling," Phys. Rev. A **50**, 5092 (1994).

125. K. Helmerson, R. Kishore, W. D. Phillips and H. H. Weetall, "Optical Tweezers-based immunosensor detects femtomolar concentration of antigens," Clinical Chemistry **43**, 379 (1997).

126. M. Mammen, K. Helmerson, R. Kishore, S.-K. Choi, W. D. Phillips and G. M. Whitesides, "Optically controlled collisions of biological Objects to evaluate potent polyvalent inhibitors of virus-cell adhesion," Chemistry & Biology **3**, 757 (1996).

PAUL D. BOYER

The first 21 years of my life were spent in Provo, Utah, then a city of about 15,000 people, beautifully situated at the foot of the Wasatch Mountains. Hardy Mormon pioneers had settled the area only 70 years before my birth in 1918. Provo was a well-designed city with stable neighbourhoods, a pride in its past and a spirit of unbounded opportunity. The geographical isolation and lack of television made world happenings and problems seem remote.

My father, Dell Delos Boyer, born in 1879 in Springville, Utah, came from the Pennsylvania Boyers, who in turn came from an earlier Bayer ancestry in what is now Holland and Germany. A small portion of my Boyer DNA has been traced to John Alden, famous as a Mayflower pilgrim who wooed for another and won for himself. Dad's education, at what was then the Brigham Young Academy, was delayed by the ill health he had endured in much of his youth. Through his ambition, and the sacrifices of his family, he acquired training in Los Angeles to become an osteopathic physician. He served humanity well. More by example than by word, my father taught me logical reasoning, compassion, love of others, honesty, and discipline applied with understanding. He also taught me such skills such as pitching horseshoes and growing vegetables. Dad loved to travel. Family trips to Yellowstone and to what are now national parks in Southern Utah, driving the primitive roads and cars of that day, were real adventures. Father became a widower when the youngest of my five siblings was only eight. Fifteen years later he married another fine woman. They shared many happy times, and she cared for him during a long illness as he died from prostate cancer at the age of 82. Prostate cancer also took the life of my only brother when he was 76. If our society continues to support basic research on how living organisms function, it is likely that my great grandchildren will be spared the agony of losing family members to most types of cancer.

Recently I scanned notes from a diary that my mother, Grace Guymon, wrote in her late teens, when living near Mancos, Colorado. The Guymons were among the Huguenots who fled religious persecution in France. My French heritage has been mixed with English and other nationalities as the Guymons descended. Mother's diary revealed to me more about her vitality and charm than I remembered from her later years, which were clouded by Addison's disease. She died in 1933, at the age of 45, just weeks after my fifteenth birthday. Discoveries about the adrenal hormones, that could have saved her life, came too late. Her death contributed to my later interest in studying biochemistry, an interest that has not been fulfilled in the sense that my accomplishments remain more at the basic than the applied level. Mother made a glorious home environment for my early years. During her long illness and after her death, all of the children helped with family chores. One of my less pleasant memories is of getting up in the middle of the night to use our allotted irrigation time to water the garden.

The large, gracious home provided by Mother and Dad at 346 North University Avenue has been replaced by a pizza parlor, although an inspection a few months ago revealed that the irrigation ditch for our garden area (now a parking lot) can still be found. Mother had a talent for home decorating. I often read from a set of the *Book of Knowledge* or *Harvard Classics* while lying in front of the fireplace, with a mantel designed and decorated by her. Staring into the glowing coals as a fire dims provided a wonderful milieu for a youthful imagination. I also remember such things as picnics in Provo Canyon, and the anticipation that I might get to lick the dasher after cranking the ice-cream freezer. My older brother, Roy, and I had a play-fight relationship. I still carry a scar on my nose from when I plunged (he pushed me!) through the mirror of the dining room closet. I am told that I had a bad temper, and remember being banished to the back hall until civility returned. Perhaps this temper was later sublimated into drive and tenacity, traits that may have come in part from my mother.

The great depression of the 1930s left lasting impressions on all our family. Father's patients became non-paying or often exchanged farm produce or some labor for medical care. Mother saved pennies to pay the taxes. The burden of paper routes and odd jobs to provide my spending money made it painful when my new Iver Johnson bicycle was stolen. We were encouraged to be creative. I recall mother's tolerance when she allowed me, at an early age, to take off the hinges and doors of cupboards if I would put them back on. My first exposure to chemistry came when I was given a chemistry set for Christmas. It competed for space in our basement with a model electric trains and an "Erector" set. After school the neighborhood yards were filled with shouts of play; games of "kick-the-can," "run-sheepy-run," "steal-the-sticks," as well as marbles, baseball and other activities. In our back yard we built tree houses, dug underground tunnels and secret passages, and made a small club house. The mountains above our house offered other outlets for adventuresome teenage boys. Days were spent in an abandoned cabin or sleeping under the sky in the shadow of Provo peak. We even took cultures of sour dough bread to the mountains and baked delicious biscuits in an a rusty stove. Mountain hikes instilled in me a life-long urge to get to the top of any inviting summit or peak.

Provo public schools were excellent. At Parker Elementary School, a few blocks from my home, I fell in love with my 3rd grade teacher, Miss McKay. Students who learned more easily were allowed to skip a grade, and I entered the new Farrer Junior High school at a younger age than my classmates. This handicapped me in two types of sporting events, athletics and courting girls. Girls did not want to dance with little Paul Boyer; boys were quite unimpressed with my physique. As I grew my status among fellows improved. Once I got into a scuffle in gym class, the instructor had the "combatants" put on boxing gloves, and I gave more than I received. It wasn't until late high school and early college that I gained enough size and skill to make me welcome on intramural basketball teams.

I was one of about 500 students of Provo High School, where the atmosphere was friendly, and scholarship and activities were encouraged by both students and faculty. I participated on debating teams and in student government, and served as senior class president. I still have a particularly high regard for my chemistry teacher, Rees Bench. I was pleased when he wrote in my Yearbook for graduation, "You have proven yourself as a most outstanding student." I graduated while still 16, and thought myself quite mature. I wish I had saved a copy of my valedictorian address. I suspect it may have sparkled with naivete.

It was always assumed that I would go to college. The Brigham Young University (BYU) campus was just a few blocks from my home and tuition was minimal. It was a small college of about 3,500 students, less than a tenth of its present size. As in high school, I enjoyed social and student government activities. Friendships abounded. New vistas were opened in a variety of fields of learning. Chemistry and mathematics seemed logical studies to emphasize, although I had little concept as to where they might lead. A painstaking course in qualitative and quantitative analysis by John Wing gave me an appreciation of the need for, and beauty of, accurate measurement. However, the lingering odor of hydrogen sulfide, used for metal identification and separation, called unwanted attention to me in later classes. "Prof" Joe Nichol's enthusiasm for general chemistry was superbly conveyed to his students. Professor Charles Maw excelled in transferring a knowledge of organic chemistry to his students. Biochemistry was not included in the curriculum.

Summers I worked as a waiter and managerial assistant at Pinecrest Inn, in a canyon near Salt Lake City. One summer a college friend and I lived there in a sheep camp trailer while managing a string of saddle horses for the guests to use. A different type of education came when as a member of a medical corps in the National Guard I spent several weeks in a military camp in California.

As my senior year progressed several career paths were considered; employment as a chemist in the mining industry, a training program in hotel management, the study of osteopathic or conventional medicine, or some type of graduate training. Little information was available about the latter possibility; but a few chemistry majors from BYU had gone on to graduate school. I have a tendency to be lucky and make the right choices based on limited information. A notice was posted of a Wisconsin Alumni Research Foundation (WARF) Scholarship for graduate studies. My application was approved, and the stage was set for a later phase of my career.

Before leaving Provo, a most important and fortunate event occurred. A beautiful and talented brunette coed, with one year of college to finish, indicated a willingness to marry me. She came from a large and loving family, impoverished financially by her father's death when she was 2 years old. She had worked and charmed her way nearly through college. My savings were limited and hers were negative. But it was clear that my choice was to have her join with me in the Wisconsin adventure or take my chances when I returned a year later. It was an easy decision. Paul, who had just turned 21, and Lyda Whicker, 20, were married in my father's home on August 31, 1939. Five days later we left by train to Wisconsin for my graduate study.

A few months after our arrival our new marriage almost ended. I was admitted to the student infirmary with diagnosed appendicitis. Through medical mismanagement my appendix ruptured and I became deathly ill. Sulfanilamides, discovered a few years earlier by Domagk, saved my life. Last summer I read an outstanding book, *The Forgotten Plague: How the Battle Against Tuberculosis Was Won and Lost,* by Frank Ryan. The book gives a stirring account, the first I have read, of Domagk's research and how he was not allowed to leave Hitler's Germany to receive the 1939 Nobel Prize.

Fortunately, the Biochemistry Department at the University of Wisconsin in Madison was outstanding and far ahead of most others in the country. A new wing on the biochemistry building had recently been opened. The excitement of vitamins, nutrition and metabolism permeated the environment. Steenbock had recently patented the irradiation of milk for enrichment with vitamin D. Elvehjem's group had discovered that nicotinic acid would cure pellagra. Petersen's group was identifying and separating bacterial growth factors. Link's group was isolating and identifying a vitamin K antagonist from sweet clover. Patents for the use of dicoumarol as a rat poison and as an anticoagulant sweetened the coffers of the WARF, the Foundation that supported my scholarship. Among younger faculty an interest in enzymology and metabolism was blossoming.

Married graduate students were rare, and the continuing economic depression made jobs hard to find. But my remarkable wife soon found a good job, and I settled into graduate studies. During our Wisconsin years she gained a perspective of art while employed in Madison's leading art retail outlet. It was years later before Lyda finished a college degree, became a professional editor at UCLA, and worked with me on the eighteen-volume series of *The Enzymes.* Our contacts in graduate school and through Lyda's employment gave us life-long friends; one was Henry Lardy, from South Dakota farm country. He and I were assigned to work under Professor Paul Phillips. Henry was highly talented, and it was my good fortune to work along side him. Phillips' main interests were in reproductive and nutritional problems of farm animals. Henry developed an egg yolk medium for sperm storage that revolutionized animal breeding.

We were encouraged by Phillips to explore metabolic and enzyme interests. I did not realize that it was unusual to be able step across the hall and attend a symposium on respiratory enzymes in which such biochemical giants as Otto Meyerhof, Fritz Lipmann, and Carl Cori spoke. Evening research discussion groups with keen young faculty such as Marvin Johnson and Van Potter, centered on enzymes and metabolism, broadened and sharpened our perspectives. One evening I presented my and Henry's evidence for the first known K^+ activation of an enzyme, pyruvate kinase. Henry kept score on the interruptions for questions or discussions–some 35 as I recall. This superb training environment set the base for my career.

My Ph.D. degree was granted in the spring of 1943, the nation was at war, and I headed for a war project at Stanford University. A few weeks after my arrival in California, on my birthday, July 31, our daughter Gail was born. I became somewhat more involved in home duties and more deeply in love with Lyda.

The wartime Committee on Medical Research sponsored a project at Stanford University on blood plasma proteins, under the direction of J. Murray Luck, founder of the nonprofit *Annual Review of Biochemistry* and other Reviews. Concentrated serum albumin fractionated from blood plasma was effective in battlefield treatment of shock. When heated to kill microorganisms and viruses, the solutions of albumin developed cloudiness from protein denaturation. The principal goal of our research project was to find some way to stabilize the solutions so that they would not show this behavior. Our small group found that acetate gave some stabilization and butyrate was better. This led to the discovery that long chain fatty acids would remarkably stabilize serum albumin to heat denaturation, and would even reverse the denaturation by heat or concentrated urea solutions. Other compounds with hydrophobic portions and a negative charge, such as acetyl tryptophan, were also effective. Our stabilization method was quickly adopted and is still in use. From the Stanford studies I gained experience with proteins and a growing respect for the beauty of their structures.

In marked contrast to the University of Wisconsin, Biochemistry was hardly visible at Stanford in 1945, consisting of only two professors in the chemistry department. The war project at Stanford was essentially completed, and I accepted an offer of an Assistant Professorship at the University of Minnesota, which had a good biochemistry department. But my local War Draft Board in Provo, Utah, had other plans and I became a member of the U.S. Navy. The Navy did not know what to do with me, the war with Japan was nearly over, and I became what is likely the only seaman second-class that has had a nearly private laboratory at the Navy Medical Research Institute in Bethesda, Maryland. In less than a year I returned to civilian life. In the spring of 1946 I, my wife, and now two daughters, Gail and Hali, became Minnesotans. But I had unknowingly acquired a latent California virus to be expressed years later.

Minnesota has generally competent and honest public officials, good support of the schools and cultural amenities, and an excellent state university. It was a fine place to rear a family, and soon our third child, Douglas, was born. A golden era for biochemistry was just starting. The NIH and NSF research grants were expanding at a rate equal to, or even ahead, of the growing number of meritorious applications. The G.I. bill provided financial support that brought excellent and mature graduate students to campus. New insights into metabolism, enzyme action, and protein structure and function were being rapidly acquired.

Housing was almost unavailable in the post war years. Initially we coped with an isolated, rat-infested farm house. In 1950, after my academic competence seemed satisfactorily established, we built a home not far from the St. Paul campus where the Department of Biochemistry was located. I served as contractor, plumber, electrician, finish carpenter etc. My warm memories of this home include looking at a sparkling, snow-covered landscape, while seated at the desk in the bedroom corner that served as my study, and struggling with the interpretation of some puzzling isotope exchanges accompanying an enzyme catalysis. The understanding that developed was rewarding and perhaps one of my best intellectual efforts. However, it did not seem that the approach would give answers to major problems.

During my early years at Minnesota I conducted an evening enzyme seminar. One participant in our lively discussions was a promising graduate student from another department, Bo Malmstrom, who became a renowned scientist in his field, and is now a retired professor from the University of Göteborg. In 1952 my family spent a memorable summer at the Woods Hole Marine Biological Laboratories on Cape Cod. A sabbatical period on a Guggenheim Fellowship in Sweden in 1955 was especially rewarding. There I did research at both the Wenner-Gren Institute of the University of Stockholm with Olov Lindberg and Lars Ernster, and at the Nobel Medical Institute, working with Hugo Theorell's group. Professor Theorell received a Nobel Prize that year, exposing us to the splendor and formality of the Nobel festivities.

Along the way, I was gratified to receive the Award in Enzyme Chemistry of the American Chemical Society in 1955. In 1959–60 I served as Chairman of the Biochemistry Section of the American Chemical Society. In 1956 I accepted a Hill Foundation Professorship and moved to the medical school campus of the University of Minnesota in Minneapolis. Much of my group's research was on enzymes other than the ATP synthase. But solving how oxidative phosphorylation occurred remained one the most challenging problems of biochemistry, and I could not resist its siren call. Mildred Cohn reported that mitochondria doing oxidative phosphorylation catalyzed an exchange of the phosphate and water oxygens, an intriguing capacity. An able physicist and a pioneer in mass spectrometry, Alfred Nier, made gaseous ^{18}O and facilities available to me, and some experiments were run using this heavy isotope of oxygen. However, much of our effort over several years was directed toward attempting to detect a possible phosphorylated intermediate in ATP (adenosine triphosphate) synthesis using ^{32}P as a probe. The combined efforts of some excellent graduate students and postdocs, most of whom went on to rewarding academic careers, culminated in the discovery of a new type of phosphorylated protein, a catalytic intermediate in ATP formation with a phosphoryl group attached to a histidine residue.

By then, time and queries had stimulated the latent California virus. Change was underway. In the summer of 1963, I and a group of graduate students and postdocs who came with me, activated laboratories in the new wing of the chemistry building at the University of California in Los Angeles (UCLA), located on a beautiful campus at the foot of the Santa Monica mountains. We soon found that the enzyme-bound phosphohistidine we had discovered was an intermediate in the substrate level phosphorylation of the citric acid cycle. It was not a key to oxidative phosphorylation. The experience reminds me of a favorite saying: Most of the yield from research efforts comes from the coal that is mined while looking for diamonds.

In 1965 I accepted the Directorship of a newly created Molecular Biology Institute (MBI) at UCLA, in part because of my disappointment that oxidative phosphorylation had resisted our efforts. A building that was promised failed to materialize, but through luck and persistence adequate funds were obtained, partly from private resources, and promising faculty were recruited. The objective was to promote basic research on how living cells function at the molecular level. I believe the best research is accomplished by a faculty member with a small group of graduate students and postdocs, who freely design, competently conduct and intensely evaluate experiments. To spend time with such a group I soon found ways to reduce my administrative chores. Probes of oxidative phosphorylation continued, and, as 1971 approached, we hit pay dirt. We recognized the first main postulate of what was to become the binding change mechanism for ATP synthesis, namely that energy input was not used primarily to form the ATP molecule, but to promote the release of an already formed and tightly bound ATP

In the following decade, the other two main concepts of the mechanism were revealed, namely that the three catalytic sites participate sequentially and cooperatively, and that our, and other, data could be best explained by what was termed a rotational catalysis. These previously unrecognized concepts in enzymology provided motivation and excitement within my research group. Richard Cross, a postdoctoral fellow trained with Jui Wang at Yale, capably probed tightly bound ATP. Jan Rosing, a gifted experimentalist from Bill Slater's group in Amsterdam, and Celik Kayalar, an intelligent, innovative graduate student from Turkey, formed a productive pair that unveiled essential facets of cooperative catalysis. David Hackney, a postdoc from Dan Koshland's stable of budding scientists at Berkeley, was an intellectual leader in our ^{18}O experimentation that led to rotational catalysis. Dan Smith, Michael Gresser, Linda Smith, and Chana Vinkler (from Israel) as postdocs, and Lee Hutton, Gary Rosen and Glenda Choate as graduate students, established the participation of bound intermediates in rapid mixing and quenching experiments, and conducted ^{18}O exchange experiments that clarified and supported our mechanistic postulates.

In ensuing years, other aspects of the complex ATP synthase were explored that solidified our feeling that the binding change mechanism was likely valid and general, and promoted its acceptance in the field. I will resist telling you here about the number, properties, and function of the six nucleotide binding sites, of the probes that agreed with rotational catalysis, of the unraveling of the complex Mg^{2+} and ADP inhibition, of the generality of the mechanism and other synthase properties revealed by studies with chloroplasts, *E. coli,* and Kagawa's thermophilic bacterium. It was a pleasure to work on such problems with Teri Melese, a postdoc who excelled in enthusiasm as well as capability, and Zhixiong Xue, an exceptional graduate student that I first met while leading a biochemical delegation to China, with Raj Kandpal a scholarly postdoc from India, with the productive postdocs John Wise (from Alan Senior's lab) and Rick Feldman (from David Sigman's lab), with Janet Wood during her sabbatical, and with June-Mei Zhou and Ziyun Du (on leave from Academia Sinica laboratories in China) as well as Dan Wu, Steven Stroop, and Karen Guerrero as graduate students. Special mention should be made of three excellent Russian researchers, Vladimir Kasho, Yakov Milgrom and Marat Murataliev, from the laboratory of Vladimir Skulachev, a respected leader in bioenergetics. With the latter two I am now writing what will likely be my last paper reporting research results. Other welcome postdocs, visitors, and graduate students at UCLA worked with other problems, including the Na^+,K^+-ATPase that Skou first isolated, and the related Ca^{++} transporting ATPase of the sarcoplasmic reticulum. During these active years it was a pleasure to receive peer recognition in the form of the Rose Award of the American Society for Biochemistry and Molecular Biology, the preeminent society in my field (I served as its President many years earlier).

An unexpected benefit of my career in biochemistry has been travel. The information exchanged and gained at scientific conferences and visits has been tremendously important for progress in my laboratory. My travelophilic wife and I thoroughly enjoyed being guests of the Australian and South African biochemical societies while visiting their countries. Meetings or laboratory visits in Japan, Sweden, France, Germany, Russia, Italy, Wales, Argentina, Iran, and elsewhere gave us a world perspective. Manuscripts that have to be produced, sometimes a bit unwillingly, offer the challenge to present speculation and perspective often not welcome by editors of prestigious journals. It was in a volume from a conference dedicated to one of the giants of the bioenergetics field, Efraim Racker, that the designation "the binding change mechanism" was introduced. Conferences at the University of Wisconsin provided opportunity to publish thoughts about rotational catalysis that had not been enthusiastically endorsed at Gordon Conferences, where information is exchanged without publication. These travels have strong scientific justification. They provided the opportunity for exchange of information, to test new ideas, to gain new perspective, and to avoid unnecessary experiments. The milieu encourages innovation and planning, as well as providing a stimulus and vitality that fosters research progress.

Other events that make up a lifetime continued. Through fortunate circumstances, Lyda and I obtained a building lot at a price that a professor could afford, in the hills north of UCLA, overlooking the city and ocean. The home we built (I was again contractor and miscellaneous laborer) has served as a focal point for family activities, and a temporary residence for grandchildren attending UCLA. The home meant much for my research, as I could readily move between home and lab, and the ambiance created was supportive for study and writing.

The study of life processes has given me a deep appreciation for the marvel of the living cell. The beauty, the design, and the controls honed by years of evolution, and the ability humans have to gain more and more understanding of life, the earth and the universe, are wonderful to contemplate. I firmly believe that our present and future knowledge of all that we are and what surrounds us depends on the tools and approaches of science. I was struck by how well Harold Kroto, one of last year's Nobelists, presented what are some of my views in his biographical sketch. As he stated, "I am a devout atheist–nothing else makes sense to me and I must admit to being bewildered by those, who in the face of what appears to be so obvious, still believe in a mystical creator." I wonder if in the United States we will ever reach the day when the man-made concept of a God will not appear on our money, and for political survival must be invoked by those who seek to represent us in our democracy.

It is disappointing how little the understanding that science provides seems to have permeated into society as a whole. All too common attitudes and approaches seem to have progressed little since the days of Galileo. Religious fundamentalists successfully oppose the teaching of evolution, and by this decry the teaching of critical thinking. We humans have a remarkable ability to blind ourselves to unpleasant facts. This applies not only to mystical and religious beliefs, but also to long-term environmental consequences of our actions. If we fail to teach our children the skills they need to think clearly, they will march behind whatever guru wears the shiniest cloak. Our political processes and a host of human interactions are undermined because many have not learned how to gain a sound understanding of what they encounter.

The major problem facing humanity is that of the survival of our selves and our progeny. In my less optimistic moments, I feel that we will continue to decimate the environment that surrounds us, even though we know of our folly and of what has happened to others. Humans could become quite transient occupants of planet earth. The most important cause of our problem is over population, which nature, as with other species, will deal with severely. I hear the cry from capable environmental leaders and organizations for movement toward sustainable societies. They are calling for sensible approaches to steer us away from impending disaster. But their voices remain largely unheard as those with power, and those misled by religious or nationality concerns, become immersed in unimportant, self-centered and short-range pursuits.

ENERGY, LIFE, AND ATP

Nobel Lecture, December 8, 1997

by

Paul D. Boyer

University of California at Los Angeles, Department of Chemistry and Biochemistry, California 90095-1469, USA

OVERVIEW

I have a deep appreciation for the unusual and unexpected chain of events that has brought me the Nobel Award. It is my good fortune to be a spokesman for a considerable number of outstanding researchers in the field of bioenergetics whose efforts have revealed an unusual and novel mechanism for one of nature's most important enzymes. Over 50 years ago a vital cellular process called oxidative phosphorylation was demonstrated. The process was recognized as the major way that our bodies capture energy from foods to be used for a myriad of essential cellular functions, but how it occurred was largely unknown. The intervening years have seen much progress. Today I will tell you how contributions of my research group in the 1970s led to new hypotheses that helped overcome the limitations of old paradigms, which were no longer applicable. We gained further support of the hypotheses and clarified other aspects of the process in the 1980s and early 1990s. Then as John Walker, my co-recipient will relate, the X-ray structural data from his group became available. The structural information, about the catalytic portion of the enzyme for the phosphorylation, supported the most novel and least accepted aspect of our hypotheses. Now on this occasion, John and I can tell you how a truly remarkable molecular machine accomplishes the oxidative phosphorylation that was left unexplained for over half a century.

A key player in the process is called ATP, the abbreviation for adenosine triphosphate. At the time I was a graduate student, Fritz Lipmann (1) recognized the broad role ATP played in biological energy capture and use. The adenosine portion for our purposes can be regarded as a convenient handle to bind the ATP to enzymes. It is the three phosphate groups attached in a row, particularly the last two, that participate in energy capture. When the energy stored in ATP is used, the terminal anhydride bond is split, forming adenosine diphosphate (ADP) and inorganic phosphate (P_i). The resynthesis of ATP, coupled to energy input, is catalyzed by an enzyme called ATP synthase, present in abundance in intracellular membranes of animal mitochondria, plant chloroplasts, bacteria and other organisms. The ATP made by your ATP synthase is transported out of the mitochondria and used for the function of muscle, brain, nerve, kidney, liver and other tissues, and for transport and for making a host of compounds that the cell needs. The ADP and phosphate formed when ATP is used return to the mitochondria and ATP is made again using the energy from the oxidations. I estimate that the net synthesis of ATP is the most prevalent chemical reaction that occurs in your body. Indeed, because plants and microorganisms capture and use energy by the same reaction, and the amount of biomass is large, the formation and use of ATP is the principal net chemical reaction occurring in the whole world. This is obviously a very important reaction. How does it occur?

All living cells contain hundreds of large, specialized protein molecules called enzymes. These catalyze the hundreds of chemical reactions that are necessary for the cell to function. Among these are the reactions by which energy is captured by the mitochondria, which are packed into muscle, brain and other cells. Inside the mitochondria and imbeded in its membranes are enzymes that catalyze oxidation of the food you eat. They essentially burn it, using oxygen and producing carbon dioxide and water, in a series of small steps, each catalyzed by a special enzyme. The oxygen you are breathing now is carried by the hemoglobin of your red blood cells, then it reaches the mitochondria where it oxidizes iron atoms that are part of a specialized enzyme, which in turn oxidizes other enzymes in a respiratory chain. The blood stream carries the carbon dioxide produced to the lungs for exhaling. The sequence of oxidations liberates protons and promotes a charge that tends to force protons across the membrane. Similarly, in chloroplasts light energy is coupled to the formation of protonmotive force. This protonmotive force, as shown by the 1978 Nobelist Peter Mitchell (2), causes protons (hydrogen ions) to be translocated through the ATP synthase accompanied by formation of ATP. The important and very difficult question that remained unanswered for many years was how the ATP synthase uses the protonmotive force to make ATP.

ATP SYNTHASE

First I will summarize what is now known about the ATP synthase, then convey aspects of how this knowledge was attained. The enzyme uses a novel mechanism that has catalytic steps different from any that had been seen before with other enzymes. A sketch that depicts the enzyme function is available on the Nobel Foundation internet site. A similar sketch was provided in a recent paper from Richard Cross's laboratory (3). The ATP synthase has three copies each of large α and β subunits, with three catalytic sites located mostly on the β subunit at the interface of the α and β subunits. A γ subunit core and smaller δ and ϵ subunits complete a portion known as F_1, with a subunit composition in order of decreasing size designated as $\alpha_3\beta_3\gamma\delta\epsilon$. This portion of the enzyme was first isolated in the laboratory of a splendid investigator, Efraim Racker, and shown to act as an ATPase (4). Several leading investigators in the bioenergetic field were trained in Racker's laboratory.

[1] Abbreviations used for the F_1-ATPase from various sources are: From heart mitochondria MF_1, from chloroplasts CF_1, from *E. coli* EcF_1, from Kagawa's thermophilic bacterium TF_1.

The F_1-ATPase[1] catalyzes ATP hydrolysis but not ATP synthesis. The rest of the enzyme, imbedded in the membrane, is known as F_0; in *E. coli* the F_0 contains a large subunit *a*, two copies of a subunit *b* and probably 12 copies of a much smaller *c* subunit. The F_0 of the mitochondrial enzyme is much more complex. The designation F_1F_0-ATPase is sometimes used in the literature for the complete ATP synthase.

During net ATP synthesis the three catalytic sites on the enzyme, acting in sequence, first bind ADP and phosphate, then undergo a conformational change so as to make a tightly bound ATP, and then change conformation again to release this ATP. These changes are accomplished by a striking rotational catalysis driven by a rotating inner core of the enzyme, which in turn is driven by the protons crossing the mitochondrial membrane. I share the view that revealing the mechanism of the ATP synthase is a fine achievement of modern biochemistry. I am also keenly aware that this achievement comes from the sum of the research of many members of the bioenergetics community, who deserve a major share in the recognition of the accomplishment. But the Nobel awards tend to make heroes of only one or a few of those responsible. It is my good fortune to be addressing you today because my research group, strongly dependent on the information provided by others, gained the first insights into three unusual features of the ATP synthase catalysis. These unusual features are energy-linked binding changes that include release of a tightly bound ATP, sequential conformational changes of three catalytic sites to accomplish these binding changes, and a rotary mechanism that drives the conformational changes. These features had not been recognized previously in enzymology.

EARLY PROBES

In the mid-1950s, some 12 years after receiving my Ph.D., some experiments on how ATP is made were conducted in my laboratory. One concerned the capture of energy in glycolysis. We found that the oxidation of glyceraldehyde 3-phosphate could occur without the participation of inorganic phosphate (5), suggesting participation of an acyl enzyme intermediate. Extension of these experiments, and salient findings in Racker's group (6), demonstrated that a sulfhydryl group on the enzyme was acylated and the acyl enzyme was cleaved by inorganic phosphate to form 1,3-diphosphoglycerate, which in turn transferred a phosphoryl group to ADP to make ATP. The demonstration that two covalent intermediates, the acyl enzyme and the phosphorylated substrate, preceded ATP formation made it seem logical to seek for similar intermediates in oxidative phosphorylation. As we and others learned years later, this was not a useful approach.

Of more relevance to ATP synthase were experiments with ^{18}O and ^{32}P, initiated because of the demonstration by Mildred Cohn that mitochondria would catalyze a rapid exchange of phosphate oxygens with those of water (7). We found from the ^{32}P experiments that the overall reaction of oxidative phosphorylation was dynamically reversible (8). The ^{18}O experiments revealed the striking finding that the exchange of inorganic phosphate oxygens with water was occurring even more rapidly. As illustrated in Fig. 1, we attributed this to the formation of a covalent intermediate, which was then cleaved by inorganic phosphate. We tried unsuccessfully to separate out fractions from mitochondria that would catalyze the first step leading to the formation of an intermediate in oxidative phosphorylation. It was some sixteen years later that we found the simple explanation that no intermediate was formed, and that the rapid ^{18}O exchange resulted from the rapid and reversible formation of a tightly bound ATP.

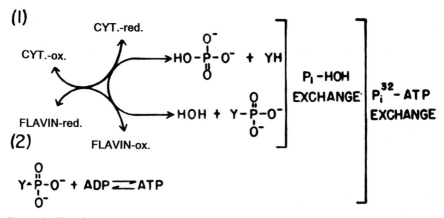

Figure 1. Phosphate oxygen exchange and dynamic reversal of oxidative phosphorylation. Adapted from (7). In this early study covalent intermediates were proposed to explain an oxygen exchange more rapid than the overall reaction reversal.

In the 1960s we embarked on another, only partially successful, series of experiments. By using ^{32}P as a sensitive tracer, we found in mitochondria a ^{32}P-labeled protein that was an intermediate between inorganic phosphate and ATP. We identified this as a previously unrecognized phosphorylated protein, with a phosphoryl group attached to a histidine residue. We mistakenly thought we had identified an intermediate in oxidative phosphorylation, but subsequently found it to be an intermediate in GTP or ATP formation by the succincyl CoA synthetase of the citric acid cycle (9). We were reaching for a gold but got a bronze instead.

^{18}O EXCHANGES AND A NEW CONCEPT

For several years we mostly studied other problems, including taking a look at active transport in *E. coli*. This study gave evidence for an intermediate and unidentified energized state (10), but we did not characterize this state or pay enough attention to the rumblings coming from Peter Mitchell's laboratory. It was difficult for me to accept protonmotive force as a driving agent for ATP formation when I could not visualize a logical way this could occur. But the lure of the ATP synthase continued, and we tried to get leads with photophosphorylation by spinach thylakoid membranes as well as oxidative phos-

189

phorylation by heart mitochondria. The use of the ^{18}O exchange measurements to study the process provided a crucial insight. The types of exchange that can be measured are readily understood with the aid of the diagram in Fig. 2. The box in Fig. 2 represents a catalytic site. ADP and P_i can bind and be converted to a tightly bound ATP. The water formed freely interchanges with medium water. Reversal of this reaction results in the incorporation of one water oxygen into the bound P_i. If the P_i can tumble freely at the catalytic site, when bound ATP is again formed there are three chances out of four that it will contain a water oxygen. Various exchanges of phosphate oxygens with water oxygens are measurable, as shown in Table 1. The oxygen exchanges thus provide sensitive probes of reaction steps that otherwise might be hidden.

The ^{18}O probes revealed a puzzling aspect, namely that the intermediate

Table 1. Exchanges of phosphate oxygens with water oxygens catalyzed by ATP synthase.

Exchange	Measurement
Intermediate $P_i \rightleftarrows HOH$	Hydrolysis of γ-^{18}O-ATP and determination of ^{18}O in P_i formed
Intermediate ATP $\rightleftarrows HOH$	Synthesis of ATP from ^{18}O-P_i and determination of ^{18}O in ATP formed
Medium $P_i \rightleftarrows HOH$	Determination of loss of ^{18}O from ^{18}O-P_i when P_i binds, undergoes exchange, and returns to the reaction medium
Medium ATP $\rightleftarrows HOH$	Determination of loss of ^{18}O from γ-^{18}O-ATP when ATP binds, undergoes exchange, and returns to the reaction medium

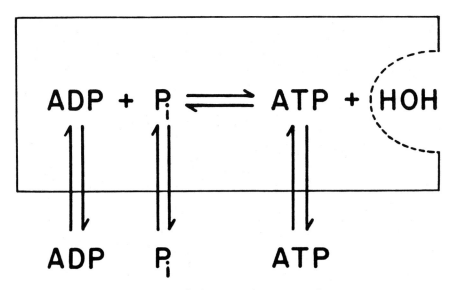

Figure 2. Binding, interconversion, and release steps for oxygen exchanges.

190

$P_i \rightleftarrows$ HOH was unusually insensitive to uncouplers of oxidative phosphorylation. As shown in Fig. 3, even though the potent uncoupler called S-13 allowed oxidation to proceed without net ATP synthesis, the rapid exchange of phosphate and water oxygens continued. The significance of this was not grasped for some time. But one day, while listening to a seminar that I did not understand, the oxygen exchange data churned in my mind. It became clear to me that the results could be explained if the energy from oxidations was not used to *make* the ATP molecule, but instead was used to bring about a *release* of a tightly bound ATP. The reversible formation of the tightly bound ATP molecule could continue at the catalytic site without involving protonmotive force, and give rise to the uncoupler-insensitive oxygen exchange. We now had a new concept for oxidative phosphorylation and were anxious to call it to the attention of the field. The editors of the *Journal of Biological Chemistry* declined the opportunity to publish this new concept. I used the privilege of my recent membership in the National Academy of Sciences (11, Fig.4) to publish this first feature of what was to become the binding change mechanism of ATP synthesis. Independently, Slater's group, based on the presence of tightly bound nucleotides on the isolated F_1-ATPases, also suggested that energy input might be involved in their release (12).

Our feeling that the new concept was valid was strengthened by companion studies with the ATPase activity of muscle myosin. Data from my and from

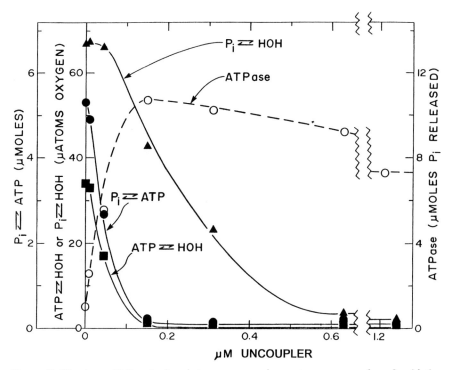

Figure 3. The insensitivity of phosphate oxygen exchange to an uncoupler of oxidative phosphorylation as compared to other measured reactions. Various uncouplers gave similar results; in this experiment an uncoupler known as "S-13" was used.

191

Koshland's laboratories (13, 14) had shown that myosin could catalyze both a medium $P_i \rightleftharpoons HOH$ and an intermediate $P_i \rightleftharpoons HOH$ exchange. It seemed possible that myosin might be able to spontaneously form a tightly bound ATP from medium ADP and P_i. Experiments showed this to be the case (15). This and other salient properties of myosin had also been revealed in contemporary studies by Trentham and associates (16, 17). Importantly, the oxygen exchange could be quantitatively accounted for by the rate of formation and cleavage of the bound ATP.

Not all bioenergeticists readily accepted the concept that a prime function of energy input was to bring about the release of a tightly bound ATP. For example, Mitchell preferred a mechanism in which the protons migrated to the catalytic site and induced the formation of ATP from ADP and P_i. It seemed logical to me that proton translocation was linked to ATP release indirectly through protein conformational changes (18). Without my being informed, my publication was accompanied by a rebuttal from Mitchell (19), and I thus presented a more complete model for conformational coupling (20). With time this indirect manner in which proton translocation drives ATP formation has become generally accepted, but this does not detract from Mitchell's salient recognition of protonmotive force as a means of capturing energy for ATP synthesis and active transport.

Reprinted from
Proc. Nat. Acad. Sci. USA
Vol. 70, No. 10, pp. 2837-2839, October 1973

A New Concept for Energy Coupling in Oxidative Phosphorylation Based on a Molecular Explanation of the Oxygen Exchange Reactions

(protein conformational change/uncouplers/mitochondria)

PAUL D. BOYER, RICHARD L. CROSS, AND WILLIAM MOMSEN

The Molecular Biology Institute and The Department of Chemistry, University of California, Los Angeles, Calif. 90024

Contributed by Paul D. Boyer, June 25, 1973

ABSTRACT   The $P_i \rightleftharpoons HOH$ exchange reaction of oxidative phosphorylation is considerably less sensitive to uncouplers than the $P_i \rightleftharpoons ATP$ and $ATP \rightleftharpoons HOH$ exchanges. The uncoupler-insensitive $P_i \rightleftharpoons HOH$ exchange is inhibited by oligomycin. These results and other considerations suggest that the relatively rapid and uncoupler-insensitive $P_i \rightleftharpoons HOH$ exchange results from a rapid, reversible hydrolysis of a tightly but noncovalently bound ATP at a catalytic site for oxidative phosphorylation, concomitant with interchange of medium and bound P_i. Such tightly bound ATP has been demonstrated in submitochondrial particles in the presence of uncouplers, P_i, and ADP, by rapid labeling from $^{32}P_i$ under essentially steady-state phosphorylation conditions. These results lead to the working hypothesis that in oxidative phosphorylation energy from electron transport causes release of preformed ATP from the catalytic site. This release could logically involve energy-requiring protein conformational change.

The beginning of the binding change mechanism.

Figure 4. From the publication presenting a new concept for oxidative phosphorylation (11).

CATALYTIC COOPERATIVITY

We were now launched on an exciting period of research. As we probed mitochondrial oxidative phosphorylation further by ^{32}P and ^{18}O isotope exchanges, some puzzling aspects emerged. For example, when submitochondrial particles capable of oxidative phosphorylation were hydrolyzing ATP, a lively medium ATP $\rightleftarrows$ HOH exchange occurred. Removal of product ADP stopped this exchange (Fig. 5), although the reversal of ATP hydrolysis was still occurring on the enzyme. Somehow the lack of medium ADP to bind to the enzyme was stopping the release of ATP. It was not apparent how this could occur if the simple scheme of Fig. 2 was used to explain the oxygen exchanges. Similarly, during net synthesis of ATP, removal of the medium ATP stopped the medium $P_i \rightleftarrows$ HOH exchange. An explanation for why these oxygen exchanges were blocked, and for other related observations, was suggested by one of my graduate students, Celik Kayalar from Turkey. Celik said he could account for these results if the catalytic sites had to work cooperatively, so that ATP could not be released from one site unless ADP and P_i were available to bind at another site, or that P_i could not be released from one catalytic site unless ATP were available to bind at another catalytic site. Celik, together with Jan Rosing from Holland, demonstrated and characterized sequential and cooperative participation of catalytic sites with the synthase in submitochondrial particles capable of or during oxidative phosphorylation (21, 22). In addition, their results gave evidence that the binding changes accompanying proton translocation also promoted the tight binding of P_i.

Adolfsen and Moudrianakis suggested that site-site cooperativity might occur with the separated F_1-ATPase, based on the observation that a tightly

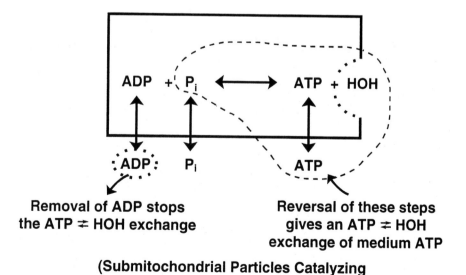

Removal of ADP stops   **Reversal of these steps**
the ATP $\rightleftarrows$ HOH exchange   **gives an ATP $\rightleftarrows$ HOH**
exchange of medium ATP

(Submitochondrial Particles Catalyzing
Synthesis and Hydrolysis of ATP)

Figure 5. Removal of medium ADP stops the medium ATP $\rightleftarrows$ HOH exchange.

bound ADP was released when ATP was cleaved by a bacterial F_1-ATPase (23). Experiments in my laboratory revealed that, as we had found with the ATP synthase, a strong cooperativity of catalytic sites occurs with the isolated ATPase. When the MF_1 hydrolyzes relatively high concentrations of ATP, the P_i formed contains only slightly more than the one water oxygen required for the hydrolysis (Fig. 6). But as the ATP concentration is lowered, an instructive change occurs. The hydrolysis velocity is of course lowered, but the number of water oxygens appearing in each P_i formed increases to almost four. It can be calculated that nearly 400 reversals of bound ATP hydrolysis occur before the P_i formed is released (10). The bound ADP and P_i formed can not be released until ATP is available to bind at another catalytic site[2].

Experiments had now made it seem likely that an unexpected catalytic cooperativity was a prominent feature of the ATP synthase. At that time the prevailing view was that the enzyme had only two catalytic sites, and a diagram depicting a bi-site mechanism appeared in my 1977 review article in the

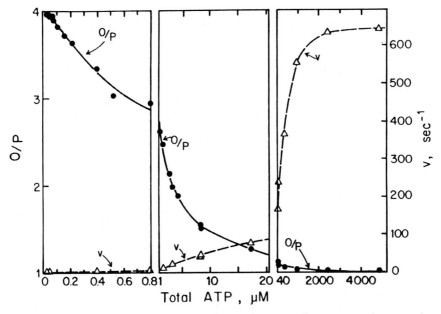

Figure 6. Effect of decrease in ATP concentration on the extent of water oxygen incorporation each phosphate released and on net hydrolysis velocity as catalyzed by the MF1-ATPase. Adapted from (10).

[2] We missed obtaining this striking result about a decade earlier. At that time Efraim Racker came to my laboratory with some F_1 ATPase so we could find if it catalyzed an oxygen exchange when ATP was hydrolyzed. We conducted the reaction at a relatively high ATP concentration, and found the incorporation of only one water oxygen, as required for the cleavage reaction. Harvey Penefksy made a similar observation (24). If we had measured what happened as the ATP concentration was lowered, we would have revealed the catalytic site cooperativity then. But we had no reason to suspect that the enzyme catalysis for each substrate cleaved would change so dramatically with substrate concentration. The strong catalytic cooperativity that we later demonstrated had not been described previously for any other enzyme.

Annual Review of Biochemistry (25). We recognized, however, that if the enzyme were found to have three catalytic sites, a tri-site mechanism, as currently known to occur, would be likely (22, 26). The crucial point was that a tightly bound ATP could not be released until ADP and P_i bound at a second or a second and third catalytic site and the binding changes driven by proton translocation occur. This positive cooperativity meant that at low substrate concentrations, during either net synthesis or hydrolysis of ATP, a tightly bound ATP should still be present at a catalytic site. We undertook experiments to find if this was so. These tests were made with submitochondrial particles (27) or chloroplast thylakoids (28) so that net ATP formation was occurring with ADP concentrations far below the apparent K_m of ADP for maximal phosphorylation rates. About one tightly bound ATP committed to net ATP formation was found on each synthase. Such data give good evidence that strong positive catalytic cooperativity takes place under conditions where ATP synthesis is actually occurring. Additional findings from our and from other laboratories consistent with or favoring the catalytic cooperativity are summarized elsewhere (29).

In 1982, Feldman and Sigman demonstrated that the CF_1-ATPase or the ATP synthase on chloroplast thylakoids, which have a tightly bound catalytic-site ADP, would slowly form an equilibrium concentration of bound ATP from relatively high concentrations of medium P_i (30, 31). Their characterization of this single site catalysis supported our concept of tight ATP formation without coupling to protonmotive force. Factors that promote formation of ATP at catalytic sites of myosin and F_1-ATPases likely include the very tight preferential binding of ATP and, as suggested by deMeis (32), low water activity.

Also in 1982, the acceptance of catalytic cooperativity by the field was considerably enhanced by the determination in Penefsky's laboratory of the rate constants for the interconversion, binding, and release steps for MF_1 exposed to ATP at molar concentrations less than the molarity of the enzyme, conditions that gave what was termed uni-site catalysis (33, 34). An additional important contribution from the same laboratory was the demonstration that the hydrolysis of a trinitrophenyl ATP bound at a single catalytic site was markedly increased by the binding of a second trinitrophenyl-ATP (35).

A number researchers subsequently found a slow uni-site catalysis with different F_1-ATPases. However, an inability to see a definite uni-site catalysis with TF_1 raised the question as to whether the cooperativity we had observed was a general phenomenon of F_1-ATPases (36). That slow uni-site catalysis was indeed occurring was demonstrated by the increase in intermediate $P_i \rightleftarrows HOH$ exchange as ATP concentration was lowered (37). For a number of years there appeared to be a general acceptance that a slow uni-site rate occurs and that the catalytic rate is markedly accelerated when ATP binds to additional sites. It was thus somewhat surprising when a quite recent claim appeared that MF_1 depleted of bound nucleotides did not show a slow uni-site catalysis (38). However, this claim is not experimentally sound; slow uni-site catalysis occurs with either native or nucleotide depleted MF_1 (39, 40).

RELATED EXPERIMENTS

My laboratory group at this time also had an experimental interest in the Na⁺K⁺-ATPase that Prof. Skou has presented. There was uncertainty whether the phosphoryl group that became attached to the enzyme as an intermediate in the catalysis was on a glutamyl or an aspartyl residue. We developed a borohydride reduction method that established that the group was attached to an aspartyl residue (41, 42). We also discovered that the enzyme in the presence of K⁺ and Mg^{2+} catalyzed a rapid exchange of oxygens of P_i with water oxygens, attributable to a dynamic reversal of enzyme phosphorylation (43). This was and remains (44) a useful way to probe this step of the reaction sequence. The related Ca⁺⁺-activated sarcoplasmic reticulum ATPase was likewise found to catalyze a rapid $P_i \rightleftarrows$ HOH exchange (45).

Our attention was also directed toward the capacity of yeast pyrophosphatase to catalyze a $P_i \rightleftarrows$ HOH exchange (46). We revealed that this exchange was due to a reversible formation of an enzyme-bound pyrophosphate (47) and the details of the exchange process were elucidated (48, 47). It was important to us that rapid mixing experiments showed that the rate of formation and cleavage of the bound pyrophosphate accounted for the oxygen exchange (47). As mentioned above, this was shown previously for the bound ATP and oxygen exchange catalyzed by myosin. For the pyrophosphatase exchange, Hackney developed a theoretical analysis of the distribution of ^{18}O-labeled species of P_i (49) that was to serve us well in studies we had underway on oxidative phosphorylation. The $P_i \rightleftarrows$ HOH exchange catalyzed by the sarcoplasmic reticulum ATPase was also shown by rapid mixing and quenching experiments to result from the dynamic reversal of the formation of the phosphorylated enzyme intermediate (50). Such results, and the demonstration by Wimmer and Rose that the ATP $\rightleftarrows$ HOH exchange catalyzed by mitochondria resulted from the reversible cleavage of the terminal P-O-P bond (51), gave us confidence that in oxidative phosphorylation and photophosphorylation the oxygen exchanges we observed were due to the reversible hydrolysis of tightly bound ATP.

THE NUMBER OF CATALYTIC SITES

Meanwhile studies in other laboratories were revealing the subunit stoichiometry of the F_1-ATPase. As noted in a review by Penefsky covering literature up through 1978 (24), considerable controversy remained. The difficulty of obtaining satisfactory molecular weights and subunit quantitation made it hard to get a clear choice between the presence of two or three copies of the major α and β subunits. Reports that measurements with EcF_1 and TF_1 isolated from bacteria grown on [¹⁴C]-amino acids (52, 53) favored a stoichiometry of $\alpha_3\beta_3\gamma_1$ seemed convincing to us. Reports on the composition of CF_1 strongly supported presence of three each of the large subunits (54). On the basis of these and other developments, the field soon widely accepted the composition of F_1-ATPases as $\alpha_3\beta_3\gamma\delta\epsilon$. All of our further experiments have been based on such a stoichiometry of subunits.

The number of nucleotide binding sites on the enzyme remained controversial until about a decade ago. Both α and β subunits were shown to have nucleotide binding sites. Reports in 1982 for MF_1 (55) and in 1983 for EcF_1 (56) gave good evidence for the presently accepted values of six potential nucleotide binding sites per enzyme. However, as late as 1987 claims were still made for only three nucleotide binding sites on CF_1 (57) and four for the liver F_1 (58). Subsequent data for CF_1 (59, 60) and the liver enzyme (61), as well as the highly conserved sequence of the β subunits, support the present view that all F_1-ATPases have six nucleotide binding sites, although differing considerably in affinity.

Chemical derivatization studies, such as those in Bragg's laboratory (62) and summarized in reviews (63, 29) showed that all three β subunits, although with identical amino acid sequence, had distinctly different chemical properties. Such heterogeneity was a prominent reason why we considered it likely that all three β subunits passed through different conformations during catalysis. The participation of all three β subunits in a cooperative, sequential manner was supported, but not proven, by observations (over twenty are given in an earlier review (29)) that derivatization of only one site per enzyme would nearly or completely block catalysis. We were also impressed by studies in Futai's laboratory showing that one defective mutant β subunit stopped catalysis (64), and by related mutational studies in Senior's laboratory (65) that favored the participation of three equivalent β subunits for catalysis.

There has, however, been considerable delay in reaching a general acceptance that three catalytic sites participate in an equivalent manner. A single catalytic and two regulatory sites have been proposed (66, 67). Various models with only two catalytic sites have been suggested (68, 69, 70, 71, 72, 73), as well as a 1991 model with four functioning catalytic sites arranged in two alternate pairs (74, 75). A 1989 review by Tiedge and Schafer (76) stresses symmetrical considerations and favors equivalent β subunit participation. Various models, and a 1991 review favoring a two-site model (77), were appraised in a review prepared in 1992, in which I attempted to consider any experiments not in harmony with the binding change mechanism (29). The conclusion I reached is that very likely three sites participate in an equivalent manner. Subsequent events (see 78) have strengthened this conclusion, although some doubts of which I am not aware may remain. The probability that three sites participate equivalently has guided experiments in my laboratory since the presence of three β subunits first seemed likely.

ROTATIONAL CATALYSIS

Toward the end of the 1970s, we initiated experiments that led to the postulation of the third feature of the binding change mechanism. The presence of three copies of the major α and β subunits and single copies of the γ, δ, and ε made it unlikely that all three β subunits could have identical interactions with single copy subunits. In particular, interactions with the larger γ subunits seemed likely to be crucial. McCarty's laboratory had reported that, with chloroplasts, light increased the reactivity of -SH groups on the subunit and that modifications in the γ subunit increased the leakage of protons across the coupling membrane (79, 80). This and other evidence suggested that the γ subunit interacted strongly with the catalytic β subunit. The growing information about the synthase gave a base for the interpretation of additional experiments with ^{18}O that were underway in my laboratory.

Water highly labeled with ^{18}O had became more available, and by nuclear magnetic resonance, as demonstrated by Cohn (81), or mass spectrometry we could measure what we designated as the ^{18}O isotopomers of P_i, containing 0, 1, 2, 3, or 4 ^{18}O atoms. Then when ATP synthesis or hydrolysis occurs with highly ^{18}O-labeled substrates, under conditions where appreciable oxygen exchange occurs, the distribution of isotopomers formed can be measured. If all the catalytic sites involved behave identically, the distributions of ^{18}O isotopomers would conform to a statistically predicted pattern. The results observed in a typical experiment for hydrolysis of ^{18}O-ATP by F_1 ATPase are given in Fig. 7 (82). They show that the distribution of isotopomers conforms very closely to that expected for identical behavior of all catalytic sites. The data rule out the possible participation of two types of catalytic sites. As shown by one example in Fig. 7, this would give a markedly different distribution of

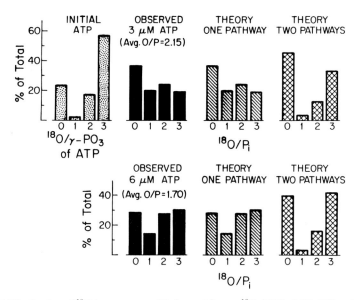

Figure 7. Distribution of ^{18}O-isotopomers of P_i formed from γ-^{18}O-ATP by MF1-ATPase hydrolysis at two relatively low ATP concentrations. The observed average number of water oxygens incorporated (O/P ratio) and distribution of species with 0 to 4 ^{18}O atoms are shown. Also shown is the theoretical distribution for one pathway as expected if the probability for exchange instead of release of bound P_i was 0.73 with 3 µM ATP and 0.55 with 6 µM ATP. This is compared to the expected distributions if two pathways were operative, one with a high an one with a low probability of exchange, that would give the observed total amount of oxygen exchange. Adapted from (82).

198

isotopomers. Importantly, experiments with the net ATP synthesis by chloroplast and mitochondrial ATP synthases also showed that all catalytic sites behave identically (83, 84, 85). The tests were sensitive and revealing; if steps of substrate binding, interconversion or release, or their concentration dependencies differed among catalytic sites, this should have been revealed in the ^{18}O experiments.

I was again confronted with unexplained results. Although it might be possible to bring a similar residue or residues on minor subunits into contact with each of the three β subunits, the interactions would not be expected to be identical. The situation might be analogous to the family of serine proteases, where markedly different sequences can appropriately position a serine residue. But the resulting proteases do not conduct their catalyses identically. To me, there seemed only one way that all catalytic sites could proceed sequentially and identically, with modulation by one or more single-copy, minor subunits. This was by a rotational catalysis, in which large catalytic subunits moved rotationally around a smaller asymmetric core. Such consideration, together with what was known about the structure of the enzyme, resulted in the postulate of rotational catalysis, presented at Gordon Research Conferences and elsewhere (86, 87, 88). A sketch of our view as presented at that time is shown in Fig. 8 (88). The internal core was likened to a cam shaft that modulated the conformation of the β subunits. The probability that the core was asymmetric was strengthened when amino acid sequence data became

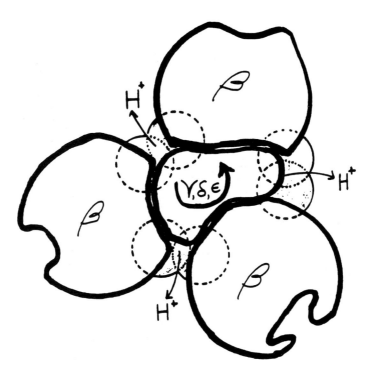

Figure 8. A sketch of possible rotational catalysis as used for 1980 presentations and discussions.

available (89); this gave no indications of possible tripartite symmetry of the minor subunits.

Later other suggestions were made of possible rotational features in the ATP synthase catalysis. Increased information about the structure of the F_0 portion of the synthase made some type of circular motion in the F_0 attractive. Cox *et al.* suggested rotational movement of circularly arranged c subunits (90, 91). Hoppe and Sebald visualized an oligomeric core of c subunits rotating against subunit a or b (92), a suggestion that still seems pertinent. Mitchell proposed a rotational model that exposed catalytic sites to a proton channel through the γ subunit (93).

The homogeneity of catalysis demonstrated by the ^{18}O technique also, to my mind, ruled out postulates, as mentioned earlier, that only two β subunits were involved in catalysis, with the other serving a regulatory function. Considerations of the need for symmetry in subunit interactions made it unlikely that two sites could alternate in catalysis identically. Their interactions on one side could not be identical with those on another side at the same stages of catalysis.

We attempted some assessments of subunit positional interchange as required by a rotational catalysis. The MF_1-ATPase after labeling one β subunit with radioactive DCCD (dicyclohexylcarbodiimide) still retained some activity. A different β subunit reacted with 2-azido-ATP. After catalytic turnover, the reactivity toward DCCD and 2-azido-ATP was randomized, as expected if a change in relative position and conformation had occurred (94). In another approach, we observed that a mild cross-linking of subunits stopped catalysis, and that cleavage of the cross-linker restored activity (95). A report from another laboratory that cross linking of the β and γ subunits did not stop catalysis (96), I regarded as inconclusive (29). None of these experiments were as edifying as those that came later from other laboratories (see below). It seemed apparent that an adequate evaluation of the possibility of rotational catalysis would need to await the knowledge of the 3-dimensional structure of the F_1-ATPase. In a review I prepared in the spring of 1992, I summarized the case for rotational catalysis at that stage (29). This included the need for a second attachment between F_0 and F_1 to act as a stator, and the suggestion that present evidence indicated that the δ subunit of the *E. coli* enzyme, or the analogous OSCP of mitochondria, could help serve this function, a prediction that has found support in recent experiments (97, 98). Attachment of a stator to the exterior of an α subunit might be partly responsible for the asymmetry of the α subunits, an asymmetry that is retained during catalysis (99). This may be analogous to the symmetry of the internal rotation of a motor not being disrupted by bolting the motor to a bench.

The occurrence of a rotational catalysis was dramatically supported by the X-ray structure for the major portion of MF_1, attained by Abrahams, Leslie, Lutter and Walker (100). This structure served as the base for innovative demonstrations of rotation in the laboratories of Cross (2, 101, 102), Capaldi (103, 104, 105), and Kagawa (97). Sabbert et al. demonstrated rotation by sophisticated fluorescent techniques (106, 107), and Noji et al. demonstrated rotation visually (108). Such developments allowed me to title a recent review as "The ATP Synthase–A Splendid Molecular Machine" (78). These more recent aspects of the ATP synthase story are more appropriately the subject of my able co-recipient John Walker's lecture. But before you have the opportunity to hear from him, I want to discuss some additional important and unsettled facets of the ATP synthase catalysis.

SOME ADDITIONAL ASPECTS

Acceptance of the binding change mechanism over the past two decades has been fostered by clarification of a number of unusual aspects of the synthase action, some of which are mentioned here. The number and properties of nucleotide binding sites needed clarification. With the use of the 2-azido-ATP, introduced for studies with F_1-ATPases by Abbot et al. (109), we established where catalytic and noncatalytic sites resided with the F_1-ATPase from different sources (59, 110, 111, 112). The characteristics of the Mg^{2+} and tightly bound ADP inhibition of the F_1-ATPase, that had harassed our, and many other, earlier studies, were established (113, 114). A role for the noncatalytic nucleotides in enabling the inhibition to be overcome was uncovered (115, 116).

A direct estimation of how many catalytic sites were filled during photophosphorylation was accomplished (117). The results gave evidence that near maximal rates of ATP synthesis were attained when a second, and not a second and a third, site were loaded with substrates. The consideration of these results, other earlier data, and recent experiments on site filling in MF_1, have led to refinements in how I consider the binding change mechanism to operate. Salient points from earlier data are that the rate of ATP formation during uni-site catalysis is much slower than the rate of ATP formation when rapid photophosphorylation is occurring, and that during photophosphorylation about one tightly bound ATP per synthase is present. In previous depictions of the mechanism (Fig. 9), after a binding change a site is depicted as having a tightly bound ADP and P_i that is being reversibly converted to tightly bound ATP, while waiting for the next binding change. We now propose that during active net ATP synthesis the interconversion of sites is as depicted in Fig. 10. As a site to which ADP and P_i have added is converted to a tight site, the capacity for the rapid formation of the terminal covalent bond in ATP is also acquired, such that essentially all the bound ADP and P_i are converted to bound ATP. A site with tightly bound ADP and P_i, as in Fig. 9, may not be a compulsory intermediate. The next rapid binding change brings about the release of the ATP to the medium.

All ATP made in oxidative phosphorylation (118) or photophosphorylation (119, 84) contains about 0.4-1.1 water oxygens. This means that some rapid reversal of ATP formation has occurred. Indeed, during net oxidative phosphorylation by mitochondria, rapid reversal of the overall process is demonstrated by ^{32}P measurements (9, 118). Thus it seems likely that the rapid incorporation of some water oxygen results from the reversal of a bind-

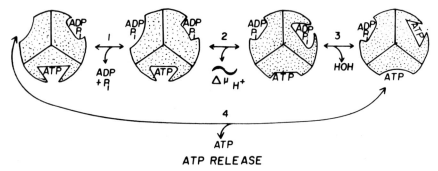

Figure 9. A typical tri-site model for cooperativity including tightly bound ADP and P_i as an intermediate.

ing change step of Fig. 10. When chloroplasts doing net ATP synthesis are separated from medium nucleotides by centrifugation and washing, bound P_i drops off and the catalytic site is left with tightly bound ADP. This is the ADP that in presence of Mg^{2+} results in a strong inhibition of ATPase activity.

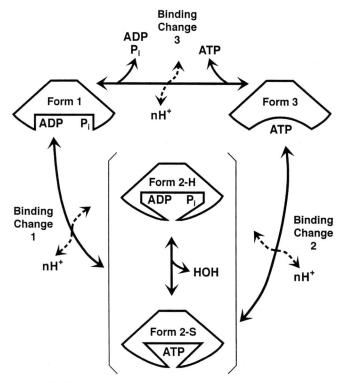

Figure 10. A proposal of how a catalytic site on the ATP synthase is modified by successive binding changes. When ADP + P_i add to Form 1, and adequate protonmotive force is present, both rapid formation and tight binding of ATP arise during Binding Change 1. Most of the site assumes the conformation of Form 2-S, and the ATP becomes loosely bound in Binding Change 2. When ATP adds to Form 3, and no protonmotive force is present, both rapid formation and tight binding of ADP + P_i arise during Binding Change 2. Most of the site assumes the conformation of Form 2-H, and the ADP + P_i become loosely bound during Binding Change 1. Both site occupancy on Forms 1 and 3 and protonmotive force modulate the quasi-equilibrium of Form 2.

202

However, when protonmotive force is applied, such tightly bound ADP is released to the medium without delay in the first binding change (120).

Other recent experiments pertinent to site occupancy during ATP hydrolysis by MF_1 were based on competition between ATP and trinitrophenyl-ATP (TNP-ATP). They revealed that TNP-ATP could bind strongly to a third catalytic site for which ATP which had a K_d in the millimolar concentration range. The near maximal ATPase rate was attained at considerably less than 1 mM ATP (121). This result, and further characterization of the transition from uni-site to multi-site catalysis and initial velocity measurements, are best explained by the filling of only two catalytic sites being necessary for near maximal rates of ATP hydrolysis (40). Interestingly, ADP had a considerably higher affinity than ATP for the third empty site of the MF_1. Our present hypothesis about catalytic site occupancy during rotational catalysis is depicted in Fig. 11. During rapid synthesis one site has a bound ATP and a site to its left (as viewed from above the F_1 portion of the synthase) can preferentially bind ADP and P_i. When adequate protonmotive force is present, rapid ATP synthesis ensues. The filling of a third site with ADP and P_i at higher substrate concentrations results in little rate acceleration. During net ATP hydrolysis, when protonmotive force is weak or absent, the preferential binding of ATP to a site to the right of the tight ATP site can result in a near maximal hydrolysis rate. Filling of the third site at millimolar concentrations of ATP gives little rate acceleration. Nature appears to have designed a way that ATP synthesis occurs with ADP addition to a site that has low affinity for ATP, helping to obviate ATP inhibition of its own synthesis.

The recognition of the principal features of the ATP synthase catalysis

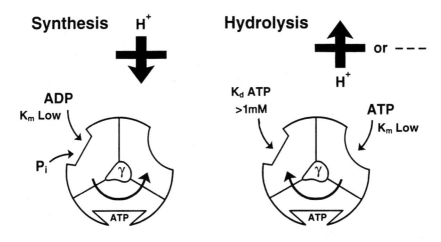

Only Two Sites Need to Be Occupied
for Rapid Synthesis or Hydrolysis

Figure 11. A proposal that near maximum rates of hydrolysis by F_1-ATPase or synthesis by ATP synthase occurs with the filling of only two sites.

creates many opportunities for gaining a better understanding of this remarkable enzyme. I will be an interested spectator in these developments. I believe that societies will, and should continue to, devote some of their resources to basic scientific research, even if the only return is the satisfaction that comes from the knowledge of how living processes occur. An additional justification is that such knowledge underlies past and future gains for attaining a healthy life. As summarized by Ernster (122), the oxygen we use to make ATP is also a toxic substance, resulting in production of harmful free radicals. The mitochondrion is particularly susceptible to such damage, and knowledge of the enzymes involved in energy capture and use may give insight into, and help find how to prevent. unwanted damage.

A final acknowledgment–I am exceptionally fortunate to have been a biochemist over the past decades when so much has been accomplished in my field. Participation in a series of researches that has revealed an unusual rotational catalysis by a vital enzyme has been warmly gratifying. I am indebted to the society that has made this possible, to my wife, Lyda, for her devotion and guidance given freely to help me and our children find our way, and to the universities and government agencies that provided the environment and the financial support for my researches.

REFERENCES

1. Lipmann, F. (1941) *Adv. Enzymol.* **1,** 99–152
2. Mitchell, P. (1979) *Science* **206,** 1148–1159
3. Duncan, T. M., Bulygin, V. V., Zhou, Y., Hutcheon, M. L., and Cross, R. L. (1995) *Proc. Natl. Acad. Sci. U. S. A.* **92,** 10964–10968
4. Penefsky, H. S., Pullman, M. E., Datta, A., and Racker, E. (1960) *J. Biol. Chem.* **235,** 3330–3336
5. Segal, H. L., and Boyer, P. D. (1953) *J. Biol. Chem.* **204,** 265–280
6. Krimsky, I., and Racker, E. (1952) *J. Biol. Chem.* **198,** 721–730
7. Cohn, M. (1953) *J. Biol. Chem.* **201,** 739–744
8. Boyer, P. D., Falcone, A. S., and Harrison, W. H. (1954) *Nature* **174,** 401–404
9. O'Neal, C. C., and Boyer, P. D. (1984) *J. Biol. Chem.* **259,** 5761–5767
10. Klein, W. L., and Boyer, P. D. (1972) *J. Biol. Chem.* **247,** 7257–7265
11. Boyer, P. D., Cross, R. L., and Momsen, W. (1973) *Proc. Natl. Acad. Sci.* **70,** 2837–2839
12. Harris, D. A., Rosing, J., van deStadt, R. J., and Slater, E. C. (1973) *Biochim. Biophys. Acta.* **314,** 149–153
13. Dempsey, M. E., Boyer, P. D., and Benson, E. S. (1963) *J. Biol. Chem.* **238,** 2708–2715
14. Levy, H. M., Sharon, N., Lindemann, E., and Koshland, D. E. (1960) *J. Biol. Chem.* **235,** 2628–2633
15. Wolcott, R. G., and Boyer, P. D. (1975) *J. Supramol. Structure* **3,** 154–161
16. Bagshaw, C. R., Eccleston, J. F., Eckstein, F., Goody, R. S., Gutfreund, H., and Trentham, D. R. (1974) *Biochem. J.* **141,** 351–364
17. Bagshaw, C. R., Trentham, D. R., Wolcott, R. G., and Boyer, P. D. (1975) *Proc. Natl. Acad. Sci. U. S. A.* **72,** 2592–2596
18. Boyer, P. D. (1975) *FEBS Lett.* **50,** 91–94
19. Mitchell, P. (1975) *FEBS Lett.* **50,** 95–97
20. Boyer, P. D. (1975) *FEBS Lett.* **58,** 1–6
21. Rosing, J., Kayalar, C., and Boyer, P. D. (1977) *J. Biol. Chem.* **252,** 2478–2485
22. Kayalar, C., Rosing, J., and Boyer, P. D. (1977) *J. Biol. Chem.* **252,** 2486–2491
23. Adolfsen, R., and Moudrianakis, E. N. (1976) *Arch. Biochem. Biophys.* **172,** 425–433

24. Penefsky, H. S. (1979) *Advances in Enzymol. and Related Areas Mol. Biol.* **49,** 223–280
25. Boyer, P. D. (1977) *Annu. Rev. Biochem.* **46,** 955–966
26. Kayalar, C. (1977) Ph. D. Thesis, University of California, Los Angeles
27. Gresser, M., Cardon, J., Rosen, G., and Boyer, P. D. (1979) *J. Biol. Chem.* **254,** 10649–10653
28. G., Gresser, M., Vinkler, C., and Boyer, P. D. (1979) *J. Biol. Chem.* **254,** 10654–10661
29. Boyer, P. D. (1993) *Biochim. Biophys. Acta* **1140,** 215–250
30. Feldman, R. I., and Sigman, D. S. (1982) *J. Biol. Chem.* **257,** 1676–1683
31. Feldman, R., and Sigman, D. S. (1983) *J. Biol. Chem.* **258,** 12178–12183
32. De Meis, L. (1989) *Biochim. Biophys. Acta* **973,** 333–349
33. Grubmeyer, C., Cross, R., and Penefsky, H. S. (1982) *J. Biol. Chem.* **257,** 12092–12100
34. Cross, R. L., Grubmeyer, C., and Penefsky, H. S. (1982) *J. Biol. Chem.* **257,** 12101–12105
35. Hisabori, T., Muneyuki, E., Odaka, M., Yokoyama, K., Mochizuki, K., and Yoshida, M. (1992) *J. Biol. Chem.* **267,** 4551–4556
36. Yohda, M. K., and Yoshida, M. (1987) *J. Biochem.* **102,** 875–883
37. Kasho, V. N., Yoshida, M., and Boyer, P. D. (1989) *Biochemistry* **28,** 6949–6954
38. Reynafarje, D. B., and Pedersen, P. L. (1996) *J. Biol. Chem.* **271,** 32546–32550
39. Milgrom, Y., and Cross, R. L. (1997) *J. Biol. Chem.* **272,** 32211–32214
40. Milgrom, Y., Murataliev, M. B., and Boyer, P. D. (1998) *Biochem. J.* **330,** 1307–1043
41. Degani, C., and Boyer, P. D. (1973) *J. Biol. Chem.* **248,** 8222–8226
42. Degani, C., Dahms, A. S., and Boyer, P. D. (1974) *Ann. N. Y. Acad. Sci.* **242,** 77–79
43. Boyer, P.D., de Meis, L., Carvalho, M.G.C., and Hackney, D.D. (1977) *Biochemistry* **16,** 136–40
44. Kasho, V. N., Stengelin, M., Smirnova, I. N., and Faller, L. D. (1997) *Biochemistry* **36,** 8045–8052
45. Kanazawa, T., and Boyer, P. D. (1973) *J. Biol. Chem.* **248,** 3163–3172.
46. Cohn, M. (1958) *J. Biol. Chem.* **230,** 369–379
47. Janson, C. A., Degani, C., and Boyer, P. D. (1979) *J. Biol. Chem.* **254,** 3743–3749
48. Hackney, D. D., and Boyer, P. D. (1978) *Proc. Natl. Acad. Sci. U. S. A.* **75,** 3133–3137
49. Hackney, D. D. (1980) *J. Biol. Chem.* **255,** 5320–5328
50. Boyer, P. D., de Meis, L., Carvalho, M. G. C., and Hackney, D. D. (1977) *Biochemistry* **16,** 136–140
51. Wimmer, M. J., and Rose, I. A. (1977) *J. Biol. Chem.* **252,** 6769–6775
52. Bragg, P. D., and Hou, C. (1975) *Arch. Biochem. Biophys.* **167,** 311–321
53. Kagawa, Y., Sone, N., Yoshida, M., Hirata, H., and Okamoto, H. (1976) *J. Biochem.* **80,** 141–151
54. Merchant, S., Shaner, S. L., and Selman, B. R. (1983) *J. Biol. Chem.* **258,** 1026–1031
55. Cross, R. L., and Nalin, C. M. (1982) *J. Biol. Chem.* **257,** 2874–2881
56. Wise, J. G., Duncan, T. M., Latchney, L. R., Cox, D. N., and Senior, A. E. (1983) *Biochem. J.* **215,** 343–350
57. McCarty, R. E., and Hammes, G. G. (1987) *Trends Biochem. Sci.* **12,** 234–237
58. Williams, N., Hullihen, J., and Pedersen, P. L. (1987) *Biochemistry* **26,** 162–169
59. Xue, Z., Zhou, J. M., Melese, T., Cross, R. L., and Boyer, P. D. (1987) *Biochemistry* **26,** 3749–3753
60. Girault, G., Berger, G., Galmiche, J. M., and Andre, F. (1988) *J. Biochem. Chem.* **263,** 14690–14695
61. Guerrero, K. J., and Boyer, P. D. (1988) *Biochem. Biophys. Res. Comm.* **154,** 854–860
62. Bragg, P. D., and Hou, C. (1990) *Biochim. Biophys. Acta* **1015,** 216–222
63. Vignais, P. V., and Lunardi, J. (1985) *Annu. Rev. Biochem.* **54,** 977–1014
64. Noumi, T., Taniai, M., Kanazawa, H., and Futai, M. (1986) *J. Biol. Chem.* **261,** 9196–9201
65. Rao, R., and Senior, A. E. (1987) *J. Biol. Chem.* **262,** 17450–17454
66. Wang, J. H., Joshi, V., and Wu, J. C. (1986) *Biochemistry* **25,** 7996–8001
67. Wang, J. H., Cesana, J., and Wu, J. C. (1987) *Biochemistry* **26,** 5527–5533

68. Di Pietro, A., Penin, F., Godinot, C., Gautheron, D. C. (1980) *Biochemistry* **19,** 5671–5678

69. Bullough, D. A., Verburg, J. G., Yoshida, A., and Allison, W. A. (1987) *J. Biol. Chem.* **262,** 11675–11683

70. Leckband, D., and Hammes, G. G. (1987) *Biochemistry* **26,** 2306–2311

71. Issartel, J. P., Dupuis, A., Junardi, J., and Vignais, P. V. (1991) *Biochemistry* **30,** 4726–4730

72. Ysern, X., Amzel, L. M., and Pedersen, P. L. (1988) *J. Bioenerg. Biomemb.* **29,** 423–450

73. Fromme, P., and Gräber, P. (1989) *FEBS Lett.* **259,** 33–36

74. Shapiro, A. B., and McCarty, R. E. (1991) *J. Biol. Chem.* **266,** 4194–4200

75. Shapiro, A. B., Gibson, K. D., Scheraga, H. A., and McCarty, R. E. (1991) *J. Biol. Chem.* **266,** 17277–17285

76. Tiedge, H., and Schafer, G. (1989) *Biochim. Biophys. Acta* **977,** 1–9

77. Berden, J. A., Hartog, A. F., and Edel, C. M. (1991) *Biochim. Biophys. Acta* **1057,** 151–156

78. Boyer, P. D. (1997) *Annu. Rev. Biochem.* **66,** 717–749

79. McCarty, R. E., and Fagan, J. (1973) *Biochemistry* **12,** 1503–1507

80. Moroney, J. V., and McCarty, R. E. (1979) *J. Biol. Chem.* **254,** 8951–8955

81. Cohn, M., and Hu, A. (1978) *Proc. Natl. Acad. Sci. U. S. A.* **75,** 200–205

82. Hutton, R. L., and Boyer, P. D. (1979) *J. Biol. Chem.* **254,** 9990–9993

83. Hackney, D. D., and Boyer, P. D. (1978) *J. Biol. Chem.* **253,** 3164–3170

84. Hackney, D. D., Rosen, G., and Boyer, P. D. (1979) *Proc. Natl. Acad. Sci. U. S. A.* **76,** 3646–3650

85. Kohlbrenner, W. E., and Boyer, P. D. (1983) *J. Biol. Chem.* **258,** 10881–10886

86. Boyer, P. D., and Kohlbrenner, W. E. (1981) in *Energy Coupling in Photosynthesis* (Selman, B., and Selman-Reiner, S., eds) pp. 231–240, Elsevier/North Holland, New York

87. Gresser, M. J., Myers, J. A., and Boyer, P. D. (1982) *J. Biol. Chem.* **257,** 12030–12038

88. Boyer, P. D. (1983) in *Biochemistry of Metabolic Processes* (Lennon, D. L. F., Stratman, F. W., and Zahlten, R. N., eds) pp. 465–477, Elsevier-Biomed., New York

89. Kanazawa, H., Kayano, T., Mabuchi, K., and Futai, M. (1981) *Biochem. Biophys. Res. Comm.* **103,** 604–612

90. Cox, G. B., Jans, D. A., Fimmel, A. L. A., Gibson, F., and Hatch, L. (1984) *Biochim. Biophys. Acta* **768,** 201–208

91. Cox, G. B., Fimmel, A. L., Gibson, F., and Hatch, L. (1986) *Biochim. Biophys. Acta* **849,** 62–69

92. Hoppe, J., and Sebald, W. (1984) *Biochim. Biophys. Acta* **768,** 1–27

93. Mitchell, P. (1985) *FEBS Lett.* **181,** 1–7

94. Melese, T., and Boyer, P. D. (1985) *J. Biol. Chem.* **260,** 15398–15401

95. Kandpal, R. P., and Boyer, P. D. (1987) *Biochim. Biophys. Acta* **890,** 97–105

96. Musier, K. M., and Hammes, G. G. (1987) *Biochemistry* **26,** 5982–5988

97. Kagawa, W., and Hamamoto, T. (1996) *J. Bioenerg. Biomembr.* **28,** 421–431

98. Ogilvie, I., Aggeler, R., and Capaldi, R. A. (1997) *J. Biol. Chem.* **272,** 19621–19624

99. Kironde, F.A.S., and Cross, R. L. (1977) *J. Biol. Chem.* **262,** 3488–3495

100. Abrahams, J. P., Leslie, A. G. W., Lutter, R., and Walker, J. E. (1994) *Nature* **370,** 621–628

101. Zhou, Y., Duncan, T. M., Bulygin, V. V., Hutcheon, M. L., and Cross, R. L. (1996) *Biochim. Biophys. Acta* **1275,** 96–100

102. Cross, R. L., and Duncan, T. M. (1996) *J. Bioenerg. Biomembr.* **28,** 403–408

103. Aggeler, R., and Capaldi, R. A. (1996) *J. Biol. Chem.* **271,** 13888–13891

104. Tang, C., and Capaldi, R. A. (1996) *J. Biol. Chem.* **271,** 3018–3024

105. Feng, Z., Aggeler, R., Haughton, M., and Capaldi, R. A. (1996) *J. Biol. Chem.* **271,** 17986–17989

106. Sabbert, D., Engelbrecht, S., Junge, W. (1996) *Nature* **381,** 623–625

107. Sabbert, D., Engelbrecht, S., Junge, W. (1997) *Proc. Natl. Acad. Sci. U. S. A.* **94,** 2312–2317

108. Noji, H., Yasuda, R., Yoshida, M., Kinosita, K., Jr. (1997) *Nature* 299–312
109. Abbott, M. S., Czarnecki, J. J., and Selman, B. R. (1984) *J. Biol. Chem.* **259,** 12271–12278
110. Cross, R. L., Cunningham, D., Miller, C. G., Xue, Z., Zhou, J. M., and Boyer, P. D. (1987) *Proc. Natl. Acad. Sci. U. S. A.* **84,** 5715–5719
111. Xue, Z., Miller, C. G., Zhou, J. M., and Boyer, P. D. (1987) *FEBS Lett.* **223,** 391–394
112. Wise, J. G., Hicke, B. J., and Boyer, P. D. (1987) *FEBS Lett.* **223,** 395–401
113. Guerrero, K. J., Xue, Z., and Boyer, P. D. (1990) *J. Biol. Chem.* **265,** 16280–16287
114. Murataliev, M. B., Milgrom, Y. M., and Boyer, P. D (1991) *Biochemistry* **30,** 8305–8310
115. Milgrom, Y. M., Ehler, L. L., and Boyer, P. D. (1991) *J. Biol. Chem.* **266,** 11551–11558
116. Murataliev, M. B., and Boyer, P. D. (1992) *Eur. J. Biochem.* **209,** 681–687
117. Zhou, J. M., and Boyer, P. D. (1993) *J. Biol. Chem.* **268,** 1531–1538
118. Berkich, D. A., Williams, G. D., Masiakos, P. T., Smith, M. B., Boyer, P. D., and LaNoue, K. F. (1991) *J. Biol. Chem.* **266,** 123–129
119. Avron, M., and Sharon, N. (1960) *Biochem. Biophys. Res. Comm.* **2,** 336–339
120. Rosing, J., Smith, D. J., Kayalar, C., and Boyer, P. D. (1976) *Biochem. Biophys. Res. Comm.* **72,** 1–8
121. Murataliev, M. B., and Boyer, P. D. (1994) *J. Biol. Chem.* **269,** 15431–15439
122. Ernster, L. (1986) *Chemica Scripta* **26,** 525–534

John E. Walker.

JOHN E. WALKER

I was born in Halifax, Yorkshire on January 7th, 1941 to Thomas Ernest Walker and Elsie Walker (née Lawton). My father was a stone mason, and a talented amateur pianist and vocalist. I was brought up with my two younger sisters, Judith and Jennifer, in a rural environment overlooking the Calder valley near Elland, and then in Rastrick. I received an academic education at Rastrick Grammar School, specializing in Physical Sciences and Mathematics in the last three years. I was a keen sportsman, and became school captain in soccer and cricket. In 1960, I went to St. Catherine's College, Oxford, and received the B.A. degree in Chemistry in 1964.

In 1965, I began research on peptide antibiotics with E. P. Abraham in the Sir Willian Dunn School of Pathology, Oxford, and was awarded the D. Phil. degree in 1969. During this period, I became aware of the spectacular developments made in Cambridge in the 1950s and early 1960s in Molecular Biology through a series of programmes on BBC television given by John Kendrew, and published in 1966 under the title "The Thread of Life". These programmes made a lasting impression on me, and made me want to know more about the subject. Two books, "Molecular Biology of the Gene" by J. D. Watson, first published in 1965, and William Hayes' "Bacterial Genetics" helped to assuage my appetite for more information. My knowledge of this new field was extended by a series of exciting lectures for graduate students on protein structure given in 1966 by David Phillips, the new Professor of Molecular Biophysics at Oxford. Another series of lectures given by Henry Harris, the Professor of Pathology and published in book form under the title "Nucleus and Cytoplasm", provided more food for thought.

Then followed a period of five years working abroad, from 1969–1971, first at The School of Pharmacy at the University of Wisconsin, and then from 1971–1974 in France, supported by Fellowships from NATO and EMBO, first at the CNRS at Gif-sur-Yvette and then at the Institut Pasteur.

Just before Easter in 1974, I attended a research workshop in Cambridge entitled "Sequence Analysis of Proteins". It was sponsored by EMBO (The European Molecular Biology Organization), and organised by Ieuan Harris from the Medical Research Council's Laboratory of Molecular Biology (LMB) and by Richard Perham from the Cambridge University Department of Biochemistry. At the associated banquet, I found myself sitting next to someone that I had not met previously, who turned out to be Fred Sanger. In the course of our conversation, he asked if I had thought about coming back to work in England. I jumped at the suggestion, and with some trepidation, approached Ieuan Harris about the possibility of my joining his group. After discussions with Fred Sanger, it was agreed that I could come to the Protein and Nucleic Acid Chemistry (PNAC) Division at the LMB for three months from June 1974. More than 23 years later, I am still there.

It goes without saying that this encounter with Fred Sanger and Ieuan Harris transformed my scientific career. In 1974, the LMB was infused throughout its three Divisions with a spirit of enthusiasm and excitement for research in molecular biology led by Max Perutz (the Chairman of the Laboratory), Fred Sanger, Aaron Klug, Francis Crick, Sidney Brenner, Hugh Huxley, John Smith and César Milstein, which was coupled with extraordinary success. For example, along the corridor from my laboratory Fred was inventing his methods for sequencing DNA, immediately across the corridor César Milstein and Georges Köhler were inventing monoclonal antibodies, and elsewhere in the building, Francis Crick and Aaron Klug and their colleagues were revealing the structures of chromatin and transfer RNA. Fred's new DNA sequencing methods were applied first to the related bacteriophages fX174 and G4, and then to DNA from human and bovine mitochondria. I analyzed the sequences of the proteins from G4 and from mitochondria using direct methods. These efforts led to the discovery of triple overlapping genes in G4 where all three DNA phases encode proteins, and to the discovery that subunits I and II of cytochrome c oxidase were encoded in the DNA in mitochondria. Later on, I helped to uncover details of the modified genetic code in mitochondria.

In 1978, I decided to apply protein chemical methods to membrane proteins, since this seemed to be both a challenging and important area. Therefore, in search of a suitable topic, I read the literature extensively. The enzymes of oxidative phosphorylation from the inner membranes of mitochondria were known to be large membrane bound multi-subunit complexes, but despite their importance, they had been studied hardly at all from a structural point of view. Therefore, the same year, I began a structural study of the ATP synthase from bovine heart mitochondria and from eubacteria. These studies resulted eventually in a complete sequence analysis of the complex from several species, and in the atomic resolution structure of the F_1 catalytic domain of the enzyme from bovine mitochondria, giving new insights into how ATP is made in the biological world. Michael Runswick has worked closely with me throughout this period, and has made contributions to all aspects of our studies.

In 1959, I received the A. T. Clay Gold Medal. I was awarded the Johnson Foundation Prize by the University of Pennsylvania in 1994, in 1996, the CIBA Medal and Prize of the Biochemical Society, and The Peter Mitchell Medal of the European Bioenergetics Congress, and in 1997 The Gaetano Quagliariello Prize for Research in Mitochondria by the University of Bari, Italy. In 1995, I was elected a Fellow of the Royal Society. In 1997, I was made a Fellow of Sidney Sussex College, Cambridge and became an Honorary Fellow of St. Catherine's College, Oxford.

I married Christina Westcott in 1963. We have two daughter, Esther, aged 21 and Miriam, aged 19. At present, both of them are university students, studying Geography and English, respectively, at Nottingham-Trent and Leeds Universities.

ATP SYNTHESIS BY ROTARY CATALYSIS

Nobel Lecture, December 8, 1997

by

JOHN E. WALKER

The Medical Research Council Laboratory of Molecular Biology, Hills Road, Cambridge, CB2 2QH, U. K.

Biological energy comes from the sun. Light energy harvested by photosynthesis in chloroplasts and phototropic bacteria, becomes stored in carbohydrates and fats. This stored energy can be released by oxidative metabolism in the form of adenosine triphosphate (ATP), and used as fuel for other biological processes. ATP is a high energy product of both photosynthesis and oxidative metabolism, and in textbooks, it is often referred to as the chemical currency of biological energy.

In the 1960s and early 1970s, the field of oxidative metabolism was dominated by a debate about the nature of the intermediate between NADH (a key product from carbohydrate and fat metabolism) and ATP itself. Many bioenergeticists believed in and sought evidence for a high energy covalent chemical intermediate. The issue was resolved by Peter Mitchell, the Nobel Laureate in Chemistry in 1978. He established that in mitochondria, energy is released from NADH via the electron transport chain and used to generate a chemical potential gradient for protons across the inner membrane of the organelle. He referred to this gradient as the proton motive force (pmf; also designated as $\Delta\mu_{H+}$). It was demonstrated that the pmf is harnessed by the ATP synthesizing enzyme (ATP synthase) to drive the synthesis of ATP from ADP and inorganic phosphate, not only in mitochondria, but also in eubacteria and chloroplasts [1].

Because of Peter Mitchell's efforts, the pmf became established as a key intermediate in biological energy conversion. In addition to being employed in ATP synthesis, it is also used by various membrane bound proteins to drive the transport of sugars, amino acids and other substrates and metabolites across biological membranes. The pmf powers the rotation of flagellae in motile bacteria. In newly born children and in hibernating animals, it is converted directly into heat by uncoupling the mitochondria in brown adipose tissue. Some bacteria that live in saline conditions generate a sodium motive force to act as an equivalent intermediate in their energy conversion processes [2]. The general notion of creating a proton (or sodium) motive force and then using it as a source of energy for other biochemical functions is known as chemiosmosis.

Today, the general outlines of chemiosmosis are well established. It is accepted that during electron transport in mitochondria, redox energy derived from NADH is used by three proton pumping enzymes called complex I

(NADH:ubiquinone oxidoreductase), complex III (ubiquinone:cytochrome c oxidoreductase) and complex IV (cytochrome c oxidase). They act consecutively and produce the pmf by ejecting protons from the matrix (the inside) of the organelle (see Figure 1). Until recently, the workings of these chemiosmotic proton pumps was obscure, but currently our understanding is being transformed by the application of modern methods of molecular biology for the analysis of their structures and functions. For example, two independent atomic resolution structures of cytochrome c oxidase isolated from bovine mitochondria [3, 4] and from the bacterium, *Paracoccus denitrificans* [5, 6], are guiding mutational and spectroscopic experiments that are providing new insights into its mechanism. Partial structures of mitochondrial complex III from two different species [7] will have a similar impact soon on our understanding of that enzmye. Complex I, the third proton pump in mitochondria, is an assembly of at least 43 different polypeptides in mammals, with a combined molecular mass in excess of 900,000 [8]. In addition, it has a non-covalently bound flavin mononucleotide, and at least five iron-sulphur clusters that act as redox centres. A consequence of this extreme complexity is that the structural analysis of complex I is less advanced than those of complexes III and IV, although the general outline of the complex has been established by electron microscopy [9, 10].

THE ATP SYNTHASE

Since 1978, my colleagues and I have concentrated on analyzing the structure of the ATP synthase, another multisubunit complex from mitochondria, where it is found in the inner membrane alongside the three proton pumping enzymes (see Figure 1). Similar complexes are found in chloroplast and eubacterial membranes. Throughout our endeavours, we have been motivated by the expectation that detailed knowledge of its structure would lead to a deeper understanding of how ATP is made. A substantial part of our efforts has been directed at establishing the subunit compositions of the ATP synthesizing enzymes from various sources, and with determining the primary sequences of the subunits [11–31]. These rather extensive analyses helped to show that the overall structure of the ATP synthase, and hence the general principles governing its operation, are very similar in mitochondria, chloroplasts and eubacteria, although the enzymes from the various sources differ in the details of both their sequences and subunit compositions (see Table 1). It is also known that the ATPases from various sources differ in the mechanisms that regulate their catalytic activities [32].

In 1962, the inside surface of the inner membranes of bovine heart mitochondria was found by electron microscopic examination to be lined with mushroom shaped knobs about 100 Å in diameter (Figure 2A) [33]. Later on, similar structures were found to be associated with the thylakoid membranes of chloroplasts (Figure 2B) [34], and with the inner membranes of eubacteria (Figure 2C). At the time of their discovery, the function of these membrane bound knobs was not known, but they were thought to be proba-

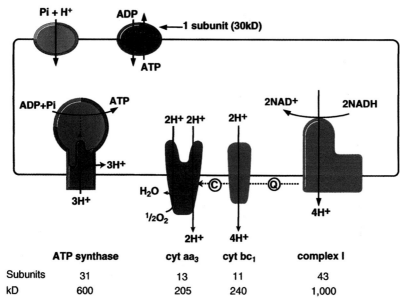

	ATP synthase	cyt aa₃	cyt bc₁	complex I
Subunits	31	13	11	43
kD	600	205	240	1,000

Figure 1. The enzyme complexes of oxidative phophorylation in the inner membranes of mammalian mitochondria. Three proton pumps, complex I, complex III (cytochrome bc₁) and complex IV (cytochrome aa₃) convert redox energy in NADH into the proton motive force (pmf) by ejecting protons from the matrix of the mitochondrion. The ATP synthase uses the energy of the pmf to produce ATP from ADP and phosphate. ADP and phosphate are brought into the mitochondrion by related proetin carriers. External ADP is exchanged for internal ATP, making the newly synthesized ATP available for many biological functions. Dotted lines indicate electron pathways. Q and C are the mobile electron carriers ubiquinone and cytochrome c, respectively.

Table 1. Equivalent subunits in ATP synthases in bacteria, chloroplasts, and bovine mitochondria

Type	Bacteria	Chloroplasts	Mitochondria
F_1	α	α	α
	β	β	β
	γ	γ	γ
	δ	δ	OSCP
	ε	ε	δ
	–	–	ε
F_0	a	a (or x)	a (or ATPase 6)
	b[a]	b and b′ (or I and II)	b
	c	c (or III)	c
Supernumerary	–	–	F_6
	–	–	inhibitor
	–	–	A6L
	–	–	d
	–	–	e
	–	–	f
	–	–	g

[a] ATP synthases in *E. coli* and bacterium PS 3 (both eight-subunit enzymes) have two identical copies of subunit b per complex. Purple non-sulphur bacteria and cyanobacteria appear to have nine different subunits, the extra subunits (known as b′) being a homologue of b. Similarly, chloroplast enzymes are made of nine non-identical subunits, and the chloroplast subunits known as I and II are the homologues of b and b′.

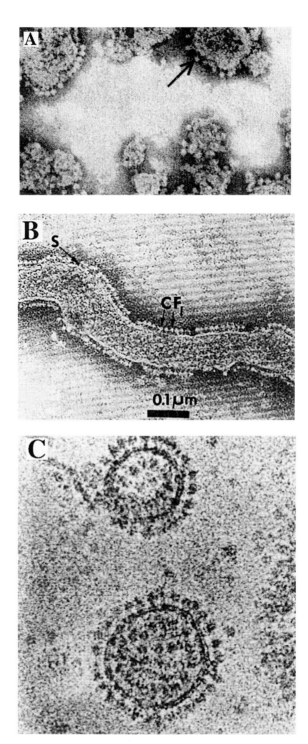

Figure 2. Knobs associated with biological membranes detected by electron microscopy in negative stain. (A), Inside-out vesicles from bovine heart mitochondria; (B), thylakoid membranes form pea chloroplasts; (C), inside-out vesicles from *E. coli*. Different magnifications have been used in parts (A)–(C), and the knobs are all about 100 Å in diameter. Reproduced with permission from references [88, 89].

bly important in biological energy conversion, and hence they were named "the fundamental particles of biology" [35]. In a brilliant series of biochemical reconstitution experiments conducted in the 1960s, Efraim Racker established that they were the ATP synthesizing enzyme complex (for example see references [36–38], and hence that these early micrographs were the first glimpses of its structure.

We now know that the head of the mushroom is a globular protein complex (known as the F_1 domain), where the catalytic sites of the ATP synthase lie. The F_1 part is attached to the membrane sector by a slender stalk about 45 Å long. The hydrophobic membrane domain (known as F_o) transports protons back through the energized membrane into the matrix, somehow releasing energy in this process and making it available to drive ATP synthesis in the catalytic F_1 domain. For some years, it has been accepted that three protons are transported back through the F_o membrane sector for each ATP molecule that is formed in F_1 [1]. However, recent experiments suggest that the chloroplast enzyme transports four protons through the membrane for each ATP that is made [39]. Therefore, it appears that either one or, less likely, both of these values of the H+:ATP ratio are incorrect, or that the mechanisms and structures of the mitochondrial and chloroplast enzymes differ significantly in their F_o domains. This point will be elaborated later in a consideration of the possible structure and mechanism of F_o.

The general model of the mechanism of the ATP synthase that will be developed below is that the F_o membrane domain contains a rotating molecular motor fuelled by the proton motive force. It is proposed that this motor is mechanically coupled to the stalk region of the enzyme, and that the rotation of the stalk affects the catalytic domain and makes the three catalytic sites pass through a cycle of conformational states in which first, substrates are bound and sequestered, then second, ATP is formed from the sequestered substrates, and finally the newly synthesized ATP is released from the enzyme. This cycle of interconversion of the three catalytic sites is part of a binding change mechanism of ATP synthesis developed by Paul Boyer (see Figure 3)

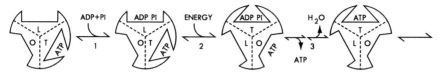

Figure 3. An energy dependent binding change mechanism of ATP synthesis. The catalytic sites in the β-subunits interact and interconvert between three forms: O, open, site with very low affinity for substrates and catalytically inactive; L, loose site, loosely binding substrates and catalytically inactive; T, tight site, tightly binding substrates and catalytically active. The proton induced conformational changes convert a T-site with bound ATP into an open site, releasing the bound nucleotide. Concomitantly, an L-site with loosely bound ADP and phosphate is converted to a T-site where substrates are bound and ATP froms. Fresh substrates bind to an O-site converting it to an L-site, and so on. One third of the catalytic cycle is illustrated. Reproduced with permission from reference [40].

216

[40]. One of its basic tenets is that the energy requiring steps in this cycle of ATP synthesis are in the binding of substrates and in the release of products. This mechanism also implies that the ATP synthase must be an asymmetrical structure, and structural asymmetry is also implicit in the molar ratios of the subunits of F_1-ATPase. Indeed, it is now clear from the asymmetrical features that are inherent in the enzyme's structure that there can be no structurally symmetrical states in the catalytic cycle.

THE STRUCTURE OF F_1-ATPase

An important practical point about the ATP synthase complex that has influenced the strategy for analyzing its structure is that, as Racker had shown in the 1960s, the globular catalytic domain F_1-ATPase can be detached from the membrane domain and studied separately in aqueous solution. Subsequently, Alan Senior and Harvey Penefsky purified the bovine F_1 complex [41, 42] and Penefsky demonstrated that it is an assembly of five different kinds of polypeptides, which he called α, β, γ, δ and ε [42]. Eventually, it was accepted that they were assembled in the complex in the molar ratios $3\alpha{:}3\beta{:}1\gamma{:}1\delta{:}1\varepsilon$. Hence, each F_1 particle is an assembly of nine polypeptides, and in the bovine heart enzyme, their combined molecular mass is about 371,000 (see Table 2).

Table 2. The subunits of bovine F_1-ATPase

Subunit	MWt	Function
α	55,247	Nucleotide binding
β	51,705	Nucleotides, catalysis
γ	30,141	Link to F_o
δ	15,065	Stalk
ε	5,632	Stalk
$\alpha3\beta3\gamma1\delta1\varepsilon1$	371,694	

Both α- and β-subunits bind nucleotides, and we now know that the catalytic nucleotide binding sites lie almost entirely within the β-subunits (see Figure 4). The nucleotides bound to α-subunits remain associated during the catalytic cycle and do not participate directly in ATP synthesis. What they are doing remains mysterious, although both structural and regulatory functions have been suggested.

In 1981, we found that the sequences of the α- and β-subunits were related weakly through most of their length [12, 13], and Matti Saraste and I wondered which regions of the sequences were contributing to the nucleotide binding sites. By examination of the known primary and atomic structures of adenylate kinase [43], and of the sequence of myosin from *Caenorhabditis elegans* (at the time unpublished information, made available to me by Jonathan Karn), we were able to propose that two short degenerate sequence motifs common to adenylate kinase, myosin and the α- and β-subunits, of F_1-ATPase were involved in helping to form their nucleotide binding pockets [44].

This proposal has had far greater consequences than we ever imagined at the time of its publication in 1982. Over the years, one of the two motifs (see

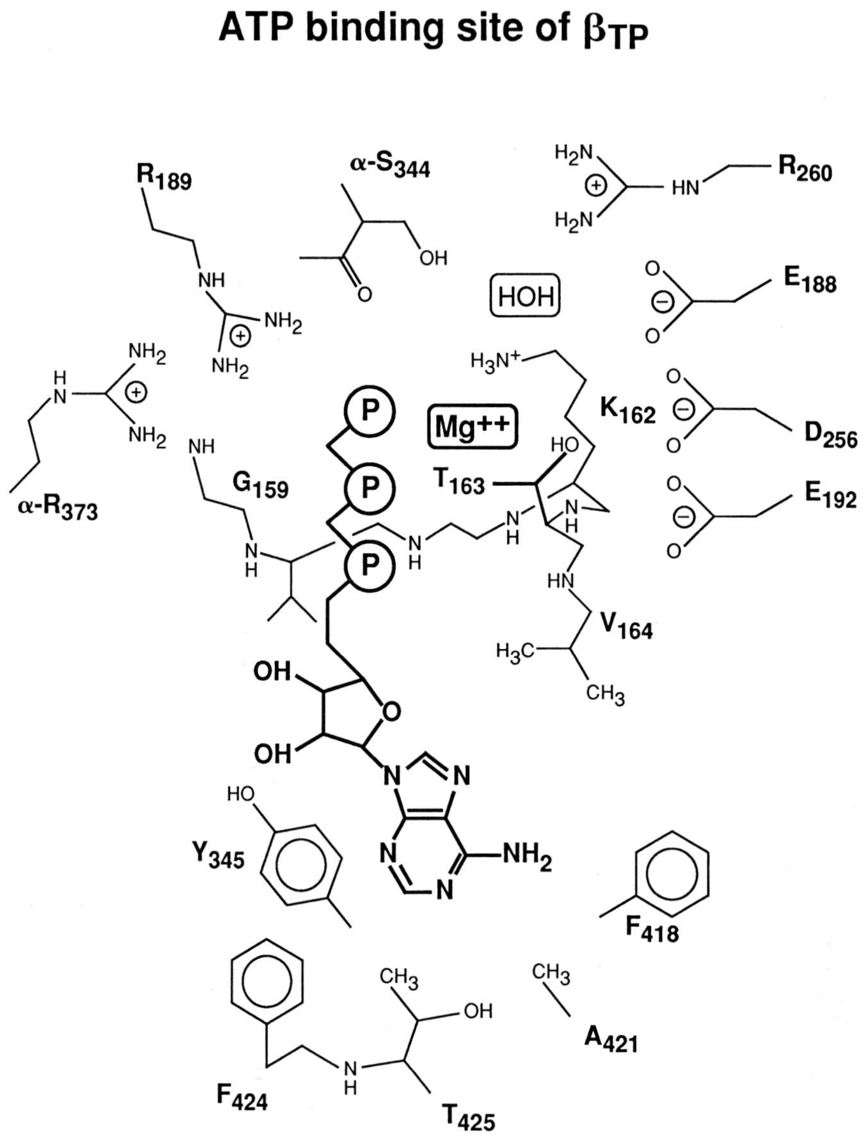

ATP binding site of βTP

Figure 4. The nucleotide binding site in the bTP-subunit of bovine F_1-ATPase. Except for αTP-Arg373 and the main chain carbonyl and the side-chain of αTP-Ser344, all of the amino acids are in bTP. Residues 159–164 are part of the P-loop sequence. The ordered water molecule is poised for nucleophilic attack on the terminal phosphate and is activated by Glu188. As an incipient negative charge develops on the terminal phosphate in a penta-coordinate transition state of ATP hydrolysis, it will be stabilized by the guanidinium of α-Arg 373. Reproduced with permission from reference [50].

Figure 5) has become established as a reliable indicator of the presence of purine nucleotide binding sites in proteins of known sequence, but of unknown biochemical function. One spectacular demonstration of its predictive value has been in the identification of members of the widely dispersed family of ABC (adenosine binding cassette) transport proteins [45], which includes the cystic fibrosis protein and multi-drug resistance proteins. Another early success was its help in the identification of the oncogene protein p21 as a GTPase [46]. The atomic structure of F_1-ATPase described below, has shown that, as in other proteins, the two sequence motifs describe amino acids that are involved in forming the phosphate binding region of its nucleotide binding sites. For this reason, one of the sequences is often referred to as the P-loop (phosphate binding loop) sequence [47] (see Figure 5).

In the determination of the atomic structure of F_1-ATPase from bovine heart mitochondria, the key problem that had to be solved was how to grow crystals of the protein complex that would diffract X-rays to appropriately high resolution. Crystals were obtained at the beginning of our efforts, but, as often happens, they diffracted X-rays rather poorly. Therefore, over a period

P-LOOP SEQUENCES IN F₁-ATPase

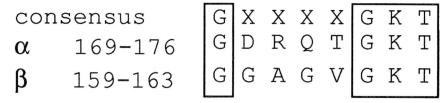

Figure 5. The phosphate binding loop sequence motif in the α- and β-subunits of bovine F_1-ATPase. In some purine binding sites, the final threonine is replaced by a serine residue.

of seven years, factors influencing crystal formation were studied systematically, and the diffraction properties of the crystals were improved gradually. Eventually, suitable cystals were obtained in 1990. In retrospect, the important factors for obtaining these crystals were to use highly pure preparations of enzyme from which trace impurities had been eliminated, to remove endogenous bound nucleotides and to replace them with a non-hydrolyzable chemical analogue of ATP, namely 5'-adenylylimidodiphosphate (AMP-PNP) which has the effect of locking the complex in a unique conformation, and to grow the crystals in the presence of deuterium oxide instead of water. By exposing the crystals to X-rays at a synchrotron source, it was demonstrated that crystals of bovine F_1-ATPase grown under these conditions diffracted to at least 2.8 Å resolution [48, 49]. Drs. René Lutter and Rose Todd were key collaborators during this critical period. At this point, for the first time the structural analysis of F_1-ATPase appeared to be a realistic possibility. Our chances of success with such a large protein complex were increased significantly by collaborating with Dr. Andrew Leslie, who is a professional protein crystallographer. Together with him and a post-doctoral visitor, Dr. J. P. Abrahams, we were able to arrive at an atomic resolution structure [50] surprisingly rapidly, given the size of the complex, and the associated problems of collecting and processing the X-ray diffraction data.

The structural model of bovine F_1-ATPase contains 2,983 amino acids. Except for short disordered stretches at their N-terminals, the sequences of the α- and β-subunits were traced in their entirety. Three α-helical segments of the γ-subunit corresponding to residues 1–45, 73–90, and 209–272 were also built into the model. The segments linking these three segments are also disordered, as are the entire δ- and ϵ-subunits (150 and 50 amino acids respectively). These disordered regions of the γ-, δ- and ϵ-subunits, comprising in total about 300 amino acids, probably lie beneath the $\alpha_3\beta_3$ sub-complex, where the γ-subunit protrudes from the structure (the γ-subunit is blue in Figures 6 and 7). The protrusion is probably a vestige of the 45 Å stalk that links the F_1 and F_o domains in the complete ATP synthase complex.

The structural model shows that the three α-subunits and the three β-subunits are arranged in alternation around a sixfold axis of pseudo-symmetry provided by an α-helical structure in the single γ-subunit (see Figures 6 and 7). Despite the large excesses of AMP-PNP and ADP in the mother liquor surrounding the crystals, five, and not six, nucleotides are bound to each enzyme complex. An AMP-PNP molecule is found in each α-subunit and a fourth one in one β-subunit. An ADP molecule is bound to the second β-subunit, and the third β-subunit has no bound nucleotide at all. A comparison of the structures of the three chemically identical β-subunits in the F_1 complex provides an explanation. The two catalytic β-subunits that have AMP-PNP and ADP bound to them (known as β_{TP} and β_{DP}, respectively; see Figures 7b and 7c) have different but rather similar conformations, whereas the structure of the third β-subunit, to which no nucleotide has bound (known as β_E; see Figure 7d), differs substantially from the other two, particularly in the central domain where the nucleotides are bound in β_{TP} and β_{DP}. In β_E, the C-terminal half of this central domain, together with the bundle of six α-helices that form the C-terminal domain, have rotated away from the sixfold axis of pseudo-symmetry. This disruption of the central domain removes the capacity of the β_E-subunit to bind nucleotides. Therefore, the crystal structure of F_1-ATPase contains the asymmetry required by the binding change mechanism, and the three different conformations of the subunits β_E, β_{TP} and β_{DP} could be interpreted as representing the "open", "loose" and "tight" states, respectively.

More recent extensive crystallographic analyses of F_1-ATPase with bound antibiotic inhibitors [51, 52], of enzyme occupied with ADP and ATP (K. Braig, M. Montgomery, A. G. W. Leslie and J. E. Walker, unpublished work), of enzyme inhibited by ADP and aluminium fluoride (K. Braig, I. Menz, M. Montgomery, A. G. W. Leslie and J. E. Walker, unpublished work), and of en-

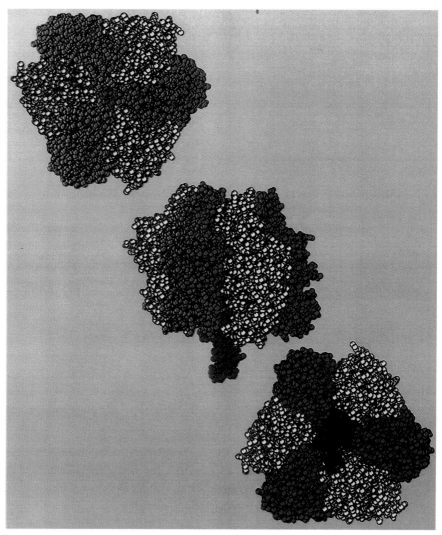

Figure 6. The three-dimensional structure of bovine F_1-ATPase shown in solid representation. The red, yellow and blue parts correspond to α-, β- and γ-subunits respecively. From top to bottom, respectively, the complex is viewed from above (towards the membrane in the intact ATP synthase), from the side, and from beneath.

zyme covalently inhibited with 4-chloro-7-nitrobenzofluorazan (G. Orriss, A. G. W. Leslie and J. E. Walker, unpublished work), leave little room for any doubt that the high resolution structure described above represents a state in the active cycle of the enzyme.

The most exciting aspect of the structure is that it suggests a mechanism for interconverting the three catalytic subunits through the cycle of conformations required by the binding change mechanism. It appears from the structure (Figure 7) that the nucleotide binding properties of the three catalytic β-subunits are modulated by the central α-helical structure in the γ-sub-

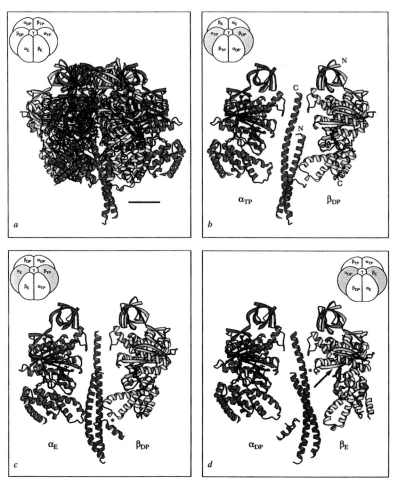

Figure 7. The three-dimensional structure of bovine F$_1$-ATPase shown in ribbon representation. The colour code for subunits is the same as used in Figure 6, and nucleotides are black, in a "ball-and-stick" representation. The axis of pseudo-symmetry is vertical. AMP-PNP is bound to the three α-subunits, and to the β-subunit defined as β$_{TP}$. Subunit β$_{DP}$ has bound ADP and subunit βE has no associated nucleotide. Subunits αTP, αE and αDP occupy the same relative positions as the corresponding β-subunits, but are rotated by -60°. The relationships of the various α- and β-subunits to each other is summarized in the icon in the top left or right corner of parts (A)–(D). In parts (C)–(D), the shaded part of the icon shows which subunits are depicted. Subunit α$_{TP}$ contributes to the nucleotide binding site of β$_{TP}$, and similarly for α$_{DP}$ and α$_E$. Subunits α and γ are numbered from 1–510 and 1–272, respectively. By convention, the fifth amino acid (serine) in subunit β is residue 1 and the first four amino acids (Ala.Ala.Gln.Ala) are referred to as residues –1 to –4. The C-terminal amino acid is residue 478. (A) A view of the entire F$_1$ particle in which subunits α$_E$ and β$_E$ point towards the viewer, revealing the anti-parallel coiled-coil of the N- and C-terminal helices of the γ-subunit through the open interface between them. The bar is 20 Å long. (B) Subunits α$_{TP}$, γ and β$_{DP}$, from a similar viewpoint to (A), but rotated 180° about the axis of pseudo-symmetry. The N- and C-termini of the β- and γ-subunit are shown. (C) Subunits α$_E$, g and β$_{TP}$ from a similar viewpoint to (A), but rotated by -60°. The asterisk indicates an interaction of the loop containing the DELSEED sequence and the γ-subunit. (D) Subunits α$_{DP}$, γ, and β$_E$ from a similar viewpoint to (A), but rotated by 60°. The arrow indicates the disruption of the β-sheet in the nucleotide binding domain. β$_E$Asp 316, β$_E$Thr 318 and β$_E$Asp 323 in a loop of the nucleotide binding domain make H-bonds with residues γ-Arg 254 and γ-Gln 255 from the C-terminal helix, 6 Å below the hydrophobic sleeve. The asterisk indicates a loop that makes an interaction with the C-terminal part of the γ-subunit. Reproduced with permission from reference [50].

222

unit. This structure is curved, and its coiled-coil region is likely to have rigidity. In the crystal structure, its curvature appears to be imposing the "open state" on the β_E subunit by pushing against the C-terminal domain of the protein, forcing the nucleotide binding domain to split and hinge outwards, thereby removing its nucleotide binding capacity. Therefore, by inspection of the model, the simplest way of interconverting the three conformations of β-subunits would be to rotate this central α-helical structure. As it is rotated, the curvature of the γ-subunit moves away from the β_E conformation, allowing that subunit to close, progressively entrapping substrates and allowing ATP to form spontaneously. At the same time, the next β-subunit will be progressively opened by the effect of the curvature of the γ-subunit, allowing the ATP that has already formed in its nucleotide binding site to be released.

EVIDENCE FOR A ROTARY MECHANISM IN ATP SYNTHASE

The suggestion that ATP synthesis involves the cyclic modulation of nucleotide binding properties of the three catalytic β-subunits by rotation of the γ-subunit was attractive because it provided a reasonable structural basis for the binding change mechanism. However, the proposal was based upon the interpretation of a static atomic model, and there was no proof that the enzyme operated in this way in reality. Therefore, in the laboratories of Richard Cross, Rod Capaldi and Wolfgang Junge, various experiments were carried out to test the rotary hypothesis [53–55]. These experiments were all consistent with the rotary model, and they provided convincing evidence of the movement of the γ-subunit through 90–240°, but conclusive proof of repeated net rotations through 360° was lacking.

Early in 1997, clear evidence of continuous rotation of the γ-subunit relative to the surrounding $\alpha_3\beta_3$ subcomplex was provided by a spectacular experiment conducted at the Tokyo Institute of Technology by Masasuke Yoshida and colleagues [56]. The essence of this experiment (summarized in Figure 8) was to bind the $\alpha_3\beta_3\gamma_1$ sub-complex to a nickel coated glass surface in a unique orientation, by introducing the nickel binding sequence (histidine)$_{10}$ at the N-terminals of the β-subunits. A cysteine residue, introduced by mutagenesis into the exposed tip of the γ-subunit, distal from the nickel surface, was biotinylated, thereby allowing a fluorescently labelled biotinylated actin filament to be attached via an intermediate streptavidin molecule, which has four biotin binding sites. The actin filaments were 1–3 μm long, and their ATP dependent anticlockwise rotation could be seen in a fluorescence microscope. The rate of rotation was approximately once per second, about one fiftieth of the rate anticipated from the turnover number of the fully active enzyme. The reduced activity can be attributed to the load of the actin filament and to the absence of the δ- and ε-subunits.

In addition to its impact in providing direct visual proof of the rotation of the γ-subunit, one crucially important aspect of this experiment is that it establishes the order of interconversion of the three conformations of β-sub-

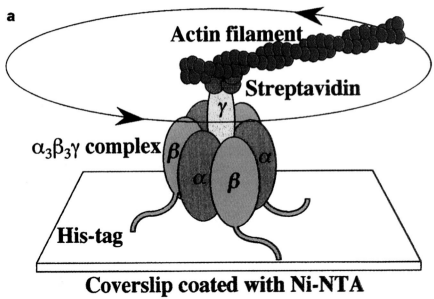

a

Actin filament

Streptavidin

γ

$\alpha_3\beta_3\gamma$ **complex** β

α

α   β

His-tag

Coverslip coated with Ni-NTA

Figure 8. Experimental observation of the ATP-depenedent rotation of the γ-subunit of the $\alpha_3\beta_3\gamma_1$ sub-complex. For explanation, see the text. Reproduced with permission from reference [56].

units observed in the crystal structure. During ATP hydrolysis, the β_{DP} sub-unit converts into the β_E state, β_E changes to β_{TP} and β_{TP} changes to β_{DP}. During ATP synthesis, it is reasonable to assume that the γ-subunit rotates in the opposite direction, and that the order of conformational changes in the β-subunits is the reverse of those occurring during ATP hydrolysis.

GENERATION OF ROTATION BY PROTON TRANSPORT THROUGH THE F_0 MEMBRANE DOMAIN

Once convincing evidence of rotation of the γ-subunit had been obtained, among the next questions for consideration were: how is rotation generated by proton transport through F_0, and what is the nature of the connections between the F_1 and the F_0 domains? High resolution structure is likely to be crucial in providing clear answers to both questions, but as yet there is no such structure for either the F_0 domain or the central stalk between F_1 and F_0, except for the ordered protrusion of the γ-subunit. Structures of the isolated ε-subunit [57, 58] and of a fragment of subunit d [59] of the *E. coli* enzyme have been established. The bacterial ε-subunit (equivalent to the bovine δ-subunit [60]) probably interacts with the γ-protrusion, and the bacterial δ-subunit (equivalent of the bovine OSCP subunit [60]) appears to interact with the N-terminal region of the α-subunits (*vide infra*), but the precise locations and functions of these proteins in ATP synthase are unclear.

Despite the lack of a detailed structure of the F_0 domain, evidence about the arrangement of the membrane subunits is accumulating. The simplest F_0

domain characterized so far is the one found in eubacterial enzymes exemplified by *E. coli*. It has three constituent subunits named a, b and c assembled in the molar ratios $a_1b_2c_{9-12}$ [61, 62]. The uncertainty in the number of c subunits per complex is a consequence of the experimental difficulties associated with making appropriate measurements. Secondary structural models for all three subunits have been advanced by interpretation of the sequences of the bacterial F_o subunits [63]. That of subunit a has been interpreted variously as indicating the presence of five, six or seven hydrophobic membrane spanning subunits in the protein, but recent experimental evidence indicates that the correct value is five [64]. In its C-terminal and in penultimate α-helices are found positively charged amino acids that are essential for a functional F_o. Subunit b is anchored in the membrane by a single N-terminal α-helix [65]. The remainder of this protein is highly charged and may form a homo-dimer by making a parallel α-helical coiled-coil. This polar extramembrane region interacts with subunits in F_1 [66]. The model of subunit c has two antiparallel transmembrane α-helices linked by an extra-membranous loop, and this has been shown by nmr studies to be the structure of the protein in a chloroform-methanol solvent mixture [64]. Cysteine residues introduced by mutation into the loop region and into the tip of the γ-subunit form a disulphide link under oxidizing conditions, showing that in the intact enzyme, these regions are either in contact (possibly transiently) or close to each other [67]. Similar kinds of experiment provide evidence of interactions between subunits e and c [68]. The most important feature of subunit c is the side chain carboxyl of an aspartate residue, which is buried in the membrane in the C-terminal α-helix. This carboxyl group is conserved throughout all known sequences of c-subunits, and it is required for transmembrane proton transport. [61, 63] Depending on the exact number of subunits c per complex, there are 9–12 such buried carboxyls in each ATP synthase complex.

The mitochondrial ATP synthase complex contains subunits that are equivalent to subunits a and c (see Table 1). Mitochondrial subunit b is also probably the equivalent of its bacterial homonym, although it appears to have two anti-parallel transmembrane a-helices at its N-terminus, rather than one, and there is only one b-subunit per enzyme complex. Presumably the role of the second b-subunit in the bacterial complex is performed by other subunits that are unique to the mitochondrial complex (for example subunits d and F_6), but such matters will only become clear when more detailed structural evidence becomes available for both bacterial and mitochondrial enzymes. Nonetheless, the bacterial and mitochondrial F_o domains have many features in common, and it is highly probable that they operate by very similar mechanisms.

Models have also been advanced about the association of the F_o subunits in the membrane domain. One such model suggests that the c-subunits form a ring by interactions though their C-terminal α-helices, with the N-terminal α-helices outside the ring [69], and annular structures of c-subunits have been visualized by atomic force microscopy [70, 71]. Some preliminary experimental evidence of this arrangement has also been obtained by formation of disulphide cross links after introduction of cysteine residues at appropriate sites (N. J. Glavas & J. E. Walker, unpublished work). In addition, the atomic force microscopy images indicate that the b-subunits are placed peripheral to a ring of c-subunits [71]. Currently, there is no experimental evidence that shows whether the a subunit lies outside or within the c-annulus.

Wolfgang Junge has proposed a model of how proton transport through F_o might generate a rotary motion [72] (see Figure 9). The essence of this hypothetical rotary motor is that the essential carboxyls in the c subunits are arranged around the external circumference of the c-annulus. Part of the external surface of the annulus interacts with subunit a, and in this region the carboxyls are negatively charged. It is envisaged that subunit a has an inlet port on the external surface of the membrane which allows a proton to neutralize one of the negatively charged carboxylates. The resulting un-ionized carboxyl will find its way by thermal vibrations to its preferred environment in contact with the phospholipid bilayer. The neutralization of this carboxylate at one point of the circumference is accompanied by re-ionization of another one further around the circumference of the c-annulus, by release of the proton on the opposite side of the membrane via an exit port in subunit a, and regeneration of a negative charge in the c-annulus:subunit a interface. These protonation-deprotonation events result in a rotary movement of the c-annulus. The rotation brings the next negatively charged carboxyl to the inlet port

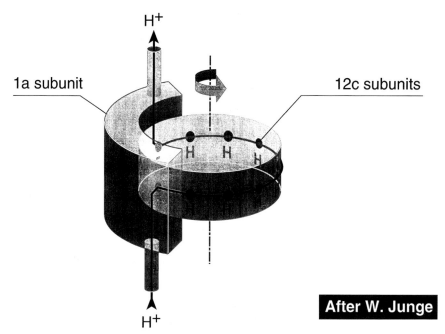

Figure 9. A hypothetical model for generation of rotation by proton transport through the F_o domain of ATP synthase. The central cylindrical part is made of c-subunits, the external curved structure is the single a subunit. The heavy black line indicates the path of the protons. For further explanation, see the text.

where in turn it is neutralized by another proton. The accompanying release of another proton via the exit port generates further rotation. It is envisaged that this rotary device is directly coupled to the γ-subunit.

The synthesis of each ATP molecule requires a rotation of the γ-subunit by 120°, and so each complete rotation of the γ-subunit in F_1 produces three ATP molecules. In a hypothetical proton motor with a c-annulus consisting of twelve c-subunits, this corresponds to the sequential neutralization of four carboxylates by proton binding (and accompanying sequential proton release from four others). In other words, a H^+: ATP ratio of four is compatible with a molar ratio of c-subunits in F_o of twelve. Likewise, a H^+:ATP ratio of three requires nine c-subunits in each F_o.

CONNECTIONS BETWEEN THE F_1 AND F_o DOMAINS OF ATP SYNTHASE

The evidence for the interaction of the central γ-subunit and the associated ε-subunit in bacterial F_1 with the loop region of a c-subunit in F_o has been described above. It is likely that these proteins are the principal components making the central interaction between F_1 and F_o, visualized as the central 45 Å stalk. There is accumulating evidence for a second link between F_1 and F_o. It is known that the bacterial δ-subunit and the equivalent bovine OSCP subunit interact with the N-terminal part of the α-subunits [73, 74], which are now known to be on top of F_1 distal from the membrane domain. Since the 1960s, it has been known that bovine OSCP is required for binding F_1 to F_o, implying that it interacts with subunits in the membrane domain. Therefore, the inescapable conclusion is that OSCP (and possibly also subunit δ in the bacterial and chloroplast enzymes) extends from the top of F_1, down its external surface, to a region associated with the membrane domain. In the bovine enzyme, the N-terminal part of OSCP interacts with the N-terminal part of the a-subunits [75, 76]. Additionally, the interactions of bovine OSCP with various F_o components have been studied by *in vitro* reconstitution experiments [77]. They indicate that OSCP binds mainly to the polar extramembranous part of subunit b (referred to as b′), and not with subunits d and F_6. However, subunits d and F_6 bind to the b′-OSCP complex to forming a stoichiometric complex containing one copy of each of the four proteins. This complex (unfortunately named as "stalk") makes no strong interactions with a complex of bovine subunits δ and ε [78], consistent with the bovine "stalk" complex being separate from the central 45 Å stalk.

By single particle analysis of negatively stained samples of monodisperse bovine ATP synthase [79–82], Simone Karrasch has obtained electron microscopic evidence for a second peripheral stalk (see Figure 10). A similar feature has been observed independently in the *E. coli* enzyme (S. Wilkens and R. A. Capaldi, personal communication), and in a V-type ATPase (a relative of ATP synthase) from *Clostridium fervidus* [83]. The image of the bovine enzyme also contains another novel feature, seen as a disc shaped structure or collar

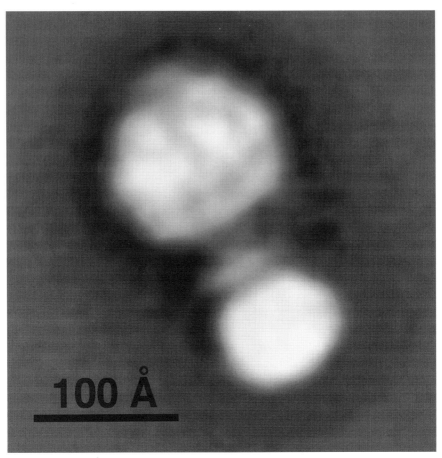

100 Å

Figure 10. Image of bovine ATP synthase obtained by averaging 4940 single negatively stained particles of the enzyme. The plane of the membrane with which the assembly is associated in mitochondria, runs upwards, left to right, at an angle of 45°. The larger sphere is the F_1 catalytic domain, and the smaller sphere beneath it is F_o (or part of F_o). The new features are the collar apparently surrounding the central stalk, and, on the right, the faint peripheral connection between the collar and F_1 which may serve as a "stator". There may also be extra material on top of the F_1 domain that is not present in isolated F_1-ATPase (for more detailed discussion, see the text).

evidently sitting between the central stalk and F_o domains, and a similar collar was observed in the Clostridial enzyme. It remains to be established which subunits of the bovine enzyme are responsible for the peripheral stalk and the collar. The OSCP and subunit b are likely candidates for being components of the former, and the collar may be composed of parts of the c subunits.

At present, we can only speculate about the role of the peripheral stalk, but it may be acting as a stator to counter the tendency of the $\alpha_3\beta_3$ sub-complex to follow the rotation of the central γ-subunit. However, it is unlikely that this peripheral stalk remains bound in a unique position because the nature of the surface of the $\alpha_3\beta_3$ sub-complex must change cyclically in response to the rotating γ-subunit, and hence the preferred binding site of the peripheral

228

structure must also move in the same way. The role of the collar is an even bigger mystery.

EVOLUTION OF ATP SYNTHASE AND ITS RELATIONSHIP TO OTHER ENZYMES

In bacterial operons coding for the subunits of ATP synthase, the genes for F_1 and F_o subunits are often clustered separately. This arrangement suggested the possibility that the two domains have evolved separately as structural modules [84], similar to the "modular evolution" of heads and tails of bacteriophages [85, 86]. If this suggestion were correct, it might be expected that the F_1 and F_o modules would be found to fulfill other biochemical functions elsewhere in biology.

It is too early to know whether there is any significant structural and mechanistic relationship between F_o and the motors that drive the flagellae of bacteria, although this remains a distinct possibility. However, there is emerging evidence of significant similarities, both functional and structural, between the F_1 domain of ATP synthase and DNA and RNA helicases that employ energy released by hydrolysis of ATP or GTP to separate the strands of nucleic acid duplexes (for example, see reference [87]). Therefore, the rotary mechanism of ATP synthase may turn out to be the first example of a more general principle in enzyme catalysis.

CONCLUDING REMARKS

The high resolution structure of the catalytic domain of the ATP synthesizing enzyme has provided new insights into our understanding of how ATP is made in biology. Nevertheless, challenging structural experiments lie ahead in the quest to understand the generation of rotation by transmembrane proton transport through its membrane sector. A short poem written by Robert Frost provides an appropriate summary of the current state of affairs.

We dance round in a ring and suppose
The secret sits in the middle and knows

I am glad to have played a role in arriving at our present level of understanding of ATP synthesis, and in the future I hope to contribute to the revelation of the secret sitting in the middle.

ACKNOWLEDGEMENTS

From what I have written, it is obvious that the work summarized above is the outcome of the joint efforts of many extremely able and highly valued colleagues and collaborators, including Ph. D. students and post-doctoral visitors, whom I have been privileged to lead. To all of them, I offer my thanks for their contributions. I am particularly grateful to The Medical Research Council, which has supported my work unstintingly for more that 20 years.

Many post-doctoral visitors were supported by Fellowships from The European Molecular Biology Organization, and others by Fellowships from the European Community and the Human Frontiers of Science Project. I thank these organizations also for their support.

REFERENCES

1. Nicholls, D. G. & Ferguson, S. J. (1992). In *Bioenergetics 2* Academic Press, London, San Diego.
2. Dimroth, P. (1991). Na$^+$-coupled alternative to H$^+$ coupled primary tarnsport system in bacteria. *Bioessays* **13**, 463–468.
3. Tsukihara, T., Aoyama, H., Yamashita, E., Tomizaki, T., Yamaguchi, H., Shinzawa-Itoh, K., Nakashima, R., Yaono, D. & Yoshikawa, S. (1995). Structures of the metal sites of oxidized cytochrome c oxidase at 2.8 Å resolution. *Science* **269**, 1069–1074.
4. Tsukihara, T., Aoyama, H., Yamashita, E., Tomizaki, T., Yamaguchi, H., Shinzawa-Itoh, K., Nakashima, R., Yaono, D. & Yoshikawa, S. (1996). The whole structure of the 13-subunit oxidized cytochrome c oxidase at 2.8 Å. *Science* **272**, 1136–1144.
5. Iwata, S., Ostermeier, C., Ludwig, B. & Michel, H. (1995). Structure at 2.8 Å resolution of cytochrome c oxidase from *Paracoccus denitrificans*. *Nature* **376**, 660–669.
6. Ostermeier, C., Harrenga, A., Ermler, U. & Michel, H. (1997). Structure at 2.7 Å of the *Paracoccus denitrificans* two-subunit cytochrome c oxidase with an antibody F$_v$ fragment. *Proc. Natl. Acad. Sci. U.S.A.* **94**, 10547–10553.
7. Xia, D., Yu, C. A., Kih, H., Xia, J. Z., Kachurin, A. M., Zhang, L., Yu, L. & Deisenhofer, J. (1997). Crystal structure of the cytochrome bc$_1$ complex from bovine heart mitochondria. *Science* **277**, 60–66.
8. Walker, J. E. (1992). The NADH:ubiquinone oxidoreductase (complex I) of respiratory chains. *Qu. Rev. Biophys.* **25**, 253–324.
9. Guénbaut, V., Vincentelli, R., Mills, D., Weiss, H. & Leonard, K. (1997). Three-dimensional structure of NADH-dehydrogenase from *Neurospora crassa* by electron microscopy and conical tilt reconstruction. *J. Mol. Biol.* **265**, 409–418.
10. Grigorieff, N. (1997). Three-dimensional structure of bovine NADH:ubiquinone oxidoreductase (complexI) at 22 Å in ice. *J. Mol. Biol.* In press.
11. Gay, N. J. & Walker, J. E. (1981). The *atp* operon: nucleotide sequence of the promoter and the genes for the membrane proteins and the δ subunit of *Escherichia coli* ATP synthase. *Nucleic Acids Res.* **9**, 3919–3926.
12. Gay, N. J. & Walker, J. E. (1981). The *atp* operon: nucleotide sequence of the region encoding the α subunit of *Escherichia coli* ATP synthase. *Nucleic Acids Res.* **9**, 2187–2194.
13. Saraste, M., Gay, N. J., Eberle, A., Runswick, M. J. & Walker, J. E. (1981). The *atp* operon: nucleotide sequence of the genes for the γ, β and ε subunits of *Escherichia coli* ATP synthase. *Nucleic Acids Res.* **9**, 5287–5296.
14. Runswick, M. J. & Walker, J. E. (1983). The amino acid sequence of the b subunit of ATP synthase from bovine heart mitochondria. *J. Biol. Chem.* **258**, 3081–3089.
15. Tybulewicz, V. L. J., Falk, G. & Walker, J. E. (1984). *Rhodopseudomonas blastica atp* operon: Nucleotide sequence and transcription. *J. Mol. Biol.* **179**, 185–214.
16. Walker, J. E., Saraste, M. & Gay, N. J. (1984). The *unc* operon: nucleotide sequence, regulation and structure of ATP synthase. *Biochim. Biophys. Acta* **768**, 164–200.
17. Falk, G., Hampe, A. & Walker, J. E. (1985). Nucleotide sequence of the *Rhodospirillum rubrum atp* operon. *Biochem. J.* **228**, 391–407.
18. Walker, J. E., Fearnley, I. M., Gay, N. J., Gibson, B. W., Northrop, F. D., Powell, S. J., Runswick, M. J., Saraste, M. & Tybulewicz, V. L. J. (1985). Primary structure and subunit stoichiometry of F$_1$-ATPase from bovine mitochondria. *J. Mol. Biol.* **184**, 677–701.
19. Cozens, A. L., Walker, J. E., Phillips, A. L., Huttly, A. K. & Gray, J. C. (1986). A sixth subunit of ATP synthase, an F$_o$ component, is encoded in the pea chloroplast genome. *EMBO J.* **5**, 217–222.

20. Fearnley, I. M. & Walker, J. E. (1986). Two overlapping genes in bovine mitochondrial DNA encode membrane components of ATP synthase. *EMBO J.* **5**, 2003–2008.

21. Cozens, A. L. & Walker, J. E. (1987). The organization and sequence of the genes for ATP synthase subunits in the cyanobacterium *Synechococcus* 6301: support for an endosymbiotic origin of chloroplasts. *J. Mol. Biol.* **194**, 359–383.

22. Walker, J. E., Gay, N. J., Powell, S. J., Kostina, M. & Dyer, M. R. (1987). ATP synthase from bovine mitochondria: sequences of imported precursors of oligomycin sensitivity conferral protein, factor 6 and adenosine triphosphatase inhibitor protein. *Biochemistry* **26**, 8613–8619.

23. Walker, J. E., Runswick, M. J. & Poulter, L. (1987). ATP synthase from bovine mitochondria: characterization and sequence analysis of two membrane associated subunits and of their corresponding c-DNAs. *J. Mol. Biol.* **197**, 89–100.

24. Falk, G. & Walker, J. E. (1988). DNA sequence of a gene cluster coding for subunits of the F_o membrane sector of ATP synthase in *Rhodospirillum rubrum*. *Biochem. J.* **254**, 109–122.

25. Walker, J. E., Powell, S. J., Vinas, O. & Runswick, M. J. (1989). ATP synthase from bovine mitochondria:complementary DNA sequence of the import precursor of a heart isoform of the alpha subunit. *Biochemistry* **28**, 4702–4708.

26. Runswick, M. J., Medd, S. M. & Walker, J. E. (1990). The δ subunit of ATP synthase from bovine heart mitochondria. Complementary DNA sequence of its import precursor cloned with the aid of the polymerase chain reaction. *Biochem. J.* **266**, 421–426.

27. Viñas, O., Powell, S. J., Runswick, M. J., Iacobazzi, V. & Walker, J. E. (1990). The epsilon subunit of ATP synthase from bovine heart mitochondria: complementary DNA, expression in bovine tissues and evidence of homologous sequences in man and rat. *Biochem. J.* **265**, 321–326.

28. Walker, J. E., Lutter, R., Dupuis, A. & Runswick, M. J. (1991). Identification of the subunits of F_1F_o-ATPase from bovine heart mitochondria. *Biochemistry* **30**, 5369–5378.

29. Van Walraven, H. S., Lutter, R. & Walker, J. E. (1993). Organization and sequence of genes for subunits of ATP synthase in the thermophilic cyanobacterium *Synechococcus* 6716. *Biochem. J.* **294**, 239–251.

30 Collinson, I. R., Runswick, M. J., Buchanan, S. K., Fearnley, I. M., Skehel, J. M., van Raaij, M. J., Griffiths, D. E. & Walker, J. E. (1994). The F_o membrane domain of ATP synthase from bovine heart mitochondria: purification, subunit composition and reconstitution with F_1-ATPase. *Biochemistry* **33**, 7971–7978.

31. Collinson, I. R., Skehel, J. M., Fearnley, I. M., Runswick, M. J. & Walker, J. E. (1996). The F_1F_o-ATPase complex from bovine heart mitochondria: the molar ratio of the subunits in the stalk region linking the F_1 and F_o domains. *Biochemistry* **35**, 12640–12646.

32. Walker, J. E. (1994). The regulation of catalysis in ATP synthase. *Curr. Opinion Struct. Biol.* **4**, 912–918.

33. Fernández-Morán, H. (1962). Cell-membrane ultrastructure. Low-temperature electron microscopy and x-ray diffraction studies of lipoprotein components in lamellar systems. *Circulation* **26**, 1039–1065.

34. Vambutas, V. K. & Racker, E. (1965). Partial resolution of the enzymes catalysing photophosphorylation. Stimulation of photophossphorylation by a preparation of a latent, Ca^{++}-dependent adenosine triphosphatase from chloroplasts. *J. Biol. Chem.* **240**, 2660–2667.

35. Green, D. E. (1964). The Mitochondrion. *Scientific American* **210**, 63–74.

36. Kagawa, Y. & Racker, E. (1966). Partial resolution of the enzymes catalyzing oxidative phosphorylation. Correlation of morphology and function in submitochondrial particles. *J. Biol. Chem.* **241**, 2475–2482.

37. Kagawa, Y. & Racker, E. (1966). Partial resolution of the enzymes catalyzing oxidative phosphorylation. Properties of a factor conferring oligmycin sensitivity on mitochondrial adenosine triphosphatase. *J. Biol. Chem.* **241**, 2461–2466.

38. Kagawa, Y. & Racker, E. (1966). Partial resolution of the enzymes catalyzing oxidative phosphorylation. Reconstruction of oligomycin-sensitive adenosine triphosphatase. *J. Biol. Chem.* **241**, 2467–2474.

39. Van Walraven, H., Strotmann, H., Schwartz, O. & Rumberg, B. (1996). The H^+/ATP ratio of the ATP synthase from the thiol modulated chloroplasts and two cyanobacterial strains is four. *FEBS Lett.* **379**, 309–313.

40. Boyer, P. D. (1993). The binding change mechanism for ATP synthase–some probabilities and possibilities. *Biochim. Biophys. Acta* **1140**, 215–250.

41. Brooks, J. C. & Senior, A. E. (1972). Methods for the purification of each subunit of the mitochondrial oligomycin-insensitive adenosine triphosphatase. *Biochemistry* **11**, 4675–4678.

42. Knowles, A. F. & Penefsky, H. S. (1972). The subunit structure of beef heart mitochondrial adenosine triphosphatase. *J. Biol. Chem.* **247**, 6616–6623.

43. Pai, E. F., Sachsenheimer, W., Schirmer, R. H. & Schulz, G. E. (1977). Substrate positions and induced-fit in crystalline adenylate kinase. *J. Mol. Biol.* **114**, 37–45.

44. Walker, J. E., Saraste, M., Runswick, M. J. & Gay, N. J. (1982). Distantly related sequences in the α and β subunits of ATP synthase, myosin, kinases and other ATP requiring enzymes and a common nucleotide binding fold. *EMBO J.* **1**, 945–951.

45. Higgins, C. F. (1992). ABC transporters: from microorganisms to man. *Ann. Rev. Cell Biol.* **8**, 67–113.

46. Gay, N. J. & Walker, J. E. (1983). Homology between human bladder carcinoma oncogene product and mitochondrial ATP synthase. *Nature* **301**, 262–264.

47. Koonin, E. V. (1993). A superfamily of ATPases with diverse functions containing either classical or deviant ATP-binding motif. *J. Mol. Biol.* **229**, 1165–1174.

48. Walker, J. E., Fearnley, I. M., Lutter, R., Todd, R. J. & Runswick, M. J. (1990). Structural aspects of proton pumping ATPases. *Phil. Trans. Royal Soc.* **326**, 367–378.

49. Lutter, R., Abrahams, J. P., van Raaij, M. J., Todd, R. J., Lundqvist, T., Buchanan, S. K., Leslie, A. G. W. & Walker, J. E. (1993). Crystallization of F_1–ATPase from bovine heart mitochondria. *J. Mol. Biol.* **229**, 787–790.

50. Abrahams, J. P., Leslie, A. G. W., Lutter, R. & Walker, J. E. (1994). Structure at 2.8 Å resolution of F_1-ATPase from bovine heart mitochondria. *Nature* **370**, 621–628.

51. van Raaij, M. J., Abrahams, J. P., Leslie, A. G. W. & Walker, J. E. (1996). The structure of bovine F_1-ATPase complexed with the antibiotic inhibitor aurovertin. *Proc. Natl. Acad. Sci. U.S.A.* **93**, 6913–6917.

52. Abrahams, J. P., Buchanan, S. K., van Raaij, M. J., Fearnley, I. M., Leslie, A. G. W. & Walker, J. E. (1996). The structure of bovine F_1-ATPase complexed with the peptide antibiotic efrapeptin. *Proc. Natl. Acad. Sci. U.S.A.* **93**, 9420–9424.

53. Duncan, T. M., Bulygin, V. V., Zhou, Y., Hutcheon, M. L. & Cross, R. L. (1995). Rotation of subunits during catalysis by *Escherichia coli* F_1-ATPase. *Proc. Natl. Acad. Sci. U. S. A.* **92**, 10964–10968.

54. Capaldi, R. A., Aggeler, R., Wilkens, S. & Grüber, G. (1996). Structural changes in the γ and ε subunits of the *Escherichia coli* F_1F_o-type ATPase during energy coupling. *J. Bioenerget. Biomemb.* **28**, 397–401.

55. Sabbert, D., Engelbrecht, S. & Junge, W. (1995). Intersubunit rotation in active F-ATPase. *Nature* **381**, 623–625.

56. Noji, H., Yasuda, R., Yoshida, M. & Kinosita Jr, K. (1997). Direct observation of the rotation of F_1-ATPase. *Nature* **386**, 299–302.

57. Wilkens, S., Dahlquist, F. W., McIntosh, L. P., Donaldson, L. W. & Capaldi, R. A. (1995). Structural features of the e subunit of the *Escherichia coli* ATP synthase determined by NMR spectroscopy. *Nature Struct. Biol.* **2**, 961–967.

58. Uhlin, U., Cox, G. B. & Guss, J. M. (1997). Crystal structure of the ε-subunit of the proton-translocating ATP synthase from *Escherichia coli*. *Structure* **5**, 1219–1230.

59. Wilkens, S., Dunn, S. D., Chandler, J., Dahlquist, F. W. & Capaldi, R. A. (1997). Solution structure of the N-terminal domain of the δ-subunit of the *E. coli* ATP synthase. *Nature Struct. Biol.* **4**, 198–201.

60. Walker, J. E., Runswick, M. J. & Saraste, M. (1982). Subunit equivalence in *Escherichia coli* and bovine heart mitochondrial F_1F_o ATPases. *FEBS Lett.* **146**, 393–396.

61. Fillingame, R. H. (1996). Membrane sectors of F- and V-type H^+-transporting ATPases. *Current Opinion Struct. Biol.* **6**, 491–498.

62. Foster, D. L. & Fillingame, R. H. (1982). Stoichiometry of subunits in the H^+-ATPase complex of *Escherichia coli*. *J. Biol. Chem.* **257**, 2009–2015.

63. Fillingame, R. H. (1990). Molecular mechanics of ATP synthesis by F_1F_o-type H^+-transporting ATPases. *The Bacteria* **12**, 345–391.

64. Fillingame, R. H., Girvin, M. E., Jiang, W., Valiyaveetil, F. & Hermolin, J. (1998). Subunit interactions coupling H^+ transport and ATP synthesis in F_1F_o ATP synthase. *Acta Physiol. Scand.* In the press.

65. Walker, J. E., Saraste, M. & Gay, N. J. (1982). *E. coli* F_1-ATPase interacts with a membrane protein component of a proton channel. *Nature* **298**, 867–869.

66. Dunn, S. D. (1992). The polar domain of the b subunit of *Escherichia coli* F_1F_o-ATPase forms an elongated dimer that interacts with the F_1 sector. *J. Biol. Chem.* **267**, 7630–7636.

67. Watts, S. D., Zhang, Y., Fillingame, R. H. & Capaldi, R. A. (1995). The gamma subunit in the *Escherichia coli* ATP synthase complex (ECF_1F_o) extends through the stalk and contacts the c subunits of the F_o part. *FEBS Lett.* **368**, 235–238.

68. Zhang, Y. & Fillingame, R. H. (1995). Subunits coupling H^+ transport and ATP synthesis in the *Escherichia coli* ATP synthase: Cys-Cys crosslinking of F_1 subunit ε to the polar loop of F_o subunit c. *J. Biol. Chem.* **270**, 24609–24614.

69. Groth, G. & Walker, J. E. (1997). Model of the c-subunit oligomer in the membrane domain of F-ATPases. *FEBS Lett.* **410**, 117–123.

70. Singh, S., Turina, P., Bustamente, C. J., Keller, D. J. & Capaldi, R. A. (1996). Topographical structure of membrane-bound *Escherichia coli* F_1F_o ATP synthase in aqueous buffer. *FEBS Lett.* **397**, 30–34.

71. Takeyasu, K., Omote, H., Nettikadan, S., Tokumasu, F., Iwamoto-Kihara, A. & Futai, M. (1996). Molecular imaging of *Escherichia coli* F_oF_1-ATPase in reconstituted membranes by atomic force microscopy. *FEBS Lett.* **392**, 110–113.

72. Junge, W., Sabbert, D. & Engelbrecht, S. (1996). Rotary catalysis by F-ATPase: real time recording of intersubunit rotation. *Ber. Bunsenges. Phys. Chem.* **100**, 2014–2019.

73. Dunn, S. D., Heppel, L. A. & Fullmer, C. S. (1980). The NH_2-terminal portion of the α-subunit of the *Escherichia coli* F_1-ATPase is required for binding the δ-subunit. *J. Biol. Chem.* **255**, 6891–6896.

74. Hundal, T., Norling, B. & Ernster, L. (1983). Lack of ability of trypsin-treated mitochondrial F_1-ATPase to bind to the oligomycin sensitivity conferring protein (OSCP). *FEBS Lett.* **162**, 5–10.

75. Joshi, S., Javed, A. A. & Gibbs, L. C. (1992). Oligomycin sensitivity-conferring protein (OSCP) of mitochondrial ATP synthase. The carboxy terminal region of OSCP is essential for the reconstitution of oligomycin-sensitive H^+-ATPase. *J. Biol. Chem.* **267**, 12860–12867.

76. Joshi, S., Pringle, M. J. & Siber, R. (1986). Topology and function of "stalk" proteins in the bovine mitochondrial H^+-ATPase. *J. Biol. Chem.* **261**, 10653–10658.

77. Collinson, I. R., van Raaij, M. J., Runswick, M. J., Fearnley, I. M., Skehel, J. M., Orriss, G., Miroux, B. & Walker, J. E. (1994). ATP synthase from bovine heart mitochondria: *in vitro* assembly of a stalk complex in the presence of F_1-ATPase and in its absence. *J. Mol. Biol.* **242**, 408–421.

78. Orriss, G. L., Runswick, M. J., Collinson, I. R., Miroux, B., Fearnley, I. M., Skehel, J. M. & Walker, J. E. (1996). The δ- and ε-subunits of bovine F_1-ATPase interact to form a heterodimeric subcomplex. *Biochem. J.* **314**, 695–700.

79. Lutter, R., Saraste, M., van Walraven, H. S., Runswick, M. J., Finel, M., Deatherage, J. F. & Walker, J. E. (1993). F_1F_o-ATPase from bovine heart mitochondria: development of the purification of a monodisperse oligomycin sensitive ATPase. *Biochem. J.* **295**, 799–806.

233

80. Walker, J. E., Collinson, I. R., Van Raaij, M. J. & Runswick, M. J. (1995). Structural analysis of ATP synthase (F_1F_o-ATPase) from bovine heart mitochondria. *Methods in Enzymol.* 163–190.

81. Buchanan, S. K. & Walker, J. E. (1996). Large scale chromatographic purification of F_1F_o-ATPase and complex I from bovine heart mitochondria. *Biochem. J.* **318**, 343–349.

82. Groth, G. & Walker, J. E. (1996). ATP synthase from bovine heart mitochondria: reconstitution into unilamellar phospholipid vesicles of the pure enzyme in a functional state. *Biochem. J.* **318**, 351–357.

83. Boekema, E., Ubbink-Kok, T., Lolkema, J. S., Brisson, A. & Konings, W. N. (1997). Visualization of a peripheral stalk in V-type ATPase: evidence for the stator structure essential to rotational catalysis. *Proc. Natl. Acad. Sci. U.S.A.* **94**, In the press.

84. Walker, J. E. & Cozens, A. L. (1986). Evolution of ATP synthase. *Chemica Scripta* **26B**, 263–272.

85. Botstein, D. (1980). A theory for molecular evolution of bacteriophages. *Ann. N. Y. Acad. Sci.* **354**, 484–491.

86. Casjens, S. & Hendrix, R. (1974). Comments on the arrangement of the morphogenetic genes of bacteriophage lambda. *J. Mol. Biol.* **90**, 20–23.

87. Yu, X. & Egelman, E. H. (1997). The RecA hexamer is a structural homologue of ring helicases. *Nature Struct. Biol.* **4**, 101–104.

88. Gogol, E. P., Aggeler, R., Sagerman, M. & Capaldi, R. A. (1989). Cryoelectron microscopy of *Escherichia coli* F_1 adenosine triphosphatase decorated with monoclonal antibodies to individual subunits of the complex. *Biochemistry* **28**, 4717–4724.

89. Weissman, G. & Claibourne, R. (1975). Cell Membranes: Biochemistry, Cell Biology and Pathology.

JENS C. SKOU

I was born on the 8th of October 1918 into a wealthy family in Lemvig, a town in the western part of Denmark. The town is nicely situated on a fjord, which runs across the country from the Kattegat in East to the North Sea in West. It is surrounded by hills, and is only 10 km, i.e. bicycling distance, from the North Sea, with its beautiful beaches and dunes. My father Magnus Martinus Skou together with his brother Peter Skou were timber and coal merchants.

We lived in a big beautiful house, had a nice summer house on the North Sea coast. We were four children, I was the oldest with a one year younger brother, a sister 4 years younger and another brother 7 years younger. The timber-yard was an excellent playground, so the elder of my brothers and I never missed friends to play with. School was a minor part of life.

When I was 12 years old my father died from pneumonia. His brother continued the business with my mother Ane-Margrethe Skou as passive partner, and gave her such conditions that there was no change in our economical situation. My mother, who was a tall handsome woman, never married again. She took care of us four children and besides this she was very active in the social life in town.

When I was 15, I went to a boarding school, a gymnasium (high school) in Haslev a small town on Zealand, for the last three years in school (student exam). There was no gymnasium in Lemvig.

Besides the 50–60 boys from the boarding section of the school there were about 400 day pupils. The school was situated in a big park, with two football fields, facilities for athletics, tennis courts and a hall for gymnastics and handball. There was a scout troop connected to the boarding section of the school. I had to spend a little more time preparing for school than I was used to. My favourites were the science subjects, especially mathematics. But there was plenty of time for sports activities and scouting, which I enjoyed. All the holidays, Christmas, Easter, summer and autumn I spent at home with my family.

After three years I got my exam, it was in 1937. I returned to Lemvig for the summer vacation, considering what to do next. I could not make up my mind, which worried my mother. I played tennis with a young man who studied medicine, and he convinced me that this would be a good choice. So, to my mother's great relief, I told her at the end of August that I would study medicine, and started two days later at the University of Copenhagen.

The medical course was planned to take 7 years, 3 years for physics, chemistry, anatomy, biochemistry and physiology, and 4 years for the clinical subjects, and for pathology, forensic medicine, pharmacology and public health. I followed the plan and got my medical degree in the summer of 1944.

I was not especially interested in living in a big town. On the other hand it was a good experience for a limited number of years to live in, and get acquainted with the capital of the country, and to exploit its cultural offers. Art galleries, classical music and opera were my favourites.

For the first three years I spent the month between the semesters at home studying the different subjects. For the last 4 years the months between the semesters were used for practical courses in different hospital wards in Copenhagen.

It was with increasing anxiety that we witnessed to how the maniac dictator in Germany, just south of our border, changed Germany into a madhouse. Our anxiety did not become less after the outbreak of the war. In 1914 Denmark managed to stay out of the war, but this time, in April 1940 the Germans occupied the country. Many were ashamed that the Danish army were ordered by the government to surrender after only a short resistance. Considering what later happened in Holland, Belgium and France, it was clear that the Danish army had no possibility of stopping the German army.

The occupation naturally had a deep impact on life in Denmark in the following years, both from a material point of view, but also, what was much worse, we lost our freedom of speech. For the first years the situation was very peculiar. The Germans did not remove the Danish government, and the Danish government did not resign, but tried as far as it was possible to minimize the consequences of the occupation. The army was not disarmed, nor was the fleet. The Germans wanted to use Denmark as a food supplier, and therefore wanted as few problems as possible.

The majority of the population turned against the Germans, but with no access to weapons, and with a flat homogeneous country with no mountains or big woods to hide in, the possibility of active resistance was poor. So for the first years the resistance only manifested itself in a negative attitude to the Germans in the country, in complicating matters dealing with the Germans as far as possible, and in a number of illegal journals, keeping people informed about the situation, giving the information which was suppressed by the German censorship. There was no interference with the teaching of medicine.

The Germans armed the North Sea coast against an invasion from the allied forces. Access was forbidden and our summer house was occupied. My grandmother had died in 1939, and we four children inherited what would have been my father's share. For some of the money my brother and I bought a yacht, and took up sailing, and this has since been an important part of my leisure time life. After the occupation the Germans had forbidden sailing in the Danish seas except on the fjord where Lemvig was situated, and another fjord in Zealand.

The resistance against the Germans increased as time went on, and sabotage slowly started. Weapons and ammunition for the resistance movement began to be dropped by English planes, and in August 1943 there were general strikes all over the country against the Germans with the demand that the Government stopped giving way to the Germans. The Government consequently resigned, the Germans took over, the Danish marine sank the fleet and the army was disarmed. An illegal Frihedsråd (the Danish Liberation Council) revealed itself, which from then on was what people listened to and took advice from.

Following this, the sabotage against railways and factories working for the Germans increased, and with this arrests and executions. One of our medical classmates was a German informer. We knew who he was, so we could take care. He was eventually liquidated by unknowns. We feared a reaction from Gestapo against the class, and stayed away from the teaching.

The Germans planned to arrest the Jews, but the date, the night between the first and second October 1943 was revealed by a high placed German. By help from many, many people the Jews were hidden. Of about 7000, the Germans caught 472, who were sent to Theresienstadt where 52 died. In the following weeks illegal routes were established across the sea, Øresund, to Sweden, and the Jews were during the nights brought to safety. From all sides of the Danish society there were strong protests against the Germans for this encroachment on fellow-countrymen.

In May and June 1944, we managed to get our exams. A number of our teachers had gone underground, but their job was taken over by others. We could not assemble to sign the Hippocratic oath, but had to come one by one at a place away from the University not known by others.

I returned to my home for the summer vacation. The Germans had taken over part of my mother's house, and had used it for housing Danes working for the Germans. This was extremely unpleasant for my mother, but she would not leave her house and stayed. I addressed the local German commander, and managed to get him to move the "foreigners" from the house at least as long as we four children were home on holiday.

The Germans had forbidden sailing, but not rowing, so we bought a canoe and spent the holidays rowing on the fjord.

After the summer holidays I started my internship in a hospital in Hjørring in the northern part of the country. I first spent 6 months in the medical ward, and then 6 months in the surgical ward. I became very interested in surgery, not least because the assistant physician, next in charge after the senior surgeon, was very eager to teach me how to make smaller operations, like removing a diseased appendix. I soon discovered why. When we were on call together and we during the night got a patient with appendicitis, it happened–after we had started the operation–that he asked me to take over and left. He was then on his way to receive weapons and explosives which were dropped by English planes on a dropping field outside Hjørring. I found that this was more important than operating patients for appendicitis, but we had of course to take care of the patients in spite of a war going on. He was finally caught by the Gestapo, and sent to a concentration camp, fortunately not in Germany, but in the southern part of Denmark, where he survived and was released on the 5th of May 1945, when the Germans in Denmark surrendered.

I continued for another year in the surgical ward. It was here I became interested in the effect of local anaesthetics, and decided to use this as a subject for a thesis. Thereafter I got a position at the Orthopaedic Hospital in Aarhus as part of the education in surgery.

In 1947 I stopped clinical training, and got a position at the Institute for Medical Physiology at Aarhus University in order to write the planned doctoral thesis on the anaesthetic and toxic mechanism of action of local anaesthetics.

During my time in Hjørring I met a very beautiful probationer, Ellen Margrethe Nielsen, with whom I fell in love. I had become ill while I was on the medical ward, and spent some time in bed in the ward. I had a single room and a radio, so I invited her to come in the evening to listen to the English radio, which was strictly forbidden by the Germans – but was what everybody did.

After she had finished her education as a nurse in 1948, she came to Aarhus and we married. In 1950 we had a daughter, but unfortunately she had an inborn disease and died after 1 1/2 year. Even though this was very hard, it brought my wife and I closer together. In 1952, and in 1954 respectively we got two healthy daughters, Hanne and Karen.

The salary at the University was very low, so partly because of this but also because I was interested in using my education as a medical doctor, I took in 1949 an extra job as doctor on call one night a week. It furthermore had the advantage that I could get a permission to buy a car and to get a telephone. There were still after war restrictions on these items.

I was born in a milieu which politically was conservative. The job as a doctor on call changed my political attitude and I became a social democrat. I realized how important it is to have free medical care, free education with equal opportunities, and a welfare system which takes care of the weak, the handicapped, the old, and the unemployed, even if this means high taxes. Or as phrased by one of our philosophers, N.F.S. Grundtvig, "a society where few have too much, and fewer too little".

We lived in a flat, so the car gave us new possibilities. We wanted to have a house, and my mother would give us the payment, but I was stubborn, and wanted to earn the money myself. In 1957 we bought a house with a nice garden in Risskov, a suburb to Aarhus not far away from the University.

I am a family man, I restricted my work at the Institute to 8 hours a day, from 8 to 4 or 9 to 5, worked concentratedly while I was there, went home and spent the rest of the day and the evening with my wife and children. All weekends and holidays, and 4 weeks summer holidays were spent with the family. In 1960 we bought an acre of land on a cliff facing the beach 45 minutes by car from Aarhus, and built a small summer house. From then on this became the centre for our leisure time life. We bought a dinghy and a rowing boat with outboard motor and I started to teach the children how to sail, and to fish with fishing rod and with net.

Later, when the girls grew older, we bought a yacht, the girls and I sailed in the Danish seas, and up along the west coast of Sweden. My wife easily gets seasick, but joined us on day tours. Later the girls took their friends on sail tours.

In wintertime the family skied as soon as there was snow. A friend of mine, Karl Ove Nielsen, a professor of physics, took me in the beginning of the 1960s at Easter time on an 8-day cross country ski tour through the high mountain area in Norway, Jotunheimen. We stayed overnight in the Norwegian Tourist Association's huts on the trail, which were open during the Easter week. It was a wonderful experience, but also a tour where you had to take all safety precautions. It became for many years a tradition. Later the girls joined us, and they also took some of their friends. When the weather situation did not allow this tour, we spent a week in more peaceful surroundings either in Norway with cross-country skiing or in the Alps with slalom. We still do, now with the girls, their husbands and the grandchildren. Outside the sporting activities, I spend much time listening to classical music, and reading, first of all biographies.

When the children left home, one for studying medicine and the other architecture, my wife, worked for several years as a nurse in a psychiatric hospital for children, then engaged herself in politics. She was elected for the County Council for the social democrats, and spent 12 years on the council, first of all working with health care problems. She was also elected to the county scientific ethical committee, which evaluates all research which involves human beings. Later she was elected co-chairman to the Danish Central Scientific Ethical Committee, which lay down the guidelines for the work on the local committees, and which is an appeal committee for the local committees as well as for the doctors. She has worked 17 years on the committees and has been lecturing nurses and doctors about ethical problems.

I had no scientific training when I started at the Institute of Physiology in 1947. It took me a good deal of time before I knew how to attack the problem I was interested in and get acquainted with this new type of work. The chairman, Professor Søren L. Ørskov was a very considerate person, extremely helpful, patient, and gave me the time necessary to find my feet. During the work I got so interested in doing scientific work that I decided to continue and give up surgery. The thesis was published as a book in Danish in l954, and written up in 6 papers published in English. The work on the local anaesthetics, brought me as described in the following paper to the identification of the sodium-potassium pump, which is responsible for the active transport of sodium and potassium across the cell membrane. The paper was published in l957. From then on my scientific interest shifted from the effect of local anaesthetics to active transport of cations.

In the 1940s and the first part of the 1950s, the amount of money allocated for research was small. Professor Ørskov, fell chronically ill. His illness developed slowly so he continued in his position, but I, as the oldest in the department after him, had partly to take over his job. This meant that besides teaching in the semesters I had to spend two months per year examining orally the students in physiology.

The identification of the sodium-potassium pump gave us contact to the outside scientific world. In 1961, I met R.W. Berliner at an international Pharmacology meeting in Stockholm. He mentioned the possibility of obtaining a grant from National Institutes of Health (NIH). I applied and got a grant for two years. The importance of this was not only the money, but that it showed interest in the work we were doing.

In 1963, Professor Ørskov resigned and I was appointed professor and chairman. In the late 1950s and especially in the 1960s, more money was allocated to the Universities, and also more positions. Due to the work with the sodium-potassium pump, it became possible to attract clever young people, and the institute staff in a few years increased from 4 to 20–25 scientists. This had also an effect on the teaching. I got a young doctor, Noe Næraa, who had expressed ideas about medical teaching, to accept a position at the Institute. He started to reorganise our old fashioned laboratory course, we got new modern equipment, and thereafter we also reorganised the teaching, made it problem-oriented with teaching in small classes. My scientific interest was membrane physiology, but I wanted also to find people who could cover other aspects of physiology, so we ended up with 5–6 groups who worked scientifically with different physiological subjects.

In 1972 we got a new statute for the Universities, which involved a democratization of the whole system. The chairman was no longer the professor (elected by the board of chairmen which made up the faculty), but he/she was now elected by all scientists and technicians in the Institute and could be anybody, scientist or technician. This was of course a great relief for me because I could get rid of all my administrative duties. A problem was, however, that I got elected as chairman, but later others took over. In the beginning it was very tedious to work with the system, not least because everybody thought that they should be asked and take part in every decision. Later we learned to hand over the responsibility to an elected board at the Institute.

In these years the money to the Institutes came from the Faculty, which got it from the University (which got it from the State). The money was then divided inside the institute by the chairman, and later by the elected board. It was usually sufficient to cover the daily expenses of the research. External funds were only for bigger equipment. Besides research-money we had a staff of very well trained laboratory assistants, whose positions–as well as the positions of the scientific staff–was paid by the University. The institute every year sent a budget for the coming year, to the faculty, who then sent a budget for the faculty to the University, and the University to the State.

This way of funding had the great advantage that there was not a steady pressure on the scientists for publication and for sending applications for external funds. It was a system that allowed everybody to start on his/her own project, independently, and test their ideas. Nobody was forced from lack of money to join a group which had money and work on their ideas. It was also a system which could be misused, by people who were not active scientifically. With an elected board it proved difficult to handle such a situation. Not least because the very active scientists tried to avoid being elected–i.e. it could be the least active who actually decided. In practice, however, the not very active scientists usually accepted to do an extra job with the teaching, thus relieving the very active scientists from part of the teaching burden.

In the 1980s this was changed, the money for science was transferred to centralized (state) funds, and had to be applied for by the individual scientist.

Not an advantage from my point of view. Applications took a lot of time, it tempted a too fast publication, and to publish too short papers, and the evaluation process used a lot of manpower. It does not give time to become absorbed in a problem as the previous system.

My research interest was concentrated around the structure and function of the active transport system, the Na^+,K^+-ATPase. A number of very excellent clever young scientists worked on different sides of the subject, either their own choice or suggested by me. Each worked independent on his/her subject. Scientists who took part in the work on the Na^+,K^+-ATPase and who made important contributions to field were, P.L. Jørgensen (purification and structure), I. Klodos (phosphorylation), O. Hansen (effect of cardiac glycosides and vanadate), P. Ottolenghi (effect of lipids), J. Jensen (ligand binding), J. G. Nørby (phosphorylation, ligand binding, kinetics), L. Plesner (kinetics), M. Esmann (solubilization of the enzyme, molecular weight, ESR studies), T. Clausen (hormonal control), A.B. Maunsbach and E. Skriver from the Institute of Anatomy in collaboration with P.L. Jørgensen (electron microscopy and crystallization), and I. Plesner from the Department of Chemistry (enzyme kinetics and evaluation of models). We also had many visitors.

We got many contacts to scientists in different parts of the world, and I spent a good deal of time travelling giving lectures. In 1973 the first international meeting on the Na^+,K^+-ATPase was held in New York. The next was 5 years later in Århus, and thereafter every third year. The proceedings from these meetings have been a very valuable source of information about the development of the field.

My wife joined me on many of the tours and we got friends abroad. Apart from the scientific inspiration the travelling also gave many cultural experiences, symphony concerts, opera and ballet, visits to Cuzco and Machu Picchu in Peru, to Uxmal and Chichén Itzá on the Yucatan Peninsula, and to museums in many different countries. Not to speak of the architectural experiences from seeing many different parts of the world. And not least it gave us good friends.

It is not always easy to keep your papers in order when travelling. Sitting in the airport in Moscow in the 1960s waiting for departure to Khabarovsk in the eastern part of Siberia, we–three Danes on our way to a meeting in Tokyo–realized that we had forgotten our passports at the hotel in town. There were twenty minutes to departure and no way to get the passports in time. We asked Intourist what to do. There was only one boat connection a week from Nakhodka, where we should embark to Yokohama, so they suggested that we should go on, they would send the passports after us. I had once had a nightmare, that I should end my days in Siberia. When we after an overnight flight arrived in Khabarovsk we were met by a lady who asked if we were the gentlemen without passports. We could not deny, and she told us that they would not arrive until after we had left Khabarovsk by train to Nakhodka. But they would send them by plane to Vladivostok and from there by car to Nakhodka. To our question if we could leave Siberia without our passports the answer was no. When the train the following morning stopped in Nakhodka, a man came into the sleeping car and asked if we were the gentlemen without passports. To our "yes" he said "here you are", and handed over the passports. Amazing. We had an uncomplicated boat trip to Yokohama.

It was not as easy some years later in Argentina. I had been at a meeting in Mendoza, had stopped in Cordoba on the way, had showed passport in and out of the airports without problems. Returning to Buenos Aires to leave for New York, the man at the counter told me that my passport had expired three months earlier, and according to rules I had to return direct to my home country. I argued that I was sure I could get into the U.S., but he would not give way. We discussed for half an hour. Finally shortly before departure he would let me go to New York if he could reserve a plane out of New York to Denmark immediately after my arrival. He did the reservation, put a label on my ticket with the time of departure, and by the second call for departure I rushed off, hearing him saying "You can always remove the label". In New York, I stepped to the rear end of the line, hoping the man at the counter would be tired when it was my turn. He was not. I asked if I had to return to Denmark. "There is always a way out" was his answer, "No, go to the other counter, sign some papers, pay 5 dollars, and I let you in".

In 1977, I was offered the chair of Biophysics at the medical faculty. It was a smaller department, with 7 positions for scientists, of which 5 were empty, which meant that we could get positions for I. Klodos and M. Esmann, who had fellowships. Besides J. G. Nørby and L. Plesner moved with us. The two members in the Institute, M. J. Mulvany and F. Cornelius became interested in the connection between pump activity and vasoconstriction, and reconstitution of the enzyme into liposomes, respectively, i.e. all in the institute worked on different sides of the same problem, the structure and function of the Na^+,K^+-ATPase. We got more space, less administration, and I were free of teaching obligations.

We all got along very well, lived in a relaxed atmosphere, inspiring and helping each other, cooperating, also with the Na^+,K^+-ATPase colleagues left in the Physiological Institute. And even if we all worked on different sides of the same problem, there were never problems of interfering in each others subjects, or about priority.

In 1988, I retired, kept my office, gave up systematic experimental work and started to work on kinetic models for the overall reaction of the pump on computer. For this I had to learn how to programme, quite interesting, and amazing what you can do with a computer from the point of view of handling even complicated models. And even if my working hours are fewer, being free of all obligations, the time I spent on scientific problems are about the same as before my retirement.

I enjoy no longer having a meeting calendar, I enjoy to go fly-fishing when the weather is right, and enjoy spending a lot of time with my grandchildren.

THE IDENTIFICATION OF THE SODIUM-POTASSIUM PUMP

Nobel Lecture, December 8, 1997

by

Jens C. Skou

Department of Biophysics, University of Aarhus, Ole Worms Allé 185,
DK-8000 Aarhus C, Denmark.

> Looking for the answer.
>
> > You hunt it,
> > you catch it,
> > You fool yourself;
> > the answer,
> > is always,
> > a step ahead.
> >
> > J. C. S.

INTRODUCTION

The cell membrane separates the cell from the surrounding medium. In 1925 Gorter and Grendel[1] extracted the lipids from red blood cells, spread them in a monomolecular layer on a water phase, and measured the compressed area. It was about the double of the surface area of the extracted red blood cells. They suggested that the cell membrane is a bilayer of lipids with the charged head groups of the phospholipids facing the water phase on the two sides of the membrane, and with the hydrocarbon chains meeting in the middle of the membrane. The thickness of the membrane is about 40 Å, much too small to be seen under a microscope.

The surface tension of invertebrate eggs and other cells is however, much lower than for a water-lipid interphase. To explain this, Danielli and Davson in 1935[2] suggested that there is an adsorbed layer of proteins on each side of the lipid bilayer. They also introduced a layer of non-oriented lipids in the middle of the bilayer.

In the cytoplasm there are proteins for which the cell membrane is impermeable. At the cell pH they carry negative charges, neutralized by potassium, K^+, which in the cell is at a concentration of about 150 meq/l, while outside the cell the K^+ concentration is 4 meq/l. The difference in K^+ concentration was explained as due to a Donnan effect of the proteins, and that the membrane is permeable to K^+. The Donnan effect gives an osmotic pressure, which is higher inside the cell than outside, and since the membrane is permeable to water, water will flow in, and as the lipid bilayer cannot resist a hydrostatic pressure the cell will swell and finally burst.

The higher osmotic pressure inside the cell is opposed by a high concentration of sodium, Na^+, outside, 140 meq/l, while the concentration inside is low, about 10–20 meq/l. A problem is to explain how this difference in the Na^+ concentration on the two sides of the membrane can be maintained. There are two possible explanations:

One is that the membrane is impermeable to Na^+, that it is an equilibrium situation. This view was advocated by Conway, an Irish biochemist from Dublin. Boyle and Conway published in 1941 a paper in which they showed that for muscle fibers soaked in solutions with varying K^+ concentrations, the calculated intracellullar K^+ concentrations, based on this assumption agreed with the measured[3]. There were, however, two problems. One was that this agreement did not hold at the normal physiological concentrations of K^+, only at higher concentrations. The other was the requirement of Na^+ impermeability. But how then to explain that there is sodium in the cell, even if it is at a low concentration. Conway gave no answers to these problems.

The other possibility is that the membrane is permeable to Na^+, and that there are secretory, energy dependent processes in the cell, which compensate for the steady influx of Na^+, a steady state distribution. This view was advocated by R.B. Dean in a paper also published in 1941 entitled: "Theories of Electrolyte Equilibrium in Muscle"[4]. Referring to investigations by L.A. Heppel (1939,1940), by L.A. Heppel and C.L.A Schmidt (1938), and by H.B. Steinbach (1940) (see ref. 4) on muscle fibers, which had shown that the muscle membrane, contrary to the view held by Conway, is permeable to Na^+, Dean concluded: "the muscle can actively move potassium and sodium against concentration gradients ... this requires work. Therefore there must be some sort of a pump possibly located in the fiber membrane, which can pump out sodium or, what is equivalent, pump in potassium."

In the following decade, helped by the introduction of radioactive isotopes of Na^+, and K^+[5], it was shown not only from experiments on muscle fibers, but on red blood cells, on nerves, and on frog skin that the membrane is permeable to Na^+ as well as to K^+, (for references see an extensive review by Ussing[6]). An energy dependent efflux of Na^+ is therefore necessary.

However, Conway strongly defended his view about the impermeability to sodium, and only reluctantly gave way. He admitted that there may be a certain permeability for Na^+ and thereby a need for a pump, but that low permeability for Na^+ is the main explanation of the concentration gradient. Conway's concern was, that it is a waste of energy to have a membrane permeable to Na^+, and then spend energy to pump Na^+ out. Krogh[7] had in a Croonian lecture in 1946 entitled "The active and passive exchange of inorganic ions through the surfaces of living cells and through living membranes generally" criticised Conway's view about impermeability to sodium. Krogh concluded: "The power of active transport of ions is of a common occurrence both in the vegetable and the animal kingdom and is possibly a general characteristic of the protoplasmic surface membrane". Conway replied the same year in a paper in Nature[8]: "Krogh ... considers the apparent impermeability to sodium as due to an active extrusion, sodium ions entering the (muscle) fibers as fast, if indeed not faster, than potassium. The following may then be considered: the minimal energy required for extrusion of sodium ions from the normal frog's sartorius if sodium enters as fast as potassium". A calculation showed that the energy requirement was about twice the resting metabolism of the muscle. Ussing[9] came to the same result, but he explained what the apparent problem was. Only a part of the measured Na^+ flux is due to active transport of Na^+, the other part is due to an exchange across the membrane of Na^+ from the one side for Na^+ from the other side, a Na:Na exchange, which is energetically neutral, and which gives no net flux of Na^+ across the membrane. Taking this into account, the energy available is more than sufficient. However, Conway's concern was relevant in the sense that with the knowledge at that time about membrane function, an active transport seemed energetically an expensive way to solve the osmotic problem of the cell.

In the 1940s and first half of the 1950s the concept of active transport developed[6]. It was defined as a transport against an electrochemical gradient[10]. It was shown that the active efflux of sodium was coupled to an influx of potassium, a pump, and that the substrate for the transport was energy rich phosphate esters (for references see[11]).

But what was the nature of the pump? With the information available in the beginning of the 1950s it was possible to foresee that the pump is a membrane bound protein with enzymatic activity, which has ATP as substrate and is activated by Na^+ on the cytoplasmic side, and by K^+ on the extracellular side. But nobody apparently thought that way. A reason may be that the membrane according to the model by Danielli and Davson is a bilayer of lipids with no room for proteins inside the bilayer spanning the bilayer. On the contrary it was assumed that protein in the bilayer would destabilize the cell membrane. It was assumed that the protein was in the interphase between the lipids and the water on the two sides of the membrane.

THE WAY TO THE SODIUM PUMP[12-13].

My scientific interest was the mechanism of action of local anaesthetics. I held a position at the Institute of Physiology at the University of Århus, and was using this problem as subject for a thesis. In 1953, I had finished a series of experiments on the problem, which was published in 1954 in book form in Danish, and accepted by the faculty to be defended for the medical doctor's degree[14]. It was also published as 6 papers in English[15].

I had received my medical degree in the summer 1944, and started my internship at a hospital in Hjørring in the northern part of the country, six months in the medical ward followed by six months in the surgical ward. I became interested in surgery, and after my internship I continued for another year in the surgical ward. We had no anaesthetists, and to avoid the unpleasant ether narcosis, we used whenever possible spinal and local anaesthesia. From the teaching of pharmacology I knew the Meyer-Overton theory[16-17], that there is a correlation between solubility of general anaesthetics in lipids, and the anaesthetic potency. General anaesthetics are non-polar substances, while local anaesthetics are weak bases, which at the physiological pH exist as a mixture of charged and uncharged molecules. I wondered which of the two components is the anaesthetic component, and whether a correlation, similar to that for the general anaesthetics, existed for the local anaesthetics. I decided to use this problem as a subject for a thesis. After the two years at the hospital in Hjørring, I took up a position for a year at the Orthopaedic Hospital in Aarhus, and after this, in 1947 I applied for and received a position at the Institute of Medical Physiology at Aarhus University.

Aarhus University was young, founded 19 years earlier. There were Institutes for Anatomy, Biochemistry and Physiology as a beginning of a Medical Faculty, which was not completed until 1957. These were the only biological Institutes at the Campus, and the scientific biology milieu was poor, with little or no contact with the outside scientific world. We were three young doctors besides the Professor, Søren L. Ørskov, in the department each working on our thesis. None of us had any scientific background, but Ørskov was very helpful, patient and let us take the necessary time. We had an intake of 140 medical students a year so the teaching load was heavy. After having passed physiology the students had to continue at the medical faculty in Copenhagen for their medical degree.

I used the intact sciatic nerve of frog legs as a test object for measuring the blocking potency of five different local anaesthetics, which are weak bases, and of butanol as a representative of a nonpolar blocking agent. After removing the sheath around the nerve to get easier access to the single nerve fibers, I measured the blocking concentration as a function of time, and from this the minimum blocking concentration at infinite time of exposure could be determined. The concentrations necessary varied from the weakest to the strongest of the local anaesthetics by a factor of 1:920 (with butanol included, 1:13.500).

The order of anaesthetic potency and solubility in lipids were the same, but the quantitative correlation was poor, i.e. local anaesthetics did not follow the Meyer-Overton rule for general anaesthetics.

I was looking for another test object. As the cell membrane is a bilayer of lipids, I decided to use a monomolecular layer of lipids on a Krebs-Ringer water phase as a model for a water cell membrane interphase. The inspiration came from reading about Langmuir's work on monomolecular layers of lipids on a water phase in "The Physics and Chemistry of Surfaces" by N.K. Adam, and that Schulmann had applied capillary active drugs in the waterphase beneath the monolayer, and observed that they penetrated up into the monolayer[18].

In a Langmuir trough the area of the monolayer can be measured as a function of the pressure that the monolayer exerts on a floating barrier, which separates the monolayer from the pure water phase without the monolayer. My first experiments were with a monolayer of stearic acid. At a given area per molecule, which also means at a given surface pressure, application of the local anaesthetics to the water phase gave an increase in pressure, indicating that the local anaesthetics penetrated up into the monolayer, and the pressure increased with the concentration. There was a certain correlation between anaesthetic potency and pressure increase, but quantitatively not clear enough. However, with a monolayer of lipids extracted from the sciatic frog nerves there was a reasonably good correlation. The order of the concentrations necessary to increase the pressure followed the order of anaesthetic potency. And the minimum blocking concentration of the five local anaesthetics, which as mentioned varied by a factor of 1:920, gave a pressure increase in the monolayer at a certain area which was of the same order, they varied by a factor of 1:3.2. Also the effect of a change in pH on the local anaesthetic potency correlated reasonable well to the effect of pH on the pressure increase at a given area.

The rising phase of the nerve impulse, the depolarization is due to a transient increase in permeability of the membrane for Na^{+}[19]. The molecular basis for this was unknown, but it seemed unlikely that it was connected to the lipids. I assumed that the permeability increase was on proteins in the membrane. The monolayer results suggested to me, that the effect of the penetration of local anaesthetics into the lipid part of the nerve membrane was a blocking of the conformational change in proteins in the membrane, which gave the increase in permeablity to Na^{+}.

To test this I wanted to see if pressure in a monolayer could influence the enzymatic activity of a protein in the monolayer, and take this as indication of an effect of pressure on conformation. And if there was an effect, then form a monolayer of a mixture of lipids and the enzyme, and test if penetration of local anaesthetics into the monolayer had an effect on the enzymatic activity. For this I needed an enzyme with high activity, which was related to membrane function. A candidate was acetylcholinesterase, which was then being prepared from electric eel by Professor Nachmansohn at Columbia University in New York. It had the further advantage that it involved a visit to New York.

The Professor of Physiology in Copenhagen Einar Lundsgaard was a close friend of David Nachmansohn and introduced me. I had planned to spend August in New York, take a break at the end of August and beginning of September to attend the 19th International Congress of Physiology in Montreal, and then return to New York in September*. This would fit with my teaching schedule. Nachmansohn would not be in New York until September, as he spent the summer at the Marine Biological Station in Woods Hole, he therefore suggested I should join him there in August. In September he would return to New York. I agreed, although I did not know what to do in Woods Hole; there was no access to electric eel.

Scientists interested in the function of the nervous system came from all over the world to Woods Hole during the summer, to use the giant axons from squids as test objects. Coming from a young University with a poor scientific milieu, this was like coming to another planet. The place was bubbling with scientific activity. I realized that science is a serious affair and not just a

* Not July and August as mentioned in references 12 and 13.

temporary hobby for young doctors writing a thesis in order to qualify for a clinical career. And also that it is competitive. I listened to lectures, met people whose names I knew from the textbooks, and from the literature, spent time in the laboratories looking on, and learning from the experiments.

In between I did some reading, and in a paper written by Nachmansohn, it was mentioned that B. Libet[20] in 1948 had shown that there is an ATP hydrolysing enzyme in the sheath part of the giant axon from squid: an ATPase. As ATP is the energy source in cells I wondered what the function could be of an ATPase in the membrane of a nerve. Situated in the membrane I assumed that it was a lipoprotein, and this was what I needed for the monolayer experiments. I decided to look for the enzyme when I came home.

I prepared acetylcholinesterase at Columbia University in September from the electric eel. Back in Aarhus I continued the monolayer experiments.

I had no access to giant axons in Aarhus, but decided to look for the putative nerve membrane ATPase in crab nerves, because the crab nerve, like the giant axon, has no myelin sheath. In 1954 I arranged with a fisherman south of Aarhus to send me some crabs, and started to isolate the sciatic nerve from the legs. The nerves were homogenized and the membrane pieces isolated by a differential centrifugation.

The experiments showed that the membrane fractions had a low magnesium (Mg^{2+}) activated ATP hydrolysing enzyme activity. Addition of Na^+ besides Mg^{2+} gave a slight increase in activity. K^+ had no effect in the presence of Mg^{2+}, Fig. 1. However the activity varied from experiment to experiment. Calcium (Ca^{2+}) was excluded as the reason for the variations. After having spent November–December trying to find a solution I gave up and went on my Christmas holiday. I resumed the experiments in June the following year, but still without being able to get reproducible results, went on summer holidays. Returning in August, I made a Na^+ salt of ATP and a K^+ salt and found to my surprise that the activity with the K^+ salt was higher than with the Na^+ salt. This could not be due to a difference in ATP but to an effect of K^+ which differed from that of Na^+. But why in this experiment and not in the previous experiments, where K^+ had no effects in the presence of Mg^{2+}. The answer was that in the experiments with the K^+ salt of ATP there was Na^+ in the medium. In other words the enzyme needed a combined effect of Na^+ and K^+ for activation. I then started a systematic investigation of the combined effect of the two cations.

As seen from Fig. 1, K^+ has two effects in the presence of Na^+. It activates, the higher the concentration is of Na^+. The K^+ affinity for the activating effect is high. At higher concentrations the activating effect of K^+ decreases, and the apparent affinity for K^+ for this effect decreases with an increase in the Na^+ concentration. With 3 mM Na^+ it is seen that K^+ not only inhibits its own activation, but also the small activation due to Na^+. The results suggest that there are two sites on the enzyme, one where Na^+ is necessary for activation, and another where K^+ activates when Na^+ is bound to the former. K^+ in higher concentrations competes for Na^+ at the Na^+ site, and by displacing Na^+ from the site decreases the activity.

250

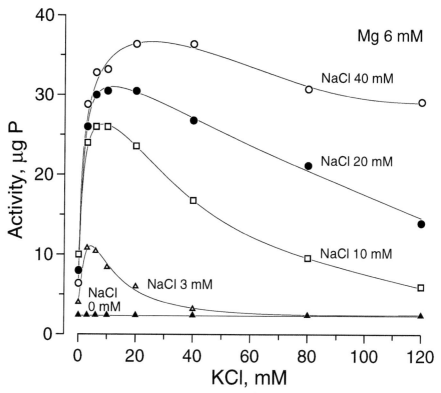

Figure 1. Effect of Na$^+$, and of K$^+$ in the presence of Mg^{2+} on the hydrolysis of ATP by membrane fractions isolated from nerves of the shore crab *Carcinus maenas*. Test solution contained 30 mM histidine HCL as buffer, pH 7.2, 3 mM ATP, 6 mM Mg^{2+}, Na$^+$ and K$^+$ in concentrations shown on the Figure. Activity is given as µg P (inorganic phosphate) hydrolysed from ATP in 30 min. at 36 °C (Reprinted by permission from.[27])

I now understood the reason for the varying results. With little effect of Na$^+$ on the activity, and of no effect of K$^+$, I had not bothered whether or not there was Na$^+$ or K$^+$ in the medium. I got ATP as an insoluble barium salt, which was converted to a soluble Na$^+$ or K$^+$ salt, sometimes the one sometimes the other, and in between instead of homogenising the nerves in glucose I used a 0.58 M KCl solution. It never occurred to me that there could be a combined effect of Na$^+$ and of K$^+$.

The problem then was, what was the physiological function of the enzyme? I was interested in the effect of local anaesthetics on nerve conduction, and my first reaction was that this was the Na$^+$ channel, which opens for the influx of Na$^+$ leading to the nerve impulse. I soon rejected the idea because the opening of the channel is voltage dependent, and not dependent on ATP. The other possibility was that it was part of or the sodium pump. I had little knowledge about the active transport of Na$^+$ and of K$^+$, I therefore started to look into the literature to see what the substrate was for the active transport in nerves. I had limited access to the literature, so there were few papers I read about active transport. The closest I could come was that A.L. Hodgkin and

R.D. Keynes[21] had shown that poisoning giant axons with dinitrophenol, cyanide or azide, decreased the active transport of sodium, suggesting that high energy phosphate esters are the substrate. And as ATP is a high energy phosphate ester, I thought it likely that it could be the substrate.

There were two papers I did not read, one was by G. Gardos[22] from Budapest published in 1954 in a Hungarian journal, which I did not have access to, and which was not cited in the paper by Hodgkin and Keynes. In this Gardos showed that ATP supported the active uptake of K^+ in red blood cells. The other was a paper published in 1956 by Hodgkin and Keynes[23], in which they reported that injecting ATP in a cyanide poisoned giant axon gave no dramatic recovery of the active extrusion of sodium. Fortunately, I did not see this last paper until I had sent my paper on the crab nerve enzyme for publication. In 1957, the experiment was repeated by Caldwell and Keynes[24], with the result that ATP was the substrate for the active transport.

In a discussion after a paper by R.D. Keynes on "Electrolytes and Nerve Activity"[25] at an international symposium on Neurochemistry in Aarhus in 1956, I showed the results with the crab nerve ATPase[26]. The same year I wrote the paper, and suggested from the characteristics of the effect of the cations, and that fact that ATP was a substrate, that the enzyme was involved in the active transport of Na^+ across the cell membrane. I considered putting the word pump in the title, but found it too provocative, so it became "The Influence of Some Cations on an Adenosine Triphosphatase from Peripheral Nerves". No wonder that few people noticed that this enzyme had to do with active transport of Na^+. It was published in 1957[27].

With my little knowledge about active transport, I was unaware of the importance of the observation on the crab nerves. Parallel with the crab nerve experiments I continued the experiments on the monolayer with the acetylcholinesterase. In 1958, I presented a paper at the 4th International Congress of Biochemistry in Vienna on "The Influence of the Degree of Unfolding and the Orientation of the Side Chains on the Activity of a Surface Spread Enzyme".

There was one important experiment I had not done. I realized this when I met Robert Post at the conference. I knew Robert from Woods Hole. We had spent time in the same laboratory, and I had driven with him and his wife Elisabeth in their car from Woods Hole to the International Congress for Physiology in Montreal. He told me that he had since worked with active transport of Na^+ and K^+ in red blood cells, and had shown that the stoichiometry between the Na^+ transport out of, and of K^+ into, the cell was 3 to 2^{28}.

I told him about the Na^+ + K^+ activated crab nerve enzyme, and that it seemed to be part of or the sodium pump. His reaction suggested to me that this was more important than surface spread enzymes. "Is it inhibited by ouabain"? he asked. "What is ouabain" was my reply. He then told me that Schatzmann in Switzerland in 1954 had shown that cardiac glycosides, of which ouabain is the most water soluble, specifically inhibits the active transport in red blood cells[29]. When Robert Post came to Aarhus after the conference I had the answer. The enzyme was inhibited by Ouabain, even if the sensitivity of the crab nerve enzyme is much lower than the sensitivity of the

252

transport in red blood cells. It convinced Robert that the enzyme had to do with active transport. I had learned that red blood cells were a classical test object for experiments on active transport, and had started to look for the enzyme in these cells. Robert asked if he could go on with these experiments when he returned to U.S.. I had no experience with this test object, and as he had the experience I agreed, and continued the experiments with the crab nerve enzyme[30], and looked for the enzyme in other tissues[31].

In 1959, after I had given my first paper on the crab nerve enzyme at the 21th International Congress for Physiology in Buenos Aires, Professor Hodgkin, who was the great name in neurophysiology and came from the famous Cambridge University, invited me for lunch to hear more about the enzyme. His interest suggested to me that the observation was of a certain importance.

Looking back, it was a very simple experiment to identify the pump. Just break the membrane and by this gain access to the Na^+ site on the inside and the K^+ site on the outside, add some ATP and test for the combined effect of Na^+ and K^+. It ought to have been done by someone who worked in the transport field and knew about active transport. I felt like an intruder in a field that was not mine.

There was however, much luck involved. First, that Nachmansohn had invited me to Woods Hole, where I learned about the giant axons and read about the observation by Libet. Next, that from the monolayer experiments I became interested in membrane proteins, especially lipoproteins, and therefore took notice of Libet's observation. Finally, that I chose crab nerves as a test object. I learned later, that after homogenization of most other tissues in order to break the membrane, the membrane pieces form vesicles, which must be opened by treatment with detergent, in order to get access to both sides of the membrane, and thereby to see the combined effect of Na^+ and K^+. This is not the case with the crab nerve membranes.

From then on the Na^+,K^+-ATPase took me away from the monolayer experiments. I never did the planned experiments on the effect of the local anaesthetics on a monolayer of a mixture of lipids and proteins; and I never used the Na^+,K^+-ATPase for monolayer experiments, first of all because it was not until 1980 that it became possible to extract the enzyme from a membrane in a pure stable water-soluble form, and secondly that was only possible with the use of detergent[32]. A problem would have been the detergent, but I had lost interest in monolayers.

In 1960, Robert Post published the paper on the red blood cell experiments, "Membrane adenosine triphosphatase as a participant in the active transport of sodium and potassium in the human erythrocytes" [33]. In this he convincingly showed that in the red blood cells there is a Na^++K^+ activated ATPase also, and that the effect of the cations on the activity correlated with the effect on transport. Robert Post was known in the transport field, and his paper had a better title than mine, so it attracted more attention.

In the following few years many papers were published, which showed that the enzyme could be found in many different tissues, and evidence was given for its involvement in active transport (for references see[34]).

In 1965, so much evidence was at hand, that in a review paper I could conclude that the enzyme system fulfilled the following requirements for a system responsible for the active transport across the cell membrane: 1) it is located in the cell membrane; 2) on the cytoplasmic side, it has a higher affinity for Na^+ than for K^+; 3) it has an affinity for K^+ on the extracellular side, which is higher than for Na^+; 4) it has enzymatic activity and catalyzes ATP hydrolysis; 5) the rate of ATP hydrolysis depends on cytoplasmic Na^+ as well as on extracellular K^+; 6) it is found in all cells that have coupled active transport of Na^+ and K^+; 7) the effect of Na^+ and of K^+ on transport in intact cells, and on the activity of the isolated enzyme, correlates quantitatively; and 8) the enzyme is inhibited by cardiac glycosides, and the inhibitory effect on the active fluxes of the cations correlates with the inhibitory effect on the isolated enzyme system[34].

The enzyme was named the Na^+- and K^+- activated ATPase, or Na^+, K^+-ATPase.

THE Na^+,K^+-ATPase AS AN ENERGY TRANSDUCER

Returning to Conway's concern about the waste of energy. Conway was right in the sense that even if the cell membrane is permeable to sodium, and therefore an energy requiring pump is needed, the ground permeability to sodium of the cell membrane is low, which is necessary in order that the maintenance of the gradient for sodium does not become energetically too costly for the cell. But what is the meaning of having a membrane permeable to sodium and then spend energy, 10–60% of the cell metabolism, to keep Na^+ out of the cell and K^+ within the cell?

1) As mentioned above it solves the osmotic problem due to the presence of impermeable protein anions in the cytoplasm.

But besides this, the gradients for Na^+ into and K^+ out of the cell sustained by the pump represent an energy source, which is used

2) for the creation of a membrane potential. The cell membrane is more permeable to K^+ than to Na^+, which means that K^+ flows out of the cell faster than Na^+ into the cell. This leads to a diffusion potential across the membrane, negative on the inside, which slows the K^+ outflux and increases the Na^+ influx until the potential reaches a value of about –70 mV, at which point the rates of the two fluxes are equal; a steady state situation. The membrane potential is the basis for the function of all excitable tissue. The nerve impulse is a depolarization of the membrane potential due to a transient increase in permeability to Na^+, with influx of Na^+ followed by a repolarization due to an outflux of K^+[35]. This leads to an increase in intracellular Na^+ and a decrease in K^+, which subsequently must be compensated for by the pump.

3) for transport of other substances in and out of the cell, see Fig. 2. In the cell membrane there are a number of protein molecules, which act as co- or countertransporters, or sym- and antiporters[36]. There are cotransporters which use the gradient for Na^+ into the cell to transport glucose[37] or amino acids[38] into cells to a higher concentration inside than outside, a Na^+/Cl^-, a

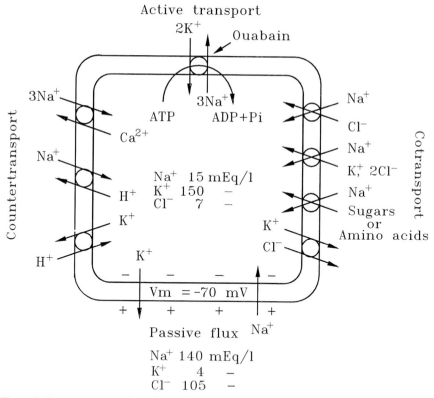

Figure 2. Transport across the cell membrane. For explanation see text. (Reproduced by permission from[73]).

Na$^+$/K$^+$ /2Cl$^-$ and a K$^+$/Cl$^-$ cotransporter, which may be involved in volume regulation (for references see[39]). A 3Na$^+$/Ca^{2+} countertransporter of importance for regulation of the intracellular Ca^{2+} concentration[40], and a Na$^+$/H$^+$ countertransport for regulation of internal pH. In addition, there are other examples.

4) for transepithelial transport in intestine, kidney and secretory glands.

The Na$^+$, K$^+$-pump thus acts as an energy transducer, that converts the chemical energy from the hydrolysis of ATP into another form of energy, a concentration gradient which is used for exchange of substances across the cell membrane. This is named a secondary active transport, while the transport, which is directly dependent on the energy from a chemical reaction, the active Na$^+$, K$^+$ transport, is named a primary active transport. The Na$^+$, K$^+$-ATPase has thus a key function in the exchange of substances across the cell membrane.

A problem was where to place the Na,K-ATPase in the membrane. The transport system, which is a protein, must have access to both sides of the membrane. As mentioned previously there is no room for proteins in the bilayer of the Danielli-Davson membrane model. Neither is there in Robertson's unit membrane model from 1959[41], which replaced it. The unit membrane was a bilayer of lipids with proteins arranged asymmetrically on the two sides of the membrane, but still with no proteins spanning the membrane. It was not until 1972 that a suitable model was introduced by Singer and Nicolson[42]. In their fluid mosaic membrane model there are globular proteins embedded with their non-polar parts in the bilayer, and with the polar parts facing the two sides of the bilayer. They can move laterally in the membrane, but do not flip-flop. They form pathways for the transport of hydrophilic substances across the membrane.

Other mammalian ion transporting pumps were identified in the following years. A Ca^{2+}-ATPase in sarcoplasmic reticulum in muscle responsible for the transport of Ca^{2+} out of the muscle fiber[43], a sarcolemma Ca^{2+}-ATPase isolated from red blood cells which transports Ca^{2+} out of the cell[44], a H^+,K^+-ATPase in the stomach, which transports H^+ out of the cells in exchange for K^+, producing the stomach acid[45]. They all have in common with the Na^+,K^+-ATPase that the reaction with ATP involves a phosphorylation, and they are therefore named P-type ATPases. A number of other P-type ATPases have been identified in bacteria and fungi (see[46]).

In the years that followed the identification of the sodium-potassium pump, many scientists from many countries took part in the elucidation of the structure of the system, and of the reaction steps in the transport process. This cannot be covered in the present lecture, but for those interested I shall refer to an extensive review by I. Glynn 1985[11], to the Proceedings from the International Conferences on the Na^+,K^+-ATPase held every third year, of which the latest is from 1996[47], to recent reviews[48–50], and to the recently published book by J. D. Robinson: "Moving Questions. A History of Membrane Transport and Bioenergetics"[46].

There is, however, one question I would like shortly to touch, without going into details, namely this: what is our present view on the way the system transports the cations?

A MODEL FOR THE TRANSPORT REACTION (see Figure 3).

The model in Fig. 3 is based on the so called Albers-Post scheme, a reaction scheme in which the system reacts consecutively with the cations, and in which the reaction with ATP in the presence of Na^+ leads to a phosphorylation, and the following reaction with K^+ to a dephosphorylation[51–56].

The transport system consists of a carrier part located in the innermost part of the membrane and with the ATP binding part on the cytoplasmic side of the membrane (see Fig. 3). The carrier is in series with a narrow channel which spans half to two thirds of the membrane and opens to the extracellular side of the membrane[57–58] (in Fig. 3 the channel part is shown only as the opening to the outside). The carrier exists in two major different conformations[51–56, 59–65], E_1 which is the high affinity sodium form, and E_2, which is the high affinity potassium form. Each of the two conformations can exist in a phosphorylated[51–56,] and a non-phosphorylated form[59–65], and each of the two major conformations has subconformations marked with primes in the

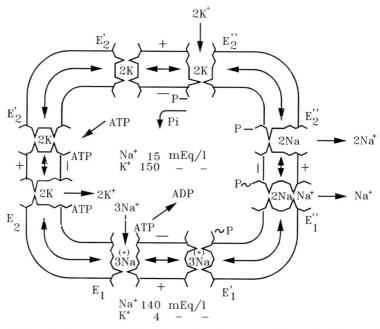

Figure 3. The active transport reaction. For explanation see text. (Reproduced by permission from[73]).

model. The carrier part has two gates, energy barriers, which can open and close access to the channel side and to the cytoplasmic side, respectively.

Referring to the model, with the system in the E_1 conformation with the gate to the cytoplasmic side open but closed to the channel side, 3 Na$^+$ are bound, two of them as a neutral complex and the third one as an ion. The system is catalytically active. The affinity for ATP is high (apparent K_D is about 0.1 μM[59–60]), and with ATP bound the enzyme is phosphorylated[51–56, 66–67], to an ADP sensitive form, which means that a high energy phosphate bond is formed, $E'_1 \sim$P, wich closes the gate to the cytoplasmic side. The 3 Na$^+$ are occluded inside the carrier part[68]. The following two steps, involve conformational changes and rearrangements of the phosphate bond from a high energy to a low energy bond, $E'_1 \sim$P to E''_2-P[51–56, 66–67], and with deocclusion and release of one Na$^+$ from $E''_1 \sim$P[67] to the extracellular side of the membrane. The transition to the E''_2-P form deoccludes, opens the gate for the remaining 2 Na$^+$, and the affinity is shifted to a low Na$^+$ high K$^+$ affinity. By this, the 2 Na$^+$ are exchanged for 2 K$^+$ from the extracellular medium, E''_2-PNa$_2$ to E''_2-PK$_2$. With 2 K$^+$ bound the system is dephosphorylated, the extracellular gate closes and the 2 K$^+$ are occluded, E'_2(K$_2$)[69–70]. ATP bound to E'_2(K$_2$) on the cytoplasmic side, with an affinity which is low (apparent K_D is about 0.1 mM), increases the rate by which the cytoplasmic gate opens and decreases the affinity for K$^+$, E'_2(K$_2$)ATP to E_2K$_2$ATP[69]. The 2 K$^+$ are exchanged for 3 Na$^+$ from the cytoplasmic medium, and this closes the cycle.

The transport system is a very efficient pump. It pumps 3 Na$^+$ out of and 2

257

K$^+$ into the cell for each ATP hydrolysed to ADP and Pi, and for this it uses 70%–85% of the free energy of the hydrolysis of ATP (see[50]). With the normal intra- and extracellular concentrations of Na$^+$ and of K$^+$, the activity of the pump is 10–15% of maximum, i.e. the pump has a considerable reserve power. At 37°C, pH 7.4 the enzyme turns over at a rate of about 160 per sec.

In the transport reaction one net positive charge is carried to the outside. The transport is therefore electrogenic, but due to a high permeability of the cell membrane to Cl⁻, it only adds a few mV to the membrane potential. Each of the two conformations E$_1$ and E$_2$ seem to have 2 negative charged binding sites on which the positive charge of the cations are neutralized, in addition the E$_1$ conformation mentioned above binds a third Na$^+$ in ionic form[71-72].

In order to obtain transport of the cations against an electrochemical gradient coupled to a chemical reaction, the hydrolysis of ATP, it is necessary that there is a tight coupling between each of the steps in the catalytic reaction, and each of the corresponding steps in the translocation reaction, as suggested in the model. The shift in affinities, and the opening and closing of the gates, are coupled to the stepwise degradation of ATP from phosphorylation with a high energy bond, to a low energy bond, and finally to dephosphorylation. This divides the translocation into steps in which local gradients are created along which the ions can flow, and thereby they are transported against their overall gradient.

The model is a working hypothesis, which explain a good deal of the experimental observations. There are however observations which do not fit with the model. And even though we have much information about the structure, there are many unanswered questions, especially at the molecular level. What is the nature of the gates, where are the binding sites for the cations, and of what nature, and how does the system discriminate between Na$^+$ and K$^+$, etc.

CONCLUSION

It may seem disappointing that 30 years of work, since the conclusion that the membrane bound Na$^+$,K$^+$-ATPase is identical with the Na$^+$,K$^+$-pump, has not given us an understanding of the basic molecular events behind the transport. However, considering that the problem is to reveal how 1320 amino acids inside a volume of $60 \times 60 \times 100$ Å^3 can be assembled to a very efficient machine, which can convert the chemical energy from the hydrolysis of ATP into work, namely the transport of cations against their electrochemical gradient, and which can distinguish between so closely related cations as Na$^+$ and K$^+$, it can be of no surprise that progress is slow.

Thirty years ago it seemed impossible to find a way to purify the enzyme not to speak of getting it into solution and reconstitute it into liposomes. Nobody dared to dream about knowing the sequence, and yet this and much much more have been accomplished.

REFERENCES

1. Gorter, E., and F. Grendel, *J. Exp. Med.*, **41**, 439 (1925).
2. Danielli, J. F., and H. Davson, *J. Cell. Comp. Physiol.*, **5**, 495 (1935).
3. Boyle, P. J., and E. F. Conway, *J. Physiol.*, **100**, 1 (1941).
4. Dean, R. B., *Biological Symposia*, **3**, 331 (1941)
5. Hevesy, G., *Enzymologia*, **5**, 138 (1938)
6. Ussing, H. H., *Physiol. Rev.*, **29**, 129 (1949)
7. Krogh, A., *Proc. Roy. Soc. London B.*, **133**, 140 (1946).
8. Conway, E. J., *Nature*, **157**, 715 (1946).
9. Ussing, H. H., *Nature*, **160**, 262 (1947).
10. Rosenberg, T., *Acta Chem. Scand.*, **2**, 14 (1948).
11. Glynn, I. M., in: *The Enzymes of Biological Membranes*, edited by A. N. Martonosi, New York: Plenum, vol. **3**, 28 (1985).
12. Skou, J. C., *Biochim. Biophys. Acta*, **1000**, 435 (1989)
13. Skou, J. C., in*: Membrane Transport: People and Ideas* (ed. D. Tosteson), American Physiol. Soc. p. 155 (1989).
14. Skou, J. C., *Lokalanestetika*. Thesis, Universitetsforlaget Aarhus, (1954).
15. Skou, J. C., *J. Pharm. Pharmacol.*, **13**, 204 (1961).
16. Meyer, H. H., *Arch. Exp. Path. Pharmak.*, **42**, 109 (1899).
17. Overton, E., *Studien über die Narkose zugleich ein Beitrag zur allgemeinen Pharmakologie*, Jena: Fisher (1901).
18. Adam, N. K., *The Physics and Chemistry of Surfaces*, London, Oxford Univ.Press (1941).
19. Hodgkin, A. L., and B. Katz, *J. Physiol.*, **108**, 37 (1949).
20. Libet, B., *Federation Proc.*, **7**, 72 (1948).
21. Hodgkin, A. L., and R. D. Keynes, *J. Physiol. Lond.*, **128**, 28 (1955).
22. Gardos, G., *Acta Physiol. Scient. Hung.*, **6**, 191 (1954).
23. Hodgkin, A. L., and R. D. Keynes, *J. Physiol. Lond.*, **131**, 592 (1956).
24. Caldwell, P. C. and R. D. Keynes, *J. Physiol. Lond.*, **137**, 12P (1957).
25. Keynes, R. D., in: *Metabolism of the Nervous System*, (ed. D. Richter). Pergamon, London, p. 159 (1957).
26. Skou, J. C., in: *Metabolism of the Nervous System*, (ed. D. Richter). Pergamon, London, p. 173 (1957).
27. Skou, J. C., *Biochim. Biophys. Acta*, **23**, 394 (1957).
28. Post, R. L., and P. Jolly, *Biochim. Biophys. Acta*, **25**, 118 (1957).
29. Schatzmann, H. J., *Helv. Physiol. Pharmacol. Acta*, **11**, 346 (1953).
30. Skou, J. C., *Biochim. Biophys. Acta*, **42**, 6 (1960).
31. Skou, J. C., *Biochim. Biophys. Acta*, **58**, 314 (1962).
32. Esmann, M., J. C. Skou, and C. Christiansen, *Biochim. Biophys. Acta*, 567, 410 (1979)
33. Post, R. L., C. R. Merritt, C. R. Kinsolving, and C. D. Albright, *J. Biol. Chem.*, **235**, 1796 (1960).
34. Skou, J. C., *Physiol. Rev.*, **45**, 596 (1965).
35. Hodgkin, A. L., and A. F. Huxley. *J. Physiol.*, **116**, 449 (1952)
36. Mitchell, P., *Biochem. Soc. Symp.*, **22**, 142 (1963).
37. Crane, R. K., *Comp. Biochem.*, **35**, 43 (1983).
38. Kromphardt, H., H. Grobecker, K. Ring, and E. Heinz, *Biochim. Biophys. Acta*, **74**, 549 (1963).
39. Hoffmann, E. K., and L. O. Simonsen, *Physiol. Rev.*, 69, 315 (1989)
40. Pitts, B. J. R., *J. Biol. Chem.*, **254**, 6232 (1979).
41. Robertson, J. D., *Biochem. Soc. Symp.*, **16**, 3 (1959).
42. Singer, S. J., and G. L. Nicolson, *Science*, **175**, 720 (1972).
43. Hasselbach, W., and M. Makinose, *Biochem. Z.*, **333**, 518 (1961).
44. Schatzmann, H. J., *Experientia*, **22**, 364 (1966).
45. Stewart, B., B. Wallmark, and G. Sachs, *J. Biol. Chem.*, **256**, 2682 (1981)

46. Robinson, J. D., *Moving Questions. A History of Membrane Transport and Bioenergetics*, American Physiological Soc., N.Y. (1997) .

47. *Na/K-ATPase and Related Transport ATPases: Structure, Mechanism and Regulation* (eds. Beaugè, L. A., D. C. Gadsby, and P. J. Garrahan), Annals New York Academy Sci. vol. 834, New York (1997).

48. Jørgensen, P. L., in: *Molecular Aspects of Transport Proteins* (ed. De Pont J. J. H. M. M.), Elsevier Service Publisher B. V., p.1 (1992).

49. Glynn, I. M., *J. Physiol.*, **462**, 1 (1993).

50. Cornelius, F., *Biomembranes*, Vol. **5**, 133 (1996).

51. Albers, R. W., *Annu. Rev. Biochem.*, **36**, 727 (1967).

52. Albers, R. W., S. Fahn, and G. J. Koval, *Proc. Natl. Acad. Sci. USA*, **50**, 474 (1963).

53. Fahn, S., G. J. Koval, and R. W. Albers, *J. Biol. Chem.*, **243**, 1993 (1968).

54. Post, R. L., and S. Kume, *J. Biol. Chem.*, **248**, 6993 (1973).

55. Post, R. L., S. Kume, T. Tobin, B. Orcutt, and A. K. Sen, *J. Gen. Physiol.*, **54**, 306S (1969).

56. Post, R. L., A. K. Sen, and A. S. Rosenthal, *J. Biol. Chem.*, **240**, 1437 (1965).

57. Läuger, P., *Biochim. Biophys. Acta*, **552**, 143 (1979).

58. Gadsby, D. C., R. F. Rakowsky, and P. De Weer, *Science*, **260**, 100 (1993).

59. Nørby, J. G., and J. Jensen, *Biochim. Biophys. Acta*, **233**, 104 (1971).

60. Hegyvary, C., and R. L. Post, *J. Biol. Chem.*, **246**, 5234 (1971).

61. Jørgensen, P. L., *Biochim. Biophys. Acta*, **401**, 399 (1975).

62. Karlish, S. J. D., and D. W. Yates, *Biochim. Biophys. Acta*, **527**, 115 (1978).

63. Karlish, S. J. D., D. W. Yates, and I. M. Glynn, *Biochim. Biophys. Acta*, **525**, 252 (1978).

64. Skou, J. C., and M. Esmann, *Biochim. Biophys. Acta*, **647**, 232 (1981).

65. Karlish, S. J. D., *J. Bioenerg. Biomembr*, **12**, 111 (1980).

66. Nørby, J. G., I. Klodos, and N. O. Christiansen, *J. Gen. Physiol.*, **82**, 725 (1983).

67. Yoda, S., and A. Yoda, *J. Biol. Chem.*, **26**, 1147 (1986).

68. Glynn, I. M., Y. Hara, and D. E. Richards, *J. Physiol.*, **351**, 531 (1984).

69. Post, R. L., C. Hergyvary, and S. Kume, *J. Biol. Chem.*, **247**, 6530 (1972).

70. Beaugé, L. A., and I. M. Glynn, *Nature*, **280**, 510 (1979).

71. Nakao, M., and D. C. Gadsby, *Nature*, **323**, 628 (1986).

72. Goldschleger, R., S. J. D. Karlish, A. Raphaeli, and W. D. Stein, *J. Physiol.* **387**, 331 (1987).

73. Skou, J. C., *News in Physiological Sciences*, **7**, 95 (1992).

Stanley Prusiner

STANLEY B. PRUSINER

My history is not atypical of many Americans: born in the midwest, educated in the East, and now living in the West. My early years were shared between Des Moines, Iowa and Cincinnati, Ohio. Shortly after I was born on May 28, 1942 in Des Moines, my father, Lawrence, was drafted into the United States Navy. I was named for my father's younger brother who died of Hodgkin's disease at the age of 24. We moved to Boston briefly where my father enrolled in Naval officer training school before being sent to the south Pacific. He served as a communications officer for the remainder of World War II on an island called Eniwetok where the first hydrogen bomb was detonated a decade later.

During my father's absence, my mother, Miriam, and I lived in Cincinnati where her mother, Mollie Spigel, also lived. Prior to moving to Cincinnati, Mollie had lived in Norfolk, Virginia, where she raised three children after her husband Benjamin was killed at age 50 in a traffic accident. Besides many special memories of my maternal grandmother, I have many fond reminiscences of my paternal grandfather, Ben, who emigrated to the United States in 1896 as a young boy from Moscow. He grew up in Sioux City, Iowa, as did my father with many other Russian Jews. Shortly after the end of World War II, we returned to Des Moines where I attended primary school and my brother, Paul, was born. In 1952, we moved back to Cincinnati with the hope that my father would be able to find a much better job as an architect. In Cincinnati, he practiced architecture for the next 25 years, which enabled him to provide a very comfortable home for his family.

During my time at Walnut Hills High School, I studied Latin for five years, which was to help me immensely later in the writing of scientific papers. But I found high school rather uninteresting and was most fortunate to be accepted by the University of Pennsylvania where I majored in Chemistry.

The intellectual environment of the University of Pennsylvania was extraordinary–there were so many internationally renowned scholars who were invariably receptive to the intrusions of undergraduate students even before the days of student evaluations of the faculty. The small size of the undergraduate student body undoubtedly contributed to the accessibility of the faculty. Besides numerous science courses, I had the opportunity to study philosophy, the history of architecture, economics, and Russian history in courses taught by extraordinarily knowledgeable professors. Although I was among the smallest of the heavyweight crew team members and thus had no chance of rowing in the varsity boat, I greatly enjoyed the many hours that I spent at this wonderful sport.

During the summer of 1963 between my junior and senior years, I began a research project on hypothermia in the Department of Surgery with Sidney Wolfson. I quickly became fascinated by the project and continued working on it throughout my senior year. I decided to remain at Penn for Medical School largely because of the wonderful experience of doing research with Sidney Wolfson. During the second year of medical school, I decided to ask Britton Chance if he would allow me to study the surface fluorescence of brown adipose tissue in Syrian golden hamsters as they arose from hibernation. Chance had reported that the surface fluorescence of other organs reflected the oxidation-reduction state of those tissues. As anticipated, large changes in the fluorescence of brown fat were found during non-shivering thermogenesis.

My research on brown fat allowed me to spend much of the fourth year of medical school at the Wenner-Gren Institute in Stockholm working with Olov Lindberg on the metabolism of isolated brown adipocytes. This was an exciting time and I began to consider seriously a career in biomedical research. Early in 1968, I returned to Philadelphia to complete my medical studies and to contemplate my options. The previous spring, I had been given a position at the NIH once I completed an internship in medicine. It was the height of the Vietnam war with 500,000 young Americans trying to control the spread of Communism in southeast Asia. But I was facing an internship at the University of California San Francisco (UCSF) that would require me to work every other night for an entire year, a prospect about which I was not enthusiastic. The privilege of serving in the US Public Health Service at the NIH clearly outweighed the unpleasant prospects of an internship. Although the workload was awesome, I managed to survive because San Francisco was such a nice place to live. During that year, I met my wife, Sandy Turk, who was teaching mathematics to high school students.

At the NIH, I worked in Earl Stadtman's laboratory where I studied glutaminases in *E. coli*. My three years at the NIH were critical in my scientific education. I learned an immense amount about the research process: developing assays, purifying macromolecules, documenting a discovery by many approaches, and writing clear manuscripts describing what is known and what remains to be investigated. As the end of my time at the NIH began to near, I examined postdoctoral fellowships in neurobiology but decided a residency in Neurology was a better route to developing a rewarding career in research. The residency offered me an opportunity to learn about both the normal and abnormal nervous system.

In July 1972, I began a residency at the University of California San Francisco in the Department of Neurology. Two months later, I admitted a female patient who was exhibiting progressive loss of memory and difficulty performing some routine tasks. I was surprised to learn that she was dying of a "slow virus" infection called Creutzfeldt-Jakob disease (CJD) which evoked no response from the body's defenses. Next, I learned that scientists were unsure if a virus was really the cause of CJD since the causative infectious agent had some unusual properties. The amazing properties of the presumed causative "slow virus" captivated my imagination and I began to think that defining the molecular structure of this elusive agent might be a wonderful research project. The more that I read about CJD and the seemingly related diseases–kuru of the Fore people of New Guinea and scrapie of sheep–the more captivated I became.

Over the next two years I completed an abbreviated residency while reading every paper that I could find about slow virus diseases. In time, I developed a passion for working on these disorders. As I plotted out a course of action, the task became more and more daunting. The tedious, slow, and very expensive assays in mice for the scrapie agent had restricted progress and I had no clever idea about how to circumvent the problem. I did think that after working with the scrapie agent for some time that I might eventually be able to develop such an assay.

Since both Sandy and I liked living in San Francisco, I accepted the offer of an assistant professor position from Robert Fishman, the Chair of Neurology, and began to set up a laboratory to study scrapie in July 1974. Although many people cautioned me about the high risk of studies on scrapie due to the assay problems, such warnings did not dull my enthusiasm. To gain a base of research support from the NIH, I initially wrote grant proposals on glutamate metabolism in the choroid plexus. Such proposals were dull but were readily funded because I had worked on glutaminases earlier. Eventually, I managed to gain modest NIH support for my scrapie studies but this was not without considerable difficulty. To rebut the disapproval of my first NIH application on scrapie, I set up a collaboration with William Hadlow and Carl Eklund who were working at the Rocky Mountain Laboratory in Hamilton, Montana. They taught me an immense amount about scrapie and helped me initiate studies on the sedimentation behavior of the scrapie agent.

I had anticipated that the purified scrapie agent would turn out to be a small virus and was puzzled when the data kept telling me that our preparations contained protein but not nucleic acid. About this time, I was informed by the Howard Hughes Medical Institute (HHMI) that they would not renew their support and by UCSF that I would not be promoted to tenure. When everything seemed to be going wrong, including the conclusions of my research studies, it was the unwavering, enthusiastic support of a few of my closest colleagues that carried me through this very trying and difficult period. Fortunately, the tenure decision was reversed and I was able to continue my work. Although my work was never supported by HHMI again, I was extremely fortunate to receive much larger funding from the R. J. Reynolds Company through a program administered by Fred Seitz and Maclyn McCarty and shortly thereafter from the Sherman Fairchild Foundation under the direction of Walter Burke. While the vast majority of my funding always came from the NIH, these private sources were crucial in providing funds for the infrastructure which was the thousands of mice and hamsters that were mandatory.

As the data for a protein and the absence of a nucleic acid in the scrapie agent accumulated, I grew more confident that my findings were not artifacts and decided to summarize that work in an article that was eventually published in the spring of 1982. Publication of this manuscript, in which I introduced the term "prion", set off a firestorm. Virologists were generally incredulous and some investigators working on scrapie and CJD were irate. The term prion derived from protein and infectious provided a challenge to find the nucleic acid of the putative "scrapie virus." Should such a nucleic acid be found, then the word prion would disappear! Despite the strong convictions of many, no nucleic acid was found; in fact, it is probably fair to state that Detlev Riesner and I looked more vigorously for the nucleic acid than anyone else.

While it is quite reasonable for scientists to be skeptical of new ideas that do not fit within the accepted realm of scientific knowledge, the best science often emerges from situations where results carefully obtained do not fit within the accepted paradigms. At times the press became involved since the media provided the naysayers with a means to vent their frustration at not being able to find the cherished nucleic acid that they were so sure must exist. Since the press was usually unable to understand the scientific arguments and they are usually keen to write about any controversy, the personal attacks of the naysayers at times became very vicious. While such scorn caused Sandy considerable distress, she and my two daughters, Helen and Leah, provided a loving and warm respite from the torrent of criticism that the prion hypothesis engendered. During the winter of 1983, I herniated a disc in my lumbar spine while skiing and this slowed the pace of my work for much of the year. After a laminectomy, I began swimming regularly, which brought relaxation and a much needed quiet time to my life.

Just prior to my back problem, the protein of the prion was found in my laboratory and the following year, a portion of the amino acid sequence was determined by Leroy Hood. With that knowledge, molecular biological studies of the prions ensued and an explosion of new information followed. I collaborated with Charles Weissmann on the molecular cloning of the gene encoding the prion protein (PrP) and with George Carlson and David Kingsbury on linking the PrP gene to the control of scrapie incubation time in mice. About the same time, we succeeded in producing antibodies that provided an extremely valuable tool that allowed us to discover the normal form of PrP. In a very important series of studies, the antibodies were used by Stephen DeArmond to study the pathogenesis of prion disease in transgenic mice. Steve brought the much needed talents of an outstanding neuropathologist to these studies. As more data accumulated, an expanding edifice in support of the prion concept was constructed. Ruth Gabizon dispersed prions into liposomes and purified scrapie infectivity on columns with PrP antibodies. Karen Hsiao discovered a mutation in the PrP gene that caused familial disease and reproduced the disease in transgenic mice while Michael Scott produced transgenic mice abrogating the prion species barrier and later artificial prions from chimeric PrP transgenes. Indeed, no experimental findings that might overturn the prion concept were reported from any laboratory. By the early 1990s, the existence of prions was coming to be accepted in many quarters of the scientific community, but the mechanism by which normal

PrP was converted into the disease-causing form was still obscure. When Fred Cohen and I began to collaborate on PrP structural studies, I was again extremely fortunate. Fred brought an extraordinary set of skills in protein chemistry and computational biology to investigations of PrP structures.

As prions gained wider acceptance among scientists, I received many scientific prizes. The first major recognition of my work was accorded by neurologists with many other awards coming soon thereafter. But the most rewarding aspect of my work has been the numerous wonderful friends that I have made during an extensive series of collaborative studies. It has been a special privilege to work with so many talented scientists including numerous postdoctoral fellows and technical associates who have taught me so much. Besides the many collaborators who have contributed their scientific skills to advancing the study of prions, I have had many colleagues who have contributed indirectly to my work by being supportive of the special needs that such a project has demanded.

PRIONS

Nobel Lecture, December 8, 1997

by

Stanley B. Prusiner

Departments of Neurology and of Biochemistry and Biophysics, University of California, San Francisco, California 94103-0518, USA

ABSTRACT

Prions are unprecedented infectious pathogens that cause a group of invariably fatal neurodegenerative diseases by an entirely novel mechanism. Prion diseases may present as genetic, infectious, or sporadic disorders, all of which involve modification of the prion protein (PrP). Bovine spongiform encephalopathy (BSE), scrapie of sheep, and Creutzfeldt-Jakob disease (CJD) of humans are among the most notable prion diseases. Prions are transmissible particles that are devoid of nucleic acid and seem to be composed exclusively of a modified protein (PrP^{Sc}). The normal, cellular PrP (PrP^C) is converted into PrP^{Sc} through a posttranslational process during which it acquires a high β-sheet content. The species of a particular prion is encoded by the sequence of the chromosomal PrP gene of the mammals in which it last replicated. In contrast to pathogens carrying a nucleic acid genome, prions appear to encipher strain-specific properties in the tertiary structure of PrP^{Sc}. Transgenetic studies argue that PrP^{Sc} acts as a template upon which PrP^C is refolded into a nascent PrP^{Sc} molecule through a process facilitated by another protein. Miniprions generated in transgenic mice expressing PrP, in which nearly half of the residues were deleted, exhibit unique biological properties and should facilitate structural studies of PrP^{Sc}. While knowledge about prions has profound implications for studies of the structural plasticity of proteins, investigations of prion diseases suggest that new strategies for the prevention and treatment of these disorders may also find application in the more common degenerative diseases.

The tortuous path of the scientific investigation that led to an understanding of familial Creutzfeldt-Jakob disease (CJD) chronicles a remarkable scientific odyssey. By 1930, the high incidence of familial (f) CJD in some families was known [1, 2]. Almost 60 years were to pass before the significance of this finding could be appreciated [3–5]. CJD remained a curious, rare neurodegenerative disease of unknown etiology throughout this period of three score years [6]. Only with transmission of disease to apes following inoculation of brain extracts prepared from patients, who died of CJD, did the story begin to unravel [7].

Once CJD was shown to be an infectious disease, relatively little attention was paid to the familial form of the disease since most cases were not found in families. It is interesting to speculate how the course of scientific investigation might have proceeded had transmission studies not been performed until after the molecular genetic lesion had been identified. Had that sequence of events transpired, then the prion concept, which readily explains how a single disease can have a genetic or infectious etiology, might have been greeted with much less skepticism [8].

Epidemiologic studies designed to identify the source of the CJD infection were unable to identify any predisposing risk factors although some geographic clusters were found [9-12]. Libyan Jews living in Israel developed CJD about 30 times more frequently than other Israelis [13]. This finding prompted some investigators to propose that the Libyan Jews had contracted CJD by eating lightly cooked brain from scrapie-infected sheep when they lived in Tripoli prior to emigration. Subsequently, the Libyan Jewish patients were all found to carry a mutation at codon 200 in their prion protein (PrP) gene [14-16].

My own interest in the subject began with a patient dying of CJD in the fall of 1972. At that time, I was beginning a residency in Neurology and was most impressed by a disease process that could kill my patient in two months by destroying her brain while her body remained unaffected by this process. No febrile response, no leucocytosis or pleocytosis, no humoral immune response, and yet I was told that she was infected with a "slow virus."

Slow viruses. The term "slow virus" had been coined by Bjorn Sigurdsson in 1954 while he was working in Iceland on scrapie and visna of sheep [17]. Five years later, William Hadlow had suggested that kuru, a disease of New Guinea highlanders, was similar to scrapie and thus, it, too, was caused by a slow virus [18]. Seven more years were to pass before the transmissibility of kuru was established by passaging the disease to chimpanzees inoculated intracerebrally [19]. Just as Hadlow had made the intellectual leap between scrapie and kuru, Igor Klatzo made a similar connection between kuru and CJD [20]. In both instances, these neuropathologists were struck by the similarities in light microscopic pathology of the CNS that kuru exhibited with scrapie or CJD. In 1968, the transmission of CJD to chimpanzees after intracerebral inoculation was reported [7].

In scrapie, kuru, CJD, and all of the other disorders now referred to as prion diseases (Table 1), spongiform degeneration and astrocytic gliosis is found upon microscopic examination of the CNS (Figure 1) [21]. The degree of spongiform degeneration is quite variable while the extent of reactive gliosis correlates with the degree of neuron loss [22].

Prions–a brief overview. Before proceeding with a detailed discussion of our current understanding of prions causing scrapie and CJD, I provide a brief overview of prion biology. Prions are unprecedented infectious pathogens that cause a group of invariably fatal neurodegenerative diseases mediated by an entirely novel mechanism. Prion diseases may present as genetic, infectious, or sporadic disorders, all of which involve modification of the prion protein (PrP), a constituent of normal mammalian cells [23]. CJD generally presents as progressive dementia while scrapie of sheep and bovine spongiform encephalopathy (BSE) are generally manifest as ataxic illnesses (Table 1) [24].

Table 1. The prion diseases

	Disease	Host	Mechanism of Pathogenesis
A.	Kuru	Fore people	Infection through ritualistic cannibalism
	Iatrogenic CJD*	Humans	Infection from prion-contaminated HGH, dura mater grafts, etc.
	Variant CJD	Humans	Infection from bovine prions?
	Familial CJD	Humans	Germline mutations in PrP gene
	GSS	Humans	Germline mutations in PrP gene
	FFI	Humans	Germline mutation in PrP gene (D178N, M129)
	Sporadic CJD	Humans	Somatic mutation or spontaneous conversion of PrP^C into PrP^{Sc}?
	FSI	Humans	Somatic mutation or spontaneous conversion of PrP^C into PrP^{Sc}?
B.	Scrapie	Sheep	Infection in genetically susceptible sheep
	BSE	Cattle	Infection with prion-contaminated MBM
	TME	Mink	Infection with prions from sheep or cattle
	CWD	Mule deer, elk	Unknown
	FSE	Cats	Infection with prion-contaminated bovine tissues or MBM
	exotic ungulate encephalopathy	Greater kudu, nyala, onyx	Infection with prion-contaminated MBM

*Abbreviations defined in Footnote a.

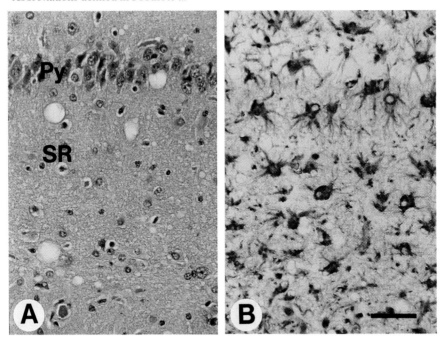

Figure 1. Neuropathologic changes in Swiss mice following inoculation with RML scrapie prions. **(A)** Hematoxylin and eosin stain of a serial section of the hippocampus shows spongiform degeneration of the neuropil, with vacuoles 10–30 μm in diameter. Brain tissue was immersion fixed in 10% buffered formalin solution after sacrificing the animals and embedded in paraffin. **(B)** GFAP immunohistochemistry of a serial section of the hippocampus shows numerous reactive astrocytes. Bar in B = 50 μm and also applies to A. Photomicrographs prepared by Stephen J. DeArmond.

Prions are devoid of nucleic acid and seem to be composed exclusively of a modified isoform of PrP designated PrP^{Sc}.[a] The normal, cellular PrP, denoted PrP^{C}, is converted into PrP^{Sc} through a process whereby a portion of its α-helical and coil structure is refolded into β-sheet [25]. This structural transition is accompanied by profound changes in the physicochemical properties of the PrP. The amino acid sequence of PrP^{Sc} corresponds to that encoded by the PrP gene of the mammalian host in which it last replicated. In contrast to pathogens with a nucleic acid genome that encode strain-specific properties in genes, prions encipher these properties in the tertiary structure of PrP^{Sc} [26-28]. Transgenetic studies argue that PrP^{Sc} acts as a template upon which PrP^{C} is refolded into a nascent PrP^{Sc} molecule through a process facilitated by another protein.

More than 20 mutations of the PrP gene are now known to cause the inherited human prion diseases and significant genetic linkage has been established for five of these mutations [4, 16, 29-31]. The prion concept readily explains how a disease can be manifest as a heritable as well as an infectious illness.

Resistance of scrapie agent to radiation. My fascination with CJD quickly shifted to scrapie once I learned of the remarkable radiobiological data that Tikvah Alper and her colleagues had collected on the scrapie agent [32-34]. The scrapie agent had been found to be extremely resistant to inactivation by UV and ionizing radiation as was later shown for the CJD agent [35]. It seemed to me that the most intriguing question was the chemical nature of the scrapie agent; Alper's data had evoked a torrent of hypotheses concerning its composition. Suggestions as to the nature of the scrapie agent ranged from small DNA viruses to membrane fragments to polysaccharides to proteins, the last of which eventually proved to be correct [36-42].

Scrapie of sheep and goats possesses a history no less fascinating than that of CJD. The resistance of the scrapie agent to inactivation by formalin and heat treatments [43], which were commonly used to produce vaccines against viral illnesses, suggested that the scrapie agent might be different from viruses, but it came at a time before the structure of viruses was understood. Later, this resistance was dismissed as an interesting observation but of little importance since some viruses can survive such treatments; indeed, this was not an unreasonable viewpoint. More than two decades were to pass before reports of the extreme resistance of the scrapie agent to inactivation by radiation again trumpeted the novelty of this infectious pathogen. Interestingly, British scientists had argued for many years about whether natural scrapie was a genetic or an infectious disease [44-46]. Scrapie, like kuru and CJD, produced

---

[a] Prions are defined as proteinaceous infectious particles that lack nucleic acid. PrP^{C} is the cellular prion protein; PrP^{Sc} is the pathologic isoform. NH$_2$-terminal truncation during limited proteolysis of PrP^{Sc} produces PrP 27-30. BSE, bovine spongiform encephalopathy; CJD, Creutzfeldt-Jakob disease; sCJD, sporadic CJD; fCJD, familial CJD; iCJD, iatrogenic CJD; vCJD, (new) variant CJD; CWD, chronic wasting disease; FFI, fatal familial insomnia; FSE, feline spongiform encephalopathy; FSI, fatal sporadic insomnia; GSS, Gerstmann-Sträussler-Scheinker disease; HGH, human growth hormone; MBM, meat and bone meal; SHa, Syrian hamster; Tg, transgenic; TME, transmissible mink encephalopathy; wt, wild-type.

death of the host without any sign of an immune response to a "foreign infectious agent."

My initial studies focused on the sedimentation properties of scrapie infectivity in mouse spleens and brains. From these studies, I concluded that hydrophobic interactions were responsible for the non-ideal physical behavior of the scrapie particle [47, 48]. Indeed, the scrapie agent presented a biochemical nightmare: infectivity was spread from one end to the other of a sucrose gradient and from the void volume to fractions eluting at 5–10 times the included volume of chromatographic columns. Such results demanded new approaches and better assays [49].

Bioassays. As the number of hypotheses about the molecular nature of the scrapie agent began to exceed the number of laboratories working on this problem, the need for new experimental approaches became evident. Much of the available data on the properties of the scrapie agent had been gathered on brain homogenates prepared from mice with clinical signs of scrapie. These mice had been inoculated 4–5 months earlier with the scrapie agent which originated in sheep but had been passaged multiple times in mice. Once an experiment was completed on these homogenates, an additional 12 months was required using an endpoint titration in mice [50]. Typically, 60 mice were required to determine the titer of a single sample. This slow, tedious, and expensive system discouraged systematic investigation.

Although the transmission of scrapie to mice had ushered in a new era of research, the 1.5–2 year intervals between designing experiments and obtaining results discouraged sequential studies. Infrequently, the results of one set of experiments were used as a foundation for the next and so on. Moreover, the large number of mice needed to measure the infectivity in a single sample prevented studies where many experiments were performed in parallel. These problems encouraged publication of inconclusive experimental results.

In 1972, when I became fascinated by the enigmatic nature of the scrapie agent, I thought that the most direct path to determining the molecular structure of the scrapie agent was purification. Fortunately, I did not appreciate the magnitude of that task although I had considerable experience and training in the purification of enzymes [51]. While many studies had been performed to probe the physicochemical nature of the scrapie agent using the mouse endpoint titration system, few systematic investigations had been performed on the fundamental characteristics of the infectious scrapie particle [42]. In fact, 12 years after introduction of the mouse bioassay, there were few data on the sedimentation behavior of the scrapie particle. Since differential centrifugation is frequently a useful initial step in the purification of many macromolecules, some knowledge of the sedimentation properties of the scrapie agent under defined conditions seemed mandatory. To perform such studies, Swiss mice were inoculated intracerebrally with the Chandler isolate of scrapie prions and the mice sacrificed about 30 and 150 days later when the titers in their spleens and brains, respectively, were expected to be at maximal levels. The two tissues were homogenized, extracted with detergent, and centrifuged for increasing times and speeds [47, 52]. The disappearance of scrapie infectivity was measured in supernatant fractions by endpoint titration which required one year to score.

Incubation time assays in hamsters. In view of these daunting logistical problems, the identification of an inoculum that produced scrapie in the golden Syrian hamster in ~70 days after intracerebral inoculation proved to be an important advance [53, 54] once an incubation time assay was developed [55, 56]. In earlier studies, Syrian hamsters (SHa) had been inoculated with prions, but serial passage with short incubation times was not reported [57]. Development of the incubation time bioassay reduced the time required to measure prions in samples with high titers by a factor of five: only 70 days were required instead of the 360 days previously needed. Equally important, 4 animals could be used in place of the 60 that were required for endpoint titrations, making possible a large number of parallel experiments. With this bioassay, research on the nature of the scrapie agent was accelerated nearly 100-fold and the hamster with high prion titers in its brain became the experimental animal of choice for biochemical studies.

The incubation time assay enabled development of effective purification schemes for enriching fractions for scrapie infectivity. It provided a means to assess quantitatively those fractions that were enriched for infectivity and those that were not. Such studies led rather rapidly to the development of a protocol for separating scrapie infectivity from most proteins and nucleic acids. With a ~100-fold purification of infectivity relative to protein, >98% of the proteins and polynucleotides were eliminated permitting more reliable probing of the constituents of these enriched fractions.

The prion concept. As reproducible data began to accumulate indicating that scrapie infectivity could be reduced by procedures that hydrolyze or modify proteins but was resistant to procedures that alter nucleic acids, a family of hypotheses about the molecular architecture of the scrapie agent began to emerge [58]. These data established, for the first time, that a particular macromolecule was required for infectivity and that this macromolecule was a protein. The experimental findings extended earlier observations on resistance of scrapie infectivity to UV irradiation at 250 nm [33] in that the four different procedures used to probe for a nucleic acid are based on physical principles that are independent of UV radiation damage.

Once the requirement of protein for infectivity was established, I thought that it was appropriate to give the infectious pathogen of scrapie a provisional name that would distinguish it from both viruses and viroids. After some contemplation, I suggested the term "prion" derived from **pro**teinaceous and **in**fectious [58]. At that time, I defined prions as proteinaceous infectious particles that resist inactivation by procedures that modify nucleic acids. I never imagined the irate reaction of some scientists to the word prion – it was truly remarkable!

Current definitions. Perhaps, the best current working definition of a prion is a proteinaceous infectious particle that lacks nucleic acid [28]. Because a wealth of data supports the contention that scrapie prions are composed entirely of a protein that adopts an abnormal conformation, it is not unreasonable to define prions as infectious proteins [25, 27, 59, 60]. But I hasten to add that we still cannot eliminate a small ligand bound to PrP^{Sc} as an essential component of the infectious prion particle. Learning how to renature PrP^{Sc} accompanied by restoration of prion infectivity or to generate de novo prion infectivity using a synthetic polypeptide should help address this as yet unresolved issue [61]. From a broader perspective, prions are elements that impart and propagate conformational variability.

Although PrP^{Sc} is the only *known* component of the infectious prion particles, these unique pathogens share several phenotypic traits with other infectious entities such as viruses. Because some features of the diseases caused by prions and viruses are similar, some scientists have difficulty accepting the existence of prions despite a wealth of scientific data supporting this concept [62–67].

Families of hypotheses. Once the requirement for a protein was established, it was possible to revisit the long list of hypothetical structures that had been proposed for the scrapie agent and to eliminate carbohydrates, lipids, and nucleic acids as the infective elements within a scrapie agent devoid of protein [58]. No longer could structures such as a viroid-like nucleic acid, a replicating polysaccharide, or a small polynucleotide surrounded by a carbohydrate be entertained as reasonable candidates to explain the puzzling properties of the scrapie agent [58, 68].

The family of hypotheses that remained after identifying a protein component was still large and required a continued consideration of all possibilities in which a protein was a critical element [49]. The prion concept evolved from a family of hypotheses in which an infectious protein was only one of several possibilities. With the accumulation of experimental data on the molecular properties of the prion, it became possible to discard an increasing number of hypothetical structures. In prion research, as in many other areas of scientific investigation, a single hypothesis is all too often championed at the expense of a reasoned approach which requires entertaining a series of complex arguments until one or more can be discarded on the basis of experimental data [69].

Genes and DNA. In some respects, the early development of the prion concept mirrors the story of DNA [70–72]. Prior to the acceptance of DNA as the genetic material of life [73, 74], many scientists asserted that the DNA preparations must be contaminated with protein which is the true genetic material [75]. The prejudices of these scientists were similar in some ways to those of investigators who have disputed the prion concept. But the scientists who attacked the hypothesis that genes are composed of DNA had no well proven alternative; they had only a set of feelings derived from poorly substantiated data sets that genes are made of protein. In contrast, those who attacked the hypothesis that the prion is composed only of protein had more than 30 years of cumulative evidence showing that genetic information in all organisms on our planet is encoded in DNA and that biological diversity resides in DNA. Studies of viruses and eventually viroids extended this concept to these small

274

infectious pathogens [76] and showed that genes could also be composed of RNA [77, 78].

Discovery of the Prion Protein. The discovery of the prion protein transformed research on scrapie and related diseases [79, 80]. It provided a molecular marker that was subsequently shown to be specific for these illnesses as well as the major, and very likely the only, constituent of the infectious prion.

PrP 27–30 was discovered by enriching fractions from SHa brain for scrapie infectivity [79, 80]. This protein is the protease-resistant core of PrP^{Sc} and has an apparent molecular weight (M_r) of 27–30 kD [81, 82]. Although resistance to limited proteolysis proved to be a convenient tool for many but not all studies, use of proteases to enrich fractions for scrapie infectivity created a problem when the NH$_2$-terminal sequence of PrP 27–30 was determined [81]. The ragged NH$_2$-terminus of PrP 27–30 yielded three sets of signals in almost every cycle of the Edman degradation. Only once these signals were properly interpreted and placed in correct register could a unique sequence be assigned for the NH$_2$-terminus of PrP 27–30. The determination of amino acid sequence of the NH$_2$-terminus of PrP 27–30 made subsequent molecular cloning studies of the PrP gene possible [83, 84].

The finding that PrP mRNA levels were similar in normal uninfected and scrapie-infected tissues caused some investigators to argue that PrP 27–30 was not related to the infectious prion particle [83]. An alternate interpretation prompted a search for a prion protein in uninfected animals which was found to be protease sensitive and soluble in non-denaturing detergents, unlike PrP 27–30. This isoform was designated PrP^C (Figure 2) [84, 85]. Deduced amino acid sequences from PrP cDNA as well as immunoblotting studies revealed that PrP 27–30 was NH$_2$-terminally truncated and was derived from a larger molecule, designated PrP^{Sc}, that was unique to infected animals [81, 82, 84–86].

With the discovery of PrP 27–30 and the production of antiserum [87], brains from humans and animals with putative prion diseases were examined for the presence of this protein. In each case, PrP 27–30 was found and it was absent in other neurodegenerative disorders such as Alzheimer's disease, Parkinson's disease, and amyotrophic lateral sclerosis [88–91]. The extreme specificity of PrP^{Sc} for prion disease is an important feature of the protein and is consistent with the postulated role of PrP^{Sc} in both the transmission and pathogenesis of these illnesses (Table 2) [92].

The accumulation of PrP^{Sc} contrasts markedly with that of glial fibrillary acid protein (GFAP) in prion disease. In scrapie, GFAP mRNA and protein levels rise as the disease progresses [93] but the accumulation of GFAP is neither specific nor necessary for either the transmission or pathogenesis of disease. Mice deficient for GFAP show no alteration in their incubation times [94, 95].

Except for PrP^{Sc}, no macromolecule has been found in tissues of patients dying of the prion diseases that is specific for these encephalopathies. In searches for a scrapie-specific nucleic acid, cDNAs have been identified that are complementary to mRNAs encoding other proteins with increased expression in prion disease [96–98]. Yet, none of the proteins has been found to be specific for prion disease.

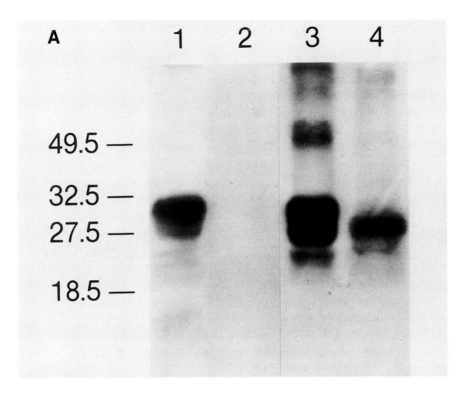

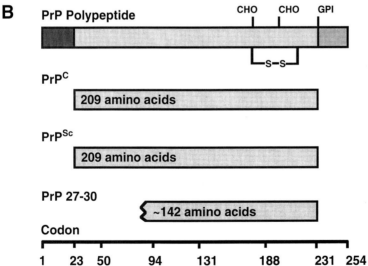

Figure 2. Prion protein isoforms. (**A**) Western immunoblot of brain homogenates from uninfected (lanes 1 and 2) and prion-infected (lanes 3 and 4) Syrian hamsters. Samples in lanes 2 and 4 were digested with 50 μg/ml of proteinase K for 30 min at 37°C. PrP^C in lanes 2 and 4 was completely hydrolyzed under these conditions, whereas approximately 67 amino acids were digested from the NH$_2$-terminus of PrP^{Sc} to generate PrP 27–30. After polyacrylamide gel electrophoresis (PAGE) and electrotransfer, the blot was developed with anti-PrP R073 polyclonal rabbit antiserum. Molecular size markers are in kilodaltons (kD). (**B**) Bar diagram of SHaPrP which consists of 254 amino acids. After processing of the NH$_2$- and COOH- termini, both PrP^C and PrP^{Sc} consist of 209 residues. After limited proteolysis, the NH$_2$-terminus of PrP^{Sc} is truncated to form PrP 27–30, which is composed of approximately 142 amino acids.

Table 2. Arguments for prions being composed largely, if not entirely, of PrP^{Sc} molecules and devoid of nucleic acid.

1. PrP^{Sc} and scrapie infectivity copurify using biochemical and immunologic procedures.
2. The unusual properties of PrP^{Sc} mimic those of prions. Many different procedures that modify or hydrolyze PrP^{Sc} inactivate prions.
3. Levels of PrP^{Sc} are directly proportional to prion titers. Non-denatured PrP^{Sc} has not been separated from scrapie infectivity.
4. No evidence for a virus-like particle or a nucleic acid genome.
5. Accumulation of PrP^{Sc} invariably associated with the pathology of prion diseases including PrP amyloid plaques that are pathognomonic.
6. PrP gene mutations are genetically linked to inherited prion disease and cause formation of PrP^{Sc}.
7. Overexpression of PrP^{C} increases the rate of PrP^{Sc} formation, which shortens the incubation time. Knock out of the PrP gene eliminates the substrate necessary for PrP^{Sc} formation and prevents both prion disease and prion replication.
8. Species variations in the PrP sequence are responsible, at least in part, for the species barrier which is found when prions are passaged from one host to another.
9. PrP^{Sc} preferentially binds to homologous PrP^{C} resulting in formation of nascent PrP^{Sc} and prion infectivity.
10. Chimeric and partially deleted PrP genes change susceptibility to prions from different species and support production of artificial prions with novel properties that are not found in nature.
11. Prion diversity is enciphered within the conformation of PrP^{Sc}. Strains can be generated by passage through hosts with different PrP genes. Prion strains are maintained by PrP^{C}/PrP^{Sc} interactions.
12. Human prions from fCJD(E200K) and FFI patients impart different properties to chimeric MHu2M PrP in transgenic mice, which provides a mechanism for strain propagation.

Attempts to falsify the prion hypothesis. Numerous attempts to disprove the prion hypothesis over the past 15 years have failed. Such studies have tried unsuccessfully to separate scrapie infectivity from protein and more specifically from PrP^{Sc}. No preparations of purified prions containing less than one PrP^{Sc} molecule per ID$_{50}$ unit have been reported [99] and no replication of prions in PrP deficient (Prnp$^{0/0}$) mice was found [100–104].

Copurification of PrP 27–30 and scrapie infectivity demands that the physicochemical properties as well as antigenicity of these two entities be similar [105] (Table 2). The results of a wide array of inactivation experiments demonstrated the similarities in the properties of PrP 27–30 and scrapie infectivity [61, 106–109]. To explain these findings in terms of the virus hypothesis, it is necessary to postulate either a virus that has a coat protein which is highly homologous with PrP or a virus that binds tightly to PrP^{Sc}. In either case, the PrP-like coat protein or the PrP^{Sc}/virus complex must display properties indistinguishable from PrP^{Sc} alone. With each species that the putative virus invades, it must incorporate a new PrP sequence during replication.

Search for a scrapie-specific nucleic acid. The inability to inactivate preparations highly enriched for scrapie infectivity by procedures that modify nucleic acids militates against the existence of a scrapie-specific nucleic acid [58, 110, 111]. To explain the findings in terms of a virus, one must argue that PrP^{Sc} or an as yet undetected PrP-like protein of viral origin protects the viral genome from inactivation. The notion that the putative scrapie virus encodes a PrP-like protein was refuted by nucleic acid hybridization studies using a PrP cDNA probe. Less than 0.002 nucleic acid molecules encoding PrP per ID_{50} unit were found in purified preparations of SHa prions [84]. To circumvent this finding, it could be hypothesized that the genetic code used by the PrP gene differs so greatly from that found in the cell that a PrP cDNA probe failed to detect it in highly purified preparations.

If prions contained a genome with a unique genetic code, then it is likely that this genome would encode some specialized proteins required for replication as well as some unique tRNAs. But both UV and ionizing radiation inactivation studies as well as physical studies have eliminated the possibility of a large nucleic acid hiding within purified preparations of prions [110-112]. Only oligonucleotides of fewer than 50 bases were found at a concentration of one molecule per ID_{50} unit in prion preparations highly enriched for scrapie infectivity [113, 114]. These small nucleic acids were of variable length and are thought to be degradation byproducts generated during purification of prions. Failure to find a bona fide genome was attributed to the unusual properties of the putative viral nucleic acid or technical incompetence on the part of the investigators who were unable to find it [63, 115].

PrP Amyloid. In preparations highly enriched for scrapie infectivity and containing only PrP 27–30 by silver staining of gels after SDS-PAGE, numerous rod-shaped particles were seen by electron microscopy after negative staining (Figure 3) [107]. Each of the rods was slightly different, in contrast to viruses which exhibit extremely uniform structures [116]. These irregular rods

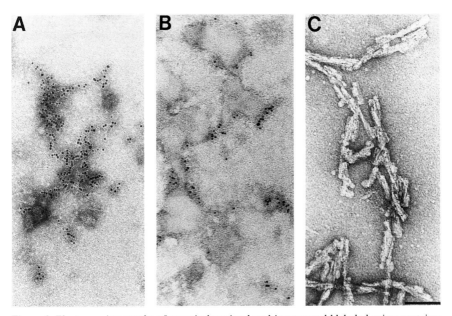

Figure 3. Electron micrographs of negatively stained and immunogold-labeled prion proteins: (A) PrP^C and (B) PrP^{Sc}. Neither PrP^C nor PrP^{Sc} form recognizable, ordered polymers. (C) Prion rods composed of PrP 27–30 were negatively stained. The prion rods are indistinguishable from many purified amyloids. Bar = 100 nm.

composed largely, if not entirely, of PrP 27–30, were indistinguishable morphologically from many other purified amyloids [117]. Studies of the prion rods with Congo red dye demonstrated that the rods also fulfilled the tinctorial criteria for amyloid [107] and immunostaining later showed that PrP is a major component of amyloid plaques in some animals and humans with prion disease [118–120]. Subsequently, it was recognized that the prion rods were not required for scrapie infectivity [121]; furthermore, the rods were shown to be an artifact of purification during which limited proteolysis of PrP^{Sc} generated PrP 27–30 that polymerized spontaneously in the presence of detergent (Figure 3) [122].

The idea that scrapie prions were composed of an amyloidogenic protein was truly heretical when it was introduced [107]. Since the prevailing view at the time was that scrapie is caused by an atypical virus, many argued that amyloid proteins are mammalian polypeptides and not viral proteins!

Some investigators have argued that the prion rods are synonymous with scrapie-associated fibrils [123–125] even though morphologic and tinctorial features of these fibrils clearly differentiated them from amyloid and as such from the prion rods [126, 127]. The scrapie-associated fibrils were identified by their unique ultrastructure in which two or four subfilaments were helically wound around each other [126] and were proposed to represent the first example of a filamentous animal virus [128]. After the argument for a filamentous animal virus causing scrapie faded, it was hypothesized that a virus induces the formation of PrP amyloid in order to explain the accumulation of PrP^{Sc} in prion diseases [129]. Besides the lack of evidence for a virus of any shape, no compelling data has been offered in support of the idea that prion diseases are caused by a filamentous bacterium called a spiroplasma [130].

Search for the ubiquitous "scrapie virus." When PrP gene mutations were discovered to cause familial prion diseases [4], it was postulated that PrP^C is a receptor for the ubiquitous scrapie virus that binds more tightly to mutant than to wt PrP^C [131]. A similar hypothesis was proposed to explain why the length of the scrapie incubation time was found to be inversely proportional to the level of PrP expression in Tg mice and why Prnp$^{0/0}$ mice are resistant to scrapie [132]. The higher the level of PrP expression, the faster the spread of the putative virus which results in shorter incubation times; conversely, mice deficient for PrP lack the receptor required for spread of the virus [63]. The inability to find virus-like particles in purified preparations of PrP^{Sc} was attributed to these particles being hidden [115] even though tobacco mosaic viruses could be detected when one virion was added per ID$_{50}$ unit of scrapie prions [121].

Recent studies on the transmission of mutant prions from FFI and fCJD(E200K) to Tg(MHu2M) mice which results in the formation of two different PrP^{Sc} molecules [27] has forced a corollary to the ubiquitous virus postulate. To accommodate this result, at least two different viruses must reside worldwide, each of which binds to a different mutant HuPrP^C and each of which induces a different MHu2M PrP^{Sc} conformer when transferred to Tg mice. Even more difficult to imagine is how one ubiquitous virus might acquire different mutant PrP^{Sc} molecules corresponding to FFI or fCJD(E200K) and then induce different MHu2M PrP^{Sc} conformers upon transmission to Tg mice.

Artificial prions. To explain the production of artificial prions from chimeric or mutant PrP transgenes in terms of a virus [133–135], mutated PrP^{Sc} molecules must be incorporated into the virus. In the case of mice expressing chimeric PrP transgenes, artificial prions are produced with host ranges not previously found in nature. Similarly, deleting specific regions of PrP resulted in the formation of "miniprions" with a unique host range and neuropathology as described below. The production of artificial prions that were generated by modifying the PrP gene sequence and exhibit unique biological properties is another compelling argument against the proposition that scrapie and CJD are caused by viruses.

Skepticism once well-justified. While the skepticism about prions was once well-justified and formed the basis for a vigorous scientific debate, the wealth of available data now renders such arguments moot. In summary, no single hypothesis involving a virus can explain the findings summarized above (Table 2); instead, a series of ad hoc hypotheses, virtually all of which can be refuted by experimental data, must be constructed to accommodate a steadily enlarging body of data.

It is notable that the search for an infectious pathogen with a nucleic acid genome as the cause of scrapie and CJD has done little to advance our understanding of these diseases. Instead, studies of PrP have created a wealth of data that now explain almost every aspect of these fascinating disorders. While no single experiment can refute the existence of the "scrapie virus", all of the data taken together from numerous experimental studies present an impressive edifice which argues that the 50 year quest for a virus has failed because it does not exist!

Prions defy rules of protein structure. Once cDNA probes for PrP became available, the PrP gene was found to be constitutively expressed in adult, uninfected brain [83, 84]. This finding eliminated the possibility that PrP^{Sc} stimulated production of more of itself by initiating transcription of the PrP gene as proposed nearly two decades earlier [37]. Determination of the structure of the PrP gene eliminated a second possible mechanism that might explain the appearance of PrP^{Sc} in brains already synthesizing PrP^C. Since the entire protein coding region was contained within a single exon, there was no possibility for the two PrP isoforms to be the products of alternatively spliced mRNAs [82]. Next, a posttranslational chemical modification that distinguishes PrP^{Sc} from PrP^C was considered but none was found in an exhaustive study [59] and we considered it likely that PrP^C and PrP^{Sc} differed only in their conformation, a hypothesis also proposed earlier [37]. However, this idea was no less heretical than that of an infectious protein.

For more than 25 years, it had been widely accepted that the amino acid sequence specifies one biologically active conformation of a protein [136]. Yet, in scrapie we were faced with the possibility that one primary structure for PrP might adopt at least two different conformations in order to explain the existence of both PrP^C and PrP^{Sc}. When the secondary structures of the PrP isoforms were compared by optical spectroscopy, they were found to be markedly different [25]. Fourier transform infrared (FTIR) and circular dichroism (CD) studies showed that PrP^C contains about 40% α-helix and little β-sheet while PrP^{Sc} is composed of about 30% α-helix and 45% β-sheet [25, 137]. Nevertheless, these two proteins have the same amino acid sequence!

Prior to comparative studies on the structures of PrP^C and PrP^{Sc}, we found by metabolic labeling studies that the acquisition of PrP^{Sc} protease-resistance is a posttranslational process [138]. In our quest for a chemical difference that would distinguish PrP^{Sc} from PrP^C, we found ethanolamine in hydrolysates of PrP 27–30 which signalled the possibility that PrP might contain a glycosylphosphatidyl inositol (GPI) anchor [139]. Both PrP isoforms were found to carry GPI anchors and PrP^C was found on the surface of cells where it could be released by cleavage of the anchor. Subsequent studies showed that PrP^{Sc} formation occurred after PrP^C reaches the cell surface [140, 141] and is localized to caveolae-like domains [142–145].

Modeling PrP structures. Molecular modeling studies predicted that PrP^C is a four-helix bundle protein containing four regions of secondary structure denoted H1, H2, H3, and H4 (Figure 4) [146, 147]. Subsequent NMR studies of a synthetic PrP peptide containing residues 90–145 provided good evidence for H1 [148]. This peptide contains the residues 113–128 that are most highly conserved among all species studied (Figure 4A) [147, 149, 150] and correspond to a transmembrane region of PrP which was delineated in cell-free translation studies [151, 152]. Recent studies show that a transmembrane form of PrP accumulates in GSS caused by the A117V mutation and in Tg mice overexpressing either mutant or wtPrP [153]. The paradoxical lack of evidence for an α-helix in this region from NMR studies of recombinant PrP in aqueous buffers [154–156] could be explained if the recombinant PrPs correspond to the secreted form of PrP that was also identified in cell-free translation studies. This contention is supported by studies with recombinant antibody fragments (Fabs) showing the GPI-anchored PrP^C on the surface of cells exhibits an immunoreactivity similar to that of recombinant PrP that was prepared with an α-helical conformation [157, 158]. GPI-anchored PrP^C is synthesized within the secretory pathway and transported to surface of the cell [139, 159].

Optical spectroscopic measurements of PrP^C provided the necessary background for more detailed structural studies [25]. Unable to produce crystals of PrP, we and others utilized NMR to determine the structure of an α-helical form of a recombinant PrP. The NMR structure of a COOH-terminal fragment of MoPrP consisting of 111 residues showed three helices, two of which corresponded to H3 and H4 in the PrP^C model, and two small β-strands each consisting of three residues [154]. How the structure of this MoPrP(121–231) fragment differs from PrP^C is of interest since this fragment is lethal when expressed in Tg mice [160]. Subsequently, structural studies were performed on a longer fragment of PrP containing residues 90–231 and corresponding to SHaPrP 27–30 [155, 161, 162]. Expression of PrP(90–231) in Tg mice did not produce spontaneous disease [163, 164]. More recently, NMR structures of recombinant full-length PrP have been reported [156, 165].

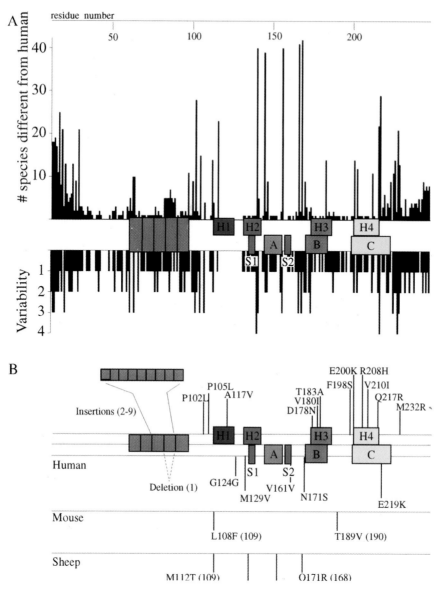

Figure 4. Species variations and mutations of the prion protein gene. (A) Species variations. The x-axis represents the human PrP sequence, with the five octarepeats and H1–H4 regions of putative secondary structure shown as well as the three α-helices A, B, and C and the two β-strands S1 and S2 as determined by NMR. The precise residues corresponding to each region of secondary structure are given in Figure 5. Vertical bars above the axis indicate the number of species that differ from the human sequence at each position. Below the axis, the length of the bars indicates the number of alternative amino acids at each position in the alignment. (B) Mutations causing inherited human prion disease and polymorphisms in human, mouse, and sheep. Above the line of the human sequence are mutations that cause prion disease. Below the lines are polymorphisms, some but not all of which are known to influence the onset as well as the phenotype of disease. Data were compiled by Paul Bamborough and Fred E. Cohen.

Models of PrP^Sc suggested that formation of the disease-causing isoform involves refolding of residues within the region between residues 90 and 140 into β-sheets [166]; the single disulfide bond joining COOH-terminal helices would remain intact since the disulfide is required for PrP^{Sc} formation (Figure 5E) [167, 168]. The high β-sheet content of PrP^{Sc} was predicted from the ability of PrP 27–30 to polymerize into amyloid fibrils [107]. Subsequent optical

Figure 5A

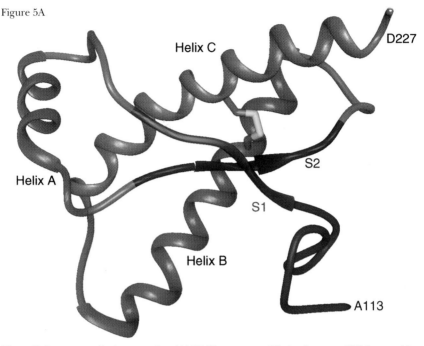

Figure 5. Structures of prion proteins. (A) NMR structure of Syrian hamster (SHa) recombinant (r) PrP(90–231). Presumably, the structure of the α-helical form of rPrP(90–231) resembles that of PrP^C. rPrP(90–231) is viewed from the interface where PrP^{Sc} is thought to bind to PrP^C. The color scheme is: α-helices A (residues 144–157), B (172–193), and C (200–227) in pink; disulfide between Cys179 and Cys214 in yellow; conserved hydrophobic region composed of residues 113–126 in red; loops in gray; residues 129–134 in green encompassing strand S1 and residues 159–165 in blue encompassing strand S2; the arrows span residues 129–131 and 161–163, as these show a closer resemblance to β–sheet [155]. (B) NMR structure of rPrP(90–231) is viewed from the interface where protein X is thought to bind to PrP^C. Protein X appears to bind to the side chains of residues that form a discontinuous epitope: some amino acids are in the loop composed of residues 165–171 and at the end of helix B (Gln168 and Gln172 with a low density van der Waals rendering) while others are on the surface of helix C (Thr215 and Gln219 with a high density van der Waals rendering) [178]. (C) PrP residues governing the transmission of prions [298]. NMR structure of recombinant SHaPrP region 121–231 [155] shown with the putative epitope formed by residues 184, 186, 203, and 205 highlighted in red. Residue numbers correspond to SHaPrP. Additional residues (138, 139, 143, 145, 148, and 155) that might participate in controlling the transmission of prions across species are depicted in green. Residues 168, 172, 215, and 219 that form the epitope for the binding of protein X are shown in blue. The three helices (A, B, and C) are highlighted in pink. (D) Schematic diagram showing the flexibility of the polypeptide chain for PrP(29–231) [156]. The structure of the portion of the protein representing residues 90–231 was taken from the coordinates of PrP(90–231) [155]. The remainder of the sequence was hand-built for illustration purposes only. The color scale corresponds to the heteronuclear {^{1}H}-^{15}N NOE data: red for the lowest (most negative) values, where the polypeptide is most flexible, to blue for the highest (most positive) values in the most structured and rigid regions of the protein.(E) Plausible model for the tertiary structure of human PrP^{Sc} [166]. Color scheme is: S1 β–strands are 108–113 and 116–122 in red; S2 β-strands are 128–135 and 138–144 in green; a-helices H3 (residues 178–191) and H4 (residues 202–218) in gray; loop (residues 142–177) in yellow. Four residues implicated in the species barrier are shown in ball-and-stick form (Asn 108, Met 112, Met 129, Ala 133).

spectroscopy confirmed the presence of β-sheet in both PrP[Sc] and PrP 27–30 [25, 169–171]. Deletion of each of the regions of putative secondary structure in PrP, except for the NH$_2$-terminal 66 amino acids (residues 23–88) [163, 172] and a 36 amino acid region (Mo residues 141 -176) prevented formation of PrP[Sc] as measured in scrapie–infected cultured neuroblastoma cells [168]. With α-PrP Fabs selected from phage display libraries [157] and two monoclonal antibodies (mAb) derived from hybridomas [173–175], the major conformational change that occurs during conversion of PrP[C] into PrP[Sc] has been localized largely, but not entirely, to a region bounded by residues 90 and 112 [158]. Similar conclusions were drawn from studies with an α-PrP IgM mAb [176]. While these results indicate that PrP[Sc] formation involves primarily a conformational change in the domain comprised of residues 90–112, mutations causing inherited prion diseases have been found throughout the protein (Figure 4B). Interestingly, all of the known point mutations in PrP with biological significance occur either within or adjacent to regions of putative secondary structure in PrP and as such, appear to destabilize the structure of PrP [147, 148, 154].

NMR structure of recombinant PrP. The NMR structure of recombinant SHaPrP(90–231) derived from *E. coli* was determined after the protein was purified and refolded (Figure 5A). Residues 90–112 are not shown since marked conformational heterogeneity was found in this region while residues 113–126 constitute the conserved hydrophobic region that also displays some structural plasticity [162]. Although some features of the structure of rPrP(90–231) are similar to those reported earlier for the smaller recombinant MoPrP(121–231) fragment [154, 177], substantial differences were found.

Figure 5B

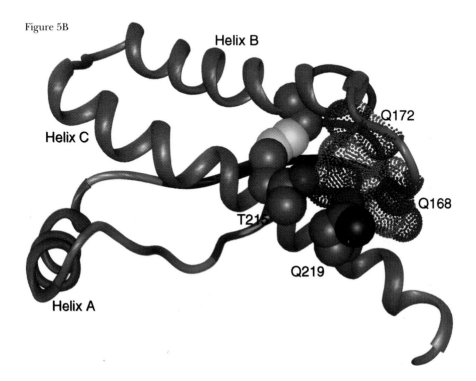

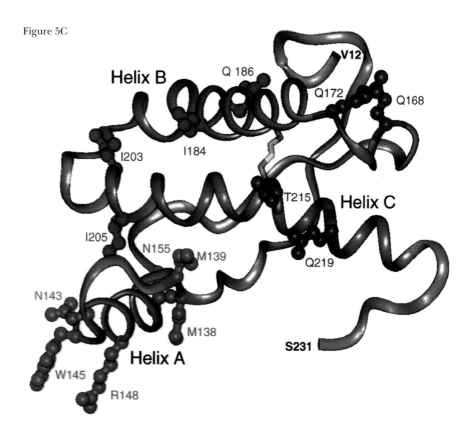

Helix B Q 186 V12

Q172 Q168

I203 I184

T215 Helix C

I205

N155 M139 Q219

N143

M138

S231

Helix A Q219

W145

R148

For example, the loop at the NH$_2$-terminus of helix B is well defined in rPrP(90–231) but is disordered in MoPrP(121–231); in addition, helix C is composed of residues 200–227 in rPrP(90–231) but extends only from 200–217 in MoPrP(121–231). The loop and the COOH-terminal portion of helix C are particularly important since they form the site to which protein X binds as described below (Figure 5B) [178]. Whether the differences between the two recombinant PrP fragments are due to (i) their different lengths, (ii) species specific differences in sequences, or (iii) the conditions used for solving the structures remains to be determined.

Studies of chimeric SHa/Mo and Hu/Mo PrP transgenes identified a domain comprised of residues 95 –170 where PrP^C binds to PrP^{Sc} [133, 179]. When chimeric Bo/Mo PrP transgenes failed to render mice sensitive to BSE prions, we examined the differences among the sequences in the chimeric and parent PrP genes [298]. The findings identified a second domain in PrP composed of residues 180–205 which seems to modulate the interaction between PrP^C and PrP^{Sc} (Figure 5C).

Recent NMR studies of full length MoPrP(23–231) and SHaPrP(29–231) have shown that the NH$_2$-termini are highly flexible and lack identifiable secondary structure under the experimental conditions employed (Figure 5D) [156, 165]. Studies of SHaPrP(29–231) indicate transient interactions between the COOH-terminal end of helix B and the highly flexible, NH$_2$-terminal ran-

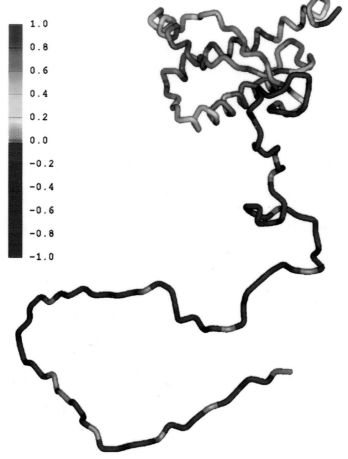

dom-coil containing the octareapeats (residues 29–125) [156]; such interactions were not reported for MoPrP(23–231) [165].

PrP appears to bind copper. The highly flexible NH_2-terminus of recombinant PrP may be more structured in the presence of copper. Each SHaPrP(29–231) molecule was found to bind two atoms of Cu^{2+}; other divalent cations did not bind to PrP [180]. Earlier studies with synthetic peptides corresponding to the octarepeat sequence demonstrated the binding of Cu^{2+} ions [181, 182] and optical spectroscopy showed that Cu^{2+} induced an α-helix formation in these peptides [183]. More recently, PrP-deficient ($Prnp^{0/0}$) mice were found to have lower levels of Zn/Cu superoxide dismutase (SOD) activity than controls [184]; SOD activity has been shown to mirror the state of copper metabolism [185]. Measurements of membrane extracts from brains of $Prnp^{0/0}$ mice showed low levels of Cu whereas Fe and Zn were unchanged suggesting PrP^C might function as a Cu^{2+} binding protein [186].

Disturbances in Cu^{2+} homeostasis leading to dysfunction of the CNS are well documented in humans and animals but are not known to be due to abnormalities in PrP metabolism: Menkes disease is manifest at birth and is due to a mutation of the MNK gene on the X chromosome while Wilson's disease

286

Figure 5E

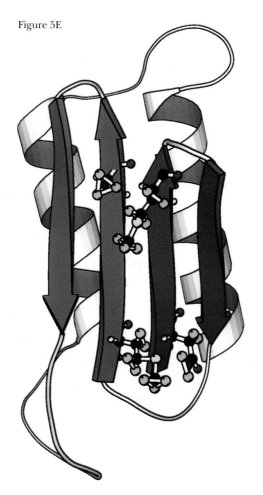

appears in childhood and is due to a mutation of the WD gene on chromosome 13 [187–190]. Both the MNK and WD genes encode copper transporting ATPases. While both Menkes and Wilson's diseases are recessive disorders, only Wilson's disease can be treated with copper chelating reagents. Interestingly, cuprizone, a Cu^{2+} chelating reagent, has been used in mice to induce neuropathological changes similar to those found in the prion diseases [191, 192].

PrP gene structure and expression. The entire open reading frame (ORF) of all known mammalian and avian PrP genes resides within a single exon [4, 82, 193, 194]. The mouse (Mo), sheep, cattle, and rat PrP genes contain three exons with the ORFs in exon 3 [195–199] which is analogous to exon 2 of the Syrian hamster (SHa) gene [82]. The two exons of the Syrian hamster (SHa) PrP gene are separated by a 10-kb intron: exon 1 encodes a portion of the 5' untranslated leader sequence while exon 2 encodes the ORF and 3' untranslated region [82]. Recently, a low abundance SHaPrP mRNA containing an additional small exon in the 5' untranslated region was discovered that is encoded by the SHaPrP gene [200]. Comparative sequencing of sheep and human (Hu) cosmid clones containing PrP genes revealed an additional putative, small untranslated 5' exon in the HuPrP gene [201]. The promoters of both the

SHa and Mo PrP genes contain multiple copies of G-C rich repeats and are devoid of TATA boxes. These G-C nonamers represent a motif that may function as a canonical binding site for the transcription factor Sp1 [202]. Mapping of PrP genes to the short arm of Hu chromosome 20 and to the homologous region of Mo chromosome 2 argues for the existence of PrP genes prior to the speciation of mammals [203, 204].

Although PrP mRNA is constitutively expressed in the brains of adult animals [83, 84], it is highly regulated during development. In the septum, levels of PrP mRNA and choline acetyltransferase were found to increase in parallel during development [205]. In other brain regions, PrP gene expression occurred at an earlier age. *In situ* hybridization studies show that the highest levels of PrP mRNA are found in neurons [206].

PrP^C expression in brain was defined by standard immunohistochemistry [207] and by histoblotting in the brains of uninfected controls [208]. Immunostaining of PrP^C in the SHa brain was most intense in the stratum radiatum and stratum oriens of the CA1 region of the hippocampus and was virtually absent from the granule cell layer of the dentate gyrus and the pyramidal cell layer throughout Ammon's horn. PrP^{Sc} staining was minimal in those regions which were intensely stained for PrP^C. A similar relationship between PrP^C and PrP^{Sc} was found in the amygdala. In contrast, PrP^{Sc} accumulated in the medial habenular nucleus, the medial septal nuclei, and the diagonal band of Broca; in contrast, these areas were virtually devoid of PrP^C. In the white matter, bundles of myelinated axons contained PrP^{Sc} but were devoid of PrP^C. These findings suggest that prions are transported along axons and are in agreement with earlier findings in which scrapie infectivity was found to migrate in a pattern consistent with retrograde transport [209–211].

Molecular genetics of prion diseases. Independent of enriching brain fractions for scrapie infectivity that led to the discovery of PrP^{Sc}, the PrP gene was shown to be genetically linked to a locus controlling scrapie incubation times [212]. Subsequently, mutation of the PrP gene was shown to be genetically linked to the development of familial prion disease [4]. At the same time, expression of a SHaPrP transgene in mice was shown to render the animals highly susceptible to SHa prions demonstrating that expression of a foreign PrP gene could abrogate the species barrier [213]. Later, PrP-deficient (Prnp$^{0/0}$) mice were found to be resistant to prion infection and failed to replicate prions, as expected [100, 101]. The results of these studies indicated PrP must play a central role in the transmission and pathogenesis of prion disease but equally important, they argued that the abnormal isoform is an essential component of the prion particle [23].

PrP gene dosage controls length of incubation time. Scrapie incubation times in mice were used to distinguish prion strains and to identify a gene controlling its length [135, 214]. This gene was initially called *Sinc* based on genetic crosses between C57Bl and VM mice that exhibited short and long incubation times, respectively [214]. Because of the restricted distribution of VM mice, we searched for another mouse with long incubation times. I/Ln mice proved to be a suitable substitute for VM mice [215]; eventually, I/Ln and VM mice were found to be derived from a common ancestor [216]. With a PrP cDNA probe, we demonstrated genetic linkage between the PrP gene and a locus controlling the incubation time in crosses between NZW/LacJ and I/Ln mice [212]. We provisionally designated these genes as components of the *Prn* complex but eventually found that the incubation time gene, *Prn-i*, is either congruent with or closely linked to the PrP gene, *Prnp* [194].

Although the amino acid substitutions in PrP that distinguish NZW *(Prnp^a)* from I/Ln *(Prnp^b)* mice argued for congruency of *Prnp* and *Prn-i*, experiments with *Prnp^a* mice expressing *Prnp^b* transgenes demonstrated a "paradoxical" shortening of incubation times [195]. We had predicted that these Tg mice would exhibit a prolongation of the incubation time after inoculation with RML prions based on *(Prnp^a* x*Prnp^b)* F1 mice which do exhibit long incubation times. We described those findings as "paradoxical shortening" because we and others had believed for many years that long incubation times are dominant traits [212, 214]. From studies of congenic and transgenic mice expressing different numbers of the *a* and *b* alleles of *Prnp*, we learned that these findings were not paradoxical; indeed, they resulted from increased PrP gene dosage [217]. When the RML isolate was inoculated into congenic and transgenic mice, increasing the number of copies of the *a* allele was found to be the major determinant in reducing the incubation time; however, increasing the number of copies of the *b* allele also reduced the incubation time, but not to the same extent as that seen with the *a* allele. From the foregoing investigations, we concluded that both *Sinc* and *Prn-i* are congruent with PrP [217], and recent gene targeting studies have confirmed this view [218].

Overexpression of wtPrP transgenes. Mice were constructed expressing different levels of the wild-type (wt) SHaPrP transgene [213]. Inoculation of these Tg(SHaPrP) mice with SHa prions demonstrated abrogation of the species barrier resulting in abbreviated incubation times [219]. The length of the incubation time after inoculation with SHa prions was inversely proportional to the level of SHaPrP^C in the brains of Tg(SHaPrP) mice [219]. Bioassays of brain extracts from clinically ill Tg(SHaPrP) mice inoculated with Mo prions revealed that only Mo prions but no SHa prions were produced. Conversely, inoculation of Tg(SHaPrP) mice with SHa prions led only to the synthesis of SHa prions. Although the rate of PrP^Sc synthesis appears to be a function of the level of PrP^C expression in Tg mice, the level to which PrP^Sc finally accumulates seems to be independent of PrP^C concentration [219].

During transgenetic studies, we discovered that uninoculated older mice harboring numerous copies of wtPrP transgenes derived from Syrian hamsters, sheep, and *Prnp^b* mice spontaneously developed truncal ataxia, hindlimb paralysis, and tremors [197]. These Tg mice exhibited a profound necrotizing myopathy involving skeletal muscle, a demyelinating polyneuropathy, and focal vacuolation of the CNS. Development of disease was dependent on transgene dosage. For example, Tg(SHaPrP^{+/+})7 mice homozygous for the SHaPrP transgene array regularly developed disease between 400 and 600 days of age, while hemizygous Tg(SHaPrP^{+/0})7 mice also developed disease, but only after >650 days.

PrP-deficient mice. The development and lifespan of two lines of PrP-deficient (Prnp$^{0/0}$) mice were indistinguishable from controls [220, 221] while two other lines exhibited ataxia and Purkinje cell degeneration at ~70 weeks of age [222] (R. Moore and D. Melton, in preparation). In the former two lines with normal development, altered sleep wake cycles have been reported [223] and altered synaptic behavior in brain slices was reported [224, 225] but could not be confirmed by others [226, 227].

Prnp$^{0/0}$ mice are resistant to prions [100, 101]. Prnp$^{0/0}$ mice were sacrificed 5, 60, 120, and 315 days after inoculation with RML prions and brain extracts bioassayed in CD-1 Swiss mice. Except for residual infectivity from the inoculum detected at 5 days after inoculation, no infectivity was detected in the brains of Prnp$^{0/0}$ mice [101]. One group of investigators found that Prnp$^{0/0}$ mice inoculated with RML prions and sacrificed 20 weeks later had $10^{3.6}$ ID$_{50}$ units/ml of homogenate by bioassay [100]. Others have used this report to argue that prion infectivity replicates in the absence of PrP [67, 132]. Neither we nor the authors of the initial report could confirm the finding of prion replication in Prnp$^{0/0}$ mice [101, 103].

Prion species barrier and protein X. The passage of prions between species is often a stochastic process, almost always characterized by prolonged incubation times during the first passage in the new host [36]. This prolongation is often referred to as the "species barrier" [36, 228]. Prions synthesized *de novo* reflect the sequence of the host PrP gene and not that of the PrP^{Sc} molecules in the inoculum derived from the donor [90]. On subsequent passage in a homologous host, the incubation time shortens to that recorded for all subsequent passages. From studies with Tg mice, three factors have been identified that contribute to the species barrier: (i) the difference in PrP sequences between the prion donor and recipient, (ii) the strain of prion, and (iii) the species specificity of protein X, a factor defined by molecular genetic studies that binds to PrP^C and facilitates PrP^{Sc} formation. This factor is likely to be a protein, hence the provisional designation protein X [134, 178]. The prion donor is the last mammal in which the prion was passaged and its PrP sequence represents the "species" of the prion. The strain of prion, which seems to be enciphered in the conformation of PrP^{Sc}, conspires with the PrP sequence, which is specified by the recipient, to determine the tertiary structure of nascent PrP^{Sc}. These principles are demonstrated by studies on the transmission of Syrian hamster (SHa) prions to mice showing that expression of a SHaPrP transgene in mice abrogated the species barrier (Table 3) [213]. Besides the PrP sequence, the strain of prion modified transmission of SHa prions to mice (Table 3) [135, 229, 230].

Transmission of human prions. Protein X was postulated to explain the results on the transmission of human (Hu) prions to Tg mice (Table 4) [134, 179]. Mice expressing both Mo and HuPrP were resistant to Hu prions while those expressing only HuPrP were susceptible. These results argue that MoPrP^C inhibited transmission of Hu prions i.e. the formation of nascent HuPrP^{Sc}. In contrast to the foregoing studies, mice expressing both MoPrP and chimeric MHu2M PrP were susceptible to Hu prions and mice expressing MHu2MPrP

Table 3. Influence of prion species and strains on transmission across a species barrier*

Inoculum	Host	Sc237		139H	
		Incubation time / [days ± SEM] (n/n$_o$)			
SHa	SHa	77 ± 1	(48/48)	167 ± 1	(94/94)
SHa	non-Tg mice	>700	(0/9)	499 ± 15	(11/11)
SHa	Tg(SHaPrP)81/ FVB mice	75 ± 2	(22/22)	110 ± 2	(19/19)
SHa	Tg(SHaPrP)81/ Prnp$^{0/0}$ mice	54 ± 1	(9/9)	65 ± 1	(15/15)

*data from references [101, 219, 230] (D. Groth and S.B. Prusiner, unpublished data). n/n$_o$ = number of diseased animals / number of injected animals.

alone were only slightly more susceptible. These findings contend that MoPrP^C has only a minimal effect on the formation of chimeric MHu2MPrP^{Sc}.

Table 4. Evidence for protein X from transmission studies of human prions†

Inoculum	Host	MoPrP gene	Incubation Time	
			[days ± SEM] (n/no)	
sCJD	Tg(HuPrP)	Prnp$^{+/+}$	721	(1/10)
sCJD	Tg(HuPrP)Prnp$^{0/0}$	Prnp$^{0/0}$	263 ± 2	(6/6)
sCJD	Tg(MHu2M)	Prnp$^{+/+}$	238 ± 3	(8/8)
sCJD	Tg(MHu2M)Prnp$^{0/0}$	Prnp$^{0/0}$	191 ± 3	(10/10)

†data with inoculum RG [134].

Genetic evidence for protein X. When the data on Hu prion transmission to Tg mice were considered together, they suggested that MoPrP^C prevented the conversion of HuPrP^C into PrP^{Sc} but had little effect on the conversion of MHu2M into PrP^{Sc} by binding to another Mo protein. We interpreted these results in terms of MoPrP^C binding to this Mo protein with a higher affinity than does HuPrP^C. We postulated that MoPrP^C had little effect on the formation of PrP^{Sc} from MHu2M (Table 4) because MoPrP and MHu2M share the same amino acid sequence at the COOH-terminus. We hypothesized that MoPrP^C only weakly inhibited transmission of SHa prions to Tg(SHaPrP) mice (Table 3) because SHaPrP is more closely related to MoPrP than is HuPrP.

Using scrapie-infected mouse (Mo) neuroblastoma cells transfected with chimeric Hu/Mo PrP genes, we extended our studies of protein X. Substitution of a Hu residue at position 214 or 218 prevented PrP^{Sc} formation (Figure 5B) [178]. The side chains of these residues protrude from the same surface of the COOH-terminal α-helix forming a discontinuous epitope with residues 167 and 171 in an adjacent loop. Substitution of a basic residue at positions 167, 171, or 218 prevented PrP^{Sc} formation; these mutant PrPs appear to act as "dominant negatives" by binding protein X and rendering it unavailable for prion propagation. Our findings within the context of protein X explain the protective effects of basic polymorphic residues in PrP of humans and sheep [198, 231, 232].

Is protein X a molecular chaperone? Since PrP undergoes a profound structural transition during prion propagation, it seems likely that other proteins such as chaperones participate in this process. Whether protein X functions as a molecular chaperone is unknown. Interestingly, scrapie-infected cells in culture display marked differences in the induction of heat-shock proteins [233, 234] and Hsp70 mRNA has been reported to increase in scrapie of mice [235]. While attempts to isolate specific proteins that bind to PrP have been disappointing [236], PrP has been shown to interact with Bcl-2 and Hsp60 by two-hybrid analysis in yeast [237, 238]. Although these studies are suggestive, no molecular chaperone involved in prion formation in mammalian cells has been identified.

Miniprions. Using the four-helix bundle model of PrP^C (Figure 4A) [147], each region of proposed secondary structure was systematically deleted and the mutant constructs expressed in scrapie-infected neuroblastoma (ScN2a) cells and Tg mice [164, 168]. Deletion of any of the four putative helical regions prevented PrP^{Sc} formation while deletion of the NH$_2$-terminal region containing residues 23–89 did not affect the yield of PrP^{Sc}. In addition to the 67 residues at the NH$_2$-terminus, 36 residues from position 141 to 176 could be deleted without altering PrP^{Sc} formation (Figures 6 and 7). The resulting PrP molecule of 106 amino acids was designated PrP106. In this mutant PrP, helix A as well as the S2 β-strand were removed. When PrP106 was expressed in ScN2a cells, PrP^{Sc}106 was soluble in 1% Sarkosyl. Whether the structure of PrP^{Sc}106 can be more readily determined than that of full-length PrP^{Sc} remains uncertain.

Transgene-specified susceptibility. Tg(PrP106)Prnp$^{0/0}$ mice that expressed PrP106 developed neurological dysfunction ~300 days after inoculation with RML prions previously passaged in CD-1 Swiss mice (S. Supattapone, T. Muramoto, D. Peretz, S. J. DeArmond, A. Wallace, F. E. Cohen, S. B. Prusiner and M. R. Scott, in preparation). The resulting prions containing PrP^{Sc}106

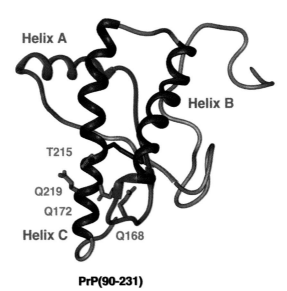

PrP(90-231)

Figure 6. Miniprions produced by deleting PrP residues 23–89 and 141–176. The deletion of residues 141–176 (green) containing helix A and the S2 β-strand is shown.

292

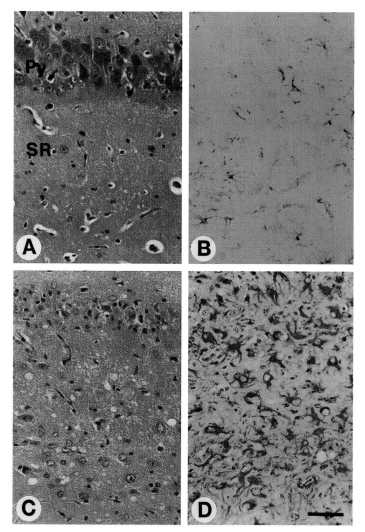

Figure 7. Tg(PrP106) Prnp$^{0/0}$ mice were inoculated with RML106 prions containing PrP^{Sc}106. Sections of the hippocampus stained with hematoxylin (A and C) and eosin (B and D). (A and B) Control Tg(PrP106) mouse uninoculated and without neurologic deficits. (C and D) Tg(PrP106) Prnp$^{0/0}$ mouse inoculated with RML106 prions and sacrificed after signs of neurologic dysfunction observed. Photomicrographs prepared by Stephen J. DeArmond.

produced CNS disease in ~66 days upon subsequent passage in Tg(PrP106)Prnp$^{0/0}$ mice. (Table 5). Besides widespread spongiform degeneration and PrP deposits, the pyramidal cells of the hippocampus comprising the CA-1, CA-2, and CA-3 fields disappeared in Tg(PrP106)Prnp$^{0/0}$ mice inoculated with prions containing PrP^{Sc}106 (Figure 7A–D). In no previous study of Tg mice have we seen similar neuropathological lesions. The Tg(MoPrP-A) mice overexpressing MoPrP are resistant to RML106 miniprions, but are highly susceptible to RML prions. These mice require more than 250 days to produce illness after inoculation with miniprions but develop disease in ~50 days when inoculated with RML prions containing full-length MoPrP^{Sc}.

Table 5. Susceptibility and resistance of transgenic mice to artificial miniprions*

Host	RML106 miniprions		RML prions	
	Incubation time [days ± SEM] (n/n_o)			
Tg(PrP106)Prnp$^{0/0}$ mice	66 ± 3	(10/10)	300 ± 2	(9/10)
Tg(MoPrP-A) mice	>250	(0/11)	50 ± 2	(16/16)

*data from references [217] (S. Supattapone, T. Muramoto, D. Peretz, S. J. DeArmond, A. Wallace, F. E. Cohen, S. B. Prusiner and M. R. Scott, in preparation).

Smaller prions and mythical viruses. The unique incubation times and neuropathy in Tg mice caused by miniprions are difficult to reconcile with the notion that scrapie is caused by an as yet unidentified virus. When the mutant or wt PrP^C of the host matched PrP^{Sc} in the inoculum, the mice were highly susceptible (Table 5). However, when there was a mismatch between PrP^C and PrP^{Sc}, the mice were resistant to the prions. This principle of homologous PrP interactions which underlies the species barrier (Table 3) is recapitulated in studies of PrP106 where the amino acid sequence has been drastically changed by deleting nearly 50% of the residues. Indeed, the unique properties of the miniprions provide another persuasive argument supporting the contention that prions are infectious proteins.

Human prion diseases. Most humans afflicted with prion disease present with rapidly progressive dementia, but some manifest cerebellar ataxia. Although the brains of patients appear grossly normal upon post-mortem examination, they usually show spongiform degeneration and astrocytic gliosis under the microscope. The human prion diseases can present as sporadic, genetic, or infectious disorders [5] (Table 1A).

Sporadic CJD. Sporadic forms of prion disease comprise most cases of CJD and possibly a few cases of Gerstmann-Sträussler-Scheinker disease (GSS) (Table 1A) [4, 239, 240]. In these patients, mutations of the PrP gene are not found. How prions causing disease arise in patients with sporadic forms is unknown; hypotheses include horizontal transmission of prions from humans or animals [241], somatic mutation of the PrP gene, and spontaneous conversion of PrP^C into PrP^{Sc} [5, 15]. Since numerous attempts to establish an infectious link between sporadic CJD and a preexisting prion disease in animals or humans have been unrewarding, it seems unlikely that transmission features in the pathogenesis of sporadic prion disease [9–12, 242].

Inherited prion diseases. To date, 20 different mutations in the human PrP gene resulting in nonconservative substitutions have been found that segregate with the inherited prion diseases (Figure 4B). Familial CJD cases suggested that genetic factors might influence pathogenesis [1, 2, 243], but this was difficult to reconcile with the transmissibility of fCJD and GSS [3]. The discovery of genetic linkage between the PrP gene and scrapie incubation times in mice [212] raised the possibility that mutation might feature in the hereditary human prion diseases. The P102L mutation was the first PrP mutation to be genetically linked to CNS dysfunction in GSS (Figure 4B)[4] and has since been found in many GSS families throughout the world [244-246]. Indeed, a mutation in the protein coding region of the PrP gene has been found in all reported kindred with familial human prion disease; besides the P102L mutation, genetic linkage has been established for four other mutations [16, 29–31].

Tg mouse studies confirmed that mutations of the PrP gene can cause neurodegeneration. The P102L mutation of GSS was introduced into the MoPrP transgene and five lines of Tg(MoPrP-P101L) mice expressing high levels of mutant PrP developed spontaneous CNS degeneration consisting of widespread vacuolation of the neuropil, astrocytic gliosis, and numerous PrP amyloid plaques similar to those seen in the brains of humans who die from GSS(P102L) [247–249]. Brain extracts prepared from spontaneously ill Tg(MoPrP-P101L) mice transmitted CNS degeneration to Tg196 mice but contained no protease-resistant PrP [248, 249]. The Tg196 mice do not develop spontaneous disease but express low levels of the mutant transgene MoPrP-P101L and are deficient for mouse PrP (Prnp$^{0/0}$) [220]. These studies, combined with the transmission of prions from patients who died of GSS to apes and monkeys [3] or to Tg(MHu2M-P101L) mice [134], demonstrate that prions are generated de novo by mutations in PrP. Additionally, brain extracts from patients with some other inherited prion diseases, fCJD(E200K) or FFI, transmit disease to Tg(MHu2M) mice [27]. An artificial set of mutations in a PrP transgene consisting of A113V, A115V, and A118V produced neurodegeneration in neonatal mice; these Val substitutions were selected for their propensity to form β sheets [153, 250]. In preliminary studies, brain extracts from two of these mice transmitted disease to hamsters and to Tg mice expressing a chimeric SHa/Mo PrP.

Genetic disease that is transmissible. Had the PrP gene been identified in families with prion disease by positional cloning or through the purification and sequencing of PrP in amyloid plaques before brain extracts were shown to be transmissible, the prion concept might have been more readily accepted. Within that scenario, it seems likely that we would have explored the possibility that the mutant protein, upon inoculation into a susceptible host, stimulated production of more of a similar protein. Postulating an infectious pathogen with a foreign genome would have been the least likely candidate to explain how a genetic disease could be experimentally transmissible.

Infectious prion diseases. The infectious prion diseases include kuru of the Fore people in New Guinea where prions were transmitted by ritualistic cannibalism [241, 251, 252]. With the cessation of cannibalism at the urging of missionaries, kuru began to decline long before it was known to be transmissible (Figure 8). Sources of prions causing infectious CJD on several different continents include improperly sterilized depth electrodes, transplanted corneas, human growth hormone (HGH) and gonadotrophin derived from cadaveric pituitaries, and dura mater grafts [253]. Over 90 young adults have developed CJD after treatment with cadaveric HGH; the incubation periods range from 3 to more than 20 years [254, 255]. Dura mater grafts implanted during neurosurgical procedures seem to have caused more than 60 cases of CJD; these incubation periods range from one to more than 14 years [256–258].

Prion diversity. The existence of prion strains raises the question of how

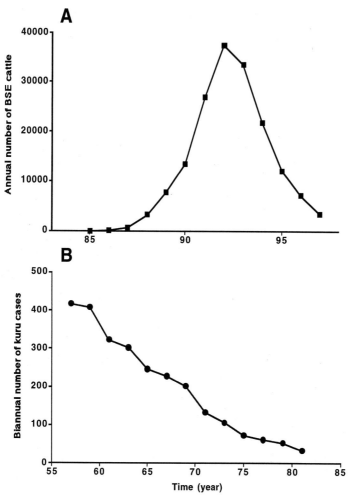

Figure 8. Disappearance of the kuru and BSE epidemics. (A) Number of annual cases of BSE in cattle in Great Britain. (B) Number of biannual cases of kuru in Papua New Guinea. Data compiled for BSE by John Wilesmith and for kuru by Michael Alpers.

heritable biological information can be enciphered in a molecule other than nucleic acid [131, 214, 259-263]. Strains or varieties of prions have been defined by incubation times and the distribution of neuronal vacuolation [214, 264]. Subsequently, the patterns of PrP^{Sc} deposition were found to correlate with vacuolation profiles and these patterns were also used to characterize strains of prions [230, 265, 266]

The typing of prion strains in C57Bl, VM, and F1 (C57Bl x VM) inbred mice began with isolates from sheep with scrapie. The prototypic strains called Me7 and 22A gave incubation times of ~150 and ~400 days in C57Bl mice, respectively [214, 267, 268]. The PrP genes of C57Bl and I/Ln (and later VM) mice encode proteins differing at two residues and control scrapie incubation times [194, 212, 216–218, 269].

Until recently, support for the hypothesis that the tertiary structure of PrP^{Sc}

296

enciphers strain-specific information [23] was minimal except for the DY strain isolated from mink with transmissible encephalopathy by passage in Syrian hamsters [26, 270, 271]. PrP^{Sc} in DY prions showed diminished resistance to proteinase K digestion as well as a peculiar site of cleavage. The DY strain presented a puzzling anomaly since other prion strains exhibiting similar incubation times did not show this altered susceptibility to proteinase K digestion of PrP^{Sc} [135]. Also notable was the generation of new strains during passage of prions through animals with different PrP genes [135, 229].

PrP^{Sc} conformation enciphers diversity. Persuasive evidence that strain-specific information is enciphered in the tertiary structure of PrP^{Sc} comes from transmission of two different inherited human prion diseases to mice expressing a chimeric MHu2M PrP transgene [27]. In fatal familial insomnia (FFI), the protease-resistant fragment of PrP^{Sc} after deglycosylation has an M_r of 19 kD; whereas in fCJD(E200K) and most sporadic prion diseases, it is 21 kD (Table 6) [272, 273]. This difference in molecular size was shown to be due to different sites of proteolytic cleavage at the NH_2-termini of the two human PrP^{Sc} molecules reflecting different tertiary structures [272]. These distinct conformations were understandable since the amino acid sequences of the PrPs differ.

Table 6. Distinct prion strains generated in humans with inherited prion diseases and transmitted to transgenic mice*

Inoculum	Host Species	Host PrP Genotype	Incubation time [days ± SEM] (n/n$_o$)		PrP^{Sc} (kD)
None	Human	FFI(D178N,M129)	19		
FFI	Mouse	Tg(MHu2M)	206 ± 7	(7/7)	19
FFI → Tg(MHu2M)	Mouse	Tg(MHu2M)	136 ± 1	(6/6)	19
None	Human	fCJD(E200K)	21		
fCJD	Mouse	Tg(MHu2M)	170 ± 2	(10/10)	21
fCJD → Tg(MHu2M)	Mouse	Tg(MHu2M)	167 ± 3	(15/15)	21

*data from reference [27] (G. Telling *et al.*, in preparation).

Extracts from the brains of FFI patients transmitted disease to mice expressing a chimeric MHu2M PrP gene about 200 days after inoculation and induced formation of the 19 kD PrP^{Sc}; whereas fCJD(E200K) and sCJD produced the 21 kD PrP^{Sc} in mice expressing the same transgene [27]. On second passage, Tg(MHu2M) mice inoculated with FFI prions showed an incubation time of ~130 days and a 19 kD PrP^{Sc} while those inoculated with fCJD(E200K) prions exhibited an incubation time of ~170 days and a 21 kD PrP^{Sc} [28]. The experimental data demonstrate that MHu2MPrP^{Sc} can exist in two different conformations based on the sizes of the protease-resistant fragments; yet, the amino acid sequence of MHu2MPrP^{Sc} is invariant.

The results of our studies argue that PrP^{Sc} acts as a template for the conversion of PrP^{C} into nascent PrP^{Sc}. Imparting the size of the protease-resistant fragment of PrP^{Sc} through conformational templating provides a mechanism for both the generation and propagation of prion strains.

Interestingly, the protease-resistant fragment of PrP^{Sc} after deglycosylation with an M_r of 19 kD has been found in a patient who developed a sporadic case of prion disease similar to FFI but with no family history. Since both PrP alleles encoded the wt sequence and a Met at position 129, we labeled this case, fatal sporadic insomnia (FSI). At autopsy, the spongiform degeneration, reactive astrogliosis, and PrP^{Sc} deposition were confined to the thalamus [274]. These findings argue that the clinicopathologic phenotype is determined by the conformation of PrP^{Sc} in accord with the results of the transmission of human prions from patients with FFI to Tg mice [27].

Selective neuronal targeting. Besides incubation times, profiles of spongiform change (Figure 1) have been used to characterize prion strains [275], but recent studies argue that such profiles are not an intrinsic feature of strains [276, 277]. The mechanism by which prion strains modify the pattern of spongiform degeneration was perplexing since earlier investigations had shown that PrP^{Sc} deposition precedes neuronal vacuolation and reactive gliosis [211, 230]. When FFI prions were inoculated into Tg(MHu2M) mice, PrP^{Sc} was confined largely to the thalamus (Figure 9A) as is the case for FFI in humans [27, 278]. In contrast, fCJD(E200K) prions inoculated into Tg(MHu2M) mice produced widespread deposition of PrP^{Sc} throughout the cortical mantle and many of the deep structures of the CNS (Figure 9B) as is seen in fCJD(E200K) of humans. To examine whether the diverse patterns of PrP^{Sc} deposition are influenced by Asn-linked glycosylation of PrP^C, we constructed Tg mice expressing PrPs mutated at one or both of the Asn-linked glycosylation consensus sites [277]. These mutations resulted in aberrant neuroanatomic topologies of PrP^C within the CNS, whereas pathologic point mutations adjacent to the consensus sites did not alter the distribution of PrP^C. Tg mice with mutation of the second PrP glycosylation site exhibited prion incubation times of >500 days and unusual patterns of PrP^{Sc} deposition. These findings raise two possible scenarios. First, glycosylation can modify the conformation of PrP^C and affect its affinity for a particular conformer of PrP^{Sc}, which results in specific patterns of PrP^{Sc} deposition; such interactions between PrP^{Sc} and PrP^C are likely to determine the rate of nascent PrP^{Sc} formation. Second, glycosylation modifies the stability of PrP^{Sc} and hence, the rate of PrP^{Sc} clearance. This latter explanation is consistent with the proposal that the binding of PrP^C to protein X is the rate-limiting step in PrP^{Sc} formation under most circumstances [255].

Bovine spongiform encephalopathy. Prion strains and the species barrier are of paramount importance in understanding the BSE epidemic in Great Britain, in which it is estimated that almost one million cattle were infected with prions [279, 280]. The mean incubation time for BSE is about 5 years. Most cattle therefore did not manifest disease since they were slaughtered between 2 and 3 years of age [281]. Nevertheless, more than 160,000 cattle, primarily dairy cows, have died of BSE over the past decade (Figure 5A) [279]. BSE is a massive common source epidemic caused by meat and bone meal (MBM) fed primarily to dairy cows [280, 282]. The MBM was prepared from the offal of sheep, cattle, pigs, and chickens as a high protein nutritional supplement. In the late 1970s, the hydrocarbon-solvent extraction method used in the rendering of offal began to be abandoned resulting in MBM with a much higher

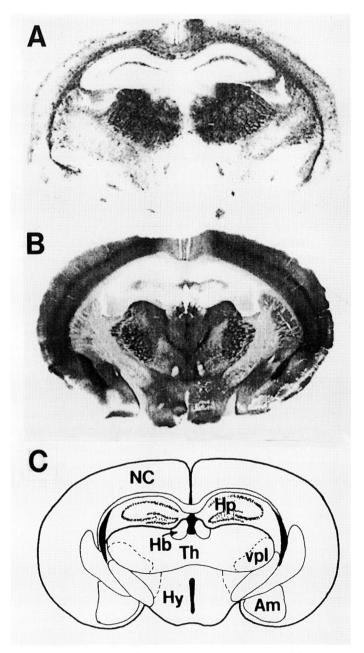

Figure 9. Regional distribution of PrP^{Sc} deposition in Tg(MHu2M)Prnp$^{0/0}$ mice inoculated with prions from humans who died of inherited prion diseases (Table 5). Histoblot of PrP^{Sc} deposition in a coronal section a Tg(MHu2M)Prnp$^{0/0}$ mouse through the hippocampus and thalamus [27]. (A) The Tg mouse was inoculated with brain extract prepared from a patient who died of FFI. (B) The Tg mouse was inoculated with extract from a patient with fCJD(E200K). Cryostat sections were mounted on nitrocellulose and treated with proteinase K to eliminate PrP^{C} [208]. To enhance the antigenicity of PrP^{Sc}, the histoblots were exposed to 3 guanidinium isothiocyanate before immunostaining using anti-PrP 3F4 mAb [174]. (C) Labelled diagram of a coronal sections of the hippocampus/thalamus region. NC, neocortex; Hp, hippocampus; Hb, habenula; Th, thalamus; vpl, ventral posterior lateral thalamic nucleus; Hy, hypothalamus; Am, amygdala. Photomicrographs prepared by Stephen J. DeArmond.

299

fat content [282]. It is now thought that this change in the rendering process allowed scrapie prions from sheep to survive rendering and to be passed into cattle. Alternatively, bovine prions were present at low levels prior to modification of the rendering process and with the processing change survived in sufficient numbers to initiate the BSE epidemic when inoculated back into cattle orally through MBM. Against the latter hypothesis is the widespread geographical distribution throughout England of the initial 17 cases of BSE, which occurred almost simultaneously [280, 283, 284]. Furthermore, there is no evidence of a pre-existing prion disease of cattle, either in Great Britain or elsewhere.

Origin of BSE prions? The origin of the bovine prions causing BSE cannot be determined by examining the amino acid sequence of PrP^{Sc} in cattle with BSE since the PrP^{Sc} in these animals has the bovine sequence whether the initial prions in MBM came from cattle or sheep. The bovine PrP sequence differs from that of sheep at 7 or 8 positions [285–287]. In contrast to the many PrP polymorphisms found in sheep, only one PrP polymorphism has been found in cattle. Though most bovine PrP alleles encode five octarepeats, some encode six. PrP alleles encoding six octarepeats do not seem to be overrepresented in BSE (Figure 4B) [288].

Brain extracts from BSE cattle cause disease in cattle, sheep, mice, pigs, and mink after intracerebral inoculation [289–293], but prions in brain extracts from sheep with scrapie fed to cattle produced illness substantially different from BSE [294]. However, no exhaustive effort has been made to test different strains of sheep prions or to examine the disease following bovine to bovine passage. The annual incidence of sheep with scrapie in Britain over the past two decades has remained relatively low (J. Wilesmith, unpublished data). In July 1988, the practice of feeding MBM to sheep and cattle was banned. Recent statistics argue that the epidemic is now disappearing as a result of this ruminant feed ban (Figure 8A) [279], reminiscent of the disappearance of kuru in the Fore people of New Guinea [241, 252] (Figure 8B).

Monitoring cattle for BSE prions. Although many plans have been offered for the culling of older cattle in order to minimize the spread of BSE [279], it seems more important to monitor the frequency of prion disease in cattle as they are slaughtered for human consumption. No reliable, specific test for prion disease in live animals is available but immunoassays for PrP^{Sc} in the brainstems of cattle might provide a reasonable approach to establishing the incidence of subclinical BSE in cattle entering the human food chain [176, 208, 287, 295–297]. Determining how early in the incubation period PrP^{Sc} can be detected by immunological methods is now possible since a reliable bioassay has been created by expressing the BoPrP gene in Tg mice [298]. Prior to development of Tg(BoPrP)Prnp$^{0/0}$ mice, non-Tg mice inoculated intracerebrally with BSE brain extracts required more than 300 days to develop disease [67, 293, 299, 300]. Depending on the titer of the inoculum, the structures of PrP^{C} and PrP^{Sc}, and the structure of protein X, the number of inoculated animals developing disease can vary over a wide range (Table 3). Some investigators have stated that transmission of BSE to mice is quite variable with incubation periods exceeding one year [67] while others report low prion titers in BSE brain homogenates [299, 300] compared to rodent brain scrapie [54, 56, 301, 302].

Have bovine prions been transmitted to humans? In 1994, the first cases of CJD in teenagers and young adults that were eventually labelled new variant (v) CJD occurred in Britain [303]. Besides the young age of these patients [304, 305], the brains of these patients showed numerous PrP amyloid plaques surrounded by a halo of intense spongiform degeneration (Figure 10A and B) [306]. Later, one French case meeting these criteria followed [307]. These unusual neuropathologic changes have not been seen in CJD cases in the United States, Australia, or Japan [306, 308]. Both macaque monkeys and marmosets developed neurologic disease several years after inoculation with bovine

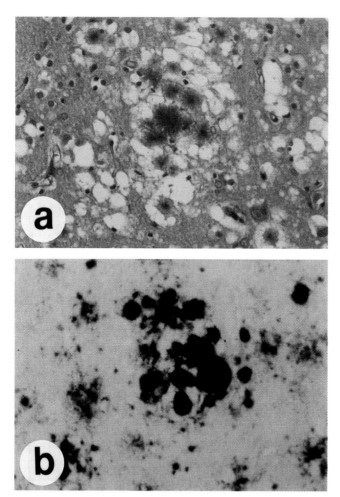

Figure 10. Histopathology of variant Creutzfeldt-Jakob disease in Great Britain. (A) Section from frontal cortex stained by the periodic acid Schiff method showing a field with aggregates of plaques surrounded by spongiform degeneration. Magnification X 100. (B) Multiple plaques and amorphous deposits are PrP immunopositive. Magnification X 500. Specimens provided by James Ironside, Jeanne Bell, and Robert Will; photomicrographs prepared by Stephen J. DeArmond.

301

prions [309], but only the macaques exhibited numerous PrP plaques similar to those found in vCJD [310] (R. Ridley and H. Baker, unpublished data).

The restricted geographical occurrence and chronology of vCJD have raised the possibility that BSE prions have been transmitted to humans. That only ~25 vCJD cases have been recorded and the incidence has remained relatively constant makes establishing the origin of vCJD difficult. No set of dietary habits distinguishes vCJD patients from apparently healthy people. Moreover, there is no explanation for the predilection of vCJD for teenagers and young adults. Why have older individuals not developed vCJD-based neuropathologic criteria? It is noteworthy that epidemiological studies over the past three decades have failed to find evidence for transmission of sheep prions to humans [9-12]. Attempts to predict the future number of cases of vCJD, assuming exposure to bovine prions prior to the offal ban, have been uninformative because so few cases of vCJD have occurred [311-313]. Are we at the beginning of a human prion disease epidemic in Britain like those seen for BSE and kuru (Figure 8) or will the number of vCJD cases remain small as seen with iCJD caused by cadaveric HGH [254, 255]?

Strain of BSE prions. Was a particular conformation of bovine PrP^{Sc} selected for heat-resistance during the rendering process and then reselected multiple times as cattle infected by ingesting prion-contaminated MBM were slaughtered and their offal rendered into more MBM? Recent studies of PrP^{Sc} from brains of patients who died of vCJD show a pattern of PrP glycoforms different from those found for sCJD or iCJD [314, 315]. But the utility of measuring PrP glycoforms is questionable in trying to relate BSE to vCJD [316, 317] because PrP^{Sc} is formed after the protein is glycosylated [138, 140] and enzymatic deglycosylation of PrP^{Sc} requires denaturation [318, 319]. Alternatively, it may be possible to establish a relationship between the conformations of PrP^{Sc} from cattle with BSE and those from humans with vCJD by using Tg mice as was done for strains generated in the brains of patients with FFI or fCJD [27, 298]. A relationship between vCJD and BSE has been suggested by finding similar incubation times in non-Tg RIII mice of ~310 days after inoculation with Hu or Bo prions [293].

Yeast and other prions. Although prions were originally defined in the context of an infectious pathogen [58], it is now becoming widely accepted that prions are elements that impart and propagate variability through multiple conformers of a normal cellular protein. Such a mechanism must surely not be restricted to a single class of transmissible pathogens. Indeed, it is likely that the original definition will need to be extended to encompass other situations where a similar mechanism of information transfer occurs.

Two notable prion-like determinants, [URE3] and [PSI], have already been described in yeast and one in another fungus denoted [Het-s*] [320-325]. Studies of candidate prion proteins in yeast may prove particularly helpful in the dissection of some of the events that feature in PrP^{Sc} formation. Interestingly, different strains of yeast prions have been identified [326]. Conversion to the prion-like [PSI] state in yeast requires the molecular chaperone Hsp104; however, no homolog of Hsp104 has been found in mammals [321, 327]. The NH$_2$-terminal prion domains of Ure2p and Sup35 that are responsible for the [URE3] and [PSI] phenotypes in yeast have been identified. In contrast to PrP, which is a GPI-anchored membrane protein, both Ure2p and Sup35 are cytosolic proteins [328]. When the prion domains of these yeast proteins were expressed in *E. coli*, the proteins were found to polymerize into fibrils with properties similar to those of PrP and other amyloids [322–324].

Whether prions explain some other examples of acquired inheritance in lower organisms is unclear [329, 330]. For example, studies on the inheritance of positional order and cellular handedness on the surface of small organisms have demonstrated the epigenetic nature of these phenomena but the mechanism remains unclear [331, 332].

Prevention of and therapeutics for prion diseases. As our understanding of prion propagation increases, it should be possible to design effective therapeutics. Because people at risk for inherited prion diseases can now be identified decades before neurologic dysfunction is evident, the development of an effective therapy for these fully penetrant disorders is imperative [333, 334]. Although we have no way of predicting the number of individuals who may develop neurologic dysfunction from bovine prions in the future [312], it would be prudent to seek an effective therapy now [28, 335]. Interfering with the conversion of PrP^C into PrP^{Sc} seems to be the most attractive therapeutic target [60]. Either stabilizing the structure of PrP^C by binding a drug or modifying the action of protein X, which might function as a molecular chaperone (Figure 5B), are reasonable strategies. Whether it is more efficacious to design a drug that binds to PrP^C at the protein X binding site or one that mimics the structure of PrP^C with basic polymorphic residues that seem to prevent scrapie and CJD remains to be determined [178, 232]. Since PrP^{Sc} formation seems limited to caveolae-like domains [142–145, 336], drugs designed to inhibit this process need not penetrate the cytosol of cells but they do need to be able to enter the CNS. Alternatively, drugs that destabilize the structure of PrP^{Sc} might also prove useful.

The production of domestic animals that do not replicate prions may also be important with respect to preventing prion disease. Sheep encoding the R/R polymorphism at position 171 seem to be resistant to scrapie [198, 231, 337–343]; presumably, this was the genetic basis of Parry's scrapie eradication program in Great Britain 30 years ago [44, 344]. A more effective approach using dominant negatives for producing prion-resistant domestic animals, including sheep and cattle, is probably the expression of PrP transgenes encoding R171 as well as additional basic residues at the putative protein X binding site (Figure 5B) [178]. Such an approach can be readily evaluated in Tg mice and once shown to be effective, it could be instituted by artificial insemination of sperm from males homozygous for the transgene. More difficult is the production of PrP-deficient cattle and sheep. Although such animals would not be susceptible to prion disease [100, 101], they might suffer some deleterious effects from ablation of the PrP gene [222–224, 227].

Whether gene therapy for the human prion diseases using the dominant negative approach described above for prion-resistant animals will prove fea-

303

sible depends on the availability of efficient vectors for delivery of the transgene to the CNS.

Concluding remarks–looking to the future. Although the study of prions has taken several unexpected directions over the past three decades, a rather novel and fascinating story of prion biology is emerging. Investigations of prions have elucidated a previously unknown mechanism of disease in humans and animals. While learning the details of the structures of PrPs and deciphering the mechanism of PrP^C transformation into PrP^{Sc} will be important, the fundamental principles of prion biology have become reasonably clear. Though some investigators prefer to view the composition of the infectious prion particle as unresolved [335, 345], such a perspective denies an enlarging body of data, none of which refutes the prion concept. Moreover, the discovery of prion-like phenomena mediated by proteins unrelated to PrP in yeast and fungi serves not only to strengthen the prion concept but also to widen it [328].

Hallmark of prion diseases. The hallmark of all prion diseases–whether sporadic, dominantly inherited, or acquired by infection–is that they involve the aberrant metabolism and resulting accumulation of the prion protein (Table 1)[23]. The conversion of PrP^C into PrP^{Sc} involves a conformation change whereby the α-helical content diminishes and the amount of β-sheet increases [25]. These findings provide a reasonable mechanism to explain the conundrum presented by the three different manifestations of prion disease.

Understanding how PrP^C unfolds and refolds into PrP^{Sc} will be of paramount importance in transferring advances in the prion diseases to studies of other degenerative illnesses. The mechanism by which PrP^{Sc} is formed must involve a templating process whereby existing PrP^{Sc} directs the refolding of PrP^C into a nascent PrP^{Sc} with the same conformation. Not only will a knowledge of PrP^{Sc} formation help in the rational design of drugs that interrupt the pathogenesis of prion diseases, but it may also open new approaches to deciphering the causes of and to developing effective therapies for the more common neurodegenerative diseases including Alzheimer's disease, Parkinson's disease, and amyotrophic lateral sclerosis (ALS). Indeed, the expanding list of prion diseases and their novel modes of transmission and pathogenesis (Table 1), as well as the unprecedented mechanisms of prion propagation and information transfer (Tables 5 and 6), indicate that much more attention to these fatal disorders of protein conformation is urgently needed.

But prions may have even wider implications than those noted for the common neurodegenerative diseases. If we think of prion diseases as disorders of protein conformation and do not require the diseases to be transmissible, then what we have learned from the study of prions may reach far beyond these common illnesses.

Multiple conformers. The discovery that proteins may have multiple biologically active conformations may prove no less important than the implications of prions for diseases. How many different tertiary structures can PrP^{Sc} adopt? This query not only addresses the issue of the limits of prion diversity but also applies to proteins as they normally function within the cell or act to affect homeostasis in multicellular organisms. The expanding list of chaperones that assist the folding and unfolding of proteins promises much new knowledge about this process. For example, it is now clear that proproteases can carry their own chaperone activity where the *pro* portion of the protein functions as a chaperone in *cis* to guide the folding of the proteolytically active portion before it is cleaved [346]. Such a mechanism might well feature in the maturation of polypeptide hormones. Interestingly, mutation of the chaperone portion of prosubtilisin resulted in the folding of a subtilisin protease with different properties than the one folded by the wild-type chaperone. Such chaperones have also been shown to work in *trans* [346]. Besides transient metabolic regulation within the cell and hormonal regulation of multicellular organisms, it is not unreasonable to suggest that polymerization of proteins into multimeric structures such as intermediate filaments might be controlled at least in part by alternative conformations of proteins. Such regulation of multimeric protein assemblies might occur either in the proteins that form the polymers or the proteins that function to facilitate the polymerization process. Additionally, apoptosis during development and throughout adult life might also be regulated, at least in part, by alternative tertiary structures of proteins.

Shifting the debate. The debate about prions and the diseases that they cause has now shifted to such issues as how many biological processes are controlled by changes in protein conformation. Although the extreme radiation-resistance of the scrapie infectivity suggested that the pathogen causing this disease and related illnesses would be different from viruses, viroids, and bacteria [32, 33], few thought that alternative protein conformations might even remotely feature in the pathogenesis of the prion diseases [37]. Indeed, an unprecedented mechanism of disease has been revealed where an aberrant conformational change in a protein is propagated. The discovery of prions and their eventual acceptance by the community of scholars represents a triumph of the scientific process over prejudice. The future of this new and emerging area of biology should prove even more interesting and productive as a multitude of unpredicted discoveries emerge.

ACKNOWLEDGEMENT

I thank O. Abramsky, M. Baldwin, R. Barry, C. Bellinger, D. Borchelt, D. Burton, D. Butler, G. Carlson, J. Cleaver, F. Cohen, C. Cooper, S. DeArmond, T. Diener, J. Dyson, S. Farr-Jones, R. Fletterick, R. Gabizon, D. Groth, C. Heinrich, L. Hood, K. Hsiao, Z. Huang, T. James, K. Kaneko, R. Kohler, T. Kitamoto, H. Kretzschmar, V. Lingappa, H. Liu, D. Lowenstein, M. McKinley, Z. Meiner, B. Miller, W. Mobley, B. Oesch, K.-M. Pan, D. Peretz, D. Riesner, G. Roberts, J. Safar, M. Scott, A. Serban, N. Stahl, A. Taraboulos, J. Tateishi, M. Torchia, P. Tremblay, M. Vey, C. Weissmann, D. Westaway, A. Williamson, P. Wright, and L. Zullianello for their contributions to many phases of these studies, and H. Baron, W. Burke, I. Diamond, H. Fields, R. Fishman, D, Gilden, S. Hauser, H. Koprowski, J. Krevans, J. Martin, M. McCarty, R. C. Morris, N.

Nathanson, F. Seitz, and C. Yanofsky for support and encouragement. This research was supported by grants from the National Institute of Aging and the National Institute of Neurologic Diseases and Stroke of the National Institutes of Health, the National Science Foundation, International Human Frontiers of Science Program, and the American Health Assistance Foundation as well as by gifts from the Sherman Fairchild Foundation, the Keck Foundation, the G. Harold and Leila Y. Mathers Foundation, the Bernard Osher Foundation, the John D. French Foundation, the Howard Hughes Medical Institute, R. J. Reynolds, National Medical Enterprises, and Centeon.

REFERENCES

1. Meggendorfer F.: Klinische und genealogische Beobachtungen bei einem Fall von spastischer Pseudosklerose Jakobs. *Z. Gesamte Neurol. Psychiatr.* 128:337–341, 1930.

2. Stender A.: Weitere Beiträge zum Kapitel "Spastische Pseudosklerose Jakobs". *Z. Gesamte Neurol. Psychiatr.* 128:528–543, 1930.

3. Masters C.L., Gajdusek D.C., and Gibbs C.J., Jr.: Creutzfeldt-Jakob disease virus isolations from the Gerstmann-Sträussler syndrome. *Brain* 104:559–588, 1981.

4. Hsiao K., Baker H.F., Crow T.J., Poulter M., Owen F., Terwilliger J.D., Westaway D., Ott J., and Prusiner S.B.: Linkage of a prion protein missense variant to Gerstmann-Sträussler syndrome. *Nature* 338:342–345, 1989.

5. Prusiner S.B.: Scrapie prions. *Annu. Rev. Microbiol.* 43:345–374, 1989.

6. Kirschbaum W.R.: *Jakob-Creutzfeldt Disease,* Elsevier, Amsterdam, 1968.

7. Gibbs C.J., Jr., Gajdusek D.C., Asher D.M., Alpers M.P., Beck E., Daniel P.M., and Matthews W.B.: Creutzfeldt-Jakob disease (spongiform encephalopathy): transmission to the chimpanzee. *Science* 161:388–389, 1968.

8. Prusiner S.B.: The prion diseases. *Sci. Am.* 272:48–57, 1995.

9. Malmgren R., Kurland L., Mokri B., and Kurtzke J.: The epidemiology of Creutzfeldt-Jakob disease. *Slow Transmissible Diseases of the Nervous System, Vol. 1.* Prusiner S.B. and Hadlow W.J., Eds. Academic Press, New York, 1979 pp. 93–112.

10. Brown P., Cathala F., Raubertas R.F., Gajdusek D.C., and Castaigne P.: The epidemiology of Creutzfeldt-Jakob disease: conclusion of 15-year investigation in France and review of the world literature. *Neurology* 37:895–904, 1987.

11. Harries-Jones R., Knight R., Will R.G., Cousens S., Smith P.G., and Matthews W.B.: Creutzfeldt-Jakob disease in England and Wales, 1980–1984: a case-control study of potential risk factors. *J. Neurol. Neurosurg. Psychiatry* 51:1113–1119, 1988.

12. Cousens S.N., Harries-Jones R., Knight R., Will R.G., Smith P.G., and Matthews W.B.: Geographical distribution of cases of Creutzfeldt-Jakob disease in England and Wales 1970–84. *J. Neurol. Neurosurg. Psychiatry* 53:459–465, 1990.

13. Kahana E., Milton A., Braham J., and Sofer D.: Creutzfeldt-Jakob disease: focus among Libyan Jews in Israel. *Science* 183:90–91, 1974.

14. Goldfarb L., Korczyn A., Brown P., Chapman J., and Gajdusek D.C.: Mutation in codon 200 of scrapie amyloid precursor gene linked to Creutzfeldt-Jakob disease in Sephardic Jews of Libyan and non-Libyan origin. *Lancet* 336:637–638, 1990.

15. Hsiao K., Meiner Z., Kahana E., Cass C., Kahana I., Avrahami D., Scarlato G., Abramsky O., Prusiner S.B., and Gabizon R.: Mutation of the prion protein in Libyan Jews with Creutzfeldt-Jakob disease. *N. Engl. J. Med.* 324:1091–1097, 1991.

16. Gabizon R., Rosenmann H., Meiner Z., Kahana I., Kahana E., Shugart Y., Ott J., and Prusiner S.B.: Mutation and polymorphism of the prion protein gene in Libyan Jews with Creutzfeldt-Jakob disease. *Am. J. Hum. Genet.* 53:828–835, 1993.

17. Sigurdsson B.: Rida, a chronic encephalitis of sheep with general remarks on infections which develop slowly and some of their special characteristics. *Br. Vet. J.* 110:341–354, 1954.

18. Hadlow W.J.: Scrapie and kuru. *Lancet* 2:289–290, 1959.

19. Gajdusek D.C., Gibbs C.J., Jr., and Alpers M.: Experimental transmission of a kuru-like syndrome to chimpanzees. *Nature* 209:794–796, 1966.

20. Klatzo I., Gajdusek D.C., and Zigas V.: Pathology of kuru. *Lab. Invest.* 8:799–847, 1959.

21. Zlotnik I. and Stamp J.L.: Scrapie disease of sheep. *World Neurology* 2:895–907, 1961.

22. Masters C.L. and Richardson E.P., Jr.: Subacute spongiform encephalopathy Creutzfeldt-Jakob disease–the nature and progression of spongiform change. *Brain* 101:333–344, 1978.

23. Prusiner S.B.: Molecular biology of prion diseases. *Science* 252:1515–1522, 1991.

24. Wells G.A.H., Scott A.C., Johnson C.T., Gunning R.F., Hancock R.D., Jeffrey M., Dawson M., and Bradley R.: A novel progressive spongiform encephalopathy in cattle. *Vet. Rec.* 121:419–420, 1987.

25. Pan K.-M., Baldwin M., Nguyen J., Gasset M., Serban A., Groth D., Mehlhorn I., Huang Z., Fletterick R.J., Cohen F.E., and Prusiner S.B.: Conversion of α-helices into β-sheets features in the formation of the scrapie prion proteins. *Proc. Natl. Acad. Sci. USA* 90:10962–10966, 1993.

26. Bessen R.A. and Marsh R.F.: Distinct PrP properties suggest the molecular basis of strain variation in transmissible mink encephalopathy. *J. Virol.* 68:7859–7868, 1994.

27. Telling G.C., Parchi P., DeArmond S.J., Cortelli P., Montagna P., Gabizon R., Mastrianni J., Lugaresi E., Gambetti P., and Prusiner S.B.: Evidence for the conformation of the pathologic isoform of the prion protein enciphering and propagating prion diversity. *Science* 274:2079–2082, 1996.

28. Prusiner S.B.: Prion diseases and the BSE crisis. *Science* 278:245–251, 1997.

29. Dlouhy S.R., Hsiao K., Farlow M.R., Foroud T., Conneally P.M., Johnson P., Prusiner S.B., Hodes M.E., and Ghetti B.: Linkage of the Indiana kindred of Gerstmann-Sträussler-Scheinker disease to the prion protein gene. *Nat. Genet.* 1:64–67, 1992.

30. Petersen R.B., Tabaton M., Berg L., Schrank B., Torack R.M., Leal S., Julien J., Vital C., Deleplanque B., Pendlebury W.W., Drachman D., Smith T.W., Martin J.J., Oda M., Montagna P., Ott J., Autilio-Gambetti L., Lugaresi E., and Gambetti P.: Analysis of the prion protein gene in thalamic dementia. *Neurology* 42:1859–1863, 1992.

31. Poulter M., Baker H.F., Frith C.D., Leach M., Lofthouse R., Ridley R.M., Shah T., Owen F., Collinge J., Brown G., Hardy J., Mullan M.J., Harding A.E., Bennett C., Doshi R., and Crow T.J.: Inherited prion disease with 144 base pair gene insertion. 1. Genealogical and molecular studies. *Brain* 115:675–685, 1992.

32. Alper T., Haig D.A., and Clarke M.C.: The exceptionally small size of the scrapie agent. *Biochem. Biophys. Res. Commun.* 22:278–284, 1966.

33. Alper T., Cramp W.A., Haig D.A., and Clarke M.C.: Does the agent of scrapie replicate without nucleic acid? *Nature* 214:764–766, 1967.

34. Latarjet R., Muel B., Haig D.A., Clarke M.C., and Alper T.: Inactivation of the scrapie agent by near monochromatic ultraviolet light. *Nature* 227:1341–1343, 1970.

35. Gibbs C.J., Jr., Gajdusek D.C., and Latarjet R.: Unusual resistance to ionizing radiation of the viruses of kuru, Creutzfeldt-Jakob diseas. *Proc. Natl. Acad. Sci. USA* 75:6268–6270, 1978.

36. Pattison I.H.: Experiments with scrapie with special reference to the nature of the agent and the pathology of the disease. *Slow, Latent and Temperate Virus Infections, NINDB Monograph 2.* Gajdusek D.C., Gibbs C.J., Jr., and Alpers M.P., Eds. U.S. Government Printing, Washington, D.C., 1965 pp. 249–257.

37. Griffith J.S.: Self-replication and scrapie. *Nature* 215:1043–1044, 1967.

38. Pattison I.H. and Jones K.M.: The possible nature of the transmissible agent of scrapie. *Vet. Res.* 80:1–8, 1967.

39. Gibbons R.A. and Hunter G.D.: Nature of the scrapie agent. *Nature* 215:1041–1043, 1967.

40. Hunter G.D., Kimberlin R.H., and Gibbons R.A.: Scrapie: a modified membrane hypothesis. *J. Theor. Biol.* 20:355–357, 1968.

41. Field E.J., Farmer F., Caspary E.A., and Joyce G.: Susceptibility of scrapie agent to ionizing radiation. *Nature* 222:90–91, 1969.

42. Hunter G.D.: Scrapie: a prototype slow infection. *J. Infect. Dis.* 125:427–440, 1972.

43. Gordon W.S.: Advances in veterinary research. *Vet. Res.* 58:516–520, 1946.

44. Parry H.B.: Scrapie: a transmissible and hereditary disease of sheep. *Heredity* 17:75–105, 1962.

45. Dickinson A.G., Young G.B., Stamp J.T., and Renwick C.C.: An analysis of natural scrapie in Suffolk sheep. *Heredity* 20:485–503, 1965.

46. Parry H.B.: Recorded occurrences of scrapie from 1750. *Scrapie Disease in Sheep*. Oppenheimer D.R., Ed. Academic Press, New York, 1983 pp. 31–59.

47. Prusiner S.B.: An approach to the isolation of biological particles using sedimentation analysis. *J. Biol. Chem.* 253:916–921, 1978.

48. Prusiner S.B., Garfin D.E., Baringer J.R., Cochran S.P., Hadlow W.J., Race R.E., and Eklund C.M.: Evidence for multiple molecular forms of the scrapie agent. *Persistent Viruses*. Stevens J., Todaro G., and Fox C.F., Eds. Academic Press, New York, 1978 pp. 591–613.

49. Prusiner S.B.: Prions. *Sci. Am.* 251:50–59, 1984.

50. Chandler R.L.: Experimental scrapie in the mouse. *Res. Vet. Sci.* 4:276–285, 1963.

51. Prusiner S., Davis J.N., and Stadtman E.R.: Regulation of glutaminase B in *Escherichia coli*. I. Purification, properties, and cold liability. *J. Biol. Chem.* 251:3447–3456, 1976.

52. Prusiner S.B., Hadlow W.J., Eklund C.M., and Race R.E.: Sedimentation properties of the scrapie agent. *Proc. Natl. Acad. Sci. USA* 74:4656–4660, 1977.

53. Marsh R.F. and Kimberlin R.H.: Comparison of scrapie and transmissible mink encephalopathy in hamsters. II. Clinical signs, pathology and pathogenesis. *J. Infect. Dis.* 131:104–110, 1975.

54. Kimberlin R. and Walker C.: Characteristics of a short incubation model of scrapie in the golden hamster. *J. Gen. Virol.* 34:295–304, 1977.

55. Prusiner S.B., Groth D.F., Cochran S.P., Masiarz F.R., McKinley M.P., and Martinez H.M.: Molecular properties, partial purification, and assay by incubation period measurements of the hamster scrapie agent. *Biochemistry* 19:4883–4891, 1980.

56. Prusiner S.B., Cochran S.P., Groth D.F., Downey D.E., Bowman K.A., and Martinez H.M.: Measurement of the scrapie agent using an incubation time interval assay. *Ann. Neurol.* 11:353–358, 1982.

57. Zlotnik I.: Experimental transmission of scrapie to golden hamsters. *Lancet* 2:1072, 1963.

58. Prusiner S.B.: Novel proteinaceous infectious particles cause scrapie. *Science* 216:136–144, 1982.

59. Stahl N., Baldwin M.A., Teplow D.B., Hood L., Gibson B.W., Burlingame A.L., and Prusiner S.B.: Structural analysis of the scrapie prion protein using mass spectrometry and amino acid sequencing. *Biochemistry* 32:1991–2002, 1993.

60. Cohen F.E., Pan K.-M., Huang Z., Baldwin M., Fletterick R.J., and Prusiner S.B.: Structural clues to prion replication. *Science* 264:530–531, 1994.

61. Prusiner S.B., Groth D., Serban A., Stahl N., and Gabizon R.: Attempts to restore scrapie prion infectivity after exposure to protein denaturants. *Proc. Natl. Acad. Sci. USA* 90:2793–2797, 1993.

62. Carp R.I., Kascsak R.J., Rubenstein R., and Merz P.A.: The puzzle of PrP[Sc] and infectivity–do the pieces fit? *Trends Neurosci.* 17:148–149, 1994.

63. Manuelidis L. and Fritch W.: Infectivity and host responses in Creutzfeldt-Jakob disease. *Virology* 216:46–59, 1996.

64. Narang H.: The nature of the scrapie agent: the virus theory. *Proc. Soc. Exp. Biol. Med.* 212:208–224, 1996.

65. Özel M., Baldauf E., Beekes M., and Diringer H.: Small virus-like particles in transmissible spongiform encephalopathies. *Transmissible Subacute Spongiform*

Encephalopathies: Prion Diseases. Court L. and Dodet B., Eds. Elsevier, Paris, 1996 pp. 369–373.

66. Caughey B. and Chesebro B.: Prion protein and the transmissible spongiform encephalopathies. *Trends Cell Biol.* 7:56–62, 1997.

67. Lasmézas C.I., Deslys J.-P., Robain O., Jaegly A., Beringue V., Peyrin J.-M., Fournier J.-G., Hauw J.-J., Rossier J., and Dormont D.: Transmission of the BSE agent to mice in the absence of detectable abnormal prion protein. *Science* 275:402–405, 1997.

68. Diener T.O., McKinley M.P., and Prusiner S.B.: Viroids and prions. *Proc. Natl. Acad. Sci. USA* 79:5220–5224, 1982.

69. Chamberlin T.C.: The method of multiple working hypotheses. *Science [Old Series]* 15:92–97, 1890.

70. Avery O.T., MacLeod C.M., and McCarty M.: Studies on the chemical nature of the substance inducing transformation of pneumococcal types. Induction of transformation by a deoxyribonucleic acid fraction isolated from pneumococcus type III. *J. Exp. Med.* 79:137–157, 1944.

71. Stanley W.M.: The "undiscovered" discovery. *Arch. Environ. Health* 21:256–262, 1970.

72. McCarty M.: *The Transforming Principle: Discovering that Genes Are Made of DNA,* W. W. Norton & Co., New York, 1985.

73. Hershey A.D. and Chase M.: Independent functions of viral protein and nucleic acid in growth of bacteriophage. *J. Gen. Physiol.* 36:39–56, 1952.

74. Watson J.D. and Crick F.H.C.: Genetical implication of the structure of deoxyribose nucleic acid. *Nature* 171:964–967, 1953.

75. Mirsky A.E. and Pollister A.W.: Chromosin, a desoxyribose nucleoprotein complex of the cell nucleus. *J. Gen. Physiol.* 30:134–135, 1946.

76. Diener T.O.: *Viroids and Viroid Diseases,* John Wiley, New York, 1979.

77. Fraenkel-Conrat H. and Williams R.C.: Reconstitution of active tobacco virus from the inactive protein and nucleic acid components. *Proc. Natl. Acad. Sci. USA* 41:690–698, 1955.

78. Gierer A. and Schramm G.: Infectivity of ribonucleic acid from tobacco mosaic virus. *Nature* 177:702–703, 1956.

79. Bolton D.C., McKinley M.P., and Prusiner S.B.: Identification of a protein that purifies with the scrapie prion. *Science* 218:1309–1311, 1982.

80. Prusiner S.B., Bolton D.C., Groth D.F., Bowman K.A., Cochran S.P., and McKinley M.P.: Further purification and characterization of scrapie prions. *Biochemistry* 21:6942–6950, 1982.

81. Prusiner S.B., Groth D.F., Bolton D.C., Kent S.B., and Hood L.E.: Purification and structural studies of a major scrapie prion protein. *Cell* 38:127–134, 1984.

82. Basler K., Oesch B., Scott M., Westaway D., Wälchli M., Groth D.F., McKinley M.P., Prusiner S.B., and Weissmann C.: Scrapie and cellular PrP isoforms are encoded by the same chromosomal gene. *Cell* 46:417–428, 1986.

83. Chesebro B., Race R., Wehrly K., Nishio J., Bloom M., Lechner D., Bergstrom S., Robbins K., Mayer L., Keith J.M., Garon C., and Haase A.: Identification of scrapie prion protein-specific mRNA in scrapie-infected and uninfected brain. *Nature* 315:331–333, 1985.

84. Oesch B., Westaway D., Wälchli M., McKinley M.P., Kent S.B.H., Aebersold R., Barry R.A., Tempst P., Teplow D.B., Hood L.E., Prusiner S.B., and Weissmann C.: A cellular gene encodes scrapie PrP 27–30 protein. *Cell* 40:735–746, 1985.

85. Meyer R.K., McKinley M.P., Bowman K.A., Braunfeld M.B., Barry R.A., and Prusiner S.B.: Separation and properties of cellular and scrapie prion proteins. *Proc. Natl. Acad. Sci. USA* 83:2310–2314, 1986.

86. Locht C., Chesebro B., Race R., and Keith J.M.: Molecular cloning and complete sequence of prion protein cDNA from mouse brain infected with the scrapie agent. *Proc. Natl. Acad. Sci. USA* 83:6372–6376, 1986.

87. Bendheim P.E., Barry R.A., DeArmond S.J., Stites D.P., and Prusiner S.B.: Antibodies to a scrapie prion protein. *Nature* 310:418–421, 1984.

88. Bockman J.M., Kingsbury D.T., McKinley M.P., Bendheim P.E., and Prusiner S.B.: Creutzfeldt-Jakob disease prion proteins in human brains. *N. Engl. J. Med.* 312:73–78, 1985.

89. Brown P., Coker-Vann M., Pomeroy K., Franko M., Asher D.M., Gibbs C.J., Jr., and Gajdusek D.C.: Diagnosis of Creutzfeldt-Jakob disease by Western blot identification of marker protein in human brain tissue. *N. Engl. J. Med.* 314:547–551, 1986.

90. Bockman J.M., Prusiner S.B., Tateishi J., and Kingsbury D.T.: Immunoblotting of Creutzfeldt-Jakob disease prion proteins: host species-specific epitopes. *Ann. Neurol.* 21:589–595, 1987.

91. Manuelidis L., Valley S., and Manuelidis E.E.: Specific proteins associated with Creutzfeldt-Jakob disease and scrapie share antigenic and carbohydrate determinants. *Proc. Natl. Acad. Sci. USA* 82:4263–4267, 1985.

92. Prusiner S.B.: Prions and neurodegenerative diseases. *N. Engl. J. Med.* 317:1571–1581, 1987.

93. Manuelidis L., Tesin D.M., Sklaviadis T., and Manuelidis E.E.: Astrocyte gene expression in Creutzfeldt-Jakob disease. *Proc. Natl. Acad. Sci. USA* 84:5937–5941, 1987.

94. Gomi H., Yokoyama T., Fujimoto K., Ikeda T., Katoh A., Itoh T., and Itohara S.: Mice devoid of the glial fibrillary acidic protein develop normally and are susceptible to scrapie prions. *Neuron* 14:29–41, 1995.

95. Tatzelt J., Maeda N., Pekny M., Yang S.-L., Betsholtz C., Eliasson C., Cayetano J., Camerino A.P., DeArmond S.J., and Prusiner S.B.: Scrapie in mice deficient in apolipoprotein E or glial fibrillary acidic protein. *Neurology* 47:449–453, 1996.

96. Duguid J.R., Rohwer R.G., and Seed B.: Isolation of cDNAs of scrapie-modulated RNAs by subtractive hybridization of a cDNA library. *Proc. Natl. Acad. Sci. USA* 85:5738–5742, 1988.

97. Duguid J.R., Bohmont C.W., Liu N., and Tourtellotte W.W.: Changes in brain gene expression shared by scrapie and Alzheimer disease. *Proc. Natl. Acad. Sci. USA* 86:7260–7264, 1989.

98. Diedrich J.F., Carp R.I., and Haase A.T.: Increased expression of heat shock protein, transferrin, and b_2-microglobulin in astrocytes during scrapie. *Microbial. Pathogenesis* 15:1–6, 1993.

99. Akowitz A., Sklaviadis T., and Manuelidis L.: Endogenous viral complexes with long RNA cosediment with the agent of Creutzfeldt-Jakob disease. *Nucleic Acids Res.* 22:1101–1107, 1994.

100. Büeler H., Aguzzi A., Sailer A., Greiner R.-A., Autenried P., Aguet M., and Weissmann C.: Mice devoid of PrP are resistant to scrapie. *Cell* 73:1339–1347, 1993.

101. Prusiner S.B., Groth D., Serban A., Koehler R., Foster D., Torchia M., Burton D., Yang S.-L., and DeArmond S.J.: Ablation of the prion protein (PrP) gene in mice prevents scrapie and facilitates production of anti-PrP antibodies. *Proc. Natl. Acad. Sci. USA* 90:10608–10612, 1993.

102. Manson J.C., Clarke A.R., McBride P.A., McConnell I., and Hope J.: PrP gene dosage determines the timing but not the final intensity or distribution of lesions in scrapie pathology. *Neurodegeneration* 3:331–340, 1994.

103. Sailer A., Büeler H., Fischer M., Aguzzi A., and Weissmann C.: No propagation of prions in mice devoid of PrP. *Cell* 77:967–968, 1994.

104. Sakaguchi S., Katamine S., Shigematsu K., Nakatani A., Moriuchi R., Nishida N., Kurokawa K., Nakaoke R., Sato H., Jishage K., Kuno J., Noda T., and Miyamoto T.: Accumulation of proteinase K-resistant prion protein (PrP) is restricted by the expression level of normal PrP in mice inoculated with a mouse-adapted strain of the Creutzfeldt–Jakob disease agent. *J. Virol.* 69:7586–7592, 1995.

105. Gabizon R., McKinley M.P., Groth D.F., and Prusiner S.B.: Immunoaffinity purification and neutralization of scrapie prion infectivity. *Proc. Natl. Acad. Sci. USA* 85:6617–6621, 1988.

106. McKinley M.P., Bolton D.C., and Prusiner S.B.: A protease-resistant protein is a structural component of the scrapie prion. *Cell* 35:57–62, 1983.

107. Prusiner S.B., McKinley M.P., Bowman K.A., Bolton D.C., Bendheim P.E., Groth D.F., and Glenner G.G.: Scrapie prions aggregate to form amyloid-like birefringent rods. *Cell* 35:349–358, 1983.

108. Bolton D.C., McKinley M.P., and Prusiner S.B.: Molecular characteristics of the major scrapie prion protein. *Biochemistry* 23:5898–5906, 1984.

109. Riesner D., Kellings K., Post K., Wille H., Serban H., Groth D., Baldwin M.A., and Prusiner S.B.: Disruption of prion rods generates 10-nm spherical particles having high α-helical content and lacking scrapie infectivity. *J. Virol.* 70:1714–1722, 1996.

110. Bellinger-Kawahara C., Cleaver J.E., Diener T.O., and Prusiner S.B.: Purified scrapie prions resist inactivation by UV irradiation. *J. Virol.* 61:159–166, 1987.

111. Bellinger-Kawahara C., Diener T.O., McKinley M.P., Groth D.F., Smith D.R., and Prusiner S.B.: Purified scrapie prions resist inactivation by procedures that hydrolyze, modify, or shear nucleic acids. *Virology* 160:271–274, 1987.

112. Bellinger-Kawahara C.G., Kempner E., Groth D.F., Gabizon R., and Prusiner S.B.: Scrapie prion liposomes and rods exhibit target sizes of 55,000 Da. *Virology* 164:537–541, 1988.

113. Kellings K., Meyer N., Mirenda C., Prusiner S.B., and Riesner D.: Further analysis of nucleic acids in purified scrapie prion preparations by improved return refocussing gel electrophoresis (RRGE). *J. Gen. Virol.* 73:1025–1029, 1992.

114. Kellings K., Prusiner S.B., and Riesner D.: Nucleic acids in prion preparations: unspecific background or essential component? *Phil. Trans. R. Soc. Lond. B* 343:425–430, 1994.

115. Manuelidis L., Sklaviadis T., Akowitz A., and Fritch W.: Viral particles are required for infection in neurodegenerative Creutzfeldt-Jakob disease. *Proc. Natl. Acad. Sci. USA* 92:5124–5128, 1995.

116. Williams R.C.: Electron microscopy of viruses. *Adv. Virus Res.* 2:183–239, 1954.

117. Cohen A.S., Shirahama T., and Skinner M.: Electron microscopy of amyloid. *Electron Microscopy of Proteins, Vol. 3.* Harris J.R., Ed. Academic Press, New York, 1982 pp. 165–206.

118. DeArmond S.J., McKinley M.P., Barry R.A., Braunfeld M.B., McColloch J.R., and Prusiner S.B.: Identification of prion amyloid filaments in scrapie-infected brain. *Cell* 41:221–235, 1985.

119. Kitamoto T., Tateishi J., Tashima I., Takeshita I., Barry R.A., DeArmond S.J., and Prusiner S.B.: Amyloid plaques in Creutzfeldt-Jakob disease stain with prion protein antibodies. *Ann. Neurol.* 20:204–208, 1986.

120. Roberts G.W., Lofthouse R., Brown R., Crow T.J., Barry R.A., and Prusiner S.B.: Prion-protein immunoreactivity in human transmissible dementias. *N. Engl. J. Med.* 315:1231–1233, 1986.

121. Gabizon R., McKinley M.P., and Prusiner S.B.: Purified prion proteins and scrapie infectivity copartition into liposomes. *Proc. Natl. Acad. Sci. USA* 84:4017–4021, 1987.

122. McKinley M.P., Meyer R., Kenaga L., Rahbar F., Cotter R., Serban A., and Prusiner S.B.: Scrapie prion rod formation *in vitro* requires both detergent extraction and limited proteolysis. *J. Virol.* 65:1440–1449, 1991.

123. Diringer H., Gelderblom H., Hilmert H., Ozel M., Edelbluth C., and Kimberlin R.H.: Scrapie infectivity, fibrils and low molecular weight protein. *Nature* 306:476–478, 1983.

124. Merz P.A., Kascsak R.J., Rubenstein R., Carp R.I., and Wisniewski H.M.: Antisera to scrapie-associated fibril protein and prion protein decorate scrapie-associated fibrils. *J. Virol.* 61:42–49, 1987.

125. Diener T.O.: PrP and the nature of the scrapie agent. *Cell* 49:719–721, 1987.

126. Merz P.A., Somerville R.A., Wisniewski H.M., and Iqbal K.: Abnormal fibrils from scrapie-infected brain. *Acta Neuropathol. (Berl.)* 54:63–74, 1981.

127. Merz P.A., Wisniewski H.M., Somerville R.A., Bobin S.A., Masters C.L., and Iqbal K.: Ultrastructural morphology of amyloid fibrils from neuritic and amyloid plaques. *Acta Neuropathol. (Berl.)* 60:113–124, 1983.

128. Merz P.A., Rohwer R.G., Kascsak R., Wisniewski H.M., Somerville R.A., Gibbs C.J., Jr.,

311

and Gajdusek D.C.: Infection-specific particle from the unconventional slow virus diseases. *Science* 225:437–440, 1984.

129. Diringer H.: Transmissible spongiform encephalopathies (TSE) virus-induced amyloidoses of the central nervous system (CNS). *Eur. J. Epidemiol.* 7:562–566, 1991.

130. Bastian F.O.: Bovine spongiform encephalopathy: relationship to human disease and nature of the agent. *ASM News* 59:235–240, 1993.

131. Kimberlin R.H.: Scrapie and possible relationships with viroids. *Semin. Virol.* 1:153–162, 1990.

132. Chesebro B. and Caughey B.: Scrapie agent replication without the prion protein? *Curr. Biol.* 3:696–698, 1993.

133. Scott M., Groth D., Foster D., Torchia M., Yang S.-L., DeArmond S.J., and Prusiner S.B.: Propagation of prions with artificial properties in transgenic mice expressing chimeric PrP genes. *Cell* 73:979–988, 1993.

134. Telling G.C., Scott M., Mastrianni J., Gabizon R., Torchia M., Cohen F.E., DeArmond S.J., and Prusiner S.B.: Prion propagation in mice expressing human and chimeric PrP transgenes implicates the interaction of cellular PrP with another protein. *Cell* 83:79–90, 1995.

135. Scott M.R., Groth D., Tatzelt J., Torchia M., Tremblay P., DeArmond S.J., and Prusiner S.B.: Propagation of prion strains through specific conformers of the prion protein. *J. Virol.* 71:9032–9044, 1997.

136. Anfinsen C.B.: Principles that govern the folding of protein chains. *Science* 181:223–230, 1973.

137. Pergami P., Jaffe H., and Safar J.: Semipreparative chromatographic method to purify the normal cellular isoform of the prion protein in nondenatured form. *Anal. Biochem.* 236:63–73, 1996.

138. Borchelt D.R., Scott M., Taraboulos A., Stahl N., and Prusiner S.B.: Scrapie and cellular prion proteins differ in their kinetics of synthesis and topology in cultured cells. *J. Cell Biol.* 110:743–752, 1990.

139. Stahl N., Borchelt D.R., Hsiao K., and Prusiner S.B.: Scrapie prion protein contains a phosphatidylinositol glycolipid. *Cell* 51:229–240, 1987.

140. Caughey B. and Raymond G.J.: The scrapie-associated form of PrP is made from a cell surface precursor that is both protease- and phospholipase-sensitive. *J. Biol. Chem.* 266:18217–18223, 1991.

141. Borchelt D.R., Taraboulos A., and Prusiner S.B.: Evidence for synthesis of scrapie prion proteins in the endocytic pathway. *J. Biol. Chem.* 267:16188–16199, 1992.

142. Taraboulos A., Scott M., Semenov A., Avrahami D., Laszlo L., and Prusiner S.B.: Cholesterol depletion and modification of COOH-terminal targeting sequence of the prion protein inhibits formation of the scrapie isoform. *J. Cell Biol.* 129:121–132, 1995.

143. Vey M., Pilkuhn S., Wille H., Nixon R., DeArmond S.J., Smart E.J., Anderson R.G., Taraboulos A., and Prusiner S.B.: Subcellular colocalization of the cellular and scrapie prion proteins in caveolae-like membranous domains. *Proc. Natl. Acad. Sci. USA* 93:14945–14949, 1996.

144. Kaneko K., Vey M., Scott M., Pilkuhn S., Cohen F.E., and Prusiner S.B.: COOH-terminal sequence of the cellular prion protein directs subcellular trafficking and controls conversion into the scrapie isoform. *Proc. Natl. Acad. Sci. USA* 94:2333–2338, 1997.

145. Naslavsky N., Stein R., Yanai A., Friedlander G., and Taraboulos A.: Characterization of detergent-insoluble complexes containing the cellular prion protein and its scrapie isoform. *J. Biol. Chem.* 272:6324–6331, 1997.

146. Gasset M., Baldwin M.A., Lloyd D., Gabriel J.-M., Holtzman D.M., Cohen F., Fletterick R., and Prusiner S.B.: Predicted α-helical regions of the prion protein when synthesized as peptides form amyloid. *Proc. Natl. Acad. Sci. USA* 89:10940–10944, 1992.

147. Huang Z., Gabriel J.-M., Baldwin M.A., Fletterick R.J., Prusiner S.B., and Cohen F.E.: Proposed three-dimensional structure for the cellular prion protein. *Proc. Natl. Acad. Sci. USA* 91:7139–7143, 1994.

148. Zhang H., Kaneko K., Nguyen J.T., Livshits T.L., Baldwin M.A., Cohen F.E., James T.L.,

and Prusiner S.B.: Conformational transitions in peptides containing two putative α-helices of the prion protein. *J. Mol. Biol.* 250:514–526, 1995.

149. Schätzl H.M., Da Costa M., Taylor L., Cohen F.E., and Prusiner S.B.: Prion protein gene variation among primates. *J. Mol. Biol.* 245:362–374, 1995.

150. Bamborough P., Wille H., Telling G.C., Yehiely F., Prusiner S.B., and Cohen F.E.: Prion protein structure and scrapie replication: theoretical, spectroscopic and genetic investigations. *Cold Spring Harb. Symp. Quant. Biol.* 61:495–509, 1996.

151. Hay B., Barry R.A., Lieberburg I., Prusiner S.B., and Lingappa V.R.: Biogenesis and transmembrane orientation of the cellular isoform of the scrapie prion protein. *Mol. Cell. Biol.* 7:914–920, 1987.

152. De Fea K.A., Nakahara D.H., Calayag M.C., Yost C.S., Mirels L.F., Prusiner S.B., and Lingappa V.R.: Determinants of carboxyl-terminal domain translocation during prion protein biogenesis. *J. Biol. Chem.* 269:16810–16820, 1994.

153. Hegde R.S., Mastrianni J.A., Scott M.R., DeFea K.A., Tremblay P., Torchia M., DeArmond S.J., Prusiner S.B., and Lingappa V.R.: A transmembrane form of the prion protein in neurodegenerative disease. *Science* 279: 827–834, 1998.

154. Riek R., Hornemann S., Wider G., Billeter M., Glockshuber R., and Wüthrich K.: NMR structure of the mouse prion protein domain PrP(121–231). *Nature* 382:180–182, 1996.

155. James T.L., Liu H., Ulyanov N.B., Farr-Jones S., Zhang H., Donne D.G., Kaneko K., Groth D., Mehlhorn I., Prusiner S.B., and Cohen F.E.: Solution structure of a 142-residue recombinant prion protein corresponding to the infectious fragment of the scrapie isoform. *Proc. Natl. Acad. Sci. USA* 94:10086–10091, 1997.

156. Donne D.G., Viles J.H., Groth D., Mehlhorn I., James T.L., Cohen F.E., Prusiner S.B., Wright P.E., and Dyson H.J.: Structure of the recombinant full-length hamster prion protein PrP(29–231): the N terminus is highly flexible. *Proc. Natl. Acad. Sci. USA* 94:13452–13457, 1997.

157. Williamson R.A., Peretz D., Smorodinsky N., Bastidas R., Serban H., Mehlhorn I., DeArmond S.J., Prusiner S.B., and Burton D.R.: Circumventing tolerance to generate autologous monoclonal antibodies to the prion protein. *Proc. Natl. Acad. Sci. USA* 93:7279–7282, 1996.

158. Peretz D., Williamson R.A., Matsunaga Y., Serban H., Pinilla C., Bastidas R., Rozenshteyn R., James T.L., Houghten R.A., Cohen F.E., Prusiner S.B., and Burton D.R.: A conformational transition at the N terminus of the prion protein features in formation of the scrapie isoform. *J. Mol. Biol.* 273:614–622, 1997.

159. Caughey B., Race R.E., Ernst D., Buchmeier M.J., and Chesebro B.: Prion protein biosynthesis in scrapie-infected and uninfected neuroblastoma cells. *J. Virol.* 63:175–181, 1989.

160. Shmerling D., Hegyi I., Fischer M., Blättler T., Brandner S., Götz J., Rülicke T., Flechsig E., Cozzio A., von Mering C., Hangartner C., Aguzzi A., and Weissmann C.: Expression of amino-terminally truncated PrP in the mouse leading to ataxia and specific cerebellar lesions. *Cell* 93:203–214, 1998.

161. Mehlhorn I., Groth D., Stöckel J., Moffat B., Reilly D., Yansura D., Willett W.S., Baldwin M., Fletterick R., Cohen F.E., Vandlen R., Henner D., and Prusiner S.B.: High-level expression and characterization of a purified 142-residue polypeptide of the prion protein. *Biochemistry* 35:5528–5537, 1996.

162. Zhang H., Stöckel J., Mehlhorn I., Groth D., Baldwin M.A., Prusiner S.B., James T.L., and Cohen F.E.: Physical studies of conformational plasticity in a recombinant prion protein. *Biochemistry* 36:3543–3553, 1997.

163. Fischer M., Rülicke T., Raeber A., Sailer A., Moser M., Oesch B., Brandner S., Aguzzi A., and Weissmann C.: Prion protein (PrP) with amino-proximal deletions restoring susceptibility of PrP knockout mice to scrapie. *EMBO J.* 15:1255–1264, 1996.

164. Muramoto T., DeArmond S.J., Scott M., Telling G.C., Cohen F.E., and Prusiner S.B.: Heritable disorder resembling neuronal storage disease in mice expressing prion protein with deletion of an α-helix. *Nat. Med.* 3:750–755, 1997.

165. Riek R., Hornemann S., Wider G., Glockshuber R., and Wüthrich K.: NMR characterization of the full-length recombinant murine prion protein, *m*PrP(23–231). *FEBS Lett* 413:282–288, 1997.

166. Huang Z., Prusiner S.B., and Cohen F.E.: Scrapie prions: a three-dimensional model of an infectious fragment. *Folding & Design* 1:13–19, 1996.

167. Turk E., Teplow D.B., Hood L.E., and Prusiner S.B.: Purification and properties of the cellular and scrapie hamster prion proteins. *Eur. J. Biochem.* 176:21–30, 1988.

168. Muramoto T., Scott M., Cohen F., and Prusiner S.B.: Recombinant scrapie-like prion protein of 106 amino acids is soluble. *Proc. Natl. Acad. Sci. USA* 93:15457–15462, 1996.

169. Caughey B.W., Dong A., Bhat K.S., Ernst D., Hayes S.F., and Caughey W.S.: Secondary structure analysis of the scrapie-associated protein PrP 27–30 in water by infrared spectroscopy. *Biochemistry* 30:7672–7680, 1991.

170. Gasset M., Baldwin M.A., Fletterick R.J., and Prusiner S.B.: Perturbation of the secondary structure of the scrapie prion protein under conditions associated with changes in infectivity. *Proc. Natl. Acad. Sci. USA* 90:1–5, 1993.

171. Safar J., Roller P.P., Gajdusek D.C., and Gibbs C.J., Jr.: Conformational transitions, dissociation, and unfolding of scrapie amyloid (prion) protein. *J. Biol. Chem.* 268:20276–20284, 1993.

172. Rogers M., Yehiely F., Scott M., and Prusiner S.B.: Conversion of truncated and elongated prion proteins into the scrapie isoform in cultured cells. *Proc. Natl. Acad. Sci. USA* 90:3182–3186, 1993.

173. Barry R.A. and Prusiner S.B.: Monoclonal antibodies to the cellular and scrapie prion proteins. *J. Infect. Dis.* 154:518–521, 1986.

174. Kascsak R.J., Rubenstein R., Merz P.A., Tonna-DeMasi M., Fersko R., Carp R.I., Wisniewski H.M., and Diringer H.: Mouse polyclonal and monoclonal antibody to scrapie-associated fibril proteins. *J. Virol.* 61:3688–3693, 1987.

175. Rogers M., Serban D., Gyuris T., Scott M., Torchia T., and Prusiner S.B.: Epitope mapping of the Syrian hamster prion protein utilizing chimeric and mutant genes in a vaccinia virus expression system. *J. Immunol.* 147:3568–3574, 1991.

176. Korth C., Stierli B., Streit P., Moser M., Schaller O., Fischer R., Schulz-Schaeffer W., Kretzschmar H., Raeber A., Braun U., Ehrensperger F., Hornemann S., Glockshuber R., Riek R., Billeter M., Wuthrick K., and Oesch B.: Prion (PrP^Sc)-specific epitope defined by a monoclonal antibody. *Nature* 389:74–77, 1997.

177. Billeter M., Riek R., Wider G., Hornemann S., Glockshuber R., and Wüthrich K.: Prion protein NMR structure and species barrier for prion diseases. *Proc. Natl. Acad. Sci. USA* 94:7281–7285, 1997.

178. Kaneko K., Zulianello L., Scott M., Cooper C.M., Wallace A.C., James T.L., Cohen F.E., and Prusiner S.B.: Evidence for protein X binding to a discontinuous epitope on the cellular prion protein during scrapie prion propagation. *Proc. Natl. Acad. Sci. USA* 94:10069–10074, 1997.

179. Telling G.C., Scott M., Hsiao K.K., Foster D., Yang S.-L., Torchia M., Sidle K.C.L., Collinge J., DeArmond S.J., and Prusiner S.B.: Transmission of Creutzfeldt-Jakob disease from humans to transgenic mice expressing chimeric human-mouse prion protein. *Proc. Natl. Acad. Sci. USA* 91:9936–9940, 1994.

180. Stöckel J., Safar J., Wallace A.C., Cohen F.E., and Prusiner S.B.: Prion protein selectively binds copper-II-ions. *Biochemistry* 37: 7185–7193, 1998.

181. Hornshaw M.P., McDermott J.R., Candy J.M., and Lakey J.H.: Copper binding to the N-terminal tandem repeat region of mammalian and avian prion protein: structural studies using synthetic peptides. *Biochem. Biophys. Res. Commun.* 214:993–999, 1995.

182. Hornshaw M.P., McDermott J.R., and Candy J.M.: Copper binding to the N-terminal tandem repeat regions of mammalian and avian prion protein. *Biochem. Biophys. Res. Commun.* 207:621–629, 1995.

183. Miura T., Hori-i A., and Takeuchi H.: Metal-dependent α-helix formation promoted by the glycine-rich octapeptide region of prion protein. *FEBS Lett.* 396:248–252, 1996.

184. Brown D.R., Schulz-Schaeffer W.J., Schmidt B., and Kretzschmar H.A.: Prion protein-

deficient cells show altered response to oxidative stress due to decreased SOD-1 activity. *Exp. Neurol.* 146:104–112, 1997.

185. Harris E.D.: Copper as a cofactor and regulator of copper, zinc superoxide dismutase. *J. Nutr.* 122:636–640, 1992.

186. Brown D.R., Qin K., Herms J.W., Madlung A., Manson J., Strome R., Fraser P.E., Kruck T., von Bohlen A., Schulz-Schaeffer W., Giese A., Westaway D., and Kretzschmar H.: The cellular prion protein binds copper *in vivo*. *Nature* 390:684–687, 1997.

187. Vulpe C., Levinson B., Whitney S., Packman S., and Gitschier J.: Isolation of a candidate gene for Menkes disease and evidence that it encodes a copper-transporting ATPase. *Nat. Genet.* 3:7–13, 1993.

188. Chelly J., Tümer Z., Tønnesen T., Petterson A., Ishikawa-Brush Y., Tommerup N., Horn N., and Monaco A.P.: Isolation of a candidate gene for Menkes disease that encodes a potential heavy metal binding protein. *Nat. Genet.* 3:14–19, 1993.

189. Bull P.C., Thomas G.R., Rommens J.M., Forbes J.R., and Cox D.W.: The Wilson disease gene is a putative copper transporting P-type ATPase similar to the Menkes gene. *Nat. Genet.* 5:327–337, 1993.

190. Petrukhin K., Fischer S.G., Pirastu M., Tanzi R.E., Chernov I., Devoto M., Brzustowicz L.M., Cayanis E., Vitale E., Russo J.J., Matseoane D., Boukhgalter B., Wasco W., Figus A.L., Loudianos J., Cao A., Sternlieb I., Evgrafov O., Parano E., Pavone L., Warburton D., Ott J., Penchaszadeh G.K., Scheinberg I.H., and Gilliam T.C.: Mapping, cloning and genetic characterization of the region containing the Wilson disease gene. *Nat. Genet.* 5:338–343, 1993.

191. Pattison I.H. and Jebbett J.N.: Clinical and histological observations on cuprizone toxicity and scrapie in mice. *Res. Vet. Sci.* 12:378–380, 1971.

192. Kimberlin R.H., Millson G.C., Bountiff L., and Collis S.C.: A comparison of the biochemical changes induced in mouse brain by cuprizone toxicity and by scrapie infection. *J. Comp. Path.* 84:263–270, 1974.

193. Gabriel J.-M., Oesch B., Kretzschmar H., Scott M., and Prusiner S.B.: Molecular cloning of a candidate chicken prion protein. *Proc. Natl. Acad. Sci. USA* 89:9097–9101, 1992.

194. Westaway D., Goodman P.A., Mirenda C.A., McKinley M.P., Carlson G.A., and Prusiner S.B.: Distinct prion proteins in short and long scrapie incubation period mice. *Cell* 51:651–662, 1987.

195. Westaway D., Mirenda C.A., Foster D., Zebarjadian Y., Scott M., Torchia M., Yang S.-L., Serban H., DeArmond S.J., Ebeling C., Prusiner S.B., and Carlson G.A.: Paradoxical shortening of scrapie incubation times by expression of prion protein transgenes derived from long incubation period mice. *Neuron* 7:59–68, 1991.

196. Yoshimoto J., Iinuma T., Ishiguro N., Horiuchi M., Imamura M., and Shinagawa M.: Comparative sequence analysis and expression of bovine PrP gene in mouse L-929 cells. *Virus Genes* 6:343–356, 1992.

197. Westaway D., Cooper C., Turner S., Da Costa M., Carlson G.A., and Prusiner S.B.: Structure and polymorphism of the mouse prion protein gene. *Proc. Natl. Acad. Sci. USA* 91:6418–6422, 1994.

198. Westaway D., Zuliani V., Cooper C.M., Da Costa M., Neuman S., Jenny A.L., Detwiler L., and Prusiner S.B.: Homozygosity for prion protein alleles encoding glutamine-171 renders sheep susceptible to natural scrapie. *Genes Dev.* 8:959–969, 1994.

199. Saeki K., Matsumoto Y., Hirota Y., Matsumoto Y., and Onodera T.: Three-exon structure of the gene encoding the rat prion protein and its expression in tissues. *Virus Genes* 12:15–20, 1996.

200. Li G. and Bolton D.C.: A novel hamster prion protein mRNA contains an extra exon: increased expression in scrapie. *Brain Res.* 751:265–274, 1997.

201. Lee I., Westaway D., Smit A., Wang K., Cooper C., Yao H., Prusiner S.B., and Hood L.: in preparation.

202. McKnight S. and Tjian R.: Transcriptional selectivity of viral genes in mammalian cells. *Cell* 46:795–805, 1986.

203. Robakis N.K., Devine-Gage E.A., Kascsak R.J., Brown W.T., Krawczun C., and Silverman W.P.: Localization of a human gene homologous to the PrP gene on the p arm of chromosome 20 and detection of PrP-related antigens in normal human brain. *Biochem. Biophys. Res. Commun.* 140:758–765, 1986.

204. Sparkes R.S., Simon M., Cohn V.H., Fournier R.E.K., Lem J., Klisak I., Heinzmann C., Blatt C., Lucero M., Mohandas T., DeArmond S.J., Westaway D., Prusiner S.B., and Weiner L.P.: Assignment of the human and mouse prion protein genes to homologous chromosomes. *Proc. Natl. Acad. Sci. USA* 83:7358–7362, 1986.

205. Mobley W.C., Neve R.L., Prusiner S.B., and McKinley M.P.: Nerve growth factor increases mRNA levels for the prion protein and the beta-amyloid protein precursor in developing hamster brain. *Proc. Natl. Acad. Sci. USA* 85:9811–9815, 1988.

206. Kretzschmar H.A., Prusiner S.B., Stowring L.E., and DeArmond S.J.: Scrapie prion proteins are synthesized in neurons. *Am. J. Pathol.* 122:1–5, 1986.

207. DeArmond S.J., Mobley W.C., DeMott D.L., Barry R.A., Beckstead J.H., and Prusiner S.B.: Changes in the localization of brain prion proteins during scrapie infection. *Neurology* 37:1271–1280, 1987.

208. Taraboulos A., Jendroska K., Serban D., Yang S.-L., DeArmond S.J., and Prusiner S.B.: Regional mapping of prion proteins in brains. *Proc. Natl. Acad. Sci. USA* 89:7620–7624, 1992.

209. Kimberlin R.H., Field H.J., and Walker C.A.: Pathogenesis of mouse scrapie: evidence for spread of infection from central to peripheral nervous system. *J. Gen. Virol.* 64:713–716, 1983.

210. Fraser H. and Dickinson A.G.: Targeting of scrapie lesions and spread of agent via the retino-tectal projection. *Brain Res.* 346:32–41, 1985.

211. Jendroska K., Heinzel F.P., Torchia M., Stowring L., Kretzschmar H.A., Kon A., Stern A., Prusiner S.B., and DeArmond S.J.: Proteinase-resistant prion protein accumulation in Syrian hamster brain correlates with regional pathology and scrapie infectivity. *Neurology* 41:1482–1490, 1991.

212. Carlson G.A., Kingsbury D.T., Goodman P.A., Coleman S., Marshall S.T., DeArmond S.J., Westaway D., and Prusiner S.B.: Linkage of prion protein and scrapie incubation time genes. *Cell* 46:503–511, 1986.

213. Scott M., Foster D., Mirenda C., Serban D., Coufal F., Wälchli M., Torchia M., Groth D., Carlson G., DeArmond S.J., Westaway D., and Prusiner S.B.: Transgenic mice expressing hamster prion protein produce species-specific scrapie infectivity and amyloid plaques. *Cell* 59:847–857, 1989.

214. Dickinson A.G., Meikle V.M.H., and Fraser H.: Identification of a gene which controls the incubation period of some strains of scrapie agent in mice. *J. Comp. Pathol.* 78:293–299, 1968.

215. Kingsbury D.T., Kasper K.C., Stites D.P., Watson J.D., Hogan R.N., and Prusiner S.B.: Genetic control of scrapie and Creutzfeldt-Jakob disease in mice. *J. Immunol.* 131:491–496, 1983.

216. Carlson G.A., Goodman P.A., Lovett M., Taylor B.A., Marshall S.T., Peterson-Torchia M., Westaway D., and Prusiner S.B.: Genetics and polymorphism of the mouse prion gene complex: the control of scrapie incubation time. *Mol. Cell. Biol.* 8:5528–5540, 1988.

217. Carlson G.A., Ebeling C., Yang S.-L., Telling G., Torchia M., Groth D., Westaway D., DeArmond S.J., and Prusiner S.B.: Prion isolate specified allotypic interactions between the cellular and scrapie prion proteins in congenic and transgenic mice. *Proc. Natl. Acad. Sci. USA* 91:5690–5694, 1994.

218. Moore R.C., Hope J., McBride P.A., McConnell I., Selfridge J., and Melton D.W.: Mice with gene targeted prion protein alterations show that *Prn-p*, *Sinc* and *Prn-i* are congruent. *Nat. Genet.* 18:118–125, 1998.

219. Prusiner S.B., Scott M., Foster D., Pan K.-M., Groth D., Mirenda C., Torchia M., Yang S.-L., Serban D., Carlson G.A., Hoppe P.C., Westaway D., and DeArmond S.J.: Transgenetic studies implicate interactions between homologous PrP isoforms in scrapie prion replication. *Cell* 63:673–686, 1990.

220. Büeler H., Fischer M., Lang Y., Bluethmann H., Lipp H.-P., DeArmond S.J., Prusiner S.B., Aguet M., and Weissmann C.: Normal development and behaviour of mice lacking the neuronal cell-surface PrP protein. *Nature* 356:577–582, 1992.

221. Manson J.C., Clarke A.R., Hooper M.L., Aitchison L., McConnell I., and Hope J.: 129/Ola mice carrying a null mutation in PrP that abolishes mRNA production are developmentally normal. *Mol. Neurobiol.* 8:121–127, 1994.

222. Sakaguchi S., Katamine S., Nishida N., Moriuchi R., Shigematsu K., Sugimoto T., Nakatani A., Kataoka Y., Houtani T., Shirabe S., Okada H., Hasegawa S., Miyamoto T., and Noda T.: Loss of cerebellar Purkinje cells in aged mice homozygous for a disrupted PrP gene. *Nature* 380:528–531, 1996.

223. Tobler I., Gaus S.E., Deboer T., Achermann P., Fischer M., Rülicke T., Moser M., Oesch B., McBride P.A., and Manson J.C.: Altered circadian activity rhythms and sleep in mice devoid of prion protein. *Nature* 380:639–642, 1996.

224. Collinge J., Whittington M.A., Sidle K.C., Smith C.J., Palmer M.S., Clarke A.R., and Jefferys J.G.R.: Prion protein is necessary for normal synaptic function. *Nature* 370:295–297, 1994.

225. Whittington M.A., Sidle K.C.L., Gowland I., Meads J., Hill A.F., Palmer M.S., Jefferys J.G.R., and Collinge J.: Rescue of neurophysiological phenotype seen in PrP null mice by transgene encoding human prion protein. *Nat. Genet.* 9:197–201, 1995.

226. Herms J.W., Kretzschmar H.A., Titz S., and Keller B.U.: Patch-clamp analysis of synaptic transmission to cerebellar purkinje cells of prion protein knockout mice. *Eur. J. Neurosci.* 7:2508–2512, 1995.

227. Lledo P.-M., Tremblay P., DeArmond S.J., Prusiner S.B., and Nicoll R.A.: Mice deficient for prion protein exhibit normal neuronal excitability and synaptic transmission in the hippocampus. *Proc. Natl. Acad. Sci. USA* 93:2403–2407, 1996.

228. Pattison I.H. and Jones K.M.: Modification of a strain of mouse-adapted scrapie by passage through rats. *Res. Vet. Sci.* 9:408–410, 1968.

229. Kimberlin R.H., Walker C.A., and Fraser H.: The genomic identity of different strains of mouse scrapie is expressed in hamsters and preserved on reisolation in mice. *J. Gen. Virol.* 70:2017–2025, 1989.

230. Hecker R., Taraboulos A., Scott M., Pan K.-M., Torchia M., Jendroska K., DeArmond S.J., and Prusiner S.B.: Replication of distinct prion isolates is region specific in brains of transgenic mice and hamsters. *Genes Dev.* 6:1213–1228, 1992.

231. Hunter N., Goldmann W., Benson G., Foster J.D., and Hope J.: Swaledale sheep affected by natural scrapie differ significantly in PrP genotype frequencies from healthy sheep and those selected for reduced incidence of scrapie. *J. Gen. Virol.* 74:1025–1031, 1993.

232. Shibuya S., Higuchi J., Shin R.-W., Tateishi J., and Kitamoto T.: Protective prion protein polymorphisms against sporadic Creutzfeldt-Jakob disease. *Lancet* 351:419, 1998.

233. Tatzelt J., Zuo J., Voellmy R., Scott M., Hartl U., Prusiner S.B., and Welch W.J.: Scrapie prions selectively modify the stress response in neuroblastoma cells. *Proc. Natl. Acad. Sci. USA* 92:2944–2948, 1995.

234. Tatzelt J., Prusiner S.B., and Welch W.J.: Chemical chaperones interfere with the formation of scrapie prion protein. *EMBO J.* 15:6363–6373, 1996.

235. Kenward N., Hope J., Landon M., and Mayer R.J.: Expression of polyubiquitin and heat-shock protein 70 genes increases in the later stages of disease progression in scrapie-infected mouse brain. *J. Neurochem.* 62:1870–1877, 1994.

236. Oesch B., Teplow D.B., Stahl N., Serban D., Hood L.E., and Prusiner S.B.: Identification of cellular proteins binding to the scrapie prion protein. *Biochemistry* 29:5848–5855, 1990.

237. Kurschner C. and Morgan J.I.: Analysis of interaction sites in homo- and heteromeric complexes containing Bcl-2 family members and the cellular prion protein. *Mol. Brain Res.* 37:249–258, 1996.

317

238. Edenhofer F., Rieger R., Famulok M., Wendler W., Weiss S., and Winnacker E.-L.: Prion protein PrP^C interacts with molecular chaperones of the Hsp60 family. *J. Virol.* 70:4724–4728, 1996.

239. Gerstmann J., Sträussler E., and Scheinker I.: Über eine eigenartige hereditär-familiäre Erkrankung des Zentralnervensystems zugleich ein Beitrag zur frage des vorzeitigen lokalen Alterns. *Z. Neurol.* 154:736–762, 1936.

240. Masters C.L., Harris J.O., Gajdusek D.C., Gibbs C.J., Jr., Bernouilli C., and Asher D.M.: Creutzfeldt-Jakob disease: patterns of worldwide occurrence and the significance of familal and sporadic clustering. *Ann. Neurol.* 5:177–188, 1978.

241. Gajdusek D.C.: Unconventional viruses and the origin and disappearance of kuru. *Science* 197:943–960, 1977.

242. Bobowick A.R., Brody J.A., Matthews M.R., Roos R., and Gajdusek D.C.: Creutzfeldt-Jakob disease: a case-control study. *Am. J. Epidemiol.* 98:381–394, 1973.

243. Rosenthal N.P., Keesey J., Crandall B., and Brown W.J.: Familial neurological disease associated with spongiform encephalopathy. *Arch. Neurol.* 33:252–259, 1976.

244. Doh-ura K., Tateishi J., Sasaki H., Kitamoto T., and Sakaki Y.: Pro->Leu change at position 102 of prion protein is the most common but not the sole mutation related to Gerstmann-Sträussler syndrome. *Biochem. Biophys. Res. Commun.* 163:974–979, 1989.

245. Goldgaber D., Goldfarb L.G., Brown P., Asher D.M., Brown W.T., Lin S., Teener J.W., Feinstone S.M., Rubenstein R., Kascsak R.J., Boellaard J.W., and Gajdusek D.C.: Mutations in familial Creutzfeldt-Jakob disease and Gerstmann-Sträussler-Scheinker's syndrome. *Exp. Neurol.* 106:204–206, 1989.

246. Kretzschmar H.A., Honold G., Seitelberger F., Feucht M., Wessely P., Mehraein P., and Budka H.: Prion protein mutation in family first reported by Gerstmann, Sträussler, and Scheinker. *Lancet* 337:1160, 1991.

247. Hsiao K.K., Scott M., Foster D., Groth D.F., DeArmond S.J., and Prusiner S.B.: Spontaneous neurodegeneration in transgenic mice with mutant prion protein. *Science* 250:1587–1590, 1990.

248. Hsiao K.K., Groth D., Scott M., Yang S.-L., Serban H., Rapp D., Foster D., Torchia M., DeArmond S.J., and Prusiner S.B.: Serial transmission in rodents of neurodegeneration from transgenic mice expressing mutant prion protein. *Proc. Natl. Acad. Sci. USA* 91:9126–9130, 1994.

249. Telling G.C., Haga T., Torchia M., Tremblay P., DeArmond S.J., and Prusiner S.B.: Interactions between wild-type and mutant prion proteins modulate neurodegeneration in transgenic mice. *Genes & Dev.* 10:1736–1750, 1996.

250. Scott M.R., Nguyen O., Stöckel J., Tatzelt J., DeArmond S.J., Cohen F.E., and Prusiner S.B.: Designer mutations in the prion protein promote β-sheet formation *in vitro* and cause neurodegeneration in transgenic mice (Abstr.). *Protein Sci.* 6 [Suppl. 1]:84, 1997.

251. Alpers M.P.: Kuru: implications of its transmissibility for interpretation of its changing epidemiological pattern. *The Central Nervous System, Some Experimental Models of Neurological Diseases.* Bailey O.T. and Smith D.E., Eds. Williams and Wilkins, Baltimore, 1968 pp. 234–251.

252. Alpers M.: Epidemiology and clinical aspects of kuru. *Prions–Novel Infectious Pathogens Causing Scrapie and Creutzfeldt-Jakob Disease.* Prusiner S.B. and McKinley M.P., Eds. Academic Press, Orlando, 1987 pp. 451–465.

253. Brown P., Preece M.A., and Will R.G.: "Friendly fire" in medicine: hormones, homografts, and Creutzfeldt-Jakob disease. *Lancet* 340:24–27, 1992.

254. Billette de Villemeur T., Deslys J.-P., Pradel A., Soubrié C., Alpérovitch A., Tardieu M., Chaussain J.-L., Hauw J.-J., Dormont D., Ruberg M., and Agid Y.: Creutzfeldt-Jakob disease from contaminated growth hormone extracts in France. *Neurology* 47:690–695, 1996.

255. Prusiner S. B., Scott M. R., Dearmond S. J., and Cohen F. E. Prion protein biology. *Cell* 93:337–348, 1998.

256. Esmonde T., Lueck C.J., Symon L., Duchen L.W., and Will R.G.: Creutzfeldt-Jakob dis-

ease and lyophilised dura mater grafts: report of two cases. *J. Neurol. Neurosurg. Psychiatry* 56:999–1000, 1993.

257. Lane K.L., Brown P., Howell D.N., Crain B.J., Hulette C.M., Burger P.C., and DeArmond S.J.: Creutzfeldt-Jakob disease in a pregnant woman with an implanted dura mater graft. *Neurosurgery* 34:737–740, 1994.

258. CDC: Creutzfeldt-Jakob disease associated with cadaveric dura mater grafts–Japan, January 1979–May 1996. *MMWR* 46:1066–1069, 1997.

259. Kimberlin R.H.: Reflections on the nature of the scrapie agent. *Trends Biochem. Sci.* 7:392–394, 1982.

260. Dickinson A.G. and Outram G.W.: Genetic aspects of unconventional virus infections: the basis of the virino hypothesis. *Novel Infectious Agents and the Central Nervous System. Ciba Foundation Symposium 135*. Bock G. and Marsh J., Eds. John Wiley and Sons, Chichester, UK, 1988 pp. 63–83.

261. Bruce M.E., McConnell I., Fraser H., and Dickinson A.G.: The disease characteristics of different strains of scrapie in *Sinc* congenic mouse lines: implications for the nature of the agent and host control of pathogenesis. *J. Gen. Virol.* 72:595–603, 1991.

262. Weissmann C.: A "unified theory" of prion propagation. *Nature* 352:679–683, 1991.

263. Ridley R.M. and Baker H.F.: To what extent is strain variation evidence for an independent genome in the agent of the transmissible spongiform encephalopathies? *Neurodegeneration* 5:219–231, 1996.

264. Fraser H. and Dickinson A.G.: Scrapie in mice. Agent-strain differences in the distribution and intensity of grey matter vacuolation. *J. Comp. Pathol.* 83:29–40, 1973.

265. Bruce M.E., McBride P.A., and Farquhar C.F.: Precise targeting of the pathology of the sialoglycoprotein, PrP, and vacuolar degeneration in mouse scrapie. *Neurosci. Lett.* 102:1–6, 1989.

266. DeArmond S.J., Yang S.-L., Lee A., Bowler R., Taraboulos A., Groth D., and Prusiner S.B.: Three scrapie prion isolates exhibit different accumulation patterns of the prion protein scrapie isoform. *Proc. Natl. Acad. Sci. USA* 90:6449–6453, 1993.

267. Dickinson A.G. and Meikle V.M.: A comparison of some biological characteristics of the mouse-passaged scrapie agents, 22A and ME7. *Genet. Res.* 13:213–225, 1969.

268. Bruce M.E. and Dickinson A.G.: Biological evidence that the scrapie agent has an independent genome. *J. Gen. Virol.* 68:79–89, 1987.

269. Hunter N., Hope J., McConnell I., and Dickinson A.G.: Linkage of the scrapie-associated fibril protein (PrP) gene and Sinc using congenic mice and restriction fragment length polymorphism analysis. *J. Gen. Virol.* 68:2711–2716, 1987.

270. Bessen R.A. and Marsh R.F.: Identification of two biologically distinct strains of transmissible mink encephalopathy in hamsters. *J. Gen. Virol.* 73:329–334, 1992.

271. Bessen R.A., Kocisko D.A., Raymond G.J., Nandan S., Lansbury P.T., and Caughey B.: Non-genetic propagation of strain-specific properties of scrapie prion protein. *Nature* 375:698–700, 1995.

272. Monari L., Chen S.G., Brown P., Parchi P., Petersen R.B., Mikol J., Gray F., Cortelli P., Montagna P., Ghetti B., Goldfarb L.G., Gajdusek D.C., Lugaresi E., Gambetti P., and Autilio-Gambetti L.: Fatal familial insomnia and familial Creutzfeldt-Jakob disease: different prion proteins determined by a DNA polymorphism. *Proc. Natl. Acad. Sci. USA* 91:2839–2842, 1994.

273. Parchi P., Castellani R., Capellari S., Ghetti B., Young K., Chen S.G., Farlow M., Dickson D.W., Sima A.A.F., Trojanowski J.Q., Petersen R.B., and Gambetti P.: Molecular basis of phenotypic variability in sporadic Creutzfeldt-Jakob disease. *Ann. Neurol.* 39:767–778, 1996.

274. Mastrianni J., Nixon F., Layzer R., DeArmond S.J., and Prusiner S.B.: Fatal sporadic insomnia: fatal familial insomnia phenotype without a mutation of the prion protein gene. *Neurology* 48 [Suppl.]:A296, 1997.

275. Fraser H. and Dickinson A.G.: The sequential development of the brain lesions of scrapie in three strains of mice. *J. Comp. Pathol.* 78:301–311, 1968.

276. Carp R.I., Meeker H., and Sersen E.: Scrapie strains retain their distinctive characteristics following passages of homogenates from different brain regions and spleen. *J. Gen. Virol.* 78:283–290, 1997.

277. DeArmond S.J., Sánchez H., Yehiely F., Qiu Y., Ninchak-Casey A., Daggett V., Camerino A.P., Cayetano J., Rogers M., Groth D., Torchia M., Tremblay P., Scott M.R., Cohen F.E., and Prusiner S.B.: Selective neuronal targeting in prion disease. *Neuron* 19:1337–1348, 1997.

278. Medori R., Tritschler H.-J., LeBlanc A., Villare F., Manetto V., Chen H.Y., Xue R., Leal S., Montagna P., Cortelli P., Tinuper P., Avoni P., Mochi M., Baruzzi A., Hauw J.J., Ott J., Lugaresi E., Autilio-Gambetti L., and Gambetti P.: Fatal familial insomnia, a prion disease with a mutation at codon 178 of the prion protein gene. *N. Engl. J. Med.* 326:444–449, 1992.

279. Anderson R.M., Donnelly C.A., Ferguson N.M., Woolhouse M.E.J., Watt C.J., Udy H.J., MaWhinney S., Dunstan S.P., Southwood T.R.E., Wilesmith J.W., Ryan J.B.M., Hoinville L.J., Hillerton J.E., Austin A.R., and Wells G.A.H.: Transmission dynamics and epidemiology of BSE in British cattle. *Nature* 382:779–788, 1996.

280. Nathanson N., Wilesmith J., and Griot C.: Bovine spongiform encephalopathy (BSE): cause and consequences of a common source epidemic. *Am. J. Epidemiol.* 145:959–969, 1997.

281. Stekel D.J., Nowak M.A., and Southwood T.R.E.: Prediction of future BSE spread. *Nature* 381:119, 1996.

282. Wilesmith J.W., Ryan J.B.M., and Atkinson M.J.: Bovine spongiform encephalopathy–Epidemiologic studies on the origin. *Vet. Rec.* 128:199–203, 1991.

283. Wilesmith J.W.: The epidemiology of bovine spongiform encephalopathy. *Semin. Virol.* 2:239–245, 1991.

284. Kimberlin R.H.: Speculations on the origin of BSE and the epidemiology of CJD. *Bovine Spongiform Encephalopathy: The BSE Dilemma.* Gibbs C.J., Jr., Ed. Springer, New York, 1996 pp. 155–175.

285. Goldmann W., Hunter N., Manson J., and Hope J.: The PrP gene of the sheep, a natural host of scrapie. *Proceedings of the VIIIth International Congress of Virology, Berlin, Aug. 26–31* 284, 1990.

286. Goldmann W., Hunter N., Martin T., Dawson M., and Hope J.: Different forms of the bovine PrP gene have five or six copies of a short, G-C-rich element within the protein-coding exon. *J. Gen. Virol.* 72:201–204, 1991.

287. Prusiner S.B., Fuzi M., Scott M., Serban D., Serban H., Taraboulos A., Gabriel J.-M., Wells G., Wilesmith J., Bradley R., DeArmond S.J., and Kristensson K.: Immunologic and molecular biological studies of prion proteins in bovine spongiform encephalopathy. *J. Infect. Dis.* 167:602–613, 1993.

288. Hunter N., Goldmann W., Smith G., and Hope J.: Frequencies of PrP gene variants in healthy cattle and cattle with BSE in Scotland. *Vet. Rec.* 135:400–403, 1994.

289. Fraser H., McConnell I., Wells G.A.H., and Dawson M.: Transmission of bovine spongiform encephalopathy to mice. *Vet. Rec.* 123:472, 1988.

290. Dawson M., Wells G.A.H., and Parker B.N.J.: Preliminary evidence of the experimental transmissibility of bovine spongiform encephalopathy to cattle. *Vet. Rec.* 126:112–113, 1990.

291. Dawson M., Wells G.A.H., Parker B.N.J., and Scott A.C.: Primary parenteral transmission of bovine spongiform encephalopathy to the pig. *Vet. Rec.* 127:338, 1990.

292. Bruce M., Chree A., McConnell I., Foster J., and Fraser H.: Transmissions of BSE, scrapie and related diseases to mice (Abstr.). *Proceedings of the IXth International Congress of Virology* 93, 1993.

293. Bruce M.E., Will R.G., Ironside J.W., McConnell I., Drummond D., Suttie A., McCardle L., Chree A., Hope J., Birkett C., Cousens S., Fraser H., and Bostock C.J.: Transmissions to mice indicate that 'new variant' CJD is caused by the BSE agent. *Nature* 389:498–501, 1997.

294. Robinson M.M., Hadlow W.J., Knowles D.P., Huff T.P., Lacy P.A., Marsh R.F., and

Gorham J.R.: Experimental infection of cattle with the agents of transmissible mink encephalopathy and scrapie. *J. Comp. Path.* 113:241–251, 1995.

295. Hope J., Reekie L.J.D., Hunter N., Multhaup G., Beyreuther K., White H., Scott A.C., Stack M.J., Dawson M., and Wells G.A.H.: Fibrils from brains of cows with new cattle disease contain scrapie-associated protein. *Nature* 336:390–392, 1988.

296. Serban D., Taraboulos A., DeArmond S.J., and Prusiner S.B.: Rapid detection of Creutzfeldt-Jakob disease and scrapie prion proteins. *Neurology* 40:110–117, 1990.

297. Grathwohl K.-U.D., Horiuchi M., Ishiguro N., and Shinagawa M.: Sensitive enzyme-linked immunosorbent assay for detection of PrP^{Sc} in crude tissue extracts from scrapie-affected mice. *J. Virol. Methods* 64:205–216, 1997.

298. Scott M.R., Safar J., Telling G., Nguyen O., Groth D., Torchia M., Koehler R., Tremblay P., Walther D., Cohen F.E., DeArmond S.J., and Prusiner S.B.: Identification of a prion protein epitope modulating transmission of bovine spongiform encephalopathy prions to transgenic mice. *Proc. Natl. Acad. Sci. USA* 94:14279–14284, 1997.

299. Taylor K.C.: The control of bovine spongiform encephalopathy in Great Britain. *Vet. Rec.* 129:522–526, 1991.

300. Fraser H., Bruce M.E., Chree A., McConnell I., and Wells G.A.H.: Transmission of bovine spongiform encephalopathy and scrapie to mice. *J. Gen. Virol.* 73:1891–1897, 1992.

301. Hunter G.D., Millson G.C., and Chandler R.L.: Observations on the comparative infectivity of cellular fractions derived from homogenates of mouse-scrapie brain. *Res. Vet. Sci.* 4:543–549, 1963.

302. Eklund C.M., Kennedy R.C., and Hadlow W.J.: Pathogenesis of scrapie virus infection in the mouse. *J. Infect. Dis.* 117:15–22, 1967.

303. Will R.G., Ironside J.W., Zeidler M., Cousens S.N., Estibeiro K., Alperovitch A., Poser S., Pocchiari M., Hofman A., and Smith P.G.: A new variant of Creutzfeldt-Jakob disease in the UK. *Lancet* 347:921–925, 1996.

304. Bateman D., Hilton D., Love S., Zeidler M., Beck J., and Collinge J.: Sporadic Creutzfeldt-Jakob disease in a 18-year-old in the UK (Lett.). *Lancet* 346:1155–1156, 1995.

305. Britton T.C., Al-Sarraj S., Shaw C., Campbell T., and Collinge J.: Sporadic CreutzfeldtJakob disease in a 16-year-old in the UK (Lett.). *Lancet* 346:1155, 1995.

306. Ironside J.W.: The new variant form of Creutzfeldt-Jakob disease: a novel prion protein amyloid disorder (Editorial). *Amyloid: Int. J. Exp. Clin. Invest.* 4:66–69, 1997.

307. Chazot G., Broussolle E., Lapras C.I., Blättler T., Aguzzi A., and Kopp N.: New variant of Creutzfeldt-Jakob disease in a 26-year-old French man. *Lancet* 347:1181, 1996.

308. CDC: Surveillance for Creutzfeldt-Jakob Disease–United States. *MMWR* 45:665–668, 1996.

309. Baker H.F., Ridley R.M., and Wells G.A.H.: Experimental transmission of BSE and scrapie to the common marmoset. *Vet. Rec.* 132:403–406, 1993.

310. Lasmézas C.I., Deslys J.-P., Demaimay R., Adjou K.T., Lamoury F., Dormont D., Robain O., Ironside J., and Hauw J.-J.: BSE transmission to macaques. *Nature* 381:743–744, 1996.

311. Collinge J., Palmer M.S., Sidle K.C., Hill A.F., Gowland I., Meads J., Asante E., Bradley R., Doey L.J., and Lantos P.L.: Unaltered susceptibility to BSE in transgenic mice expressing human prion protein. *Nature* 378:779–783, 1995.

312. Cousens S.N., Vynnycky E., Zeidler M., Will R.G., and Smith P.G.: Predicting the CJD epidemic in humans. *Nature* 385:197–198, 1997.

313. Raymond G.J., Hope J., Kocisko D.A., Priola S.A., Raymond L.D., Bossers A., Ironside J., Will R.G., Chen S.G., Petersen R.B., Gambetti P., Rubenstein R., Smits M.A., Lansbury P.T., Jr., and Caughey B.: Molecular assessment of the potential transmissibilities of BSE and scrapie to humans. *Nature* 388:285–288, 1997.

314. Collinge J., Sidle K.C.L., Meads J., Ironside J., and Hill A.F.: Molecular analysis of prion strain variation and the aetiology of "new variant" CJD. *Nature* 383:685–690, 1996.

315. Hill A.F., Desbruslais M., Joiner S., Sidle K.C.L., Gowland I., Collinge J., Doey L.J., and Lantos P.: The same prion strain causes vCJD and BSE. *Nature* 389:448–450, 1997.

316. Parchi P., Capellari S., Chen S.G., Petersen R.B., Gambetti P., Kopp P., Brown P., Kitamoto T., Tateishi J., Giese A., and Kretzschmar H.: Typing prion isoforms (Lett.). *Nature* 386:232–233, 1997.

317. Somerville R.A., Chong A., Mulqueen O.U., Birkett C.R., Wood S.C.E.R., and Hope J.: Biochemical typing of scrapie strains. *Nature* 386:564, 1997.

318. Haraguchi T., Fisher S., Olofsson S., Endo T., Groth D., Tarantino A., Borchelt D.R., Teplow D., Hood L., Burlingame A., Lycke E., Kobata A., and Prusiner S.B.: Asparagine-linked glycosylation of the scrapie and cellular prion proteins. *Arch. Biochem. Biophys.* 274:1–13, 1989.

319. Endo T., Groth D., Prusiner S.B., and Kobata A.: Diversity of oligosaccharide structures linked to asparagines of the scrapie prion protein. *Biochemistry* 28:8380–8388, 1989.

320. Wickner R.B.: [URE3] as an altered URE2 protein: evidence for a prion analog in *Saccharomyces cerevisiae. Science* 264:566–569, 1994.

321. Chernoff Y.O., Lindquist S.L., Ono B., Inge-Vechtomov S.G., and Liebman S.W.: Role of the chaperone protein Hsp104 in propagation of the yeast prion-like factor [*psi*+]. *Science* 268:880–884, 1995.

322. Glover J.R., Kowal A.S., Schirmer E.C., Patino M.M., Liu J.-J., and Lindquist S.: Self-seeded fibers formed by Sup35, the protein determinant of [*PSI*+], a heritable prion-like factor of S. cerevisiae. *Cell* 89:811–819, 1997.

323. King C.-Y., Tittman P., Gross H., Gebert R., Aebi M., and Wüthrich K.: Prion-inducing domain 2–114 of yeast Sup35 protein transforms *in vitro* into amyloid-like filaments. *Proc. Natl. Acad. Sci. USA* 94:6618–6622, 1997.

324. Paushkin S.V., Kushnirov V.V., Smirnov V.N., and Ter-Avanesyan M.D.: In vitro propagation of the prion-like state of yeast Sup35 protein. *Science* 277:381–383, 1997.

325. Coustou V., Deleu C., Saupe S., and Begueret J.: The protein product of the *het-s* heterokaryon incompatibility gene of the fungus *Podospora anserina* behaves as a prion analog. *Proc. Natl. Acad. Sci. USA* 94:9773–9778, 1997.

326. Derkatch I.L., Chernoff Y.O., Kushnirov V.V., Inge-Vechtomov S.G., and Liebman S.W.: Genesis and variability of [*PSI*] prion factors in *Saccharomyces cerevisiae. Genetics* 144:1375–1386, 1996.

327. Patino M.M., Liu J.-J., Glover J.R., and Lindquist S.: Support for the prion hypothesis for inheritance of a phenotypic trait in yeast. *Science* 273:622–626, 1996.

328. Wickner R.B.: A new prion controls fungal cell fusion incompatibility [Commentary]. *Proc. Natl. Acad. Sci. USA* 94:10012–10014, 1997.

329. Sonneborn T.M.: The determination of hereditary antigenic differences in genically identical Paramecium cells. *Proc. Natl. Acad. Sci. USA* 34:413–418, 1948.

330. Landman O.E.: The inheritance of acquired characteristics. *Annu. Rev. Genetics* 25:1–20, 1991.

331. Beisson J. and Sonneborn T.M.: Cytoplasmid inheritance of the organization of the cell cortex of *Paramecium aurelia. Proc. Natl. Acad. Sci. USA* 53:275–282, 1965.

332. Frankel J.: Positional order and cellular handedness. *J. Cell Sci.* 97:205–211, 1990.

333. Chapman J., Ben-Israel J., Goldhammer Y., and Korczyn A.D.: The risk of developing Creutzfeldt-Jakob disease in subjects with the *PRNP* gene codon 200 point mutation. *Neurology* 44:1683–1686, 1994.

334. Spudich S., Mastrianni J.A., Wrensch M., Gabizon R., Meiner Z., Kahana I., Rosenmann H., Kahana E., and Prusiner S.B.: Complete penetrance of Creutzfeldt-Jakob disease in Libyan Jews carrying the E200K mutation in the prion protein gene. *Mol. Med.* 1:607–613, 1995.

335. Aguzzi A. and Weissmann C.: Prion research: the next frontiers. *Nature* 389:795–798, 1997.

336. Gorodinsky A. and Harris D.A.: Glycolipid-anchored proteins in neuroblastoma cells form detergent-resistant complexes without caveolin. *J. Cell Biol.* 129:619–627, 1995.

337. Goldmann W., Hunter N., Smith G., Foster J., and Hope J.: PrP genotype and agent effects in scrapie: change in allelic interaction with different isolates of agent in sheep, a natural host of scrapie. *J. Gen. Virol.* 75:989–995, 1994.

338. Belt P.B.G.M., Muileman I.H., Schreuder B.E.C., Ruijter J.B., Gielkens A.L.J., and Smits M.A.: Identification of five allelic variants of the sheep PrP gene and their association with natural scrapie. *J. Gen. Virol.* 76:509–517, 1995.

339. Clousard C., Beaudry P., Elsen J.M., Milan D., Dussaucy M., Bounneau C., Schelcher F., Chatelain J., Launay J.M., and Laplanche J.L.: Different allelic effects of the codons 136 and 171 of the prion protein gene in sheep with natural scrapie. *J. Gen. Virol.* 76:2097–2101, 1995.

340. Ikeda T., Horiuchi M., Ishiguro N., Muramatsu Y., Kai-Uwe G.D., and Shinagawa M.: Amino acid polymorphisms of PrP with reference to onset of scrapie in Suffolk and Corriedale sheep in Japan. *J. Gen. Virol.* 76:2577–2581, 1995.

341. Hunter N., Moore L., Hosie B.D., Dingwall W.S., and Greig A.: Association between natural scrapie and PrP genotype in a flock of Suffolk sheep in Scotland. *Vet. Rec.* 140:59–63, 1997.

342. Hunter N., Cairns D., Foster J.D., Smith G., Goldmann W., and Donnelly K.: Is scrapie solely a genetic disease? *Nature* 386:137, 1997.

343. O'Rourke K.I., Holyoak G.R., Clark W.W., Mickelson J.R., Wang S., Melco R.P., Besser T.E., and Foote W.C.: PrP genotypes and experimental scrapie in orally inoculated Suffolk sheep in the United States. *J. Gen. Virol.* 78:975–978, 1997.

344. Parry H.B.: *Scrapie Disease in Sheep*, Academic Press, New York, 1983.

345. Chesebro B.: Prion diseases: BSE and prions: uncertainties about the agent. *Science* 279:42–43, 1998.

346. Shinde U.P., Liu J.J., and Inouye M.: Protein memory through altered folding mediated by intramolecular chaperones. *Nature* 389:520-522, 1997.

Dario Fo

DARIO FO

In addition to playwright, Dario Fo is also director, stage and costume designer, and on occasion he even composes the music for his plays.

Franca Rame, in addition to being his leading actress, has assisted in and contributed to the writing of many of the plays they have produced in their 45 years of theatre together. She has also assumed the administrative and organizational responsibility for the Fo–Rame Company.

FRANCA RAME

Franca Rame was born in Parabiago, a small town in the Province of Milan. That she happened to be born there was pure chance: her family was performing in the town at the time. Her father Domenico, her mother Emilia and her brother, along with aunts, uncles, cousins and other actors and actresses hired on contract, were all part of a travelling theatre troupe touring the towns and villages of Lombardy and Piedmont.

The Rame family's ties to the theatre are very old. Since the late 17th century, they have been actors, and puppet masters, as the occasion required.

With the arrival of the cinema they shifted from puppet theatre to real theatre, enriched with all the "special effects" of the puppet theatre. They travelled from town to town, and were well received wherever they went.

Even today, her personal success in theatre and television notwithstanding, people in these towns still often refer to Franca as "the daughter of Domenico Rame". In the best tradition of the Commedia dell'Arte, the family improvised its performances, drawing on a rich repertoire of tragic and comical situations and dialogues.

They often opened in a new town – following a poll among the townspeople – with an enactment of the life of the local patron saint.

The family's repertoire ranged from the biblical texts over Shakespeare to Chekhov and Pirandello; from Niccodemi to the great 19th century historical novels – especially those with a socialist or anticlerical bent. Often their performances included enactments of the lives of men such as Giordano Bruno, Arnaldo da Brescia and Galileo Galilei.

Domenico Rame was the troupe's poet; a devout socialist, he often saw to it that the revenue from a performance was given in support of striking workers or used to build child-care facilities, or in other ways spent to improve the lives of the common people. The minutely documented records of this activity, which remains in the Rame–Fo archives, was probably maintained by

Franca's mother Emilia Baldini, a school teacher and daughter of a municipal engineer in Bobbio.

As a young school teacher, Emilia fell in love with Domenico – twenty years her senior – who was passing through Bobbio with his marionettes and puppets. She married him, against the strong wishes of her family, and together they continued to tour all of Lombardy. Emilia soon learned the trades of acting and costume designer. It was she who taught their four children to act and to move on the stage. She was an outstanding woman, meticulous in all her work and an excellent organizer. In the end it was she who carried the troupe on her shoulders.

It was in this environment that Franca earned her apprenticeship. She has always felt at home on the stage because – as she says – "I was born there: I was only eight days old when I made my debut in my mother's arms [she played the new-born son of Geneviève of Brabant] … I didn't say much that evening!".

Some years later, in the 1950–51 theatre season, Franca – following the lead of her sister Pia – left the family and joined the company of Tino Scotti for a part in Marcello Marchesi's "Ghe pensi mi" at the Teatro Olimpia in Milan.

DARIO FO

Dario Fo was born on 26 March 1926 in San Giano, a small town on Lago Maggiore in the province of Varese. His family consisted of: his father Felice, socialist, station master and actor in an amateur theatre company; his mother Pina Rota, a woman of great imagination and talent (in the 1970s her autobiographical account "Il paese delle rane", telling the history of her home town, was published by Einaudi); his brother Fulvio and his sister Bianca; and his maternal grandfather, who had a farm in Lomellina, where young Dario spent his childhood vacations.

During Dario's visits, his grandfather would travel around the countryside selling his produce from a big, horse-drawn wagon. To attract customers he would tell the most amazing stories, and in these stories he would insert news and anecdotes about local events. His satirical and timely chronicles earned him the nickname *Bristìn* (pepper seed). It was from his grandfather, sitting beside him on the big wagon, that Dario began to learn the rudiments of narrative rhythm.

Dario spent his childhood moving from one town to another, as his father's postings were changed at the whim of the railway authorities. But even though the geography remained in a flux, the cultural setting was always the same. As the boy grew, he became schooled in the local narrative tradition. With growing passion, he would sit in the taverns or the *piazze* and listen tirelessly to the master glass-blowers and fishermen, who – in the oral tradition of the *fabulatore* – would swap tall tales, steeped in pungent political satire.

In 1940 he moved to Milan (commuting from Luino) to study at the Brera Art Academy. After the war, he begins to study architecture at the Polytechnic, but interrupts his studies with only a few exams left to complete his degree.

Towards the end of the war, Dario is conscripted into the army of the Salò republic. He manages to escape, and spends the last months of the war hidden in an attic store room. His parents are active in the resistance, his father organizing the smuggling of Jewish scientists and escaped British prisoners of war into Switzerland by train; his mother caring for wounded partisans.

At the end of the war, Dario returns to his studies at the Academy of Brera in Milan while attending courses in architecture at the Polytechnic, commuting each day from his home on Lago Maggiore.

1945–41 he turns his attention to stage design and theatre décor. He begins to improvise monologues.

He moves with his family to Milan. Mamma Fo, in order to help her husband put the three children through college, does her best as a shirt-maker.

For the younger Fos, this is a period of ravenous reading. Gramsci and Marx are devoured along with American novelists and the first translations of Brecht, Mayakovsky and Lorca.

In the immediate postwar years, Italian theatre undergoes a veritable revolution, pushed along mainly by the new phenomenon of *piccoli teatri* ["small theatres"] that play a key role in developing the idea of a "popular stage".

Fo is captured by this effervescent movement and proves to be an insatiable theatregoer – even though he usually can't afford to buy a seat and has to stand through the performances. Mamma Fo keeps an open mind and an open house for her children's new acquaintances, among them Emilio Tadini, Alik Cavalieri, Piccoli, Vittorini, Morlotti, Treccani, Crepax, some of them already famous.

During his architecture studies, while working as decorator and assistant architect, Dario begins to entertain his friends with tales as tall as those he heard in the lakeside taverns of his childhood.

In the summer of 1950, Dario seeks out Franco Parenti who is enthralled by the young man's comical rendering of the parable of Cain and Abel, a satire in which Cain, *poer nano* ["poor little thing"], a miserable fool, is anything but evil. It's just that every time he tries, *poer nano*, to mimic the splendid, blond and blue-eyed Abel, he gets into trouble. After suffering one disaster after another, he finally goes crazy and kills the splendid Abel. Franco Parenti enthusiastically invites Fo to join his theatre company.

Dario starts performing in Parenti's summer variety show. This is when he has his first "encounter" with Franca Rame – not in person, mind, but in the form of a photograph he sees at the home of some friends. He is thunderstruck!

For a while he continues to work as assistant architect. But he soon decides to abandon his work and studies, disgusted by the corruption already rampant in the building sector.

The 1951– 52 theatre season	Franca Rame and Dario Fo meet by chance: they are both engaged in a production of **"Sette giorni a Milano"** by Spiller and Carosso, staged by the Nava-Parenti company at the Odeon Theatre in Milan.

The 1951–52 theatre season Franca Rame and Dario Fo meet by chance: they are both engaged in a production of **"Sette giorni a Milano"** by Spiller and Carosso, staged by the Nava-Parenti company at the Odeon Theatre in Milan.

Dario's courting technique is drastic: he pretends not to see Franca. After a couple of weeks of this, she grabs him backstage, pushes him up against a wall and gives him a passionate kiss. They are engaged.

1951 Fo's performance is a minor success, and he is invited to participate in RAI's (the Italian national radio's) show **"Cocoricò"**, where he earns a certain notoriety with his "poer nano" monologues, transmitted in 18 episodes. His innovative use of language subverts the rhetoric of "official" narrative. It is the first experiment with a narrative technique that combines re-examinations of history with excursions into popular lore, a technique he is later to develop further with **"Mistero buffo"**. Created in this period are his grotesque renditions of the stories of Cain and Abel, Samson and Delilah, Abraham and Isaac, Romeo and Juliet, Moses, Othello, Rigoletto, Hamlet, Julius Caesar, King David, Nero and others.

The series is interrupted after the eighteenth show, as the producers – who are slow to catch on to the social and political satire that permeates the monologues – at last see fit to censure them.

1951–52 Dario makes his debut with a series of monologues entitled **"Poer Nano"** ("poor little thing", an affectionate expression in the Lombard dialect) in the revue **"Sette giorni a Milano"**, where he meets Franca Rame. Fo's monologues are a success, leading to an own show on Italian national radio. He becomes a celebrity.

1952 **"Papaveri e papere"**, a film by Marcello Marchesi, with Franca Rame and Walter Chiari. Franca has roles in some ten-odd other commercial films.

1952–53 Dario Fo is on stage with the satirical performance **"Cocoricò"**, with Giustino Durano, Viky Enderson and others.

Franca Rame is engaged by Remigio Paone to play in a big revue company, Billi and Riva in **"I fanatici"** by Marchesi and Mertz, music by Kramer. Teatro Nuovo, Milan.

1953–54 For a performance at the Piccolo Teatro in Milan, Fo writes, together with Franco Parenti and Giustino Durano, directs (in collaboration with Lecoq) and plays **"Il dito nell'occhio"**. (He is also responsible for stage design and costumes.) Franca Rame also participates in the production, which is the first really satirical post-war revue. The show sparks both approval and controversy.

The company has difficulty in finding theatres to stage the play. Drastic efforts of censorship by the government as well as the Church: signs on church doors exhort parishioners not to see the play. This becomes a praxis that will hound the Fo–Rame theatre company for many years.

24 June   Franca and Dario are married in Milan's Saint Ambrose Basilica. From this moment on, Franca is Fo's main collaborator behind the desk as well as on the stage.

1954–55   Together with Parenti and Durano, Fo writes and at the Piccolo Teatro in Milan, directs and plays **"I sani da legare"**. Also this play is subject to the same type of censorship as is described above. These two plays are the first real satirical postwar revues, and both enjoy great success with the public.

1955   Attracted by the possibility to work in the cinema, the couple moves to Rome. Dario works as screen-writer (gag-man) with Age, Scarpelli, Scola and Pinelli, and for Ponti and De Laurentis as well as for other productions.

31 March   Their son Jacopo is born.

Franca with Memo Benassi in **"King Lear"** at the Teatro Stabile of Bolzano.

1956   Fo writes the script for and plays against Franca Rame in the film **"Lo svitato"**, directed by Carlo Lizzani.

1956–57   Fo collaborates in various film script projects and plays against Franca in several films.

1957   Franca Rame in **"Non andartene in giro tutta nuda"** ["Mais n'te promène donc pas tout nue!"] by G. Feydeau at the Arlecchino Theatre in Rome.

1957–58   The "Fo–Rame Company" is established. Franca and Dario return to Milan to establish their own theatre company, with Dario as playwright, actor, director, stage- and costume designer. Franca is Dario's main text collaborator and leading actress. She also assumes responsibility for the company's administration.

The Fo–Rame company makes its debut at Milan's Piccolo Teatro. The company then leaves for a first long, annual tour (there were to be many, lasting up to 10 months and bringing the company to every part of Italy) with a performance entitled **"Ladri, manichini e donne nude"** and comprising four one-act farces: **"l'uomo nudo, l'uomo in frack"** [**"One Was Nude and One Wore Tails"**], **"Non tutti i ladri vengono per nuocere"** [**"The Virtuous Burglar"**], **"Gli imbianchini non hanno ricordi"** and **"I cadaveri si spediscono e le donne si spogliano"**. The four farces make the most of an endless series of misunderstandings, mistaken identities, people running up and down stairs, gags and slapstick.

1958–59   **"Comica finale"** is another collection of four one-act plays: **"Quando sarai povero sarai re"**, **"La Marcolfa"**, **"Un morto da vendere"** and **"I tre bravi"**. These are short, comical stories structured much like the ones Franca's family played at the end of their performances ("comic closures"). From the Teatro Stabile, Dario Fo and Franca Rame buy scenery, props and costumes, and set out on tour with their company. They also revive "Ladri, manichini e donne nude".

THE FO–RAME COMPANY HAS ITS FIRST OPENING AT A MAJOR, DOWNTOWN THEATRE IN MILAN

1959–60   With **"Gli arcangeli non giocano a flipper"** ["Archangels Don't Play Pinball"], at Milan's Odeon Theatre, The Fo–Rame Company finally earns national recognition. The play becomes the greatest box-office hit in Italian theatre.

1960   Fo writes **"La storia vera di Piero d'Angera, che alla crociata non c'era"**, produced by other companies with great success.

1960–61   Teatro Odeon, Milan: **"Aveva due pistole con gli occhi bianchi e neri"**.

1961   First performance abroad with his play: **"Ladri, manichini e donne nude",** first at Stockholm's Arena Theatre, then with a production in Poland.

1961–62   Teatro Odeon, Milan: **"Chi ruba un piede è fortunato in amore"**.

1962   In the spring, RAI (Italian national television) broadcasts on its second channel the televised variety show **"Chi l'ha visto?"** with Fo–Rame and others.

Together with Franca Rame, Dario Fo is invited to write, direct and present **"Canzonissima"**, a highly popular TV show built around the national lottery, with a different host each year. Fo's and Rame's sketches become an issue for the entire nation, provoking wild controversy. For the first time, television is used to portray the lives and difficulties of common people: the work-related illness of a signal woman, bricklayers that fall to their death from the scaffolding, etc.

The show is very successful; during broadcasts even taxi drivers stop working, and bars with televisions are smack full of people. RAI's management starts to get nervous. Cuts are demanded in texts that have already been approved. All hell breaks loose over a sketch with a Mafia theme that tells the story of a murdered journalist. Malagodi, a senator from Italy's Liberal Party, reports the sketch to the Italian Parliament's oversight committee for television, on the grounds that "the honour of the Sicilian people is insulted by the claim that there exists a criminal organization called the Mafia". (In 1985, Prime Minister Andreotti appoints Malagodi senator-for-life for his political services.) Fo and Rame also receive death threats, written with blood and delivered with the typical miniature, wooden coffin. The Fo family (including Franca's and Dario's seven-year old son) is placed under police protection.

A fight begins with RAI about censorship. Just a few hours before the scheduled broadcast of the eighth programme in the series, RAI's management declares that further cuts must be made. Dario and Franca refuse and threaten to leave the programme. As **"Canzonissima"** is about to be aired it is still unclear what is going to happen. At the last minute RAI confirms the cuts. Dario and Franca walk off the show as a sign of protest.

The support they receive for their act is overwhelming, including thousands of letters and telegrams. RAI is unable to find substitutes for Fo and Rame, as all who are asked to replace them follow the instructions of SAI (the Italian actors union) to turn down the offer.

Fo and Rame face five law suits as a consequence and are ordered to pay several billion lire in damages. For 15 years they are banned by RAI from participating in either programmes or commercials on national radio or television (at that time, both radio and television were state monopolies).

1963–64	Opening at Milan's Odeon Theatre of **"Isabella , tre caravelle e un cacciaballe"**, which tells the story of the "discovery" of America on the basis of a thorough historical investigation of the life of Christopher Columbus, the court of Isabella of Castille and the "ethnic cleansing" of Spain's Arabs and Jews. The play marks the beginning of a major effort to trace the history and "dogmas" of the dominant culture. The play, blatantly exposing the mystifications of "school-book" history and of militarist and patriotic rhetoric, comes under violent attack by right-wing groups. On one occasion, Fo and Rame are assaulted as they leave the Valle Theatre in Rome. Only through the presence of groups of militant workers from the Italian Communist Party (PCI) can the performances continue.
1964–65	**"Settimo: ruba un po' meno"** opens at the Odeon in Milan. The play is dedicated to Franca Rame, who in the leading comic role portrays a rather odd grave digger whose highest ambition is to become a prostitute. With its minutely detailed description of the corruption rampant in Italy, it anticipates by some thirty years the

331

revolution brought about by the **"Mani Pulite"** ("Clean hands") movement.

1965–66   Milan's Odeon Theatre: **"La colpa è sempre del diavolo"**.

1966–67   Two productions: **"Gli amici della battoniera"**, translated from French and adapted by Fo; and **"Ci ragiono e canto"**, in collaboration with Nuovo Canzoniere Italiano, a performance built on traditional folk songs, compiled by Gianni Bosio and elaborated by Fo.

1967   Following the Soviet invasion of Czechoslovakia, Dario Fo withdraws his permission for his plays to be staged in Czech theatres. He later refuses to authorize cuts, proposed by Soviet censors, in a play scheduled to open at a Soviet theatre. After these incidents, production of his work all but ceases throughout the Soviet block.

1967–68   Teatro Manzoni in Milan: **"La signora è da buttare"**.

1968–69   Stimulated by the political events of those years, Dario and Franca disband their company and establish the Associazione Nuova Scena, composed of more than thirty young technicians, actors and actresses. It is an independent theatre collective, organized in three groups that tour Italy with productions staged mainly before working class audiences and at venues other than those offered by the official theatre circuit, such as *case del popolo* (workers' community halls), sport arenas, cinemas, boccia courts, town squares, etc. To allow mobility and use of available space, foldable stages are built on Dario's design. Nuova Scena's first production opens at the *Casa del popolo* in Cesena (Romagna) with a performance of **"Grande pantomima per pupazzi piccoli, grandi e medi"**. The production is also staged at Milan's Union Hall and is played on tour. Back in Milan, Nuova Scena – encountering difficulties in finding a fixed venue – rents an old, abandoned factory which it transforms into a theatrical centre. The centre becomes the home stage of a new company, *Il Capannone di Via Colletta*, supported by the theatre collective and by a large group of members: workers and students who contribute with their creativity and practical skills.

1969–70   At Genua's Union Hall and in various localities, Franca Rame is on stage with two new comic productions by Fo: **"L'operaio conosce 300 parole, il padrone 1000, per questo lui è il padrone"** and a double feature consisting of two one-act farces: **"Legami pure, tanto spacco tutto lo stesso"** and **"Il funeral e del padrone"**. Because of the plays' expressed critique of Stalinism and of the social-democratic position of the Italian Communist Party, the tour is heavily sabotaged by the Party leadership. Some ten-odd performances are cancelled. The situation is very tense, Franca's planned opening at Milan's Union Hall is cancelled. Instead she is invited to play at the **"Circus Medini",** a real circus with horses, tigers, lions and elephants, luckily all kept in cages around the tent. After some initial difficulties, the production can continue – thanks to support organized among the Party rank and file and among the extraparliamentary left – to enjoy great public success. Franca sends her Party card back to PCI Secretary Enrico Berlinguer (Dario has never been a member).

Dario stages **"Mistero buffo" ["Mistero Buffo"]**. The performance takes the form of a lesson in the history of literature that departs from a questioning of school dogma, in particular the text-book interpretation of the earliest known text in Italian (**"Rosa fresca e aulentissima"**), in which the text's blatant – and scurrilous – allusion to the feminine genitalia is altogether censored. The actor reconstructs the language of the medieval jesters, reciting their monologues in such a way as to make them accessible to a wide audience today. The play is a terrific success; it even becomes necessary to stage it at sport arenas that can hold thousands. It is the play that more than any other establishes Fo's fame worldwide. More than 5000 performances.

Due to political differences, Dario Fo and Franca Rame leave "Nuova Scena". The "Collettivo Teatrale La Comune" sees the light of day, directed by Dario Fo and Franca Rame.

1970–71   1970 Arturo Corso begins as assistant director to Fo. La Comune produces (at the *Capannone di via Colletta*): **"Vorrei morire anche stasera se dovessi sapere che non è servito niente"**, a play about the Italian and Palestinian resistance.

Following the terrorist attack on the Banca Nazionale dell'Agricoltura in Milan, Dario writes and produces one of his most famous pieces: **"Morte accidentale di un anarchico" ["Accidental Death of an Anarchist"]**, about the *strage di Stato* [a massacre thought to be organized by organs of the state].

Franca Rame on stage in **"Tutti uniti, tutti inseme! Ma, scusa, quello non è il padrone?!"**, a play about the birth of the Italian Communist Party in 1921.

1971   **"Fedayin"**, a piece by Fo, with Franca on stage with 10 authentic Palestinian freedom fighters to gather funds and medicine for the Palestinian resistance. Franca went to fetch the fedayeen herself in the training camps in Lebanon, with the help of the Popular Democratic Front.

1971-72   **"Ordine per Dio.ooo.ooo.ooo"** with Franca Rame and other actors, while Dario tours Italy with **"Mistero buffo numero 2"**.

Due to the economic crisis, many factories are closed. To defend their jobs, workers go on strike and occupy the factories. In support of this struggle, from 1971 to 1985 the La Comune collective stages hundreds of performances, donating the revenues to the workers.

La Comune is forced to leave the *Capannone di via Colletta*. The contract has expired and the owner refuses to renew it.

1973–74　Dario, Franca and their colleagues are not deterred. They rent the Rossini Cinema on the outskirts of Milan, where they stage **"Pum pum, chi è? La Polizia!"** [**"Bang bang, who's there? Police!"**] (still addressing the *strage di Stato*) with Dario Fo and other actors.

The theatre collective is subjected to various acts of repression by the police as well as to efforts at censorship.

8 March　A group of fascists kidnaps, tortures and rapes Franca Rame.

Through this beastly act, they seek to punish Franca and Dario for their political activism, in particular Franca's work in the prisons since 1970. Outcries of indignation and support throughout Italy.

May　Following a two-month break, Franca returns to the stage with a performance entitled **"Basta con i fascisti"**, a slide presentation with monologues by Fo–Rame and Lanfranco Binni. The performance is dedicated to young people and addresses the cultural and political presence of fascism within the Italian state, retelling the birth, history and violence of fascism (opening: Milan's *Casa del popolo* and tour).

Paris: **"Mistero buffo"** with Théâtre National Populaire at Salle Gemier–Trocadero.

"Ci ragiono e canto N.3" written by Fo for the Sicilian street singer Ciccio Busacca.

Having searched in vain for a permanent stage, La Comune occupies an abandoned, dilapidated building in central Milan, the *Palazzina Liberty*, formerly an indoor vegetable market. Within a year they have 80 000 season-ticket holders in Milan alone.

September　A few days after the death of Allende, La Comune opens its new home stage – repaired and put in order with the help of neighbours and workers from various Milan factories – with **"Guerra di popolo in Cile"**. The revenues go to the Chilean resistance. During a guest performance in Sassari, Fo is arrested for having blocked access to the theatre for policemen seeking to stop the performance.

1974–75   *Palazzina Liberty*: **"Non si paga, non si paga!"** [**"Can't pay? Won't pay!"**]. In the course of the season, Fo and Rame organize performances, demonstrations and concerts in support of the campaign for a referendum on divorce and as manifestations of solidarity with workers occupying factories and in other ways taking part in the political struggle. Many immigrants have in the *Palazzina Liberty* found a place to meet to discuss their common concerns and to celebrate their faiths.

June 1975   **"Fanfani rapito"**: Fo writes this piece in four days in support of the campaign for a referendum for the legalization of abortion. The performances of **"Non si paga, non si paga!"** are interrupted and the new play is staged within eight days!

1975   The La Comune collective visits the People's Republic of China for one month.

A group of Swedish intellectuals nominate Fo as candidate for the Nobel Prize in literature.

1975–76   **"La marijuana della mamma è la più bella"**, a play about the drug fad making headway also in Italy.

1976–77   On the invitation of Massimo Fichera, Director of RAI 2, Dario and Franca return to television after 15 years. The series **"Il teatro di Dario Fo"** includes **"Mistero buffo"**, **"Settimo: ruba un po' meno!"**, **"Ci ragiono e canto"**, **"Isabella, tre caravelle e un cacciaballe"**, **"La signora è da buttare"** and **"Parliamo di donne"**, for a total television time of 21 hours. The political right and the Church complain … and attack the programme at every opportunity! Franca Rame receives the IDI Prize as best television actress for her performance in **"Parliamo di donne"**.

1977–78   During this theatre season, the third edition of **"Mistero buffo"** is born (*Palazzina Liberty*, followed by tour.)

In November opens at *Palazzina Liberty* a production of **"Tutta casa, letto e chiesa"** [**"Female parts"**], a piece mixing the grotesque, comic and dramatic to illustrate the situation of women today. Alone on the stage is Franca Rame, who for the first time puts her name besides Fo's on the author by-line. The performance is staged more than 3000 times.

It is in these years that Fo becomes Italy's most translated author. He is published in more than 50 countries and in more than 30 languages.

1979   Dario and Franca participate in the International Theatre Festival in Berlin with **"Mistero buffo"** and **"Tutta casa, letto e chiesa"**.

Fo writes **"La tragedia di Aldo Moro"**, on the kidnapping and assassination of the Italian Christian Democratic Party leader at the hands of the Red Brigades. The play, which has never been performed, is built on Sophocles' *Philoctetes*.

Re-elaborates and directs for Milan's La Scala Theatre "L'Histoire du Soldat" by Igor Stravinsky. Writes and directs **"Storia della tigre ['The Tale of the Tiger'] e altre storie"**.

1980   Franca, Dario and their son Jacopo found the *Libera Università di Alcatraz*, a cultural and agricultural retreat and study centre located in the hills between Gubbio and Perugia. By buying up, little by little, 3 700 000 square metres of forest (that otherwise would have been felled) and olive groves, the Fos prevent the destruction of a beautiful valley. They also restore eleven ancient and abandoned farm houses and medieval towers. Alcatraz becomes a gathering place for various artists and cultural groups – including Sergio Angese, Stefano Benni, Dacia Maraini, Milo Manara, Andrea Pazienza, Elena Cranco – who hold workshops in theatre, cartoon drawing, dance, writing, psychophysical techniques, psychology and craftsmanship. Alcatraz also arranges educational programmes and summer camps for young people, social outcasts and persons with handicap. The activities at the centre include equine therapy, comic therapy, nature walks and pool swimming including a swimming school. In addition, the centre offers natural gardening, an ecological restaurant and a facility to preserve organically grown fruit and produce. To date, the centre has had more than 3000 guests. It is directed by Jacopo Fo.

"Buona sera con Franca Rame" – by and with Fo – RAI 2 (20 shows).

March   Sweden: Stockholms Stadsteater (The City Theatre of Stockholm) stages **"Mistero buffo"** and **"Tutta casa, letto e chiesa"**.

May   Fo is invited by East Berlin's **Berliner Ensemble** to stage a production at Bertolt Brecht's prestigious theatre in the spring of 1981. Dario Fo prepares an adaptation of Brecht's "Three-penny Opera" that is rejected for its political content. The main resistance comes from Brecht's daughter (the Berlin Wall has not yet fallen). The same adaptation is used when the play is staged a year later at Turin's Teatro Stabile.

Dario and Franca are invited to participate at the Italian Theatre Festival in New York. However, the US Department of State denies them entry visas to the United States. On 29 May, a large group of US artists and intellectuals organize a protest against the ruling. Among the protesters are Arthur Miller, Norman Mailer, Martin Scorsese, Ellen Stewart, Sol Yurrick, Eve Merriam and others.

December	France: Théâtre de L'Est Parisien stages **"Mistero buffo"** and **"Tutta casa, letto e chiesa"**.
	Germany: Franca on stage with **"Tutta casa, letto e chiesa"** at the Volkshochschule in Frankfurt and the Deutsches Schauspielhaus in Bochum and in Hamburg.
1981–	The University of Copenhagen awards Fo with the prestigious Sonning Prize, which he dedicates to Franca.
1981	Franca in a production by RAI: "Mrs Warren's Profession" by G. B. Shaw, directed by Giorgio Albertazzi.
1981–82	**"Tutta casa, letto e chiesa"** in a new version, Milan's Odeon Theatre followed by tour. Franca writes **"Lo stupro"** and, with Dario, **"Una madre"** (about political prisoners), two monologues that are inserted in various performances.
	Fo writes **"Clacson, trombette e pernacchi"** [**"Trumpets and raspberries"**], a comedy about terrorism.
1982	Turin's Teatro Stabile produces and Fo directs his new play **"L'Opera dello sghignazzo"**, a free adaptation of John Gay's "The Beggar's Opera", which also served as point of departure for Brecht's "Three-penny Opera". Dario Fo writes and produces **"Il fabulazzo osceno"**, based on **"Mistero buffo"** and "Storia della tigre". With him on stage is Franca Rame who recites the two monologues **"Lo stupro"** and **"La madre"**.
	London: Franca's performance of **"Tutta casa, letto e chiesa"** at the Riverside Studios is received with loud acclaim by critics and public alike. The same piece, in English translation ["Female Parts"], is performed by Yvonne Bryceland at the National Theatre.
	Dario and Franca together write **"Coppia aperta"** [**"The Open Couple"**], which is immediately staged at Stockholm's famous Pistol Theatre, translated and directed by Anna and Carlo Barsotti. The play enjoys great success with critics and public.
1983 May	London: Fo at the Riverside Studios with **"Mistero buffo"**.
	Canada: Franca is invited to participate in the Festival Québécois du Jeune Théâtre with **"Tutta casa, letto e chiesa"**.
1983–84	Following the play's clamorous success in Sweden, Dario and Franca stage **"Coppia aperta"** with Nicola de Buono in the role of the husband (Teatro Ciak in Milan). The Ministerial Commission for Censorship bans the play to minors under 18 (!). The ruling is later recalled after protests from the press and the public.
January	Cuba: Festival de teatro de la Habana with **"Tutta casa, letto e chiesa"**.

| May | Argentina: Teatro Municipal General San Martìn with **"Tutta casa, letto e chiesa"** and **"Mistero buffo"**. During a performance, a youth throws a military tear-gas grenade into the theatre. It explodes, creating panic among the audience of well over 1000 persons. Every evening throughout the stay in Argentina, young – and not so young – fascists in black leather jackets throw stones at the windows of the theatre – while tens of policemen stand by, watching complacently. Windows up to the third floor are broken. Meanwhile, groups of Catholics (instigated by fiery press articles by the Bishop of Buenos Aires, written before the arrival of the company), carrying oversized images of Jesus on their chests, pray in the lobby of the theatre. Others interrupt the performances with shouts every time the word "pope" was mentioned. These people are carried out of the theatre by the police. Reactions of support from authorities and the public, including the mothers of Plaza de Mayo. |

Colombia: Teatro Colon with **"Tutta casa, letto e chiesa"** and **"Mistero buffo"**.

| August | Franca and Dario at Edinburgh's Fringe Theatre Festival with **"Tutta casa, letto e chiesa"** and **"Mistero buffo"**. |

Tour in Finland, Tampere: Festival of the Theatre of Dario Fo. Plays and performances by Fo–Rame are staged all over the city. Dario presents **"Mistero buffo"** and Franca **"Tutta casa, letto e chiesa"**.

They are invited by Joseph Papp to stage a production at New York's Public Theatre, but are denied entry into the USA for a second time.

Fo writes **"Patapunfete"**, a text for clowns, performed and directed by Ronald and Alfred Colombaioni.

During the summer, Fo writes **"Quasi per caso una donna: Elisabetta"** ["Elizabeth: Almost by Chance a Woman"], **"Dio li fa poi li accoppa"** and **"Lisistrata romana"**, the latter a monologue that has never been staged.

London: Riverside Studios with **"La storia della maschera"**.

Fo–Rame at Edinburgh's Fringe Theatre Festival.

| 1984–85 | The first production of **"Quasi per caso una donna: Elisabetta"** opens in the autumn. The large number of people who come to see the play during the season earn Dario and Franca AGIS's "Golden Ticket" award. |

| May–June | Germany: The International Theatre Festival in Munich with **"Tutta casa, letto e chiesa"** and **"Mistero buffo"**. |

May	Genua's Teatro della Tosse stages **"La vera storia di Piero d'Angera che alla crociata non c'era"**, directed by Tonino Conte, stage design and costumes by Lele Luzzati.
November	American producer Alexander Cohen stages a Broadway production of "Accidental Death of an Anarchist", with adaptations by Richard Nelsan, at New York's Belasco Theatre. The US Department of State finally – after personal intervention by President Reagan! – grants Fo and Rame a limited, six-day entry visa.
1985–86	For the Biennial exhibition in Venice, Fo writes and stages (with Rome University's Teatro Ateneo) **"Hellequin, Harlekin, Arlecchino"** at Venice's Palazzo del Cinema. He also writes **"Diario di Eva"** for Franca; but has yet to stage it.
September	Franca is invited to Copenhagen by the Danish actors' union to present a few of her monologues at a benefit performance. Franca visits Tübingen, Heidelberg, Stuttgart and Frankfurt with the Theater Am Turm to perform **"Coppia aperta"** with Giorgio Biavati.
May–June	USA: Dario and Franca are finally granted a normal entry visa for the United States. On the invitation of Harvard University, they perform **"Mistero buffo"** and **"Tutta casa, letto e chiesa"** at Cambridge's American Repertory Theater, the New Haven University Repertory Theatre, Washington's Kennedy Center, Baltimore's Theater of Nations and New York's Joyce Theater. They hold a five-day theatre seminar at New York University as well as various workshops. Franca gives a lesson/performance at Wheaton College in Norton, Massachusetts.
August	Fo receives the Premio Eduardo from Taormina Arte.
	Franca at the Free Festival in Edinburgh with **"Coppia aperta"**. Participating in the festival are various companies presenting Fo–Rame texts in English translation: Yorick Theatre Co., Catwalk Theatre Productions, Fo–Rame Theatre Project, Warehouse Theatre, The Drama Department and Borderline Theatre.
1986–87	Franca opens at Milan's Teatro Nuovo with **"Parti femminili"**, two one-act plays by Dario Fo and Franca Rame: **"Una giornata qualunque"** [**"An Ordinary Day"**] and an updated version of **"Coppia aperta"**. The same season sees the opening of **"Il ratto della Francesca"** with Franca Rame and others.
December	Pagani (Naples): Dario Fo receives the "Fifth national award against violence and the Camorra" from the Associazione Torre.
February	Dario Fo directs Rossini's "The Barber of Seville" at *De Nederlandse Opera* in Amsterdam. The same production – with another cast – is later staged at the Teatro Petruzzelli in Bari.

April	Dario and Franca are in Cambridge, Massachusetts, to direct "Archangels Don't Play Flipper" at the American Repertory Theatre.
June	In New York to receive the Obie Prize.
July	Franca Rame at the San Francisco Theater Festival with **"Coppia aperta"**. She holds a theatre workshop with well over a hundred participants, numbering actors, mimes, acrobats and magicians who have come from all parts of the United States to share experiences.
1987–88	At the Festival dell'Unità, before an audience of over 10 000, Dario Fo presents his piece **"La rava e la fava"** (title later changed to **"La parte del leone"**), a tragicomic monologue on the political situation in Italy.
	Franca Rame continues with **"Parti femminili"** and participates in a production for RAI 2, **"Una lepre con la faccia da bambina"**, a film by Gianni Sera on the ecological disaster in Seveso. In the meantime, Fo writes scripts for the eight episodes of **"Trasmissione forzata"** planned for RAI 3, where he also assumes the roles of director, costume designer, stage designer and actor (with Franca and others). Eleven more years have again passed since their last collaboration with RAI television.
	They are awarded the Agro Dolce Prize in Campione d'Italia.
June	Franca tours Turin for RAI 2's production of **"Parti femminili"**.
1988–89	Franca Rame continues her Italian tour of **"Parti femminili"**. Fo has a film role in "Musica per vecchi animali", directed by Stefano Benni.
March	*De Nederlandse Opera* reopens with "The Barber of Seville", again directed by Fo.
1989	**"Lettera dalla Cina"** by Dario Fo staged at Milan's *Arco della Pace* and in other Italian cities as part of demonstrations against the events at Tienanmen Square.
May	Brazil: As part of the exhibition "Italia Viva", the Teatro Petruzzelli stages Fo's production of "The Barber of Seville" in São Paolo and Rio de Janeiro. In the same cities, Dario and Franca perform **"Mistero buffo"** and **"Parti femminili"** to a public already acquainted with their theatre through several productions by various Brazilian theatre companies.
1989–90	Fo writes two plays: **"Il braccato"**, a never-played piece with a Mafia theme, and **"Il papa e la strega"** [**"The Pope and the Witch"**], on the legalization of drugs. The latter is staged with Franca Rame,

who thanks to the large audience she reaches during the season again receives the "Golden ticket" award from AGIS.

April–June   Paris: on the invitation of Antoine Vitez, Artistic Director of the *Comédie Française*, Fo stages Molière's "Le médecin malgré lui" and "Le médecin volant". Sadly, Vitez – who had fought to have Fo inaugurate his planned Molière cycle – is unable to witness the triumphs that the productions reap with critics and public alike. He passes away towards the end of April. Fo is the first Italian director to stage a production at the *Comédie Française*. Among the spectators is President Mitterrand, who praises the productions in a personal letter to Dario Fo.

May   Fo is invited by the Berliner Ensemble to stage a production in Bertolt Brecht's old theatre in the spring of 1991. The project is never finalized.

July   Franca Rame films **"Coppia aperta"** for Swiss national television.

1990–91   Fo writes and produces at Milan's Teatro Nuovo **"Zitti! Stiamo precipitando!"**, a comic-grotesque farce about AIDS. The piece – with Dario Fo, Franca Rame and others on stage – is played at many of the country's major theatres. In several cities, it is alternated with **"Mistero buffo"**, always in high demand.

The open-ended structure of **"Mistero buffo"** allows it to evolve over the years, permitting Fo to address the various issues which over time attracts his interest and that of the public.

April   As part of the Eleventh International Theatre Festival, Dario and Franca stage **"Mistero buffo"** in Palma and Seville.

May   Fo is invited to participate with a new production at Seville's 1992 World Exhibition on the occasion of the fifth anniversary of the discovery of America.

May   Fo's production of "The Barber of Seville" at *De Nederlandse Opera* is filmed by Dutch national television.

1991–92   Dario Fo on stage with his new monologue **"Johan Padan a la descoverta de le Americhe"**. The text is the fruit of his research on the lives of a group of Europeans shipwrecked in the early 16th Century. Using testimonials recovered from that time, Fo tells the story – in a reinvented, antique language – of a group of Mississippi Indians resisting the European incursion. This five centuries old struggle marks the beginning of the undefeated Seminole nation's fight for its survival, an epic story that from the beginning has been censored from the pages of history.

October   Dario and Franca at the Italian Theatre festival in Moscow, organized by the Russian Writers Association and ETI. They stage **"Mistero buffo"** at the Taganka Theatre.

April	Spain: the Centro Dramatico in Valencia puts on a production of Fo's 1962 play **"Isabella, tre caravelle e un cacciaballe"**, slightly revised on occasion of the "celebration" of the quincentenial anniversary of the "discovery" of America.
	Fo participates with "**Johan Padan**" in the World Exhibition in Seville in 1992.
	"Parliamo di donne", consisting of two one-act pieces (**"L'Eroina"** and **"Grassa è bello"**), is staged in September at Milan's Teatro Nuovo. The pieces are written with Franca Rame who also plays the leading roles. **"L'Eroina"** tells the tragic story of a mother of three drug-addicted children, of which one dies of an overdose and another of AIDS. To save the life of the third child, the mother prostitutes herself to afford to keep him with drugs: "A drug addiction can be cured but AIDS can only kill". In **"Grassa è bello"**, Franca – in a foam rubber body suit to make her look grossly overweight – airs thoughts on femininity, what it means to be sexy, slimming, dieting, love and life in general. As often happens when Franca is on stage, several performances are cancelled because the theatre owners get cold feet following a bigoted press campaign.
June	Fo directs a new production of "The Barber of Seville", this time for the Paris Opera playing at the *Opera Garnier*.
October	*De Nederlandse Opera* opens with "The Barber of Seville" for yet another season.
	Also continuing for another season are Fo's productions of Molière's "Le médecin malgré lui" and "Le médecin volant" at the *Comédie Française*.
1992–93	**"Settimo: ruba un po' meno! n. 2"** by Dario Fo and Franca Rame. In this one-act play, staged as the flood-gates of the wide-reaching graft scandal known in Italy as "*tangentopoli*" ["bribe city"] opened, Franca Rame talks in simple terms about the thievery that has become custom in Italy's political establishment. No embellishments are necessary for dramatic effects.
July 1993	At the Festival dei Due Mondi in Spoleto, Franca Rame and others read **"Dario Fo incontra Ruzzante"**.
1993–94	Dario Fo writes and plays in **"Mamma! I sanculotti!"**, a piece that, in the tradition of comic theatre, through dance, mime and song, tells the story of a public prosecutor who investigates graft and corruption in and out of Parliament.
1994	**"Un palcoscenico per le donne"**: At Milan's Porta Romana Theatre, Franca Rame organizes a theatrical review, by and for

women, with young playwright/actresses. In August, the review is played in Cesenatico with great success.

April   Franca: a new season with **"Settimo: ruba un po' meno n. 2"**.

May   In cooperation with the Municipality of Cervia, Franca organizes a performance for a group of Italian and foreign actors and actresses. Participants come from Denmark, the United Kingdom, the United States and Turkey.

August   At the Rossini Opera Festival in Pesaro, Fo directs Rossini's "L'Italiana in Algeri".

1994–95   In October, Franca opens in Milan with **"Sesso? grazie, tanto per gradire!"**, by Franca Rame and Jacopo and Dario Fo, based on Jacopo Fo's book *Lo zen e l'arte di scopare* (more than 300 000 copies sold). In the grotesque and ironic text, Franca Rame – departing from her own first sexual experiences – illustrates how we are kept in the dark as we grow up, with the idea that sexuality – above all women's sexuality – is something indecent. At first, the Ministerial Commission for Censorship bans the performance for minors under 18 years. After two months of press campaigns and litigation, the ban is dropped, and the performance is described as "brimming with profound maternal love and therefore recommended to minors".

December Fo's production of Rossini's "L'Italiana in Algeri" is staged at *De Nederlandse Opera* to resounding international acclaim. The production is filmed by Dutch national television.

Franca visits Toronto with an enthusiastically received performance of **"Sesso? Grazie, tanto per gradire!"**.

January   Dario Fo opens in Florence with **"Dario Fo recita Ruzzante"**, a satirical monologue and an homage to Angelo Beolco. The text is an elaboration of the one already read at the Festival in Spoleto, enriched with new material. The performance meets with unanimous praise from Italy's theatre critics and draws a large audience.

Walter Valeri, who manages the Fo–Rame company's foreign bookings, prepares an international tour in France, the United Kingdom, Germany and the United States. Scheduled for the tour are performances of **"Johan Padan a la scoperta de le Americhe"** and **"Sesso? Grazie, tanto per gradire!"**, as well as seminars at leading universities with central figures in American theatre.

On 17 July, Dario is struck by cerebral ischaemia and loses 80 per cent of his sight. All plans are put on hold. In order to honour commitments to technical and administrative personnel, Franca Rame continues in the autumn with her Italian tour of **"Sesso? Grazie, tanto per gradire!"**, while Dario rests and recuperates. His condition is good and improves day by day.

1996–97   Dario begins to reassume his tasks: he holds classes in theatre schools and at universities, and gives a special performance of **"Arlecchino"** at Venice's Teatro Goldoni.

July   He writes **"Bibbia dei villani"** for the festival of Benevento. The performance is staged in September.

May   Dario and Franca visit Copenhagen, where they hold an open seminar at Folketeatret. Franca arranges a theatre evening with Danish actresses and gives performances of **"Sesso? Grazie, tanto per gradire!"**. The couple also inaugurates an exhibition of their drawings, costumes and puppets at the National Museum.

In the autumn, Dario and Franca continue with their Italian tour of **"Mistero buffo"** and **"Sesso? Grazie, tanto per gradire!"**, merging the two pieces into a single performance played at major theatres as well at sports arenas before large audiences (up to 5000 people). In order not to tire Dario too much, the activities of the company are otherwise reduced.

During this tour, Dario and Franca write **"Il diavolo con le zinne"**, a comic–grotesque spectacle that for its richness and variety in language, its theatrical invention and its elements of song and dance, is best described as an opera. It is a great success.

Dario is now cured of his illness, and his eyesight has improved so much that Franca gives him a computerized typewriter (he refuses to use a computer). They are very happy!

1997–98   For the Festival of Taormina, CTFR, GIGA and Taormina Arte produce **"Il diavolo con le zinne",** directed by Dario Fo, who also designs costumes and décor. On stage are Franca Rame and Giorgio Albertazzi. The play opens on 7 August 1997 at the Teatro Vittorio Emanuele in Messina.

The production continues the following season and is taken on tour throughout Italy, where it meets with great success.

9 October 1997 Dario Fo receives the Nobel Prize in literature.

PLAYS DIRECTED BY DARIO FO AND FRANCA RAME

1962   GLI AMICI DELLA BATTONIERA – Teatro Ridotto, Venice
1963   CHI RUBA UN PIEDE È FORTUNATO IN AMORE – Lilla Teatern, Helsinki

1967   LA PASSEGGIATA DELLA DOMENICA – by M. Archard, translation and arrangement by Dario Fo; Teatro Durini, Milan

1968   ENZO JANNACCI: 22 CANZONI – Teatro Odeon, Milan

1978   LA STORIA DI UN SOLDATO (L'HISTOIRE DU SOLDAT) – by I. Stravinsky; Teatro alla Scala, Milan

1981   L'OPERA DELLO SGHIGNAZZO – elaboration of "The Beggars Opera" by J. Gay; Teatro Stabile, Turin

1986   TUTTA CASA, LETTO E CHIESA – Belgium and France

1987   THE BARBER OF SEVILLE – by G. Rossini; De Nederlandse Opera, Amsterdam

1987   ARCHANGELS DON'T PLAY FLIPPER – American Repertory Theater, Cambridge (Mass.)

1988   THE BARBER OF SEVILLE – by G. Rossini; Teatro Petruzzelli, Bari

1989   THE BARBER OF SEVILLE – by G. Rossini; tour with Teatro Petruzzelli in Brazil (São Paolo and Rio de Janeiro)

1990   LE MÉDECIN MALGRÉ LUI/LE MÉDECIN VOLANT – by Molière; Comédie Française, Paris

1990   THE BARBER OF SEVILLE – by G. Rossini; De Nederlandse Opera, Amsterdam

1991   IL MEDICO PER FORZA/IL MEDICO VOLANTE – by Molière; Comédie Française, Paris

1992   ISABELLA, TRE CARAVELLE E UN CACCIABALLE – Centro Dramatico Nacional, Valencia

1992   THE BARBER OF SEVILLE – by G. Rossini; De Nederlandse Opera, Amsterdam (filmed for Dutch TV)

1992   THE BARBER OF SEVILLE – by G. Rossini; Opera Garnier, Paris

1994   L'ITALIANA IN ALGERI – by G. Rossini; Pesaro Opera Festival, Pesaro

1994   THE BARBER OF SEVILLE – by G. Rossini; De Nederlandse Opera, Amsterdam

1996   THE BARBER OF SEVILLE – by G. Rossini; Israel (produced by Arturo Corso)

1997   THE BARBER OF SEVILLE – by G. Rossini; Sweden (staged by Carlo Barsotti)

WORK IN FILM AND TELEVISION

1952   PAPAVERI E PAPERE, a film by Marcello Marchesi with Franca Rame and Walter Chiari.

1956   MONETINE DA 5 LIRE, a television comedy by Dario Fo for RAI.

1956   LO SVITATO, a film by Carlo Lizzani with Franca Rame, script by Dario Fo.

1961   CHI L'HA VISTO?, a television series for RAI 2 (6 episodes).

1962   CANZONISSIMA, a television series for RAI 1 (13 episodes). Fo writes the texts, directs and – with Franca Rame – hosts the show, which is one of the most popular on Italian television. Due to the political content of some of the sketches, the show is censured. Dario Fo and Franca Rame leave the show in protest. As a consequence, they are sued by RAI's management which bans them from television for 15 years.

1976 FANFANI RAPITO, film.

1977 IL TEATRO DI DARIO FO, seven televised comedies by and with Dario Fo and Franca Rame, for RAI 2.

1978 BUONASERA CON FRANCA RAME, a television series for RAI 2 (20 episodes).

1978 PARLIAMO DI DONNE, 2 episodes with Franca Rame.

1981 MRS WARREN'S PROFESSION by G. B. Shaw, directed for television by G. Albertazzi, with Franca Rame.

1988 TRASMISSIONE FORZATA with Dario Fo and Franca Rame, for RAI 3.

1989 UNA LEPRE CON LA FACCIA DA BAMBINA, film for television by G. Serra, with Franca Rame.

1989 UNA GIORNATA QUALUNQUE and COPPIA APERTA for RAI 2, with Franca Rame.

1989 PROMESSI SPOSI, Dario Fo.

1989 MUSICA PER VECCHI ANIMALI, film for television by S. Benni, with Dario Fo.

1990 COPPIA APERTA, Swiss national television, with Franca Rame.

1991 SETTIMO: RUBA UN PO' MENO, for RAI 2.

1991 MISTERO BUFFO, for RAI 2, with Dario Fo and Franca Rame.

1993 RUZZANTE, for RAI 2.

COUNTRIES IN WHICH THE THEATRE OF DARIO FO AND
FRANCA RAME HAS BEEN PLAYED

Argentina	Greenland	Poland
Australia	Hungary	Portugal
Austria	Iceland	Puerto Rico
Belgium	India	Romania
Brazil	Ireland	Scotland
Bulgaria	Israel	Singapore
Canada	Japan	South Africa
Chile	Kenya	Spain
China	Luxembourg	Sweden
Colombia	Malta	Switzerland
Czechoslovakia	Mexico	Turkey
Denmark	Monaco	South Korea
England	The Netherlands	Soviet Union
Estonia	New Guinea	United States
Finland	New Zealand	Uruguay
France	Norway	Venezuela
Germany	Paraguay	Yugoslavia
Greece	Peru	Zimbabwe

CITIES HOSTING EXHIBITS OF THE THEATRE OF DARIO FO AND
FRANCA RAME

ITALY: Bergamo, Cesena, Forlì, Milan, Palermo, Pesaro, Riccione, Venice

SPAIN: Barcelona, Madrid

DENMARK: Copenhagen

FINLAND: Helsinki

The NETHERLANDS: Amsterdam

The exhibits contain paintings, masks, hand- and string puppets, tapestries,
sketches for stage design, stage machinery, direction notes and costumes.

Translated by Paul Claesson

NOBEL LECTURE

Contra jogulatores obloquentes

Legge emessa da Federico II (1221, Messina) che permetteva di infliggere violenza ai giullari senza incorrere in alcuna pena o sanzione

DISCORSO DEL NOBEL PER LA LETTERATURA DARIO FO

Le tavole che vi sto mostrando sono state disegnate e dipinte da me.

A voi sono state distribuite delle immagini leggermente ridotte rispetto a queste.

Ecco, io sono abituato da tanto tempo a realizzare dei discorsi con le immagini, invece di scriverli li disegno. Questo mi permette di andare a soggetto, di improvvisare, di esercitare la mia fantasia e di costringere voi ad usare la vostra.

Mentre io leggerò questi testi, ogni tanto vi mostrerò dove siamo, così non perderete il filo, e questo servirà soprattutto a coloro che non conoscono né l'italiano né lo svedese; gli inglesi avranno un vantaggio straordinario perché si immagineranno cose che io non ho detto né pensato. C'è il problema delle due risate: quelli che capiscono l'italiano rideranno subito, quelli che debbono aspettare per ridere la traduzione in svedese di Anna (Anna Barsotti, la traduttrice, n.d.t.) e gli altri che non sanno se ridere alla prima battuta o alla seconda. Ad ogni modo cominciamo.

Signore e Signori: il titolo di questa mia chiaccherata è "contra jogulatores obloquentes" e avete capito tutti che si tratta di latino, latino medievale. Questo è il frontespizio di una legge che è stata promulgata nel 1221 in Sicilia dall'Imperatore Federico II di Svevia, un "Unto del Signore" che a scuola ci presentano come un imperatore illuminato straordinario, liberale. Ora voi, da quello che segue, giudicherete se questo prossimo a Dio fosse veramente liberale. "Joculatores obloquentes" significa "giullari che diffamano e insultano". La legge in questione permetteva a tutti i cittadini di insultare i giullari, di bastonarli e, se si era un po' nervosi, anche di ammazzarli senza rischiare alcun processo con relativa condanna. Vi avverto subito che questa legge è decaduta e quindi posso continuare, tranquillo.

Signore e Signori…

Alcuni amici miei, letterati, artisti famosi, intervistati da giornali e televisioni, hanno dichiarato: "Il premio più alto va dato senz'altro quest'anno ai Membri dell'Accademia Svedese che hanno avuto il coraggio di assegnare il Nobel a un giullare!" Eh sì, il Vostro è stato davvero un atto di coraggio che rasenta la provocazione.

Basta vedere il putiferio che ha causato: poeti e pensatori sublimi che normalmente volano alto… e poco si degnano di quelli che campano rasoterra… si sono trovati all'istante travolti da una specie di tromba d'aria.

Ebbene, io applaudo e sono d'accordo con loro.

Stavano già beati nel Parnaso degli eletti e Voi, con questa Vostra insolenza, li avete abbattuti e precipitati giù a sbattere musi e pance nel fango della normalità.

Si son levati urla e improperi tremendi, rivolti all'Accademia di Svezia, ai suoi Membri e ai loro parenti prossimi e lontani fino alla settima generazione.

I più scatenati hanno gridato: "Abbasso il Re... di Norvegia!".

Nel trambusto si sono sbagliati di dinastia.

A questo punto potete voltare pagina... vedete che c'è l'immagine di un poeta nudo travolto da un turbine di vento.

Qualcuno ha battuto anche la parte bassa: ci sono stati dei poeti e scrittori che hanno avuto crisi di nervi e di fegato spaventose.

In quei giorni in Italia, nelle farmacie, non si trovavano più calmanti.

Ma bisogna ammetterlo, diciamo la verità, cari Membri dell'Accademia, stavolta avete esagerato: andiamo, avete cominciato una diecina d'anni fa col premiare un nero... un Nobel di colore. Poi avete dato il Nobel a un ebreo... adesso addirittura a un giullare!! Ma che, – come dicono i napoletani – pazziamme?

Anche nel clero alto ci sono stati momenti di pazzia... proprio i grandi elettori del Papa: vescovi, cardinali, prelati dell'Opus Dei sono andati in escandescenze. Tant'è che costoro hanno richiesto che venga ripristinata la legge che permette di bruciare i giullari sul rogo: una cosa delicata, a fuoco lento.

Per contrasto devo dirVi che però ci sono state masse straordinarie di persone che hanno gioito con me in modo incredibile per questa Vostra scelta.

E io Vi porto il più festoso dei ringraziamenti da parte di una caterva di guitti, di giullari, di clown, di saltimbanchi, di contastorie.

Siamo arrivati qua (mostra una tavola).

E a proposito di contastorie non posso dimenticare i fabulatori del mio paese sul Lago Maggiore, dove sono nato e cresciuto e dove c'è una grande tradizione di fabulatori; loro, i vecchi fabulatori, maestri soffiatori di vetro, che hanno insegnato a me e ad altri ragazzi il mestiere, l'arte, di raccontare assurde favole, che noi ascoltavamo commentandole con sghignazzi e silenzi improvvisi a strozzagola per la tragica allegoria che di colpo sormontava ogni sarcasmo. Ancora mi ricordo la favola della Rocca di Caldé. "Tanti anni fa... – raccontava il maestro soffiatore -sul dorso scosceso di quel cocuzzolo che si erge dal lago... lassù, stava arroccato un paese di nome Caldé, che giorno dopo giorno franava tutt'in blocco giù verso il fondo del dirupo. Era uno splendido paese con il campanile, con le torri arroccate proprio in cima, con tutte le case una dietro l'altra. E' un paese che esisteva e adesso non c'è più: nel 1400 è sparito. 'Ehi... – gli gridavano i contadini e i pescatori di fondovalle – attenti, state franando... sloggiate di lassù!'. Ma i roccaroli non ascoltavano, anzi ridevano, scherzavano, sfottevano: 'Furbi voi, cercate di terrorizzarci per convincerci a scappare, andare via lasciando le case, i nostri terreni per poi fregarveli voi. Non ci caschiamo.' E così continuavano a potare le viti, seminare i campi, sposarsi, fare all'amore. Andavano a messa. Sentivano slittare la roccia sotto le fondamenta delle case… ma non se ne curavano più di tanto: 'Normali mosse d'assestamento…' si rassicuravano.

La grande scheggia di roccia stava affondando nel lago. 'Attenti, avete i piedi nell'acqua!', gridavano dalla costa. 'Macché, è l'acqua di scolo delle fontane, è soltanto un po' più umido'; e così, piano piano ma inesorabilmente, il paese intero s'affonda nel lago.

Glu… glu… pluf… affondano… case, uomini, donne, due cavalli, tre asini… iaa… glu… Il prete continuava imperterrito a confessare una suora: 'Te absolvi… animus… santi… gluu… Aame… Glu…'. Scompare la torre, va sotto il campanile con le campane: don… din… dop…plok…'

"Ancora oggi – raccontava il vecchio soffiatore di vetro – se ci si affaccia dallo spuntone di roccia rimasto a picco in quel punto del lago… se in quell'istante scoppia un temporale, i lampi riescono ad illuminare il fondo dell'acqua e, incredibile, là sotto si scorge il paese affondato con le case e le strade ancora intatte e, come in un presepe vivente, si scoprono loro, gli abitanti della vecchia Rocca, che si muovono ancora… e imperterriti ripetono: 'Non è successo niente'. I pesci passano loro davanti agli occhi di qua e di là… fin nelle orecchie… 'Niente paura!… è solo un tipo di pesce che ha imparato a nuotare nell'aria', commentano. 'Eccì!'. 'Salute!'. 'Grazie… fa un po' umido oggi… fa più umido di ieri… ma va tutto bene!' Sono sprofondati… ma per loro non è successo assolutamente nulla."

Non si può negare che una favola del genere sia ancora oggi di sconvolgente attualità.

Ripeto, devo molto a quei miei maestri soffiatori di vetro e anche loro, Vi assicuro, oggi sono immensamente grati a Voi, Signori Membri dell'Accademia, per aver premiato un loro allievo

E in modo follemente esplosivo Ve lo manifestano. Infatti al mio paese giurano che la notte in cui si è saputo del Nobel a un loro concittadino fabulatore, si è sentito un tremendo botto! Dal grande forno della vetreria spenta da cinquant'anni, è esplosa una bordata di lava infuocata e una miriade di schegge di vetro fuso colorato s'è proiettata altissima in aria come in un finale di fuochi d'artificio… ed è ricaduta rovente nel lago, sparando gran vapore.

Mentre voi applaudite bevo un po' d'acqua; (rivolgendosi all'interprete) ne vuoi anche tu? Importante è che mentre beviamo voi parliate tra di voi perché se tentate di sentire il glu glu glu che fa l'acqua che scende ci va tutto di traverso e cominciamo a tossire. Allora parlate: "o che bella serata che è questa".

Secondo tempo: pagina nove. Ma adesso sarò veloce, non preoccupatevi.

Sopra tutti, questa sera a Voi si leva il grazie solenne e fragoroso di uno straordinario teatrante della mia terra, poco conosciuto non soltanto da voi e in Francia, Norvegia, Finlandia… ma poco noto anche in Italia. Ma che è senz'altro il più grande autore di teatro che l'Europa abbia avuto nel Rinascimento prima ancora dell'avvento di Shakespeare.

Sto parlando di Ruzzante Beolco, il mio più grande maestro insieme a Molière: entrambi attori-autori, entrambi sbeffeggiati dai sommi letterati del loro tempo. Disprezzati soprattutto perché portavano in scena il quotidiano, la gioia e la disperazione della gente comune, l'ipocrisia e la spocchia dei potenti, la costante ingiustizia. E soprattutto avevano un difetto tremendo: raccontavano queste cose facendo ridere. Il riso non piace al potere. Ruzzante poi, vero padre dei comici dell'Arte, si costruì una lingua, un lessico del tutto teatrale, composto di idiomi diversi; dialetti della Padania, espressioni latine, spagnole, perfino tedesche, miste a suoni onomatopeici completamente inventati. Da lui, dal Beolco Ruzzante ho imparato a liberarmi della scrittura letteraria convenzionale e ad esprimermi con parole da masticare, con suoni inconsueti, ritmiche e respiri diversi, fino agli sproloqui folli del grammelot.

A lui, al Ruzzante, permettetemi di dedicare una parte del riconoscimento prestigioso che Voi mi offrite.

Qualche giorno fa, un giovane attore di grande talento mi ha detto: "Maestro, tu devi cercare di proiettare la tua energia, il tuo entusiasmo ai giovani. Questa carica che tu hai devi darla a loro. Ai giovani devi dare la conoscenza e la sapienza del tuo mestiere". Io e Franca (mia moglie) ci siamo guardati e abbiamo detto: "Ha ragione". Ma quando noi insegneremo un mestiere, daremo una carica effervescente di fantasia, poi a che cosa servirà, dove verrà portata questa fantasia, questa vitalità, questo entusiasmo, questo mestiere?

A che scopo e verso cosa far proiettare vitalità e entusiasmo?

Negli ultimi mesi mi è capitato con Franca di girare per parecchie Università tenendo stages e organizzando conferenze davanti a platee di giovani. La cosa che più ci ha colpiti e quasi sconvolti, è stato scoprire la loro ignoranza rispetto al tempo in cui stiamo vivendo. Raccontavamo loro del processo che si sta svolgendo in Turchia contro gli esecutori della strage di Sivas. In Anatolia trentasette intellettuali democratici fra i più prestigiosi del paese, riuniti per ricordare un famoso giullare del Medioevo ottomano, venivano bruciati vivi, intrappolati dento un Hotel, in piena notte. Ad appiccare il fuoco era stata una banda di fanatici integralisti ben protetta da elementi di governo. In una notte, trentasette fra i più importanti artisti, scrittori, registi, attori e attrici, famose danzatrici del rito curdo, sono stati all'istante cancellati dalla terra. In un sol colpo quei fanatici avevano distrutto, si può dire, gli uomini più importanti della cultura di quel paese.

Ascoltavano questo nostro racconto migliaia di studenti, che ci guardavano attoniti, increduli. Non sapevano nulla di quel massacro. La cosa che mi ha impressionato è che anche i professori presenti a questo mio discorso non ne sapevano niente. Eppure la Turchia è lì, nel Mediterraneo, quasi di fronte a noi, insiste per essere ammessa nella Comunità Economica Europea… ma loro del massacro nulla sapevano. Giustamente Salvini, un grande democratico del nostro Paese, diceva: "L'ignoranza diffusa dei fatti è il maggior supporto all'ingiustizia." Ma questa assenza distratta dei giovani viene da chi li educa e li dovrebbe informare, e costoro sono invece i primi assenti e disinformati, parlo dei maestri e dei responsabili della scuola. I giovani, in gran parte, soccombono al bombardamento di banalità e oscenità gratuite che ogni giorno i mass-media propinano loro: telefilms truculenti dove in dieci minuti avvengono tre stupri, due assassinii... un pestaggio e uno scontro di dieci auto su un ponte che crolla e tutti, macchine, autisti e passeggeri, precipitano nel mare... solo uno si salva, però non sa nuotare e annega fra le risate dei curiosi accorsi in massa.

In un'altra Università abbiamo denunciato il progetto, ormai in via di realizzazione, della manipolazione genetica... cioè di brevettare organismi viventi, proposto dal Parlamento Europeo... abbiamo sentito un gran gelo salire dalla platea. Io e Franca spiegavamo come i nostri eurocrati, stimolati dalle strapotenti e onnipresenti multinazionali, stanno preparando un piano degno di un film di fantascienza-trucida dal titolo "Il fratello porco di Frankenstein". Vogliono cioè approvare una direttiva che (attenti alla trovata) autorizzi le industrie a brevettare esseri viventi, o loro parti, create con quella tecnica da apprendista stregone che è la manipolazione genetica.

Le cose andrebbero così: uno scienziato riesce, andando a mettere le mani nel corredo genetico di un maiale, a renderlo più simile all'uomo, col risultato, stravolgente, che grazie a questo arrangiamento sarà più facile staccargli il fegato, o un rene... a scelta, per trapiantarlo in un uomo. Ma per essere più sicuri che gli organi trapiantati attecchiscano, bisognerà inserire nell'uomo delle particelle del maiale che ne condizionino e modifichino la struttura; avremo così, finalmente, un uomo-maiale (voi direte che ne abbiamo già tanti) o un maiale-uomo... e ogni parte di questo nuovo essere si potrà brevettare, imporgli il copyright; e chi vorrà un pezzo di questo porco umanizzato dovrà pagare i diritti d'autore all'industria che lo avrà "inventato". Malattie conseguenti, deformazioni mostruose, morbi trasmettibili in massa... tutti sono optional inclusi nel prezzo.

Il Papa è rimasto indignato da questa operazione, da questa mostruosità genetica da bassa stregoneria, e l'ha chiamata un obbrobrio contro l'umanità, contro la dignità dell'uomo, l'ha insultata ricordando che la morale in questo caso è spenta ed è ridotta a livello sotto-animale.

La cosa incredibile è che nello stesso tempo c'è un americano, uno stregone straordinario, voi l'avete letto sul giornale sicuramente: è quello che taglia la testa a un babbuino e poi mozza la testa a un altro babbuino, prende la prima testa e la seconda testa e le scambia. Il babbuino rimane un po' male. In verità rimangono sempre paralizzati, tanto l'uno che l'altro, poi muoiono ma l'esperimento è riuscito che è una meraviglia. La cosa incredibile è che questo personaggio che si chiama White, professor White, sembra proprio Frankenstein. Questo White è membro dell'Accademia delle Scienze del Vaticano. Bisognerebbe avvertire il Papa.

Ecco, noi raccontavamo queste farse criminali ai ragazzi, agli studenti e loro ridevano come dei matti: dicevano di me e di Franca: "Ma come sono simpatici, si inventano delle storie incredibili"; non avevano assolutamente, neanche per l'anticamera del cervello, l'idea che quello che raccontavamo fosse vero. Allora sempre di più siamo convinti, come incitava Savinio, un grande poeta italiano: "raccontate, uomini, la vostra storia". Il nostro dovere di intellettuali, di gente che monta in cattedra o sul palcoscenico, che parla soprattutto con i giovani è quello non soltanto di insegnare come si muovono le braccia, come si respira per recitare, come si usa lo stomaco, la voce, il falsetto, il contraccampo. Non basta insegnare uno stile: bisogna informarli di quello che succede intorno. Loro devono raccontare la loro storia. Un teatro, una letteratura, una espressione d'arte che non parli del proprio tempo è inesistente.

Io sono andato ultimamente a un grande congresso con tantissima gente e cercavo di spiegare a loro e soprattutto ai giovani un processo che si è svolto in Italia, un processo che si è sviluppato in sette processi; alla fine di questi processi, tre politici di sinistra sono stati condannati a 21 anni di carcere, accusati di aver trucidato un commissario di polizia. Io ho studiato le carte del processo come avevo fatto con "Morte accidentale di un anarchico". Ebbene, raccontavo i fatti di questo processo assurdo, addirittura farsesco nel modo in cui è stato condotto, e a un certo punto ho capito che parlavo nel vuoto perché la gente non era al corrente degli antefatti, non conosceva cosa era successo cinque anni prima, dieci anni prima: le violenze, il terrorismo, niente sapeva, non sapeva delle stragi di stato avvenute in Italia, né dei treni che sono saltati in aria, né delle bombe nelle piazze, né dei processi che sono stati portati avanti come farse. Il guaio terribile è che per raccontare la storia di oggi devo cominciare a raccontare la storia da trent'anni fa a venire avanti, non mi basta raccontare di adesso; e state attenti, questo succede dappertutto, in tutta l'Europa. Io ho provato in Spagna ed era lo stesso discorso, ho provato in Francia, ho provato in Germania, devo ancora provare qui da voi in Svezia, ma verrò a provare.

E per finire permettete che io dedichi una buona metà della medaglia che mi offrite, a Franca.

Franca Rame, la mia compagna di vita e d'arte che Voi, Membri dell'Accademia, ricordate nella motivazione del premio come attrice e autrice, che con me ha scritto più di un testo del nostro teatro.

Franca proprio in questo momento sta recitando in Italia ma dopodomani sarà qui: arriva a mezzogiorno, se volete venire andiamo tutti insieme a prenderla all'aeroporto. Franca è molto spiritosa, ve lo assicuro. A dei giornalisti che le chiedevano: "Ma scusi, lei come si sente adesso ad essere la moglie di un Nobel? Con un monumento in casa?" rispondeva: "Non sono preoccupata, non mi sento a disagio perché mi sono sempre allenata. Tutte le mattine faccio flessioni: mi piego in due appoggiando le mani a terra, così mi sono abituata a diventare piedestallo al monumento. Ci riesco benissimo." Vi avevo detto che è molto spiritosa... e a volte addirittura autolesionista nella sua ironia. Ma davvero senza di lei per una vita al mio fianco personalmente non ce l'avrei mai fatta a meritare questo premio. Insieme abbiamo montato e recitato migliaia di spettacoli in teatri, fabbriche occupate, Università in lotta... perfino in chiese sconsacrate, in carceri, in piazza col sole e la pioggia, sempre insieme. Abbiamo sopportato vessazioni, cariche della polizia, insulti dei benpensanti e le violenze. E soprattutto è lei, Franca, che ha subito la più atroce delle aggressioni. Lei, più di tutti, sulla sua pelle, ha pagato per la solidarietà che davamo agli umili e ai battuti.

Il giorno in cui mi è stato designato il Nobel mi trovavo davanti al Teatro in via di Porta Romana, a Milano, dove Franca stava recitando, con Giorgio Albertazzi, "Il diavolo con le zinne." All'istante è arrivata una turba di fotoreporter, cronisti, operatori con le loro telecamere. Un tram che transitava in quel momento s'è fermato, il conduttore s'è sporto a salutarmi, sono scesi tutti i passeggeri, mi applaudivano, mi volevano stringere la mano per felicitarsi... ma poi si sono bloccati e tutti in coro hanno gridato: "E Franca dov'è?" e hanno chiamato a gran voce "Francaaa!" e lei dopo un po' è apparsa... frastornata... commossa alle lacrime, ed è venuta ad abbracciarmi.

All'improvviso, come dal nulla, è apparsa una banda musicale di soli fiati con tamburi, erano tutti ragazzi, che accorrevano da punti diversi della città, musici che suonavano insieme per la prima volta, hanno intonato "Porta Romana bella, Porta Romana" a ritmo di samba. Non ho mai sentito stonare a quel modo ma era la più bella musica che Franca e io avessimo mai ascoltato.

Credetemi, questo premio l'avete proprio dato a tutti e due.

Grazie

CONTRA JOGULATORES OBLOQUENTES

AMICI
LETTERATI
ARTISTI
FAMOSI

MEMBRI DELL'ACCADEMIA

INTERVISTA

GIULLARE

PROVOCAZIONE

PUTIFERIO

MA CHE? PAZIAMMO?

LA CURIA È IMPAZZITA

TEATRANTI HANNO STRAGIOITO

GUITTI

GIULLARI

CLOWN

SALTIMBANCHI⁴

FABULATORI DEL LAGO

FAVOLE ASSURDE CHE NOI RAGAZZI
COMMENTAVAMO CON SCHIGNAZZI

SILENZI PER LA TRAGICA 5
ALLEGORIA

TANTI ANNI FA
RACCONTAVA IL
MAESTRO
SOFFIATORE

STAVA
ARROCCATO
UN PAESE
DI NOME
CALDÉ

CHE GIORNO DOPO GIORNO

FRANAVA TUTTO
IN BLOCCO

362

SI LEVA SOLENNE E' FRAGOROSO IL SALUTO

RUZZANTE

SHAKESPEARE MOLIÈRE

ENTRAMBI DISPREZZATI DAI SACCENTI

10
PADRE DEI
COMICI DELL'ARTE
LESSICO
IDIOMI
PROIETTARE
L'ENERGIA
AI GIOVANI
INSIEME
ALL'UNIVERSITÀ

TURCHIA **11**

STRAGE DI SIVAS

37 IN ANATOLIA

SCRITORI AUTORI
ATTORI DANZATRICI
RITO CURDO

ASCOLTAVANO INCREDULI 12

IGNORANZA DEL NOSTRO TEMPO

SAVINIO

L'IGNORANZA DIFFUSA DEI FATTI È IL MAGGIOR SUPPORTO ALL'INGIUSTIZIA

L'ASSENZA

IL SILENZIO

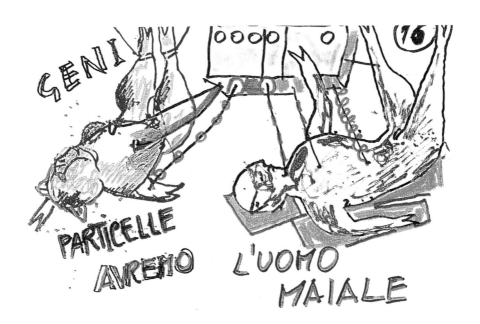

IMPORRE A OGNI PARTE
IL COPY-RIGHT

BREVETTARE

PASARE I DIRITTI D'AUTORE
PER OGNI PEZZO

ALL'INDUSTRIA
PADRONA DEL BREVETTO

INFORMARE 18

CRITICAME NTE

I GIOVANI

NON SANNO ! DELLE STRAGI

DI STATO

INCHIESTE DEVIATE

PROCESSI FARSA

DI STATO

CANTATE 19
UOMINI
LA VOSTRA
STORIA

SAVINIO

CONTINUIAMO
A CANTARE PER
L'INDIGNAZIONE
DEI GIOVANI

A COROLLARIO DI (20) QUESTA SERIE DI

SOFRI SOPRAFFAZIONI PIETROSTEFANI BOMPRESSI

FARSA DI GIUSTIZIA ALLA INSULTO RAGIONE

MI STO ALLENANDO

22

SENZA DI LEI

NON AVREI VINTO

NELLE FABBRICHE 23 OCCUPATE

LA VIOLENZA SUBITA INSIEME

MANIPO
LAZIONE

GENETICA

PARLAMENTO

EUROCRATI

BREVETTAZIONE
o ovvsi DEGLI
ORGANISMI VIVENTI

CONTRA JOGULATORES OBLOQUENTES
AGAINST JESTERS WHO DEFAME AND INSULT

Nobel Lecture, December 7, 1997

by

Dario Fo

Milan, Italy.

> "Against jesters who defame and insult." Law issued by emperor Frederick II (Messina 1221), declaring that anyone may commit violence against jesters without incurring punishment or sanction.

The drawings I'm showing you are mine. Copies of these, slightly reduced in size, have been distributed among you.

For some time it's been my habit to use images when preparing a speech; rather than write it down, I illustrate it. This allows me to improvise, to exercise my imagination–and to oblige you to use yours.

As I proceed, I will from time to time indicate to you where we are in the manuscript. That way you won't lose the thread. This will be of help especially to those of you who don't understand either Italian or Swedish. English-speakers will have a tremendous advantage over the rest because they will imagine things I've neither said nor thought. There is of course the problem of the two laughters: those who understand Italian will laugh immediately, those who don't will have to wait for Anna [Barsotti]'s Swedish translation. And then there are those of you who won't know whether to laugh the first time or the second. Anyway, let's get started.

Ladies and gentlemen, the title I've selected for this little chat is "contra jogulatores obloquentes", which you all recognize as Latin, mediaeval Latin to be precise. It's the title of a law issued in Sicily in 1221 by Emperor Frederick II of Swabia, an emperor "anointed by God", who we were taught in school to regard as a sovereign of extraordinary enlightenment, a liberal. "Jogulatores obloquentes" means "jesters who defame and insult". The law in question allowed any and all citizens to insult jesters, to beat them and even – if they were in that mood – to kill them, without running any risk of being brought to trial and condemned. I hasten to assure you that this law no longer is in vigour, so I can safely continue.

Ladies and gentlemen,
Friends of mine, noted men of letters, have in various radio and television interviews declared: "The highest prize should no doubt be awarded to the members of the Swedish Academy, for having had the courage this year to award the Nobel Prize to a jester." I agree. Yours is an act of courage that borders on provocation.

It's enough to take stock of the uproar it has caused: sublime poets and writers who normally occupy the loftiest of spheres, and who rarely take interest in those who live and toil on humbler planes, are suddenly bowled over by some kind of whirlwind.

Like I said, I applaud and concur with my friends.

These poets had already ascended to the Parnassian heights when you, through your insolence, sent them toppling to earth, where they fell face and belly down in the mire of normality.

Insults and abuse are hurled at the Swedish Academy, at its members and their relatives back to the seventh generation. The wildest of them clamour: "Down with the King . . . of Norway!". It appears they got the dynasty wrong in the confusion.

(At this point you may turn the page. As you see there is an image of a naked poet bowled over by a whirlwind.)

Some landed pretty hard on their nether parts. There were reports of poets and writers whose nerves and livers suffered terribly. For a few days thereafter there was not a pharmacy in Italy that could muster up a single tranquillizer.

But, dear members of the Academy, let's admit it, this time you've overdone it. I mean come on, first you give the prize to a black man, then to a Jewish writer. Now you give it to a clown. What gives? As they say in Naples: *pazziàmme?* Have we lost our senses?

Also the higher clergy have suffered their moments of madness. Sundry potentates – great electors of the Pope, bishops, cardinals and prelates of Opus Dei – have all gone through the ceiling, to the point that they've even petitioned for the reinstatement of the law that allowed jesters to be burned at the stake. Over a slow fire.

On the other hand, I can tell you there is an extraordinary number of people who rejoice with me over your choice. And so I bring you the most festive thanks, in the name of a multitude of mummers, jesters, clowns, tumblers and storytellers.

(This is where we are now [indicates a page].)

And speaking of storytellers, I mustn't forget those of the small town on Lago Maggiore where I was born and raised, a town with a rich oral tradition.

They were the old storytellers, the master glass-blowers who taught me and other children the craftsmanship, the art, of spinning fantastic yarns. We would listen to them, bursting with laughter – laughter that would stick in our throats as the tragic allusion that surmounted each sarcasm would dawn on us. To this day I keep fresh in my mind the story of the Rock of Caldé.

"Many years ago", began the old glass-blower, "way up on the crest of that steep cliff that rises from the lake there was a town called Caldé. As it happened, this town was sitting on a loose splinter of rock that slowly, day by day, was sliding down towards the precipice. It was a splendid little town, with a campanile, a fortified tower at the very peak and a cluster of houses, one after the other. It's a town that once was and that now is gone. It disappeared in the 15th century.

"'Hey', shouted the peasants and fishermen down in the valley below. 'You're sliding, you'll fall down from there'.

"But the cliff dwellers wouldn't listen to them, they even laughed and made fun of them: 'You think you're pretty smart, trying to scare us into running away from our houses and our land so you can grab them instead. But we're not that stupid.'

"So they continued to prune their vines, sow their fields, marry and make love. They went to mass. They felt the rock slide under their houses but they didn't think much about it. 'Just the rock settling. Quite normal', they said, reassuring each other.

"The great splinter of rock was about to sink into the lake. 'Watch out, you've got water up to your ankles', shouted the people along the shore. 'Nonsense, that's just drainage water from the fountains, it's just a bit humid', said the people of the town, and so, slowly but surely, the whole town was swallowed by the lake.

"Gurgle … gurgle … splash … they sink … houses, men, women, two horses, three donkeys … heehaw … gurgle. Undaunted, the priest continued to receive the confession of a nun: 'Te absolvi … animus … santi … guurgle … Aame … gurgle …' The tower disappeared, the campanile sank with bells and all: Dong … ding … dop … plock …

"Even today", continued the old glass-blower, "if you look down into the water from that outcrop that still juts out from the lake, and if in that same moment a thunderstorm breaks out, and the lightning illuminates the bottom of the lake, you can still see – incredible as it may seem! – the submerged town, with its streets still intact and even the inhabitants themselves, walking around and glibly repeating to themselves: 'Nothing has happened'. The fish swim back and forth before their eyes, even into their ears. But they just brush them off: 'Nothing to worry about. It's just some kind of fish that's learned to swim in the air'.

"'Atchoo!' 'God bless you!' 'Thank you … it's a bit humid today … more than yesterday … but everything's fine'. They've reached rock bottom, but as far as they're concerned, nothing has happened at all."

Disturbing though it may be, there's no denying that a tale like this still has something to tell us.

I repeat, I owe much to these master glass-blowers of mine, and they – I assure you – are immensely grateful to you, members of this Academy, for rewarding one of their disciples.

And they express their gratitude with explosive exuberance. In my home town, people swear that on the night the news arrived that one of their own storytellers was to be awarded the Nobel Prize, a kiln that had been standing cold for some fifty years suddenly erupted in a broadside of flames, spraying high into the air – like a fireworks *finale* – a myriad splinters of coloured glass, which then showered down on the surface of the lake, releasing an impressive cloud of steam.

(While you applaud, I'll have a drink of water. [Turning to the interpreter:] Would you like some?

It's important that you talk among yourselves while we drink, because if you try to hear the gurgle gurgle gurgle the water makes as we swallow we'll choke on it and start coughing. So instead you can exchange niceties like "Oh, what a lovely evening it is, isn't it?".

End of intermission: we turn to a new page, but don't worry, it'll go faster from here.)

Above all others, this evening you're due the loud and solemn thanks of an extraordinary master of the stage, little-known not only to you and to people in France, Norway, Finland ... but also to the people of Italy. Yet he was, until Shakespeare, doubtless the greatest playwright of renaissance Europe. I'm referring to Ruzzante Beolco, my greatest master along with Molière: both actors-playwrights, both mocked by the leading men of letters of their times. Above all, they were despised for bringing onto the stage the everyday life, joys and desperation of the common people; the hypocrisy and the arrogance of the high and mighty; and the incessant injustice. And their major, unforgivable fault was this: in telling these things, they made people laugh. Laughter does not please the mighty.

Ruzzante, the true father of the *Commedia dell'Arte*, also constructed a language of his own, a language of and for the theatre, based on a variety of tongues: the dialects of the Po Valley, expressions in Latin, Spanish, even German, all mixed with onomatopoeic sounds of his own invention. It is from him, from Beolco Ruzzante, that I've learned to free myself from conventional literary writing and to express myself with words that you can chew, with unusual sounds, with various techniques of rhythm and breathing, even with the rambling nonsense-speech of the *grammelot*.

Allow me to dedicate a part of this prestigious prize to Ruzzante.

A few days ago, a young actor of great talent said to me: "Maestro, you should try to project your energy, your enthusiasm, to young people. You have to give them this charge of yours. You have to share your professional knowledge and experience with them". Franca – that's my wife – and I looked at each other and said: "He's right". But when we teach others our art, and share this charge of fantasy, what end will it serve? Where will it lead?

In the past couple of months, Franca and I have visited a number of university campuses to hold workshops and seminars before young audiences. It has been surprising – not to say disturbing – to discover their ignorance about the times we live in. We told them about the proceedings now in course in Turkey against the accused culprits of the massacre in Sivas. Thirty-seven of the country's foremost democratic intellectuals, meeting in the Anatolian town to celebrate the memory of a famous mediaeval jester of the Ottoman period, were burned alive in the dark of the night, trapped inside their hotel. The fire was the handiwork of a group of fanatical fundamentalists that enjoyed protection from elements within the Government itself. In one night, thirty-seven of the country's most celebrated artists, writers, directors, actors and Kurdish dancers were erased from this Earth.

In one blow these fanatics destroyed some of the most important exponents of Turkish culture.

Thousands of students listened to us. The looks in their faces spoke of their astonishment and incredulity. They had never heard of the massacre. But what impressed me the most is that not even the teachers and professors present had heard of it. There Turkey is, on the Mediterranean, practically in front of us, insisting on joining the European Community, yet no one had heard of the massacre. Salvini, a noted Italian democrat, was right on the mark when he observed: "The widespread ignorance of events is the main buttress of injustice". But this absent-mindedness on the part of the young has been conferred upon them by those who are charged to educate and inform them: among the absent-minded and uninformed, school teachers and other educators deserve first mention.

Young people easily succumb to the bombardment of gratuitous banalities and obscenities that each day is served to them by the mass media: heartless TV action films where in the space of ten minutes they are treated to three rapes, two assassinations, one beating and a serial crash involving ten cars on a bridge that then collapses, whereupon everything – cars, drivers and passengers – precipitates into the sea . . . only one person survives the fall, but he doesn't know how to swim and so drowns, to the cheers of the crowd of curious onlookers that suddenly has appeared on the scene.

At another university we spoofed the project – alas well under way – to manipulate genetic material, or more specifically, the proposal by the European Parliament to allow patent rights on living organisms. We could feel how the subject sent a chill through the audience. Franca and I explained how our Eurocrats, kindled by powerful and ubiquitous multinationals, are preparing a scheme worthy the plot of a sci-fi/horror movie entitled "Frankenstein's pig brother". They're trying to get the approval of a directive which (and get this!) would authorize industries to take patents on living beings, or on parts of them, created with techniques of genetic manipulation that seem taken straight out of "The Sorcerer's Apprentice".

This is how it would work: by manipulating the genetic make-up of a pig, a scientist succeeds in making the pig more human-like. By this arrangement it becomes much easier to remove from the pig the organ of your choice – a liver, a kidney – and to transplant it in a human. But to assure that the transplanted pig-organs aren't rejected, it's also necessary to transfer certain pieces of genetic information from the pig to the human. The result: a human pig (even though you will say that there are already plenty of those).

And every part of this new creature, this humanized pig, will be subject to patent laws; and whosoever wishes a part of it will have to pay copyright fees to the company that "invented" it. Secondary illnesses, monstrous deformations, infectious diseases – all are optionals, included in the price . . .

The Pope has forcefully condemned this monstrous genetic witchcraft. He has called it an offence against humanity, against the dignity of man, and has gone to pains to underscore the project's total and irrefutable lack of moral value.

The astonishing thing is that while this is happening, an American scientist, a remarkable magician – you've probably read about him in the papers – has succeeded in transplanting the head of a baboon. He cut the heads off two baboons and switched them. The baboons didn't feel all that great after the operation. In fact, it left them paralysed, and they both died shortly there-after, but the experiment worked, and that's the great thing.

But here's the rub: this modern-day Frankenstein, a certain Professor White, is all the while a distinguished member of the Vatican Academy of Sciences. Somebody should warn the Pope.

So, we enacted these criminal farces to the kids at the universities, and they laughed their heads off. They would say of Franca and me: "They're a riot, they come up with the most fantastic stories". Not for a moment, not even with an inkling in their spines, did they grasp that the stories we told were true.

These encounters have strengthened us in our conviction that our job is – in keeping with the exhortation of the great Italian poet Savinio – "to tell our own story". Our task as intellectuals, as persons who mount the pulpit or the stage, and who, most importantly, address to young people, our task is not just to teach them method, like how to use the arms, how to control breathing, how to use the stomach, the voice, the falsetto, the *contraccampo*. It's not enough to teach a technique or a style: we have to show them what is hap-pening around us. They have to be able to tell their own story. A theatre, a literature, an artistic expression that does not speak for its own time has no relevance.

Recently, I took part in a large conference with lots of people where I tried to explain, especially to the younger participants, the ins and outs of a particular Italian court case. The original case resulted in seven separate proceedings, at the end of which three Italian left-wing politicians were sentenced to 21 years of imprisonment each, accused of having murdered a police commissioner. I've studied the documents of the case – as I did when I prepared *Accidental Death of an Anarchist* – and at the conference I recounted the facts pertaining to it, which are really quite absurd, even farcical. But at a certain point I rea-lized I was speaking to deaf ears, for the simple reason that my audience was ignorant not only of the case itself, but of what had happened five years earlier, ten years earlier: the violence, the terrorism. They knew nothing about the massacres that occurred in Italy, the trains that blew up, the bombs in the *piazze* or the farcical court cases that have dragged on since then.

The terribly difficult thing is that in order to talk about what is happening today, I have to start with what happened thirty years ago and then work my way forward. It's not enough to speak about the present. And pay attention, this isn't just about Italy: the same thing happens everywhere, all over Europe. I've tried in Spain and encountered the same difficulty; I've tried in France, in Germany, I've yet to try in Sweden, but I will.

To conclude, let me share this medal with Franca.

Franca Rame, my companion in life and in art who you, members of the Academy, acknowledge in your motivation of the prize as actress and author; who has had a hand in many of the texts of our theatre.

(At this very moment, Franca is on stage in a theatre in Italy but will join me the day after tomorrow. Her flight arrives midday, if you like we can all head out together to pick her up at the airport.)

Franca has a very sharp wit, I assure you. A journalist put the following question to her: "So how does it feel to be the wife of a Nobel Prize winner? To have a monument in your home?" To which she answered: "I'm not worried. Nor do I feel at all at a disadvantage; I've been in training for a long time. I do my exercises each morning: I go down on my hand and knees, and that way I've accustomed myself to becoming a pedestal to a monument. I'm pretty good at it."

Like I said, she has a sharp wit. At times she even turns her irony against herself.

Without her at my side, where she has been for a lifetime, I would never have accomplished the work you have seen fit to honour. Together we've staged and recited thousands of performances, in theatres, occupied factories, at university sit-ins, even in deconsecrated churches, in prisons and city parks, in sunshine and pouring rain, always together. We've had to endure abuse, assaults by the police, insults from the right-thinking, and violence. And it is Franca who has had to suffer the most atrocious aggression. She has had to pay more dearly than any one of us, with her neck and limb in the balance, for the solidarity with the humble and the beaten that has been our premise.

The day it was announced that I was to be awarded the Nobel Prize I found myself in front of the theatre on Via di Porta Romana in Milan where Franca, together with Giorgio Albertazzi, was performing *The Devil with Tits*. Suddenly I was surrounded by a throng of reporters, photographers and camera-wielding TV-crews. A passing tram stopped, unexpectedly, the driver stepped out to greet me, then all the passengers stepped out too, they applauded me, and everyone wanted to shake my hand and congratulate me … when at a certain point they all stopped in their tracks and, as with a single voice, shouted "Where's Franca?". They began to holler "Francaaa" until, after a little while, she appeared. Discombobulated and moved to tears, she came down to embrace me.

At that moment, as if out of nowhere, a band appeared, playing nothing but wind instruments and drums. It was made up of kids from all parts of the city and, as it happened, they were playing together for the first time. They struck up "Porta Romana bella, Porta Romana" in samba beat. I've never heard anything played so out of tune, but it was the most beautiful music Franca and I had ever heard.

Believe me, this prize belongs to both of us.

Thank you   *Translation: Paul Claesson*

International CAMPAIGN TO BAN LANDMINES

THE INTERNATIONAL CAMPAIGN TO BAN LANDMINES (ICBL)

In the course of 1991, several nongovernmental organizations and individuals began simultaneously to discuss the necessity of coordinating initiatives and calls for a ban on antipersonnel landmines.

Handicap International, Human Rights Watch, Medico International, Mines Advisory Group, Physicians for Human Rights, and Vietnam Veterans of America Foundation came together in October 1992 to formalize the International Campaign to Ban Landmines.

From the beginning the International Campaign to Ban Landmines has defined itself as a fexible network of organizations that share common objectives. The campaign calls for an international ban on the use, production, stockpiling and transfer of antipersonnel landmines, for increased international resources for humanitarian mine clearance, and increased international resources for mine victim assistance programs.

In 1993 the Campaign Steering Committee consisting of the original six organizations was formalized, and the coordinator recognized. As dozens of national campaigns formed and hundreds of organizations joined the Campaign, the Steering Committee was expanded in 1996 and 1997 to reflect the growth and diversity of the Campaign. New members included the Afghan Campaign to Ban Landmines, Cambodia Campaign to Ban Landmines, Kenyan Coalition Against Landmines, Rädda Barnen, and South African Campaign to Ban Landmines.

Today, this network represents over 1,000 human rights, humanitarian, children's, peace, veteran's, medical, development, arms control, religious, environmental, and women's groups in over 60 countries. These groups work locally, nationally, and internationally to ban antipersonnel landmines. ICBL was an important force behind the convention to ban antipersonel landmines signed in Ottawa in December 1997 by more than 120 countries. In 1997 the ICBL and its coordinator Jody Williams received the Nobel Peace Prize.

NOBEL LECTURE

in Oslo, December 10, 1997

by

RAE MCGRATH

on behalf of the INTERNATIONAL CAMPAIGN TO BAN LANDMINES

Vietnam Veterans of America Foundation, 2001 "S" Street, NW, Washington DC 20009, USA

Your Majesties, Members of the Norwegian Nobel Committee, Excellencies, Ladies and Gentlemen,

Almost exactly fifteen years ago somewhere close to the Thai-Cambodian border, Tun Channareth was lying helpless in a minefield, both legs shattered by an anti-personnel mine. As his terrified friend looked on he took an axe and attempted, in his own words, *"... to cut off the dead weight of my legs"*. Horrified by the sight his companion snatched away the axe and dragged him from the minefield. Mercifully unconscious through loss of blood for most of the hours that followed he awoke to find his legs amputated. Today he lives with his wife and six children in Cambodia, he designs wheelchairs and works with disabled children, encouraging them to live full and active lives. Tun Channareth is one of tens of thousands of campaigners from more than sixty countries who work in a worldwide partnership; the International Campaign to Ban Landmines (the ICBL). Reth was chosen to accept this prestigious award because he exemplifies the experience, commitment and activism which form the roots of this campaign, a coalition of more than 1100 non-governmental organisations. We were, and still are, driven, not by the wish to ban a weapon of war, but to bring to a halt the unacceptable impact of the anti-personnel mines on people.

It is the indiscriminate nature of the anti-personnel landmine, the fact that it is triggered by its victim, that it remains active indefinitely after conflicts cease, which make it different from any other weapon. However, it was also its impact over such a wide area of human activity which singled it out – and made the birth of the ICBL inevitable. How could organisations committed to work with communities affected by landmines fail to recognise the fact which governments and the manufacturers had chosen to ignore – that the situation was already out of control and extending further beyond our capacity to respond with every new conflict? And armed with the facts about this weapon, how could civil society fail to respond?

Clearing landmines while others were being planted, manufactured and traded was no solution. Amputating limbs and providing prostheses for one survivor while another bled to death unaided was no solution. Why provide improved seeds for farmers whose fields were mined, or vaccinate animals which graze in minefields? We saw a world where peace had few advantages over war. The circle of manufacture, supply and use had to be broken. The answer was a ban – and so the campaign was born.

We called for a global ban on use, production, transfer and stockpiling and demanded adequate resources for demining and victim assistance. That call remains unchanged – a demand by civil society that governments throughout the world could not ignore.

In Ottawa last week more than 120 nations signed a treaty banning anti-personnel mines – a treaty which overcame the slow progress which had become the hallmark of international legislation. We applaud those governments who initiated and drove this process which began as a direct result of civil activism expressed through the work of the ICBL. The campaign, because of its diversity of experience and direct links to the minefields of the world, has been able to support the Ottawa process from the beginning; providing the humanitarian and technical data which underpins the urgent need to ban anti-personnel mines. We have praised the comprehensive nature of the treaty. But at the same time a key role of the campaign has been to identify and challenge areas of concern in the treaty since these could cost lives and deny land. For example; the treaty excludes *"..mines designed to be detonated by the presence, proximity or contact of a vehicle as opposed to a person, that are equipped with anti-handling devices…"* from definition as an anti-personnel mine.

Anti-handling devices are designed to kill or maim deminers. The Ottawa treaty rightly calls for signatories to assist and fund humanitarian mine clearance initiatives. It is, therefore, contradictory and against the spirit in which this treaty was conceived to include a specific exemption for a device which is designed to make that task more dangerous. Delegates at the Oslo conference which finalised the text of the treaty established for the diplomatic record that landmines equipped with devices which would explode as a result of an innocent or unintentional act were considered anti-personnel mines and therefore banned, the campaign will hold them accountable if this diplomatic understanding is not honoured. Allow me to put this in perspective.

Less than three weeks ago, on November 21st at ten-thirty in the morning, David Licumbi, an experienced humanitarian deminer, was working on the Lucusse Road in Moxico Province, Eastern Angola. David died when an anti-tank mine exploded less than a metre from him. He did nothing wrong, he broke no rules – a magnetic-influence anti-handling device fitted to the mine responded to the presence of David's mine detector. The implications of this incident go far beyond the tragic death of a deminer, work on this key road has ceased and this will threaten the resettlement of displaced Angolans and damage community confidence in the peace process. How can we ask these brave men and women to continue their work when their very detection devices may become the instrument of their deaths?

And so we view the Ottawa Treaty as a first and valuable step, a milestone in a battle to rid this world of anti-personnel mines. While these weapons remain in the world's armouries there is no nation immune from their effects–they can be delivered by aeroplane or missile and once they are deployed there is no magic technology to remove them – it would take no more than a few days to turn this country, Norway, into one of the world's worst-mined nations. It would take years to make it safe again and during those years Norwegians would become so familiar with the sight of limbless, blind and scarred compatriots that they would no longer turn their heads to look. Norwegians would become deminers of their own land and learn too late, as the people of Bosnia today are learning, that there is no immunity from the impact of this weapon.

To sign the Treaty is not enough, forty countries must ratify this treaty before its entry into force and no nation which seeks to reverse the damage done to our world by this weapon can justify any delay in ratification.

The International Campaign will do everything in its power in the coming months to achieve a legally binding ban by December 1998. To this end we, as Nobel Peace Prize Laureates – issue a challenge directly to the Heads of State of each signatory country – make sure that your country is among the first forty nations who ratify the Ottawa Treaty.

What of those nations which have failed to sign the Treaty or those which have not even attended the preparatory conferences? It would be easy to focus totally on China, the United States and Russia, nations whose stubborn refusal to put humanitarian concern above ill-judged military policy is inconsistent with their status as UN Security Council members and major regional powers. But what of those countries like South and North Korea, India, Pakistan, Israel and Syria whose, often valid, concern for their border defences blinds them to the damaging nature of the anti-personnel mine? What of Egypt, a country which is itself blighted by landmines emplaced decades ago, which argues it needs anti-personnel mines to deter smugglers from crossing its borders? We have heard much about the South Korean minefields. South Korea and the US government argue that the Demilitarised Zone minefields are of such importance they wish to make them exempt from any landmine ban. The ICBL does not accept the defensive utility of and necessity for the retention of those minefields.

Freedom is so often the justification for war. But where is the sense in fighting for the freedom of a people employing a weapon which will deny those same people, in peacetime, freedom to live without fear, freedom to farm their land, freedom merely to walk in safety from place to place – deny them the freedom to let their children play without being torn apart by a landmine? That is no freedom.

All those States who have failed to sign this treaty have failed humanity–size, power and economy are irrelevant – they are intransigent and uncaring in the face of compelling humanitarian, economic and environmental evidence that anti-personnel mines should be banned.

We are determined that the Ottawa Treaty will become a global legal instrument applicable to all states and will leave no avenues of action unexplored to achieve that aim. Together we have achieved so much but our progress must be measured against an obscene reality – that there are warehouses overflowing with anti-personnel mines throughout the world. These weapons must be destroyed – their mere presence is a threat since, while they remain in store, any country which goes to war will be tempted to deploy them. The destruction of stockpiles removes that possibility.

The Campaign will focus particular attention on those nations which have not signed the Ottawa Treaty, especially those which manufacture, export or use anti-personnel mines. It is our contention that the treaty establishes a norm which is equally applicable to nonsignatories, that the use of anti-personnel mines by any force, from any nation including guerilla armies, is no longer acceptable.

And here we would offer another challenge to signatory states; illustrate your commitment by destroying stockpiles of anti-personnel mines and enact domestic legislation outlawing the design, manufacture, trading and use of this weapon immediately – do not wait for the treaty to enter into force, do it now.

Arms manufacturers have driven and encouraged the trade in landmines and profited from the misery of millions – we intend to hold governments to their treaty obligations which require them to stop all production of anti-personnel mines and their components. Who can forget the competition to ship millions of mines to Iran and Iraq, mainly from Italy, and the role of countries like Singapore in providing a "legal" conduit for those mines to reach their destination? Happily the Italian government has enacted legislation which has driven the worst offenders out of the business of landmine manufacture, a process initiated and supported by the ICBL – but our business with those companies is not concluded until we are assured that they have not merely transferred their production overseas. The supply of components implies no lesser culpability than primary manufacture. We should remember the lesson learned by the people of Sweden, who believed their country to have had no involvement in the export of landmines during the Iran - Iraq conflict. They were wrong – because the explosive which filled millions of Italian mines came from Sweden. And so we can be sure that today as a result of that trade cooperation, many years after hostilities between those two countries ended, a Kurdish farmer or a mother searching for firewood or a child playing in the snow will be killed or maimed by a mine like this (holds up VS-69).

This is not an attempt to vilify selected nations – it is a plea for civil society to demand transparency from the arms industry, the military and from their governments. It is no moral excuse to wring your hands and cry *"but I never knew"* – if you never asked to know.

We have this target in view – that no soldier will carry an anti-personnel mine into battle. That no government or company anywhere in this world will make anti-personnel mines nor any weapon, by any name or in any shape, that is, in effect, an anti-personnel mine.

We will investigate all possibilities to achieve that target. Member organisations of the ICBL will continue examining the potential for mounting legal actions which may result in the payment of damages to mine victims, their families and mine-affected communities. Neither will we neglect the environmental impact of landmines. If a company can be held legally liable for an oil-spill we must ask why similar sanctions should not apply to arms manufacturers who have supplied landmines.

A small girl once explained patiently to me the moments following her crippling by a mine:

"We were playing a game by the railroad track on the hillside, we had to hop up the hill, we each took our turn. I was hopping and then there was a flash – a very bright light – and I thought there was a bang but my ears hurt and I could not tell. It was frightening and my friends ran away and I ran after them. But I fell over which made me more scared and I got up very quickly and then fell over ... and I slipped down the hill and I could hear my friends shouting and there was a strange smell and I started crying, I wanted my mother because I couldn't get up and run away or even sit up properly. Then I saw that something was wrong with my leg – it was twisted and very dirty and I saw it was bleeding – then I forget. When I woke up my face was wet, my mother was holding me very close and her tears were dropping on me. She said "Don't worry – you will be alright", I hurt a lot but I was happy then."

Anti-personnel mines do not only sever limbs, they can break the human spirit. We talk not of mine victims, but of survivors – but to survive such trauma requires support, encouragement and love. That responsibility must not be left to the survivors' family and friends, who are often struggling themselves against poverty and the damaging effects of conflict, but to a greater family – the human family. In most mine affected countries we, the international community, must offer more than the surgeon's knife and protheses as support to those who survive the blast of a landmine – in some countries even that basic level of care may not be available. This is not support – it is little more than first aid. In the same way as the Ottawa Treaty is only the first step towards a global ban, so prostheses should be seen as the first stage in the support process for the victim of a mine blast. That is not the case today, and the reason for this lack of response is evident and shames us all – we simply do not care enough. This is a responsibility which the ICBL places high on its action agenda. We must have respect for the rights of those who fall victim to landmines, most importantly their right to control their own lives and their right to be heard.

Through our member organisations, especially those who deal directly with landmine survivors and their families, we will seek effective and innovative ways to ensure support for their treatment to match the scale of the problem. That support must incorporate social and economic integration. The ICBL expects governments to join us in this attempt to redress the wrong suffered by the victims of mine explosions.

There are tens of millions of landmines around our world – no-one knows how many and it simply does not matter. What matters is that we eradicate them. There is a popular myth that mine clearance costs too much – the ICBL does not accept that is true and, faced with the obscenity of the effects of the anti-personnel mines, it would be difficult to understand what scale of measurement could be used to make such a calculation. The problem is that most funding for mine clearance is allocated from aid and development budgets and, we would agree, those sources are inadequate to the task and are already struggling to meet their commitments in other sectors, often exacerbated by the peripheral impact of landmines especially in the fields of health, agriculture and resettlement. It follows, therefore, that other sources of funding must be identified. There should be no misunderstanding – the cost of global eradication of landmines will be billions of dollars, assuming that sustainable methodologies are employed and emphasis is placed on developing an indigenous capacity in each affected country.

We must afford it, we cannot talk of having concern for the global environment and yet leave future generations a blighted world with land made unusable by this deadly military garbage. We need to look for relevant funding sources which can meet the requirements of the task we face. It is worth making a comparison which illustrates the priorities which must be challenged before global mine eradication becomes an achievable objective.

The tens of millions of dollars spent annually on mine clearance pale in comparison to the hundreds of billions spent on the military. In 1995 alone the military expenditure by European Union nations was more than US$ 166 billion – in the same year world military expenditure was over US$ 695 billion. Based on these figures it would seem that the military, who are responsible for the laying of landmines, are polluters who can afford to pay the price of clearance.

But it is not merely a matter of making funds available, it is vital that they are expended on relevant, effective and integrated response. Mine action is a sector of development – that this approach works on a national level is well illustrated in Afghanistan.

To achieve these aims the campaign will continue to expand our activities and develop new national campaigns, particularly in countries which have not signed the treaty. We open our arms to new members who support our aims, particularly those from mined countries and from mine-producing states.

Your Majesties, Excellencies, Ladies and Gentlemen we are greatly honoured by the award of the Nobel Peace Prize and are proud but humbled to share this award with previous Laureates such as Nelson Mandela, Aung San Suu Kyi, Desmond Tutu, Bishop Belo and José Ramos Horta who have given so much in the service of peace. We would also like to take this opportunity to pay tribute to a fellow nominee and champion of civil action, Wei Jingsheng, and wish him well in the hope that he can one day return to his home in happier times.

The International Campaign to Ban Landmines dedicates this award to all victims of landmines and their families, to those communities who struggle to exist surrounded by minefields and to humanitarian deminers. It is the wish of every reasonable human being to leave this world a better place for their having lived, it is a wish we rarely can hope to achieve. By eradicating landmines we can leave future generations a better and safer world in which to live – it is possible; we should grasp that opportunity.

Thank you.

The International Campaign to Ban Landmines is represented at the Nobel Peace Prize ceremony through its Steering Committee, comprising the following:

Afghan Campaign to Ban Landmines	Sayed Aqa
Cambodian Campaign to Ban Landmines	Sister Denise Coghlan
Handicap International	Phillippe Chabasse
Human Rights Watch	Steve Goose
Kenya Coalition of NGOs against Landmines	Mereso Agina
Medico International	Thomas Gebauer
Mines Advisory Group	Lou McGrath
Physicians for Human Rights	Susannah Sirkin
Rädda Barnen, Sweden	Carl von Essen
South African Campaign to Ban Landmines	Noel Stott
Vietnam Veterans of America Foundation	Robert Muller

JODY WILLIAMS

Born 9 Ocober 1950.

Professional:

Ms. Jody Williams is the founding coordinator of the International Campaign to Ban Landmines (ICBL), which was formally launched by six NGOs in October of 1992. Ms. Williams has overseen the growth of the ICBL to more than 1,000 NGOs in more than sixty countries. She has served as the chief strategist and spokesperson for the campaign. Working in a unprecedented cooperative effort with governments, UN bodies and the International Committee of the Red Cross, the ICBL achieved its goal of an international treaty banning antipersonnel landmines during the diplomatic conference held in Oslo in September 1997.

In her capacity as ICBL coordinator, she has written and spoken extensively on the problem of landmines and the movement to ban them. In recognition of her expertise on the issue, Ms. Williams was invited to serve as a technical adviser to the UN's Study on the Impact of Armed Conflict on Children, led by Ms. Graca Machel, former first lady of Mozambique.

Prior to beginning the ICBL, Ms. Williams worked for eleven years to build public awareness about U.S. policy toward Central America. From 1986 to 1992, she developed and directed humanitarian relief projects as the deputy director of the Los Angeles-based Medical Aid for El Salvador. From 1984 to 1986, she was co-coordinator of the Nicaragua-Honduras Education Project, leading fact-finding delegations to the region. Previously, she taught English as a Second Language (ESL) in Mexico, the United Kingdom, and Washington, D.C.

Education:

Ms. Williams has a Master's Degree in International Relations from the Johns Hopkins School of Advanced International Studies (Washington, D.C., 1984), a Master's Degree in Teaching Spanish and ESL from the School for International Training (Brattleboro, Vermont, 1976), and a Bachelor of Arts degree from the University of Vermont (Burlington, Vermont, 1972).

Presentations/publications:

In her capacity as ICBL coordinator, she has written and spoken extensively on the problem of landmines and the movement to ban them. She has spoken in various fora, including at the United Nations, the European Parliament, and the Organization of African Unity. Ms. Williams co-authored a seminal study, based on two years of field research in four mine-affected countries, detailing the socioeconomic consequences of landmine contamination. She has written articles for journals produced by the United Nations and the ICRC, among others. Papers and publications include: *After the Guns Fall Silent: The Enduring Legacy of Landmines,* Shawn Roberts and Jody Williams, Vietnam Veterans of America Foundation, Washington, D.C., 1995. "Landmines and measures to eliminate them," *International Review of the Red Cross,* July–August 1995. No. 307. "Landmines: Dealing with the Environmental Impact," *Environment & Security,* 1997, Vol. 1. No. 2. "Social Consequences of Widespread Use of Landmines," Landmine Symposium, International Committee of the Red Cross, Montreux, Switzerland, April 1993. "The Protection of Children Against Landmines and Unexploded Ordnance," Impact of Armed Conflict on Children: Report of the Expert Group of the Secretary-General, Ms. Graca Machel, A/51/306, 26 August 1996.

NOBEL LECTURE

December 10, 1997

by

JODY WILLIAMS

Vietnam Veterans of America Foundation, 5803 Harvey Place, Alexandria, VA 23450, USA

Your Majesties, Honorable Members of the Norwegian Nobel Committee, Excellencies and Honored Guests,

It is a privilege to be here today, together with other representatives of the International Campaign to Ban Landmines, to receive jointly the 1997 Nobel Peace Prize. Our appreciation goes to those who nominated us and to the Nobel Committee for chosing this year to recognize, from among so many other nominees who have worked diligently for peace, the work of the International Campaign.

I am deeply honored–but whatever personal recognition derives from this award, I believe that this high tribute is the result of the truly historic achievement of this humanitarian effort to rid the world of one indiscriminate weapon. In the words of the Nobel Committee, the International Campaign "started a process which in the space of a few years changed a ban on anti-personnel mines from a vision to a feasible reality."

Further, the Committee noted that the Campaign has been able to "express and mediate a broad range of popular commitment in an unprecedented way. With the governments of several small and medium-sized countries taking the issue up ... this work has grown into a convincing example of an effective policy for peace."

The desire to ban landmines is not new. In the late 1970s, the International Committee of the Red Cross, along with a handful of nongovernmental organizations (NGOs), pressed the world to look at weapons that were particularly injurious and/or indiscriminate. One of the weapons of special concern was landmines. People often ask why the focus on this one weapon. How is the landmine different from any other conventional weapon?

Landmines distinguish themselves because once they have been sown, once the soldier walks away from the weapon, the landmine cannot tell the difference between a soldier or a civilian–a woman, a child, a grandmother going out to collect firewood to make the family meal. The crux of the problem is that while the use of the weapon might be militarily justifiable during the day of the battle, or even the two weeks of the battle, or maybe even the two months of the battle, once peace is declared the landmine does not recognize that peace. The landmine is eternally prepared to take victims. In common parlance, it is the perfect soldier, the "eternal sentry." The war ends, the landmine goes on killing.

Since World War II most of the conflicts in the world have been internal conflicts. The weapon of choice in those wars has all too often been land-mines–to such a degree that what we find today are tens of millions of land-mines contaminating approximately 70 countries around the world. The overwhelming majority of those countries are found in the developing world, primarily in those countries that do not have the resources to clean up the mess, to care for the tens of thousands of landmine victims. The end result is an international community now faced with a global humanitarian crisis.

Let me take a moment to give a few examples of the degree of the epidem-ic. Today Cambodia has somewhere between four and six million landmines, which can be found in over 50 percent of its national territory. Afghanistan is littered with perhaps nine million landmines. The U.S. military has said that during the height of the Russian invasion and ensuing war in that country, up to 30 million mines were scattered throughout Afghanistan. In the few years of the fighting in the former Yugoslavia, some six million landmines were sown throughout various sections of the country–Angola nine million, Mozambique a million, Somalia a million–I could go on, but it gets tedious. Not only do we have to worry about the mines already in the ground, we must be concerned about those that are stockpiled and ready for use. Estimates range between one and two hundred million mines in stockpiles around the world.

When the ICRC pressed in the 1970s for the governments of the world to consider increased restrictions or elimination of particularly injurious or in-discriminate weapons, there was little support for a ban of landmines. The end result of several years of negotiations was the 1980 Convention on Conventional Weapons (CCW). What that treaty did was attempt to regulate the use of landmines. While the Convention tried to tell commanders in the field when it was okay to use the weapon and when it was not okay to use the weapon, it also allowed them to make decisions about the applicability of the law in the midst of battle. Unfortunately, in the heat of battle, the laws of war do not exactly come to mind. When you are trying to save your skin you use anything and everything at your disposal to do so.

Throughout these years the Cold War raged on, and internal conflicts that often were proxy wars of the Super Powers proliferated. Finally, with the col-lapse of the Soviet Bloc, people began to look at war and peace differently. Without the overarching threat of nuclear holocaust, people started to look at how wars had actually been fought during the Cold War. What they found was that in the internal conflicts fought during that time, the most insidious weapon of all was the antipersonnel landmine–and that it contaminated the globe in epidemic proportion.

As relative peace broke out with the end of the Cold War, the U.N. was able to go into these nations that had been torn by internal strife, and what they found when they got there were millions and millions of landmines which af-fected every aspect of peacekeeping, which affected every aspect of post-conflict reconstruction of those societies. You know, if you are in Phnom Penh in Cambodia, and you are setting up the peacekeeping operations, it might seem relatively easy. But when you want to send your troops out into the hinterlands where four or six million landmines are, it becomes a problem, because the main routes are mined. Part of the peace agreement was to bring the hundreds of thousands of refugees back into the country so that they could participate in the voting, in the new democracy being forged in Cambodia. Part of the plan to bring them back included giving each family enough land so that they could be self-sufficient, so they wouldn't be a drain on the country, so that they could contribute to reconstruction. What they found: So many landmines they couldn't give land to the families. What did they get? Fifty dollars and a year's supply of rice. That is the impact of landmines.

It was the NGOs, the nongovernmental organizations, who began to seriously think about trying to deal with the root of the problem–to eliminate the problem, it would be necessary to eliminate the weapon. The work of NGOs across the board was affected by the landmines in the developing world. Children's groups, development organizations, refugee organizations, medical and humanitarian relief groups–all had to make huge adjustments in their programs to try to deal with the landmine crisis and its impact on the people they were trying to help. It was also in this period that the first NGO humanitarian demining organizations were born–to try to return contaminated land to rural communities.

It was a handful of NGOs, with their roots in humanitarian and human rights work, which began to come together, in late 1991 and early 1992, in an organized effort to ban antipersonnel landmines. In October of 1992, Handicap International, Human Rights Watch, Medico International, Mines Advisory Group, Physicians for Human Rights and Vietnam Veterans of America Foundation came together to issue a "Joint Call to Ban Antipersonnel Landmines." These organizations, which became the steering committee of the International Campaign to Ban Landmines called for an end to the use, production, trade and stockpiling of antipersonnel landmines. The call also pressed governments to increase resources for humanitarian mine clearance and for victim assistance.

From this inauspicious beginning, the International Campaign has become an unprecedented coalition of 1,000 organizations working together in 60 countries to achieve the common goal of a ban of antipersonnel landmines. And as the Campaign grew, the steering committee was expanded to represent the continuing growth and diversity of those who had come together in this global movement. We added the Afghan and Cambodian Campaigns and Rädda Barnen in 1996, and the South African Campaign and Kenya Coalition early this year as we continued to press toward our goal. And in six years we did it. In September of this year, 89 countries came together–here in Oslo –and finished the negotiations of a ban treaty based on a draft drawn up by Austria only at the beginning of this year. Just last week in Ottawa, Canada, 121 countries came together again to sign that ban treaty. And as a clear indication of the political will to bring this treaty into force as soon as possible, three countries ratified the treaty upon signature–Canada, Mauritius and Ireland.

In its first years, the International Campaign developed primarily in the North–in the countries which had been significant producers of antipersonnel landmines. The strategy was to press for national, regional and international measures to ban landmines. Part of this strategy was to get the governments of the world to review the CCW and in the review process–try to get them to ban the weapon through that convention. We did not succeed. But over the two and one-half years of the review process, with the pressure that we were able to generate–the heightened international attention to the issue–began to raise the stakes, so that different governments wanted to be seen as leaders on what the world was increasingly recognizing as a global humanitarian crisis.

The early lead had been taken in the United States, with the first legislated moratorium on exports in 1992. And while the author of that legislation, Senator Leahy, has continued to fight tirelessly to ban the weapon in the U.S., increasingly other nations far surpassed that early leadership. In March of 1995, Belgium became the first country to ban the use, production, trade and stockpiling domestically. Other countries followed suit: Austria, Norway, Sweden, and others. So even as the CCW review was ending in failure, increasingly governments were calling for a ban. What had once been called a utopian goal of NGOs was gaining in strength and momentum.

While we still had that momentum, in the waning months of the CCW review, we decided to try to get the individual governments which had taken action or had called for a ban to come together in a self-identifying bloc. There is, after all, strength in numbers. So during the final days of the CCW we invited them to a meeting and they actually came. A handful of governments agreed to sit down with us and talk about where the movement to ban landmines would go next. Historically, NGOs and governments have too often seen each other as adversaries, not colleagues, and we were shocked that they came. Seven or nine came to the first meeting, 14 to the second, and 17 to the third. By the time we had concluded the third meeting, with the conclusion of the Review Conference on May 3rd of 1996, the Canadian government had offered to host a governmental meeting in October of last year, in which pro-ban governments would come together and strategize about how to bring about a ban. The CCW review process had not produced the results we sought, so what do we do next?

From the third to the fifth of October we met in Ottawa. It was a very fascinating meeting. There were 50 governments there as full participants and 24 observers. The International Campaign was also participating in the conference. The primary objectives of the conference were to develop an Ottawa Declaration, which states would sign signalling their intention to ban landmines, and an "Agenda for Action," which outlined concrete steps on the road to a ban. We were all prepared for that, but few were prepared for the concluding comments by Lloyd Axworthy, the Foreign Minister of Canada. Foreign Minister Axworthy stood up and congratulated everybody for formulating the Ottawa Declaration and the Agenda for Action, which were clearly seen as giving teeth to the ban movement. But the Foreign Minister did not end with congratulations. He ended with a challenge. The Canadian government challenged the world to return to Canada in a year to sign an international treaty banning antipersonnel landmines.

Members of the International Campaign to Ban Landmines erupted into cheers. The silence of the governments in the room was defeaning. Even the truly pro-ban states were horrified by the challenge. Canada had stepped outside of diplomatic process and procedure and put them between a rock and a hard place. They had said they were pro-ban. They had come to Ottawa to develop a road map to create a ban treaty and had signed a Declaration of intent. What could they do? They had to respond. It was really breath-taking. We stood up and cheered while the governments were moaning. But once they recovered from that initial shock, the governments that really wanted to see a ban treaty as soon as possible, rose to the challenge and negotiated a ban treaty in record time.

What has become known as the Ottawa Process began with the Axworthy Challenge. The treaty itself was based upon a ban treaty drafted by Austria and developed in a series of meetings in Vienna, in Bonn, in Brussels, which culminated in the three-week long treaty negotiating conference held in Oslo in September. The treaty negotiations were historic. They were historic for a number of reasons. For the first time, smaller and middle-sized powers had come together, to work in close cooperation with the nongovernmental organizations of the International Campaign to Ban Landmines, to negotiate a treaty which would remove from the world's arsenals a weapon in widespread use. For the first time, smaller and middle-sized powers had not yielded ground to intense pressure from a superpower to weaken the treaty to accommodate the policies of that one country. Perhaps for the first time, negotiations ended with a treaty stronger than the draft on which the negotiations were based! The treaty had not been held hostage to rule by consensus, which would have inevitably resulted in a gutted treaty.

The Oslo negotiations gave the world a treaty banning antipersonnel landmines which is remarkably free of loopholes and exceptions. It is a treaty which bans the use, production, trade and stockpiling of antipersonnel landmines. It is a treaty which requires states to destroy their stockpiles within four years of its entering into force. It is a treaty which requires mine clearance within ten years. It calls upon states to increase assistance for mine clearance and for victim assistance. It is not a perfect treaty–the Campaign has concerns about the provision allowing for antihandling devices on antivehicle mines; we are concerned about mines kept for training purposes; we would like to see the treaty directly apply to nonstate actors and we would like stronger language regarding victim assistance. But, given the close cooperation with governments which resulted in the treaty itself, we are certain that these issues can be addressed through the annual meetings and review conferences provided for in the treaty.

As I have already noted, last week in Ottawa, 121 countries signed the treaty. Three ratified it simultaneously–signalling the political will of the international community to bring this treaty into force as soon as possible. It is remarkable. Landmines have been used since the U.S. Civil War, since the Crimean War, yet we are taking them out of arsenals of the world. It is amazing. It is historic. It proves that civil society and governments do not have to see themselves as adversaries. It demonstrates that small and middle powers can work together with civil society and address humanitarian concerns with breathtaking speed. It shows that such a partnership is a new kind of "super-power" in the post-Cold War world.

It is fair to say that the International Campaign to Ban Landmines made a difference. And the real prize is the treaty. What we are most proud of is the treaty. It would be foolish to say that we are not deeply honored by being awarded the Nobel Peace Prize. Of course, we are. But the receipt of the Nobel Peace Prize is recognition of the accomplishment of this Campaign. It is recognition of the fact that NGOs have worked in close cooperation with governments for the first time on an arms control issue, with the United Nations, with the International Committee of the Red Cross. Together, we have set a precedent. Together, we have changed history. The closing remarks of the French ambassador in Oslo to me were the best. She said, "This is historic not just because of the treaty. This is historic because, for the first time, the leaders of states have come together to answer the will of civil society."

For that, the International Campaign thanks them–for together we have given the world the possibility of one day living on a truly mine-free planet.

Thank you.

THE PRIZE IN ECONOMIC SCIENCES
IN MEMORY OF ALFRED NOBEL

THE INSTITUTION

On the occasion of its tercentenary, in 1968, Sveriges Riksbank (Bank of Sweden) made a donation to the Nobel Foundation for the purpose of awarding, through the Royal Swedish Academy of Sciences, *The Sveriges Riksbank (Bank of Sweden) Prize in Economic Sciences in Memory of Alfred Nobel.*

The statutes for the distribution of the Prize are, *mutatis mutandis,* the same as those for the Nobel Prizes. The presentation of the Prize is to take place at the Nobel Ceremony on December 10, at the same time as that of the Nobel Prizes. The first Prize in Economy was awarded in 1969.

The amount of the Prize is the same as that of the Nobel Prizes for the year. A special diploma and a gold medal are presented on this occasion.

In 1997, the Committee responsible for preparing matters was composed of the following members:

BERTIL NÄSLUND, Professor of Economics at Stockholm School of Economics, *Chairman of the Committee;* LARS CALMFORS, Professor of Economics at Stockholm University; KARL GUSTAV JÖRESKOG, Professor of Statistics at Uppsala University; LARS E. O. SVENSSON, Professor of International Economics at Stockholm University; *Secretary of the Committee:* TORSTEN PERSSON, Professor of Economics at Stockholm University; *adjoint members:* KARL-GUSTAF LÖFGREN, Professor of Economics at Umeå University; ROBERT ERIKSON, Professor of Sociology at Stockholm University; JÖRGEN WEIBULL, Professor of Economics at Stockholm School of Economics; PETER ENGLUND, Professor of Economics at Uppsala University.

THE PRIZE-WINNERS AND CITATION

THE ROYAL SWEDISH ACADEMY OF SCIENCES
decided on October 14, 1997, to award The Sveriges Riksbank (Bank of Sweden) Prize in Economic Sciences in Memory of Alfred Nobel jointly to

ROBERT C. MERTON
Harvard Business School, Boston, USA, and

MYRON S. SCHOLES
Stanford University, Stanford, USA

for a new method to determine the value of derivatives.

The number of candidates formally proposed was 119.

THE INSIGNIA AND THE AMOUNT OF THE PRIZE

The Prize-Winners received a *diploma*, a *medal*. The amount of the Prize was, like that of the Nobel Prizes, 7,500,000 Swedish kronor.

The diplomas presented to the Prize-Winners have been designed by the Swedish artist Bengt Landin. Calligraphy by Annika Rücker.

THE SVERIGES RIKSBANK (BANK OF SWEDEN) PRIZE IN ECONOMIC SCIENCES IN MEMORY OF ALFRED NOBEL

Speech by Professor Bertil Näslund of the Royal Swedish Academy of Sciences.
Translation of the Swedish text.

Your Majesties, Your Royal Highnesses, Ladies and Gentlemen,

If a Swedish company has to pay 10 million dollars for a machine in six months, it runs the risk that the exchange rate will change. In order to protect itself against a future increase in the value of the dollar, the company can purchase an option with the right, but not the obligation, to buy dollars in six months at a predetermined price.

A financial option contract is an example of a derivative instrument. The price of a derivative depends on an underlying financial instrument. The price of the above-mentioned currency option is determined by the value of the dollar. Derivative instruments serve a highly useful purpose in society by redistributing risks to those who are willing and able to take them.

Options have a long history. As far back as in ancient Greece Aristotle described the use of option-type contracts. We also know that options were actively traded in Amsterdam, the financial center of Europe in the seventeenth century. In spite of its potential importance, option trading remained rather limited. Up until the end of the 1960s, there did not exist a fully acceptable method of evaluating and pricing option contracts.

Three young Ph.D.'s connected with the Massachusetts Institute of Technology – Fischer Black, Robert Merton and Myron Scholes – worked on option valuation around 1970. In 1973, Black and Scholes published the so-called Black-Scholes formula for pricing stock options, which solved the evaluation problem. Merton had a direct influence on the development of the formula and has generalized it in important ways.

Soon afterwards, the formula was applied on the new options exchange in Chicago; it is now used daily by thousands of agents on markets all over the world. More important than the formula itself, however, was the method that this year's Laureates used to derive it. In one stroke they solved the problem which had been an obstacle in the pricing of all kinds of options, that is: what risk premium should be used in the evaluation.

The answer given by the Prize-Winners was: no risk premium at all! This answer was so unexpected and surprising that they had considerable difficulties in getting their first articles accepted for publication. But this insight

410

proved to be the key to a very general and powerful method for determining the value of *all* kinds of options and other derivative securities. In combination with advances in information technology, it is this method which has generated the explosive growth of new financial products and markets over the past 10-15 years.

The method developed by Merton and Scholes has also had a great impact in several areas *outside* of financial markets. In deciding between investment alternatives, it is often important to determine the value of flexibility. One investment alternative may be more flexible than another regarding, for example, the use of different sources of energy. The possibility of switching from one type of energy to another is an option, and the economic value of flexibility can now be determined. The methodology can also be used to determine the value of corporate liabilities and the value of insurance and economic guarantees.

Dear Professor Merton, Dear Professor Scholes,

In collaboration with Fischer Black, who sadly passed away just two years ago, you have developed a new method to determine the value of derivatives. Your methodology has paved the way for economic valuations in many areas. It has also generated new financial instruments and facilitated more effective risk management in society. It is a great honor and a privilege for me to convey to you, on behalf of the Royal Swedish Academy of Sciences, our warmest congratulations.

I now ask you to receive the Prize from his Majesty the King.

Robert C. Merton

ROBERT C. MERTON

I was born in New York, New York, on July 31, 1944, the middle child between two sisters, Stephanie and Vanessa. I grew up in Hastings-on-Hudson, a village of about 8000 outside the city, in a house that Vanessa and her family live in today. My father, born in Philadelphia the son of immigrant parents, was a professor of sociology at Columbia University. He is now University Professor Emeritus at Columbia, having meanwhile been awarded the National Medal of Science for founding the sociology of science and for his contributions to sociological knowledge such as the self-fulfilling prophecy and the focus group. My mother, from a multigenerational southern New Jersey Methodist/ Quaker family, stayed at home. She died in 1992. My mother's mother and many (at one time 25) cats completed the household that shared my childhood.

Hastings was a mixed middle-class and blue-collar town with local employment dominated by a wire and cable company and a chemical plant. Despite this composition and the town's small size, the local public school provided a fine education opportunity. In a graduating class of only some 90, I nevertheless was able to take mathematics through the calculus and five years of science (two in physics including a MIT-designed course). I was a good student but not at the top of my class. I played varsity football and ran track, neither with great distinction. Among my classmates were the sons of the Columbia physicists and Nobel laureates, James Rainwater and Jack Steinberger. Other long-time Hastings residents were the laureate in medicine, Max Theiler, and the laureate in economics, William Vickrey, as well as the sculptor Jacques Lipchitz.

School work and intellectual interests such as music and the arts were not especially important to me while I was growing up, although mathematics, my favorite subject, was fun. Baseball was my first passion: I played sand lot and Little League, and rooted for the Brooklyn Dodgers. Around age 11, that passion began to turn toward cars. On my bedroom wall, I put a large sheet of paper with 1800-plus numbers: one to be crossed out each day until I would be old enough for my driver's license. As I had known all the batting averages and pitching records of big league baseball players, so I came to know the horsepower, cubic inches of engines size, and other detailed specifications of just about every automobile in the post-war era. Going to auto shows and stock car races and handing tools to older, amateur buffs working on their cars were outlets for my passion until, at age 15, I bought and rebuilt my first car. After getting my driver's license, I built street hot rods which I raced at drag strips in upstate New York and Long Island. I thought that I would become an automobile engineer when I grew up. Indeed, while in college, I spent two summers working for Ford in its headquarters in Dearborn, Michigan: one as an engineer in advanced vehicle design and the other in the Lincoln-Mercury division trying to figure out optimal importing patterns for the English Ford. Other than working in a local cemetery after school and in the summer during high school and a summer spent in information technology at IBM, these automotive jobs were the only full-time, non-academic ones I have had.

Both of my parents played important roles in my early life of learning. My father introduced me to baseball, poker, magic, and the stock market (only magic didn't take root). And books of every kind were everywhere. He said nothing directly about expected academic performance. There was no need to. Simply by self-exemplification, he set the standards for work effort and for clarity of thought and expression. I had the normal father-son tensions as a teenager, but we subsequently became very close: for more than 30 years, we have talked to each other, at least once, nearly every day. My mother taught me caring and sensitivity towards the feelings of others, animals as well as humans. She gave me much good, practical advice for getting through life. One such counsel in particular I have applied often and in varied arenas: "First show them that you can do it their way, so that you earn the right to do it your way."

One week before my 17th birthday, I had a blind date with June Rose, a television actress on network soap operas, a model, and a regular on the popular Dick Clark's Saturday night American Bandstand show from New York. We were married five years later, one week after my graduation from Columbia. We devoted much energy to and derived enormous pleasure from raising three wonderful and talented children, Samantha J., Robert F., and Paul J. June and I separated in 1996.

My arrival at college marked the beginning of serious focus on academic matters. Just one day after entering Columbia College I switched to the Engineering School. With its small and flexible program and fine faculty, it was a great place for an undergraduate to explore mathematics and its uses. I took several undergraduate and graduate mathematics courses, both applied and pure: my tastes were however clear, preferring partial differential equations to real analysis and the calculus of variations to functions of a complex variable. Along with a number of engineering courses including drawing, I also took Columbia's famous Contemporary Civilization course, humanities, one introductory course in economics (using Samuelson's *Economics*), a graduate course in mathematical sociology, and two general studies night courses in accounting and stock market investments. The C- or D received in my English literature course in my sophomore year did not help my grade point average. The paper on *Gulliver's Travels* written for that course, however, became my first published article (in the *Journal of the History of Ideas*).

After Columbia, I went west to pursue a Ph.D. in applied mathematics at the California Institute of Technology. My time at Cal Tech (1966–67), brief as it was, added significantly to my stock of mathematics. Even more valuable to me was its creed of placing students from the outset in a research framework, "playing" with their subject instead of merely passively learning the material. Sometime during the year, I decided to leave Cal Tech (and mathematics) to study economics. Although he thought it was a bizarre idea, Gerald Whitham (the department head) provided generous help. I applied to half a dozen good departments, but only one, M.I.T., accepted me, and it gave me a full fellowship.

My decision to leave applied mathematics for economics was in part tied to the widely-held popular belief in the 1960s that macroeconomics had made fundamental inroads into controlling business cycles and stopping dysfunctional unemployment and inflation. Thus, I felt that working in economics could "really matter" and that potentially one could affect millions of people. I also believed that my mathematics and engineering training might give me some advantage in analyzing complex situations. Most important in my decision was the sense that I had a much better intuition and "feel" into economic matters than physical ones. Nowhere was that more apparent to me than in the stock market.

As early as 8 or 9 years of age, I developed an interest in money and finance, even at play. I created fictitious banks such as the RCM Savings of Dollars and Cents Company. I gladly balanced my mother's check book. As already noted, my father introduced me to the stock market. At 10 or 11, I drew up an "A" list of stocks, and bought my first one, General Motors. In college, I spent time doing some trading, learning tape watching, and hearing the lore of the market from retail traders in brokerage houses. In late 1963, I had my first experience in what is now known as "risk arbitrage". The trade surrounding the merger of Friden Company and Singer Company involved buying Friden shares and shorting Singer shares in a ratio of 1.75-to-1. The current difference in value between the two would become a "sure-thing" profit, provided the merger went through. Fortunately for me, it did. At Cal Tech, many mornings I would get to a local brokerage house at 6:30 am (9:30 am in New York) for the opening of the stock market, spend a couple of hours watching the tape and trading, and then go to my classes. In addition to stocks, I traded warrants, convertible bonds, and over-the-counter options. Although I did apply mathematical skills, my valuation approaches were essentially *ad hoc*. Nevertheless, I learned much from those varied transactional experiences about markets and institutions which proved useful in my later research. For instance, in discovering specialized banks that would legally finance my convertible bond positions at 85 percent of their value (leveraging terms considerably superior to the 50 percent financing offered by standard margin accounts), I learned early on that the "institutional rigidities," often postulated as inviolate in academic financial-market modeling, can be more flexible and permeable in their real-world counterparts.

When I arrived at MIT in the fall of 1967, I discovered why they had admitted me when no other institution had: Harold Freeman, statistician and member of the economics department from pre-Samuelson days. Harold had recognized some of the mathematicians who had written my letters of recommendation and convinced the department to take a flyer. Now in the role of first-year advisor, he saw my proposed, "traditional" course plan and told me "…you follow that and you'll leave here by the end of the term out of boredom … go take Paul Samuelson's mathematical economics course." I did. Not only did I get to interact with Paul Samuelson, but I met the then second-year students, Stanley Fischer and Michael Rothschild. I learned economics from Paul's *Foundations* and wrote a term paper on an optimal growth model with endogenous population changes which was later published in 1969. As a result of our meeting in his course, Paul hired me as his research assistant that spring. Quite a yield from a single course!

In the course of my work for Paul, we discovered shared interests and some common knowledge about the stock market, warrants and convertible securities. I found out that my "after/before-hours" interest in such things could also be a legitimate part of my day-hours devoted to research. In the summer of 1968, we began a joint effort to advance Paul's 1965 theory of warrant pricing, which was subsequently published in 1969. Later in October, I would have my first experience presenting in a formal seminar. My co-author decided that I, the second-year grad student, and not he, the Institute Professor, would give our paper at the *inaugural* session of the MIT-Harvard Mathematical Economics seminar. With a full audience of Harvard economics faculty including Kenneth Arrow, Wassily Leontief, and Hendrik Houthakker, it was surely a memorable baptism.

The research with Paul on warrant pricing introduced me to the expected-utility maxim and its application to optimal portfolio selection in a static framework. As a consequence of that effort, I began to think about combining the static theory of portfolio selection with the intertemporal optimization of lifetime consumption under certainty found in the growth-model literature. Ignorant of the important work underway by Nils Hakansson and Hayne Leland, then graduate students elsewhere, I attacked the problem of dynamic portfolio theory in a continuous-time framework without having the benefit of their discrete-time formulations. Despite all the mathematics courses that I had taken, I had seen neither stochastic dynamic programming nor the Itô calculus, both of which turned out to be key mathematical tools needed for this research. Instead, driven by "need," I found them and learned them on my own. Presented first at a Harvard-MIT graduate student seminar in November 1968, my paper on lifetime consumption and portfolio selection under uncertainty was published the following August as a companion paper to one by Paul investigating the effect of age on portfolio risk tolerance.

Despite having Paul Samuelson, Franco Modigliani, Robert Solow, Frank Fisher, Robert Bishop, Evsey Domar, Peter Diamond, Peter Temin, and Ed Kuh as teachers, I must confess that my focus was more on research than classes from the beginning (and my course grades reflected that). However, no one could have had a better introduction to economics than I did, with these great teachers and the opportunity to live in Paul Samuelson's office as his assistant for two and a half years. Three of the five chapters of my thesis were published before the thesis was submitted. A fourth, "Optimum Consumption and Portfolio Rules in a Continuous-Time Model," was presented at the Second World Congress of the Econometric Society in August 1970 and was published in 1971. During those most productive days of graduate study, I also developed much of my 1970 working paper on equilibrium asset pricing and the pricing of the capital structure of the firm which formed the core of my later papers on the intertemporal capital asset pricing model, the rational theory of option pricing, and the pricing of corporate debt.

Paul nominated me to be a Junior Fellow at Harvard. After being rejected, however, I had no choice but to get a job. I spent the fall and winter of 1969 interviewing only with departments of economics, but I ended up taking an appointment to teach finance at M.I.T.'s Sloan School of Management. It was Franco Modigliani, with a foot in both the department and Sloan, who made the invitation and who convinced me that I could teach there even though I had no formal training in finance. I had been a student of Franco's and my research on optimal lifetime consumption and portfolio selection supported his Life-Cycle Hypothesis. Our relationship, however, became even stronger in the years after I joined Sloan. I was especially honored and greatly touched when he invited me to be the speaker at the traditional American Economics Association luncheon honoring him for receiving the 1985 Nobel Prize. That occasion (the remarks later published in *Economic Perspectives*) provided the opportunity to express, albeit inadequately, the deep respect and affection I hold for Franco. Some years later, he made a physically very demanding trip to Rome specifically to be the speaker at the National Academy of Lincei on the occasion celebrating my receiving the International INA-Accademia Nazionale dei Lincei Prize.

It was in the process of interviewing for the job at Sloan that I met Myron Scholes, a recent arrival to the faculty from the University of Chicago. As I note in the accompanying lecture, the story of my meeting Myron Scholes and Fischer Black and our subsequent interactions and collaborations are well described in Myron's Nobel Lecture, in our joint tribute in memory of Fischer Black, in Fischer's own writings, and in the book by Peter Bernstein. Thus, even with its obvious central importance to my professional life, both its academic and practitioner parts, there is no need to repeat it here.

When I joined the finance group at M.I.T., the faculty consisted of assistant professors Myron Scholes, Stewart Myers, and Gerry Pogue and senior professors Daniel Holland and Franco Modigliani. Dan specialized in tax matters and Franco was involved in many things everywhere. As a consequence, *de facto*, the junior faculty "ran" everything in the group with respect to both teaching and research. It was a wonderful environment of benign neglect in which all of us could grow. I enjoyed teaching from the start. My first experience was in 1969 as one of four graduate students (Karen Johnson, David Scheffman, and Jeremy Siegel were the others) who team-taught the second monetary course usually taught by Paul Samuelson. I began, however, full-time teaching at Sloan in the fall of 1970 with two regular courses in the Master's degree program in management: general finance and advanced capital markets. In the basic course involving both capital markets and corporate finance, I taught Markowitz-Tobin portfolio theory, the Sharpe(-Lintner-Mossin) Capital Asset Pricing Model, and the Modigliani-Miller theorems, learning much of the material barely before I presented it to the students. For my own sense of security and to provide some evidence of preparation to the students, I gave them detailed (handwritten) teaching notes for each class. Lecturing from them saved me from having to write everything down on the blackboard and saved the students from having to copy what I would have otherwise written. This in turn left more time for in-class discussion. These notes became so popular that I prepared similar ones for every course I taught at Sloan, long after I had learned the subject matter. In the capital markets course that first year, I introduced intertemporal portfolio selection, Black-Scholes type option pricing and hedging and its application to the pricing of corporate liabilities. I did so not as an "outlet" for presenting my research interests but because I thought that the training would be quite useful in practice. I believed that teaching this material, even before it was published, was more important for the M.S. students than for the Ph.D. students since non-academic jobs were not likely to provide the same opportunity as academics to keep up with the research literature after graduation. At Sloan in those days, M.S. and Ph.D. students in finance took the same courses, and so both groups were exposed to this research long before its publication.

Throughout the 18 years I spent at the Sloan School, it was a stimulating and happy place to do research. I shall always owe a great debt to my brilliant colleagues there: Myron Scholes and Fischer Black, Franco Modigliani, Stewart Myers, John Cox, Chi-fu Huang, Terry Marsh, Richard Ruback, Douglas Breeden (unfortunately, only as a visitor), and from the Economics Department, Stanley Fischer and Paul Samuelson. The tenure and the tenor of the finance area varied considerably and it was small, rarely having more than a half dozen members at a time. But the quality of mind, diversity of thought, devotion to the subject of finance, and genuine affection for one another were reliable constants throughout those years.

I see my research interests as fitting into three regimes of roughly equal lengths across time: 1968 to 1977, 1977 to 1987, and 1988 to the present, with a reflective year 1987–1988. The first period was my most productive one for basic research, in terms of both the number of papers produced and the originality and significance of contribution. The central modeling theme was continuous-time stochastic processes with continuous-decision-making by agents. Locating this modeling approach within mathematical economics, I see my models falling in the middle range between simple models (e.g., one or two-periods with a representative agent) designed to give insights (associated by some with the "M.I.T. School") and full general equilibrium models on a grand scale involving an arbitrary number of agents with general preferences and production technologies (often associated with the "Berkeley School"). Compared with discrete-time dynamic formulations, the continuous-time models are mathematically more complex. But by explicitly setting the trading interval and modeling the evolution of the system as diffusion processes, the derived results of the continuous-time models were often more precise and easier to interpret than their discrete-time counterparts. As a consequence, these theoretical models combined enough richness and tractability to be applied normatively for decisions in practice and positively in empirical tests. Of course, all models involve abstractions from complex reality. I see the relative importance of my contribution to be more in selecting "good" abstractions than in introducing and applying mathematical power.

My first decade's research focus on developing dynamic models of optimal lifetime consumption and portfolio selection, equilibrium asset pricing, and contingent-claim pricing shifted in the 1978–1987 period to applications of those models. A series of papers examined the various risk-bearing roles of pay-as-you-go and funded social security and defined-benefit, defined-contribution, and integrated private-sector pension plans. I also applied option-pricing theory to the valuation of deposit insurance, market-timing information, corporate investment decisions, and implicit labor contracts. I worked on models for estimating expected returns on the market portfolio, for fitting dividend and earnings behavior, and for testing of investor market-timing skills. A number of papers including my Presidential address to the American Finance Association examined the rationality of capital-market prices and the effects of market imperfections on equilibrium asset prices. With Stanley Fischer, I also wrote on issues common to macroeconomics and finance. Others whom I was fortunate to publish with during this period were Zvi Bodie, Mathew Gladstein, Roy Henriksson, Alan Marcus, Terry Marsh, Scott Mason and, for the first time, Myron Scholes. In contrast, during the prior decade, I had had only two co-authors: (three papers with) Paul Samuelson and (one with) Marti Subrahmanyam.

In 1987, I took my first-ever sabbatical year to write a book based on my work in continuous-time finance. Peter Dougherty, then an editor at Basil Blackwell, had suggested a book nearly a year before that would use my previously published papers as the core. As it happened, I had been thinking about putting my ideas on the subject together and Peter's expressed interest served as a catalyst. M.I.T. graciously provided my full salary for the year and the Harvard Business School kindly offered an office in which to work. It was a most enjoyable and productive time. With no other commitments, I wrote nearly every day with no limit on length and no set deadline for either any piece or the whole. Earlier writings were corrected and, in some cases, significantly expanded. Five new chapters were created incorporating my cumulative thoughts in the fields of optimal portfolio selection, option pricing, financial intermediation, and general equilibrium theory. I even took pleasure in developing my own extensive index and bibliography.

This reflective year was a watershed, both for my research and for where it would take place. In effect, *Continuous-Time Finance* was the crowning synthesis of my earlier work. Its Chapter 14 on intermediation and institutions, however, represented a bridge to a new direction of my research. From that time until the present, I have focused on understanding the financial system with special emphasis on the dynamics of institutional change. In particular, I am studying the role of financial technology and innovation in driving changes in financial institution and market design, the management of financial-service firms, and the regulatory and the accounting systems. There is, however, continuity of this line of inquiry with the past: Fischer's, Myron's and my derivative-security research provided much of the foundation for the contracting and security-design technology that is central to the extraordinary wave of real-world financial innovation of the past two decades.

My decision to move from M.I.T. to the Harvard Business School in 1988 was significantly influenced by this turn in my research interests. Although it was a difficult decision to make, I have never since doubted that it was the right one. Both the institution and my colleagues have treated me in extraordinary fashion. A prime exemplifying case: shortly after my joining the HBS faculty, then-Dean John McArthur resigned from the George Fisher Baker professorship in order to give it to me. Giving the name chair of the founding-sponsor of the School–known as the "Dean's Chair" since the beginning–to a newly arrived professor of mathematical finance who had not yet taught a single HBS student, was a towering symbol and statement of confidence and support. That recognition meant all the more to me because it was given *after* I had happily accepted the School's offer and this timing made it altogether clear that it was not part of any negotiation. Now, a decade later, I am especially pleased to become the first John and Natty McArthur University Professor and to have the Baker chair become once again the "Dean's Chair."

For nearly a decade, I have enjoyed developing the new work on the financial system: to begin with, on my own, but then quite soon after, in a delightful, productive and multi-faceted collaboration with Zvi Bodie, professor of finance at Boston University, whom I have known since the early 1970s when he was a student in the M.I.T. department of economics. Together we have developed the idea of using a "functional" perspective to analyze and to predict financial institutional change over time and to provide a better understanding of contemporaneous institutional differences across geopolitical borders. Zvi and I have refined and applied this idea in a series of working papers, published articles, and book chapters. In 1992, Zvi and my HBS colleague and my former MIT student, Carliss Baldwin, led the way to the creation of the Global Financial System project at the Harvard Business School. The project which involves several of my finance colleagues (and Zvi) working together with senior management from 15 major global financial-service firms has considerably expanded the research effort devoted to applying the functional approach to the financial system and to the management of financial institutions. Whether published as jointly or singly authored, my work with Zvi in this area has always been collaborative. Conceived at the outset as a parallel development to our research, but completed only now, is our textbook on basic finance that applies this perspective and presents the subject as a set of principles much like first-courses in economics and the physical sciences.

Throughout the last 30 years of academic research, I have been involved in finance practice. The vast bulk of my research has been in mathematical finance theory, but I believe that my involvement in practice has shaped that research and in turn has been shaped by it, this interplay to the benefit of both. A targeted instance can be found in the section of my 1973 rational option pricing paper on pricing and hedging the risk of the "down-and-out" call option. I became aware of such instruments in the early 1970s only as a consequence of a consulting assignment from a firm that was issuing them in Asia. In the decades since, the down-and-out option has become the prototype example of the exotic option, which is now a large, mainstream class of financial-product offerings.

My first consulting experience was in 1969 for a southern California bank on the pricing of warrants. Ironically, had the "equal-yield-for-equal sigma-risk" model I developed *ad hoc* for them been taken to its continuous-trading limit, it would have led to the Black-Scholes pricing formula but of course without any of the rigorous foundation underlying that formula which includes the key hedging insight of Black and Scholes. Myron Scholes and I began working together on consulting projects shortly after I joined the Sloan faculty. In 1972, we were engaged by Mathew Gladstein of the options department of Donaldson, Lufkin, & Jenrette to develop option pricing and hedging models for the over-the-counter market and later for the new Chicago Board Options Exchange. In 1973, Leo Pomerance, head of the DLJ options department, became the first chairman of the CBOE. Myron and I learned much from our DLJ experience and indeed, our first publications together in 1978 and 1982 evolved directly from a mutual-fund project which DLJ helped us to underwrite.

As a consequence of the extraordinary decline in the stock market in 1973–74, Myron and I had an idea for a mutual-fund product that would provide significant downside protection to the investor while at the same time affording significant exposure to upside movements in the stock market. The strategy designed to do this was to purchase a diversified portfolio of call options with 10 percent of the assets and to invest the balance of the assets in short-term money-market instruments, with those proportions rebalanced every 6 months. Since the strategy involved option buying instead of option writing, many cautioned us that the SEC might see it as "too speculative" for the first option-based mutual fund in the United States and thus, would create serious roadblocks. They were wrong: the staff of the SEC apparently understood the fund's relatively conservative design and approved it with essentially no delays. The strategy was thus implemented with the creation of Money Market/Options Investment, Inc., an open-ended mutual fund, which went effective in February 1976. The portfolio's subsequent performance fit the simulations projected for it. Nevertheless, and despite being a direct predecessor to the portfolio-insurance products of the 1980s and the various successful "floor" products offered around the globe in the 1990s, MM/OI was not a commercial success. Still, it was for us a broadening experience about the multi-dimensional aspects of setting up a new financial entity. As Myron is fond of observing, "Sometimes the early bird gets the worm … and sometimes, it gets frozen."

For the rest of the 1970s and much of 1980s, I kept my hand in practice, serving on a few mutual fund boards and being elected a trustee of College Retirement Equities Fund. During the early 1980s, several of my former students from M.I.T., most of them Ph.D.s, were attracted to Salomon Brothers, the global investment bank, by John Meriwether and under his leadership, they helped build an enormously successful proprietary trading group focused on arbitrage in the fixed-income markets. The core financial technology used in the group was based on the Black-Scholes-Merton derivative-security models, but it was highly refined to take account of much greater empirical detail and practical market experience. In 1988, one of those former students, Eric Rosenfeld, and Thomas Strauss, then President of Salomon, came to see me about becoming a special consultant to the Office of the Chairman. They made me an offer I couldn't refuse: unlike the simple model-building/product-design role of my past consultancies, this one also called for a role as trusted advisor (with technical skills) to the CEO on business matters of the firm and on the direction of institutional change in the global financial system. One could hardly imagine a better fit to inform, and to be informed by, my then-new direction of research on the functional perspective. Over the next four years, I learned much about the operations and management of a global intermediary, and trust that I contributed something as well. I definitely strengthened old friendships with former students and developed new friendships with their colleagues, and Myron and I got back together in practice when he joined Salomon from Stanford.

In early 1993, John Meriwether who had left Salomon in 1991, Eric Rosenfeld who had recently left and James McEntee, former chairman and cofounder of Carroll-McEntee, the primary government-bond dealer, and John's long-time friend, had the idea of building a new firm to undertake fixed-income arbitrage on a global basis. The thought of working with John and Eric once again and having a hand in building a large-scale financial firm from scratch was exciting and I immediately volunteered to help out.

Over the ensuing months, one at a time, senior members of John's old group left Salomon and showed up ready to get involved in what became Long-Term Capital Management (LTCM): Victor Haghani arrived in the spring; Gregory Hawkins and Myron Scholes (bringing us back together in practice once again) in the summer; William Krasker in the fall; and Richard Leahy and Larry Hilibrand at year end. The last of the founders, David Mullins, who joined LTCM in late winter, never worked at Salomon. With a Ph.D. from M.I.T. and 15 years on the finance faculty at Harvard Business School before going into government service, he exemplifies the strong M.I.T. and HBS connections among the founders of LTCM: seven of the eleven founders (and nine of the current sixteen principals of the firm) were either graduates, or on their faculties, or both.

This small group of founding principals, together with a few key early employees, put together and tested the financial, telecommunication, and computer technologies, hired the strategists and operations people to run them, designed the organizational structure of the business, executed the complex contractual agreements with investors and counterparties, found and outfitted physical quarters in both the United States and London, and helped to raise over $1 billion from investors. The design and development efforts along each of these dimensions attempted to marry the best of finance theory with the best of finance practice. It all came together in February 1994 when the firm began active business. Today, LTCM has 180 employees, a third office in Tokyo, and its capital has grown considerably.

It was deliciously intense and exciting to have been a part of creating LTCM. For making it possible, I will never be able to adequately express my indebtedness to my extraordinarily talented LTCM colleagues.

The distinctive LTCM experience from the beginning to the present characterizes the theme of the productive interaction of finance theory and finance practice. Indeed, in a twist on the more familiar version of that theme, the major investment magazine, *Institutional Investor*, characterized the remarkable collection of people at LTCM as "The best finance faculty in the world."

In long retrospect, unexpected roads happily traveled.

Personal

Born: July 31, 1944
          New York, New York

Address: Harvard Business School
          Morgan Hall 397
          Soldiers Field
          Boston, MA 02163

Education

B.S., Columbia University (Engineering Mathematics), 1966
M.S., California Institute of Technology (Applied Mathematics), 1967
Ph.D., Massachusetts Institute of Technology (Economics), 1970

Honorary Degrees

Masters of Arts, Harvard University, 1989
Doctor of Laws, University of Chicago, 1991
Professeur Honoris Causa, Hautes Etudes Commerciales (Paris), 1995
Doctoris Honoris Causa, University of Lausanne, 1996
Doctoris Honoris Causa, University Paris-Dauphine, 1997
Honorary Doctor, National Sun Yat-sen University, 1998

Academic Appointments

John and Natty McArthur University Professor, Graduate School of Business
    Administration, Harvard University, 1998–

George Fisher Baker Professor of Business Administration, Graduate School of Business Administration, Harvard University, 1988–1998

Invited Professor of Finance, Faculté des Sciences Economiques, Université de Nantes, June 1993

Visiting Professor of Finance, Graduate School of Business Administration, Harvard University, 1987–1988

J.C. Penney Professor of Management, A.P. Sloan School of Management, Massachusetts Institute of Technology, 1980–1988

Assistant Professor of Finance, 1970–73, Associate Professor, 1973–74; Professor 1974–80, A.P. Sloan School of Management, Massachusetts Institute of Technology

Instructor, Department of Economics, Massachusetts Institute of Technology, 1969–1970

Research Assistant to Paul Samuelson, Massachusetts Institute of Technology, 1968–1970

Other Professional Appointments

Principal, co-founder, Limited Partner, Long-Term Capital Management, L.P. (1993–)

Research Associate, National Bureau of Economic Research, 1979–

Trustee, College Retirement Equities Fund (1988–1996)

Director, Travelers Investment Management Company (1987–1991)

Director, ABT Investment Series (1983–1988)

Director, ABT Utility Income Fund (1982–1988)

Trustee, ABT Growth and Income Trust (1982–1988)

Director, Nova Fund (1980–1988)

Elected Societies and Positions

Member, Tau Beta Pi, Columbia University, 1965

Member, Sigma Xi, Massachusetts Institute of Technology, 1970

Director, American Finance Association, 1982–84; 1987–88

Fellow, Econometric Society, 1983

Fellow, American Academy of Arts and Sciences, 1986

President, American Finance Association, 1986

Vice President, The Society for Financial Studies, 1993–96

Member, National Academy of Sciences, 1993

Senior Fellow, International Association of Financial Engineers, 1994

Fellow, Institute for Quantitative Research in Finance ("Q Group"), 1997

Honorary Member, the Bachelier Finance Society, 1997

Awards

1964	Faculty Scholar Award, Columbia University
1971–72	Salgo-Noren Award for Excellence in Teaching, Massachusetts Institute of Technology

1977–78	Graduate Student Council Teaching Award, Massachusetts Institute of Technology
1983	Leo Melamed Prize, University of Chicago
1985, 1986	First Prize, Roger Murray Prize Competition, Institute for Quantitative Research in Finance
1989	Distinguished Scholar Award, Eastern Finance Association
1993	International INA - Accademia Nazionale dei Lincei Prize, National Academy of Lincei, Rome
1993	FORCE Award for Financial Innovation, Fuqua School of Business, Duke University
1993	Financial Engineer of the Year Award, International Association of Financial Engineers
1997	The Bank of Sweden Prize in Economic Sciences in Memory of Alfred Nobel
1998	Inducted, Derivatives Hall of Fame, *Derivatives Strategy*

Selected Lectures

1975	Distinguished Speaker Lecture, Western Finance Association
1985	Mortimer Hess Memorial Lecture, Association of the Bar of the City of New York
1988	12th Annual Lecture, Geneva Association, Paris
1992	Scholl Chair in Finance Distinguished Speaker Lecture, DePaul University
1993	Lecture, Discussion Meeting on Mathematical Finance, The Royal Society, London
1993	Keynote, 10th International Conference in Finance, Association Francaise de France
1994	AEA/AFA Speaker, Allied Social Sciences Meetings
1994	Speaker, International Monetary Conference, London
1995	Lecture, Newton Institute Seminar, Isaac Newton Institute for Mathematical Sciences, Cambridge
1995	Keynote, 12th International Conference in Finance, Association Francaise de France
1995	Keynote, 25th Anniversary, Financial Management Association
1996	Oxford University Press and Massachusetts Institute of Technology Sloan School of Management Distinguished Lectures in Business, Massachusetts Institute of Technology, Cambridge
1996	Donor's Lecture, London Business School, London
1996	Inaugural, Dean's Research Seminar, Harvard Business School
1996	Faculty Inaugural Session, University of Lausanne
1996	Paolo Baffi Lecture on Money and Finance, Bank of Italy, Rome
1997	Edgar Lorch Memorial Lecture, Sigma Xi, Columbia University
1998	Lionel McKenzie Lecture, University of Rochester
1998	Martin H. Crego Lecture, Vassar College

1998   I.E. Block Community Lecture, Society for Industrial and Applied
       Mathematics

Advisory and Editorial Boards

Current:
International Board of Scientific Advisers, Tinbergen Institute (1995–)
Advisory Board, Brookings-Wharton (1997–)
Advisory Board, *International Journal of Theoretical & Applied Finance* (1997–)
Advisory Board, Center for Global Management and Research, George
   Washington University (1996–)
Advisory Board, *European Finance Review* (1997–)
Advisory Board, *Journal of Financial Education* (1995–)
Advisory Board, *Review of Derivatives Research* (1993–)
Advisory Board, *Japan Financial Economics Association* (1993–)
Advisory Board, *Mathematical Finance* (1989–)
Editorial Board, *Finance India* (1988–)
Associate Editor, *Journal of Fixed Income* (1991–)
Associate Editor, *Journal of Banking and Finance* (1977–1979,1992–)

Past:
Advisory Board, *The New Palgrave Dictionary of Money and Finance* (1989–1992)
Selection Editor, *Papers and Proceedings, Journal of Finance,* July 1986
Co-Editor, *Journal of Financial Economics* (1974–1977)
Associate Editor, *Financial Review* (1992–1997)
Associate Editor, *Geneva Papers on Risk and Insurance* (1989–1996)
Associate Editor, *Journal of Financial Economics* (1977–1983)
Associate Editor, *Journal of Money, Credit and Banking* (1974–1979)
Associate Editor, *Journal of Finance* (1973–1977)
Associate Editor, *International Economic Review* (1972–1977)
Founding Committee, *Review of Financial Studies* (1986)

Publications, Cases and Unpublished Papers

Books
Finance, with Zvi Bodie, New Jersey: Prentice-Hall, 1998.
The Global Financial System: A Functional Perspective, with D. Crane, K.
   Froot, S. Mason, A. Perold, Z. Bodie, E. Sirri, and P. Tufano, Boston:
   Harvard Business School Press, 1995.
Cases in Financial Engineering: Applied Studies of Financial Innovation, with
   S. Mason, A.F. Perold, and P. Tufano, Prentice-Hall, 1995.
Continuous-Time Finance, Basil Blackwell, Inc. 1990; Revised Edition 1992.
The Collected Scientific Papers of Paul A. Samuelson Volume III, editor,
   Cambridge, MIT Press 1972.

426

Published Papers

"The Global Financial System Project," with P. Tufano, in T.K. McCraw, ed., **Intellectual Venture Capital: Essays in Honor of Dean John H. McArthur**, Boston: Harvard Business School Press, forthcoming 1998.

"Applications of Option-Pricing Theory: Twenty-Five Years Later," *Les Prix Nobel 1997*, Stockholm: Nobel Foundation.

"Foreword," **Mathematics of Derivative Securities,** M.A.H. Dempster and S. Pliska, eds., Cambridge University Press, 1997.

"A Model of Contract Guarantees for Credit-Sensitive, Opaque Financial Intermediaries," *European Finance Review*, Vol. 1, No. 1, 1997, pp. 1–13.

"On the Role of the Wiener Process in Finance Theory and Practice: The Case of Replicating Portfolios," in D. Jerison, I.M. Singer, and D.W. Stroock, eds., **The Legacy of Norbert Wiener: A Centennial Symposium**, PSPM Series, Vol. 60, Providence, RI: American Mathematical Society, 1997.

"Foreword," **Managing Derivative Risks**, L. Chew, Chichester: John Wiley & Sons, 1996.

"Fischer Black," with M. Scholes, *Journal of Finance*, 50, December 1995.

"A Functional Perspective of Financial Intermediation," *Financial Management*, Volume 24, Summer 1995.

"Financial Innovation and the Management and Regulation of Financial Institutions," *Journal of Banking and Finance*, 19, July 1995.

"Mark-to-Market Accounting for Banks and Thrifts: Lessons from the Danish Experience," with V. Bernard and K. Palepu, *Journal of Accounting Research*, 33, 1, Spring 1995.

"Influence of Mathematical Models in Finance on Practice: Past, Present and Future," **Philosophical Transactions of the Royal Society of London**, Series A, Volume 347, June 1994. Reprinted in *Financial Practice and Education*, Spring 1995.

"Pension Benefit Guarantees in the United States: A Functional Analysis," with Z. Bodie in R. Schmitt, ed., **The Future of Pensions in the United States**, Pension Research Council, Philadelphia: University of Pennsylvania Press, 1993.

"Theory of Risk Capital in Financial Firms," with A. Perold, *Journal of Applied Corporate Finance*, Fall 1993.

"Management of Risk Capital in Financial Firms," with A. Perold, in S.L. Hayes III, ed., **Financial Services: Perspectives and Challenges**, Boston: Harvard Business School Press 1993.

"Deposit Insurance Reform: A Functional Approach," with Z. Bodie, in A. Meltzer and C. Plosser, eds., **Carnegie-Rochester Conference Series on Public Policy**, Volume 38, June 1993.

"Operation and Regulation in Financial Intermediation: A Functional Perspective," in P. Englund, ed., **Operation and Regulation of Financial Markets**, Stockholm: The Economic Council 1993.

"Optimal Investment Strategies for University Endowment Funds," in C. Clotfelter and M. Rothschild, eds., **Studies of Supply and Demand in**

Higher Education, Chicago: University of Chicago Press 1993. Chapter 21 in **Continuous-Time Finance**.

"On the Management of Financial Guarantees," with Z. Bodie, *Financial Management,* 21, Winter 1992.

"Labor Supply Flexibility and Portfolio Choice in a Life-Cycle Model," with Z. Bodie and W. Samuelson, *Journal of Economic Dynamics and Control,* 16, July/October 1992.

"Financial Innovation and Economic Performance," *Journal of Applied Corporate Finance,* Winter 1992.

"The Financial System and Economic Performance," *Journal of Financial Services Research,* 4, December 1990.

"Capital Market Theory and the Pricing of Financial Securities," in B. Friedman and F. Hahn, eds., **Handbook of Monetary Economics**, Amsterdam: North-Holland 1990.

"The Changing Nature of Debt and Equity: A Discussion," in R.W. Kopeke and E.S. Rosengren, eds., **Are the Distinctions Between Debt and Equity Disappearing?** Conference Series #33, Federal Reserve Bank of Boston, 1990.

"On the Application of the Continuous-Time Theory of Finance to Financial Intermediation and Insurance," Twelfth Annual Lecture of the Geneva Association, *The Geneva Papers on Risk & Insurance,* 14, July 1989.

"Options," in **The New Palgrave: A Dictionary of Economic Theory and Doctrine**, London: MacMillan Press, Ltd. 1987. Revised in **The New Palgrave Dictionary of Money and Finance**, London: MacMillan Press, Ltd. 1992.

"Continuous-Time Stochastic Models," in **The New Palgrave: A Dictionary of Economic Theory and Doctrine**, London: MacMillan Press, Ltd. 1987. Revised in **The New Palgrave Dictionary of Money and Finance**, London: MacMillan Press, Ltd. 1992.

"In Honor of Nobel Laureate, Franco Modigliani," *Economic Perspectives,* 1, Fall 1987.

"Defined Benefit Versus Defined Contribution Pension Plans: What Are the Real Tradeoffs?" with Z. Bodie and A.J. Marcus in **Pensions in the U.S. Economy**, J. Shoven and D. Wise, eds., Chicago: University of Chicago Press 1987.

"A Simple Model of Capital Market Equilibrium With Incomplete Information," *Journal of Finance,* 42, July 1987.

"On the Current State of the Stock Market Rationality Hypothesis," in **Macroeconomics and Finance: Essays in Honor of Franco Modigliani**, R. Dornbusch, S. Fischer and J. Bossons, eds., Cambridge: MIT Press 1987.

"Pension Plan Integration as Insurance Against Social Security Risk," with Z. Bodie and A.J. Marcus, in **Issues in Pension Economics**, Z. Bodie, J.B. Shoven, and D.A. Wise, eds., Chicago: University of Chicago Press 1987.

"Dividend Behavior for the Aggregate Stock Market," with T.A. Marsh, *Journal of Business,* 60, January 1987.

"Dividend Variability and Variance Bounds Tests for the Rationality of Stock Market Prices," with T.A. Marsh, *American Economic Review,* 76, June 1986.

"Implicit Labor Contracts Viewed as Options: A Discussion of 'Insurance

Aspects of Pensions','" in **Pensions, Labor, and Individual Choice**, D.A. Wise, ed., Chicago: University of Chicago Press 1985.

"The Role of Contingent Claims Analysis in Corporate Finance," with S. Mason, in **Recent Advances in Corporate Finance**, E.I. Altman and M.G. Subrahmanyam, eds., Homewood: Richard D. Irwin 1985.

"Macroeconomics and Finance: The Role of the Stock Market," with S. Fischer, in **Essays on Macroeconomic Implications of Financial and Labor Markets and Political Processes**, K. Brunner and A.H. Meltzer, eds., Vol. 21 Amsterdam: North-Holland, Autumn 1984.

"On Consumption-Indexed Public Pension Plans," in **Financial Aspects of the U.S. Pension System**, Z. Bodie and J. Shoven, eds., Chicago: University of Chicago Press 1983. Chapter 18 in **Continuous-Time Finance.**

"On the Role of Social Security As a Means for Efficient Risk-Bearing in an Economy Where Human Capital Is Not Tradeable," in **Financial Aspects of the U.S. Pension System**, Z. Bodie and J. Shoven, eds., University of Chicago Press 1983.

"Financial Economics," in **Paul Samuelson and Modern Economic Theory**, E.C. Brown and R.M. Solow, eds., New York: McGraw-Hill 1983.

"On the Mathematics and Economic Assumptions of Continuous-Time Financial Models," in **Financial Economics: Essays in Honor of Paul Cootner**, W.F. Sharpe and C.M. Cootner, eds., Englewood Cliffs: Prentice Hall 1982. Chapter 3 in **Continuous-Time Finance.**

"On the Microeconomic Theory of Investment Under Uncertainty," in **Handbook of Mathematical Economics**, Volume II, K. Arrow and M. Intriligator, eds., Amsterdam: North-Holland Publishing Company, 1982.

"The Returns and Risk of Alternative Put Option Portfolio Investment Strategies," with M.S. Scholes and M.L. Gladstein, *Journal of Business,* 55, January 1982.

"On Market Timing and Investment Performance Part II: Statistical Procedures for Evaluating Forecasting Skills," with R.D. Henriksson, *Journal of Business,* 54, October 1981.

"On Market Timing and Investment Performance Part I: An Equilibrium Theory of Value for Market Forecasts," *Journal of Business,* 54, July 1981.

"On Estimating the Expected Return on the Market: An Exploratory Investigation," *Journal of Financial Economics,* 8, December 1980.

"Capital Requirements in the Regulation of Financial Intermediaries: A Discussion," in **Proceedings, The Regulation of Financial Institutions**, Conference Series #21, Federal Reserve Bank of Boston, October 1979.

"On the Cost of Deposit Insurance When There Are Surveillance Costs," *Journal of Business,* 51, July 1978. Chapter 20 in **Continuous-Time Finance.**

"The Returns and Risk of Alternative Call Option Portfolio Investment Strategies," with M.S. Scholes and M.L. Gladstein, *Journal of Business,* 51, April 1978.

"On the Pricing of Contingent Claims and the Modigliani-Miller Theorem," *Journal of Financial Economics,* 5, November 1977. Chapter 13 in **Continuous-Time Finance.**

"An Analytic Derivation of the Cost of Loan Guarantees and Deposit Insurance: An Application of Modern Option Pricing Theory," *Journal of Banking and Finance*, 1, June 1977.

"A Reexamination of the Capital Asset Pricing Model," in **Studies in Risk and Return**, J. Bicksler and I. Friend, eds., Cambridge, MA: Ballinger 1977.

"The Impact on Option Pricing of Specification Error in the Underlying Stock Price Returns," *Journal of Finance*, 31, May 1976.

"Option Pricing When Underlying Stock Returns are Discontinuous," *Journal of Financial Economics*, 3, January–February 1976. Chapter 9 in **Continuous-Time Finance.**

"Theory of Finance From the Perspective of Continuous Time," *Journal of Financial and Quantitative Analysis*, 10, November 1975.

"An Asymptotic Theory of Growth Under Uncertainty," *Review of Economic Studies*, 42, July 1975. Chapter 17 in **Continuous-Time Finance.**

"On the Pricing of Corporate Debt: The Risk Structure of Interest Rates," *Journal of Finance*, 29, May 1974. Chapter 12 in **Continuous-Time Finance.**

"Fallacy of the Log-Normal Approximation to Optimal Portfolio Decision Making Over Many Periods," with P.A. Samuelson, *Journal of Financial Economics*, 1, May 1974.

"Generalized Mean-Variance Tradeoffs for Best Perturbation Corrections to Approximate Portfolio Decisions," with P.A. Samuelson, *Journal of Finance*, 29, March 1974.

"The Optimality of a Competitive Stock Market," with M.C. Subrahmanyam, *Bell Journal of Economics and Management Science*, 5, Spring 1974.

"An Intertemporal Capital Asset Pricing Model," *Econometrica*, 41, September 1973. Chapter 15 in **Continuous-Time Finance.**

"Book Review: Studies in the Theory of Capital Markets, M.C. Jensen, ed.," *Journal of Money, Credit, and Banking*, May 1973.

"Theory of Rational Option Pricing," *Bell Journal of Economics and Management Science*, 4, Spring 1973. Chapter 8 in **Continuous-Time Finance.**

"The Relationship Between Put and Call Option Prices: Comment," *Journal of Finance*, 28, March 1973.

"Appendix: Continuous-Time Speculative Processes," in P.A. Samuelson, 'Mathematics of Speculative Price,' *SIAM Review*, 15, January 1973.

"An Analytical Derivation of the Efficient Portfolio Frontier," *Journal of Financial and Quantitative Analysis*, 10, September 1972.

"Optimum Consumption and Portfolio Rules in a Continuous-Time Model," *Journal of Economic Theory*, 3, December 1971. Chapter 5 in **Continuous-Time Finance.**

"A Golden Golden-Rule for Welfare-Maximization in an Economy With a Varying Population Growth Rate," *Western Economic Journal*, 4, December 1969. Chapter III of Ph.D. dissertation.

"Lifetime Portfolio Selection Under Uncertainty: The Continuous-Time Case," *Review of Economics and Statistics*, 51, August 1969. Chapter II of Ph.D. dissertation. Chapter 4 in **Continuous-Time Finance.**

"A Complete Model of Warrant Pricing That Maximizes Utility," with P.A.

Samuelson, *Industrial Management Review,* 10, Winter 1969. Chapter IV of Ph.D. dissertation. Chapter 7 in **Continuous-Time Finance.**

"The 'Motionless' Motion of Swift's Flying Island," *Journal of the History of Ideas,* 27, April–June 1966.

Cases and Unpublished Papers

Harrington Financial Group," with A. Moel, Harvard Business School Case #9-297-088, April 1997.

"Smith Breeden Associates: The Equity Plus Fund," with A. Moel, Harvard Business School Case #9-297-089, April 1997.

"Savings and Loans and the Mortgage Markets," with A. Moel, Harvard Business School Case #N9-297-090, February 1997.

"Financial Infrastructure and Public Policy: A Functional Perspective," with Z. Bodie, Harvard Business School, Working Paper #95-064, February 1995.

"The Informational Role of Asset Prices: The Case of Implied Volatility," with Z. Bodie, Harvard Business School, Working Paper #95-063, February 1995.

"A Conceptual Framework for Analyzing the Financial Environment," with Z. Bodie, Harvard Business School, Working Paper #95-062, February 1995.

"On the Management of Deposit Insurance and Other Guarantees," with Z. Bodie, Working Paper #92-081, May 1992.

"Pension Reform and Privatization in International Perspective: The Case of Israel," with Z. Bodie, Harvard Business School, Working Paper #92-082, May 1992. Published (in Hebrew), *The Economics Quarterly,* 152 (August 1992).

"A Framework for the Economic Analysis of Deposit Insurance and Other Guarantees," with Z. Bodie, Harvard Business School, Working Paper #92-063, January 1992.

"Optimal Portfolio Rules in Continuous Time When the Nonnegativity Constraint on Consumption is Binding," Harvard Business School, Working Paper #90-042, December 1989. Chapter 6 in **Continuous-Time Finance.**

"Earnings Variability and Variance Bounds Tests for the Rationality of Stock Market Prices," with T.A. Marsh, MIT Sloan School of Management, Working Paper #1559-84, April 1984.

"Aggregate Dividend Behavior and Its Implications for Tests of Stock Market Rationality," with T.A. Marsh, MIT Sloan School of Management, Working Paper #1475-83, September 1983.

"Continuous-Time Portfolio Theory and the Pricing of Contingent Claims," MIT Sloan School of Management, Working Paper, November 1976.

"A Dynamic General Equilibrium Model of the Asset Market and Its Application to the Pricing of the Capital Structure of the Firm," MIT Sloan School of Management, Working Paper #497-70, December 1970. Chapter 11 in **Continuous-Time Finance.**

"Analytical Optimal Control Theory as Applied to Stochastic and Non-Stochastic Economics," Ph.D. dissertation, Massachusetts Institute of Technology, September 1970.

"An Empirical Investigation of the Samuelson Rational Warrant Pricing Theory," Chapter V in Ph.D. dissertation, class paper, Massachusetts Institute of Technology, Spring 1969.

"Restrictions on Rational Option Pricing: A Set of Arbitrage Conditions," mimeographed, Massachusetts Institute of Technology, August 1968.

APPLICATIONS OF OPTION-PRICING THEORY: TWENTY-FIVE YEARS LATER*

Nobel Lecture, December 9, 1997

by

ROBERT C. MERTON

Graduate School of Business Administration, Harvard University, Boston, MA 02163, USA and Long-Term Capital Management, L.P., Greenwich, CT 06831, USA

INTRODUCTION[1]

The news from Stockholm that the prize in economic sciences had been given for option-pricing theory provided unique and signal recognition to the rapidly advancing, but still relatively new discipline, within economics which relates mathematical finance theory and finance practice. The special sphere of finance within economics is the study of allocation and deployment of economic resources, both spatially and across time, in an uncertain environment. To capture the influence and interaction of time and uncertainty effectively requires sophisticated mathematical and computational tools. Indeed, mathematical models of modern finance contain some truly elegant applications of probability and optimization theory. These applications challenge the most powerful computational technologies. But, of course, all that is elegant and challenging in science need not also be practical; and surely, not all that is practical in science is elegant and challenging. Here we have both. In the time since publication of our early work on the option-pricing model, the mathematically complex models of finance theory have had a direct and wide-ranging influence on finance practice. This conjoining of intrinsic intellectual interest with extrinsic application is central to research in modern finance.

It was not always thus. The origins of much of the mathematics in modern finance can be traced to Louis Bachelier's 1900 dissertation on the theory of speculation, framed as an option-pricing problem. This work marks the twin births of both the continuous-time mathematics of stochastic processes and the continuous-time economics of derivative-security pricing. Kiyoshi Itô (1987) was greatly influenced by Bachelier's work in his development in the

* I am grateful to Robert K. Merton, Lisa Meulbroek, and Myron Scholes for their helpful suggestions on this lecture and for so much more. Over the past thirty years, I have come to owe an incalculable debt to Paul A. Samuelson, my teacher, mentor, colleague, co-researcher, and friend. Try as I have (cf. Merton, 1983, 1992), I cannot find the words to pay sufficient tribute to him. I dedicate this lecture to Paul and to the memory of Fischer Black. Copyright © Nobel Foundation.
[1] This section draws on Merton (1994, 1995, 1997b).

1940s and early 1950s of the stochastic calculus, later to become an essential mathematical tool in finance. Paul Samuelson's theory of rational warrant pricing, published in 1965, was also motivated by the same piece. However, Bachelier's important work was largely lost to financial economists for more than a half century. During most of that period, mathematically complex models with a strong influence on practice were not at all the hallmarks of finance theory. Before the pioneering work of Markowitz, Modigliani, Miller, Sharpe, Lintner, Fama, and Samuelson in the late 1950s and 1960s, finance theory was little more than a collection of anecdotes, rules of thumb, and shuffling of accounting data. It was not until the end of the 1960s and early 1970s that models of finance in academe become considerably more sophisticated, involving both the intertemporal and uncertainty dimensions of valuation and optimal decision-making. The new models of dynamic portfolio theory, intertemporal capital asset pricing, and derivative-security pricing employed stochastic differential and integral equations, stochastic dynamic programming, and partial differential equations. These mathematical tools were a quantum level more complex than had been used in finance before and they are still the core tools employed today.

The most influential development in terms of impact on finance practice was the Black-Scholes model for option pricing. Yet paradoxically, the mathematical model was developed entirely in theory, with essentially no reference to empirical option-pricing data as motivation for its formulation. Publication of the model brought the field to almost immediate closure on the fundamentals of option-pricing theory. At the same time, it provided a launching pad for refinements of the theory, extensions to derivative-security pricing in general, and a wide range of other applications, some completely outside the realm of finance. The Chicago Board Options Exchange (CBOE), the first public options exchange, began trading in April 1973, and by 1975, traders on the CBOE were using the model to both price and hedge their option positions. It was so widely used that, in those pre-personal-computer days, Texas Instruments sold a handheld calculator specially programmed to produce Black-Scholes option prices and hedge ratios. That rapid adoption was all the more impressive, as the mathematics used in the model were not part of the standard mathematical training of either academic economists or practitioner traders.

Academic finance research of the 1960s including capital asset pricing, performance and risk measurement, and the creation of the first large-scale databases for security prices essential for serious empirical work have certainly influenced subsequent finance practice. Still the speed of adoption and the intensity of that influence was not comparable to the influence of the option model. There are surely several possible explanations for the different rates of adoption in the 1960s and the 1970s. My hypothesis is that manifest "need" determined that difference. In the 1960s, especially in the United States, financial markets exhibited unusually low volatility: the stock market rose steadily, interest rates were relatively stable, and exchange rates were fixed. Such a market environment provided investors and financial-service firms with little incentive to adopt new financial technology, especially technology designed to help manage risk. However, the 1970s experienced several events that caused both structural changes and large increases in volatility. Among the more important events were: the shift from fixed to floating exchange rates with the fall of Bretton Woods and the devaluation of the dollar; the world oil-price shock with the creation of OPEC; double-digit inflation and interest rates in the United States; and the extraordinary real-return decline in the U.S. stock market from a peak of around 1050 on the Dow Jones Industrial Average in the beginning of 1973 to about 580 at the end of 1974. As a result, the increased demand for managing risks in a volatile and structurally different economic environment contributed to the major success of the derivative-security exchanges created in the 1970s to trade listed options on stocks, futures on major currencies, and futures on fixed-income instruments. This success in turn increased the speed of adoption for quantitative financial models to help value options and assess risk exposures.

The influence of option-pricing theory on finance practice has not been limited to financial options traded in markets or even to derivative securities generally. As we shall see, the underlying conceptual framework originally used to derive the option-pricing formula can be used to price and evaluate the risk in a wide array of applications, both financial and non-financial. Option-pricing technology has played a fundamental role in supporting the creation of new financial products and markets around the globe. In the present and in the impending future, that role will continue expanding to support the design of entirely new financial institutions, decision-making by senior management, and the formulation of public policy on the financial system. To underscore that point, I begin with a few remarks about financial innovation of the past, this adumbration to be followed in later sections with a detailed listing of applications of the options technology that include some observations on the directions of future changes in financial services.

New financial product and market designs, improved computer and telecommunications technology and advances in the theory of finance during the past quarter-century have led to dramatic and rapid changes in the structure of global financial markets and institutions. The scientific breakthroughs in financial modeling in this period both shaped and were shaped by the extraordinary flow of financial innovation which coincided with those changes. Thus, the publication of the option-pricing model in 1973 surely helped the development and growth of the listed options and over-the-counter (OTC) derivatives markets. But, the extraordinary growth and success of those markets just as surely stimulated further development and research focus on the derivative-security pricing models. To see this in perspective, consider some of the innovative changes in market structure and scale of the global financial system since 1973. There occurred the aforementioned fall of Bretton Woods leading to floating-exchange rates for currencies; the development of the national mortgage market in the United States which in turn restructured that entire industry; passage of the Employee Retirement Income Security Act (ERISA) in 1974 with the subsequent development of the U.S. pension-fund industry; the first money-market fund with check writing that also took place in 1974; and the explosive growth in mutual fund assets from $48 billion 25 years ago to $4.3 trillion today (a ninety-fold increase), with one institution, Fidelity Investments, accounting for some $500 billion by itself. In this same period, average daily trading volume on the New York Stock Exchange grew from 12 million shares to more than 300 million. Even more dramatic were the changes in Europe and in Asia. The cumulative impact has significantly affected all of us–as users, producers, or overseers of the financial system.

Nowhere has this been more the case than in the development, refinement and broad-based implementation of contracting technology. Derivative securities such as futures, options, swaps and other contractual agreements–the underlying substantive instruments for which our model was developed–provide a prime example. Innovations in financial-contracting technology have improved efficiency by expanding opportunities for risk sharing, lowering transactions costs and reducing information and agency costs. The numbers reported for the global use of derivative securities are staggering (the figure of $70 trillion appeared more than once in the news stories surrounding the award of the Prize and there are a number of world banking institutions with reported multi-trillion dollar, off-balance-sheet derivative positions). However, since these are notional amounts (and often involve double-counting), they are meaningless for assessing either the importance or the risk-exposure to derivative securities.[2] Nevertheless, it is enough to say here that, properly measured, derivatives are ubiquitous throughout the world financial system and that they are used widely by non-financial firms and sovereigns as well as by institutions in virtually every part of their financing and risk-managing activities. Some observers see the extraordinary growth in the use of derivatives as fad-like, but a more likely explanation is the vast saving in transactions costs derived from their use. The cost of implementing financial strategies for institutions using derivatives can be one-tenth to one-twentieth of the cost of executing them in the underlying cash-market securities.[3] The significance of reducing spread costs in financing can be quite dramatic for corporations and for sovereigns: for instance, not long ago, a 1 percent (i.e., 100-basis-point) reduction in debt-spread cost on Italian government debt would have reduced the deficit by an amount equal to 1.25 percent of the gross domestic product of Italy.

Further improved technology, together with growing breadth and experience in the applications of derivatives, should continue to reduce transactions costs as both users and producers of derivatives move along the learning curve. Like retail depositors with automatic-teller machines in banks, initial

---

[2] Notional amounts typically represent either the total value of the underlying asset on which payments on the derivative is determined (e.g interest-rate swap contracts) or the exercise price on an option. The value of the derivative contract itself is often a small fraction of its notional amount.

[3] See André F. Perold (1992) for a case study illustrating the savings in transactions costs, taxes, and custodial fees from using derivatives instead of the cash market. Myron S. Scholes (1976) provides an early analysis of the effect of taxes on option prices.

resistance by institutional clients to contractual agreements can be high, but once customers use them they tend not to return to the traditional alternatives for implementing financial strategies.

A central process in the past two decades has been the remarkable rate of globalization of the financial system. Even today, inspection of the diverse financial systems of individual nation-states would lead one to question how effective integration across geopolitical borders could have realistically taken place since those systems are rarely compatible in institutional forms, regulations, laws, tax structures, and business practices. Still, significant integration did take place. This was made possible in large part by derivative securities functioning as "adapters". In general, the flexibility created by the widespread use of contractual agreements, other derivatives, and specialized institutional designs provides an offset to dysfunctional institutional rigidities.[4] More specifically, derivative-security contracting technologies provide efficient means for creating cross-border interfaces among otherwise incompatible domestic systems, without requiring widespread or radical changes within each system. For that reason, implementation of derivative-security technology and markets within smaller and emerging-market countries may help form important gateways of access to world capital markets and global risk-sharing. Such developments and changes are not limited only to the emerging-market countries with their new financial systems. Derivatives and other contracting technologies are likely to play a significant role in the financial engineering of the major transitions required for European Monetary Union and for the major restructuring of financial institutions in Japan.

With this introduction as background, I turn now to the key conceptual and mathematical framework underlying the option-pricing model and its subsequent applications.

GENERAL DERIVATION OF DERIVATIVE-SECURITY PRICING

I understand that it is customary in these lectures for the Laureates to review the background and the process leading up to their discoveries. Happily, there is no need to do so here since that has been done elsewhere in Black (1989), Bernstein (1992, Ch.11), Merton and Scholes (1995), and Scholes (1998). Instead, I briefly summarize. My principal contribution to the Black-Scholes option-pricing theory was to show that the dynamic trading strategy prescribed by Black and Scholes to offset the risk exposure of an option would provide a perfect hedge in the limit of continuous trading. That is, if one could trade continuously without cost, then following their dynamic trading strategy using the underlying traded asset and the riskless asset would exactly replicate the payoffs on the option. Thus, in a continuous-trading fi-

[4] Scholes and Mark A. Wolfson (1992) develop the principles of security and institutional design along these lines. See also Perold (1992) and Merton (1993, 1995). Inspection of the weekly *International Financing Review* will find the widespread and varied applications of financial engineering, derivatives, special-purpose vehicles and securities for private-sector and sovereign financing in every part of the world.

nancial environment, the option price must satisfy the Black-Scholes formula or else there would be an opportunity for arbitrage profits. To demonstrate this limit-case result, I applied the tools developed in my earlier work (1969; 1971) on the continuous-time theory of portfolio selection. My 1973 paper also extended the applicability of the Black-Scholes model to allow for stochastic interest rates on the riskless asset, dividend payments on the underlying asset, a changing exercise price, American-type early-exercise of the option, and other "exotic" features such as the "down-and-out" provision on the option. I am also responsible for naming the model, "the Black-Scholes Option-Pricing Model."[5]

The derivations of the pricing formula in both of our 1973 papers make the following assumptions:

I)   *"Frictionless" and "continuous" markets*: there are no transactions costs or differential taxes. Markets are open all the time and trading takes place continuously. Borrowing and short-selling are allowed without restriction. The borrowing and lending rates are equal.

II) *Underlying asset-price dynamics*: let $V = V(t)$ denote the price at time t of a limited-liability asset, such as a share of stock. The posited dynamics for the instantaneous returns can be described by an Itô-type stochastic differential equation with continuous sample paths given by

$$dV = [\alpha V - D_1(V,t)]\,dt + \sigma V dZ$$

where: $\alpha \equiv$ instantaneous expected rate of return on the security; $\sigma^2 \equiv$ instantaneous variance rate, which is assumed to depend, at most, on $V(t)$ and t (i.e., $\sigma^2 = \sigma^2(V,t)$); dZ is a Wiener process; and $D_1 \equiv$ dividend payment flow rate. With limited liability, to avoid arbitrage, $V(t) = 0$ for all $t \geq t^*$ if $V(t^*) = 0$. Hence D_1 must satisfy $D_1(0,t) = 0$. Other than a technical requirement of bounded variation, α can follow a quite general stochastic process, dependent on V, other security prices, or state variables. In particular, the assumed dynamics permit a mean-reverting process for the underlying asset's returns.

III) *Default-free bond-price dynamics*: bond returns are assumed to be described by Itô stochastic processes with continuous sample paths. In the original Black and Scholes formulation and for exposition convenience here, it is assumed that the riskless instantaneous interest rate, $r(t) = r$, is a constant over time.

IV) *Investor preferences and expectations*: investor preferences are assumed to prefer more to less. All investors are assumed to agree on the function σ^2

---

[5] My 1970 working paper was the first to use the "Black-Scholes" label for their model (cf. Merton 1992, p. 379). This same paper was given at the July 1970 Wells Fargo Capital Market Conference, since made "famous" (or notorious) by Bernstein (1992, p. 223) as the one at which I "...inconveniently overslept..." the morning session and missed the Black and Scholes presentation. The second instance naming their model was in the 1971 working-paper version of Merton (1973a). Samuelson (1972) is the first published usage: both in the main text and in my appendix to that paper which derives the model and refers to it as the "Black-Scholes formula." The formula is cited in Roger J. Leonard (1971) and Carliss Baldwin (1972), the earliest theses to apply the model. Somewhat ironically, all these references to the "Black-Scholes model" appear before the actual publication of either Black and Scholes (1972) or (1973).

and on the Itô process characterization for the return dynamics. It is not assumed that they agree on the expected rate of return, α.

V) *Functional dependence of the option-pricing* formula: the option price is assumed to be a twice-continuously differentiable function of the asset price, V, default-free bond prices, and time.

In the particular case of a nondividend-paying asset $(D_1 = 0)$ and a constant variance rate, σ^2, these assumptions lead to the Black-Scholes option-pricing formula for a European-type call option with exercise price L and expiration date T, written as

(1) $C(V, t) = V N(d) - L \exp(-r[T-t]) N(d - \sigma \sqrt{T-t})$

where $d = (\ln[V/L] + [r + \sigma^2/2][T-t]) / \sigma \sqrt{T-t}$ *and* $N(\ )$ *is the cumulative density function for the standard normal distribution.*

Subsequent research in the field proceeded along three dimensions: applications of the technology to other than financial options (which is discussed in the next section); empirical testing of the pricing formula, which began with a study using over-the-counter data from a dealer's book obtained by Black and Scholes (1972); attempts to weaken the assumptions used in the derivation, and thereby to strengthen the foundation of the applications developed from this research. The balance of this section addresses issues of the latter dimension.

Early concerns raised about the model's theoretical foundation came from Long (1974) and Smith (1976), who questioned Assumption *V*: namely, how does one know that the option prices do not depend on other variables than the ones assumed (for instance, the price of beer), and why should the pricing function be twice-continuously differentiable? These concerns were resolved in an alternative derivation in Merton (1977b) which shows that Assumption *V*. is a derived consequence, not an assumption, of the analysis.[6]

A broader, and still open, research issue is the robustness of the pricing formula in the absence of a dynamic portfolio strategy that exactly replicates the payoffs to the option security. Obviously, the conclusion on that issue depends on why perfect replication is not feasible as well as on the magnitude of the imperfection. Continuous trading is, of course, only an idealized prospect, not literally obtainable; therefore, with discrete trading intervals, replication is at best only approximate. Subsequent simulation work has shown that within the actual trading intervals available and the volatility levels of speculative prices, the error in replication is manageable, provided, however, that the other assumptions about the underlying process obtain. Cox

---

[6] As another instance of early questioning of the core model, a paper I refereed argued that Black-Scholes must be fundamentally flawed because a different valuation formula is derived from the replication argument if the R. L. Stratonovich (1968) stochastic calculus is used for modeling instead of the Itô calculus. My report showed that while the paper's mathematics were correct, its economics were not: A Stratonovich-type formulation of the underlying price process implies that traders have a partial knowledge about future asset prices that the non-anticipating character of the Itô process does not. The "paradox" is thus resolved because the assumed information sets are essentially different and hence, so should the pricing formulas.

and Ross (1976) and Merton (1976a, b) relax the continuous sample-path assumption and analyze option pricing using a mixture of jump and diffusion processes to capture the prospect of non-local movements in the underlying asset's return process.[7] Without a continuous sample path, replication is not possible and that rules out a strict no-arbitrage derivation. Instead, the derivation of the option-pricing model is completed by using equilibrium asset pricing models such as the Intertemporal CAPM [Merton (1973b)] and the Arbitrage Pricing Theory [Ross (1976a)].[8] This approach relates back to the original way in which Black and Scholes derived their model using the classic Sharpe-Lintner CAPM.[9] There has developed a considerable literature on the case of imperfect replication (Cf. Bertsimas, Kogan, and Lo [1997], Breeden [1984], Davis [1997], Figlewski [1989], Föllmer and Sondermann [1986], and Romano and Touzi [1997]).

On this occasion, I re-examine the imperfect-replication problem for a derivative security linked to an underlying asset that is not continuously available for trading in an environment in which some assets are tradable at any time. As is discussed in the section to follow, non-tradability is the circumstance for several important classes of applications that have evolved over the last quarter century, which include among others, the pricing of financial guarantees such as deposit and pension insurance and the valuation of non-financial or "real" options. Since the Black-Scholes model was derived by assuming that the underlying asset is continuously traded, questions have been raised about whether the pricing formula can be properly applied in those applications. The derivation follows along the lines presented in Merton (1977b, 1997b) for the perfect-replication case.

A *derivative security* has contractually determined payouts that can be described by functions of observable asset prices and time. These payout functions define the derivative. We express the terms as follows:

Let $W(t)$ = price of a derivative security at time t.

$$\text{If} \quad V(t) \geq \overline{V}(t) \text{ for } 0 \leq t < T, \text{ then } W(t) = f\big[V(t), t\big]$$

$$(2) \qquad \text{If} \quad V(t) \leq \underline{V}(t) \text{ for } 0 \leq t < T, \text{ then } W(t) = g\big[V(t), t\big]$$

$$\text{If} \quad t = T, \text{ then } W(T) = h\big[V(T)\big]$$

---

[7] Since a discontinuous sample-path price process for the underlying asset rules out perfect hedging even with continuous trading but a continuous-sample-path process with stochastic volatility does not, there is considerable interest in testing which process fits the data better. See Eric Rosenfeld (1980), an early developer of such tests and James B. Wiggins (1987).

[8] The important Douglas T. Breeden (1979) Consumption-based Capital Asset Pricing Model, which was not published at the time of these papers, can also be used to complete those models.

[9] See Black (1989) and Scholes (1998). Fischer Black always maintained with me that the CAPM-version of the option-model derivation was more robust because continuous trading is not feasible and there are transactions costs. As noted in Merton (1973a, p. 116), the discrete-time Samuelson-Merton (1969) model also gives the Balck-Scholes formula under special conditions.

For $0 \leq t \leq T$, the derivative security receives a payment flow rate specified by $D_2(V,t)$. The terms as described in (2) are to be interpreted as follows: the first time that $V(t) \geq \overline{V}(t)$ or $V(t) \leq \underline{V}(t)$, the owner of the derivative must exchange it for cash according to the schedule in (2). If no such events occur for $t < T$, then the security is redeemed at $t = T$ for cash according to (2). T is called the *maturity date* (or expiration date, or redemption date) of the derivative. The derivative security is thus defined by specifying the contingent payoff functions f, g, h, D_2, and T. In some cases, the schedules or the boundaries $\overline{V}(t)$ and $\underline{V}(t)$ are contractually specified; in others, they are determined endogenously as part of the valuation process, as in the case of the early-exercise boundary for an American-type option.

By arbitrage restrictions, the derivative security will have *limited liability* if and only if $g \geq 0$, $h \geq 0$, $f \geq 0$, and $D_2(0, t) = 0$.

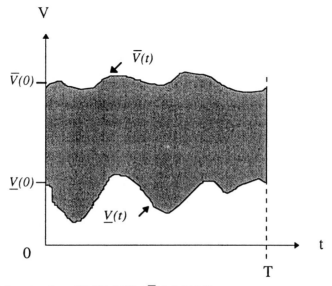

Figure 1. Relevant region of V: $\underline{V}(t) \leq V(t) \leq \overline{V}(t)$, $0 \leq t \leq T$

If (as drawn in Figure 1) the boundaries $\underline{V}(t)$, and $\overline{V}(t)$ are continuous functions, then because $V(t)$ has a continuous sample path in t by Assumption II, one has that (i) if $V(t) < \underline{V}(t)$ for some t, then there is a $\underline{t}$, $\underline{t} < t$, so that $V(\underline{t}) = \underline{V}(\underline{t})$ and (ii) if $V(t) > \overline{V}(t)$ for some t, then there is a $\bar{t}$, $\bar{t} < t$, so that $V(\bar{t}) = \overline{V}(\bar{t})$. Hence, in this case, the inequalities for V can be neglected in (2) and the only relevant region for analysis is $\underline{V}(t) \leq V(t) \leq \overline{V}(t)$, $0 \leq t \leq T$.

With the derivative-security characteristics fully specified, we turn now to the fundamental production technology for hedging the risk of issuing a derivative security and for evaluating the cost of its production. To locate the derivation in a more substantive framework, I posit a hypothetical financial intermediary that creates derivative securities in principal transactions for its customers by selling them contracts which are its obligation. It uses the capital markets or transactions with other institutions to hedge the contractual liabilities so created by dynamically trading in the underlying securities following a strategy designed to reproduce the cash flows of the issued contracts as accurately as it can. If the intermediary cannot perfectly replicate the payoffs to the issued derivative, it either obtains adequate equity to bear the residual risks of its imperfectly hedged positions or it securitizes those positions by bundling them into a portfolio for a special-purpose financial vehicle which it then sells either in the capital market or to a consortium of other institutions in a process similar to the traditional reinsurance market. Although surely a caricature, the following description is nevertheless not far removed from real-world practice.

The objective is to find a feasible, continuous-trading portfolio strategy constructed from all available traded assets including the riskless asset that comes "closest" to satisfying the following four properties: if $P(t)$ denotes the value of the portfolio at time t, then for $0 \leq t \leq T$:

(i)   at t, if $V(t) = \underline{V}(t)$, then $P(t) = g\,[\,\underline{V}(t),\, t]$

(ii) at t, if $V(t) = \overline{V}(t)$, then $P(t) = f\,[\,\overline{V}(t),\, t]$

(iii) for each t, the payout rate on the portfolio is $D_2(V,\, t)\,dt$

(iv) at $t = T$, $P(T) = h\,[\,V(T)\,]$.

Call this portfolio the "hedging portfolio" for the derivative security defined by (2). That portfolio is labeled as "portfolio (*)." In the special, but important, case in which the portfolio meets the above conditions exactly, the hedging portfolio is called the "replicating portfolio" for the derivative security.

Bertsimas, Kogan, and Lo(1997) study the complementary problem of "closeness" of dynamic replication where they assume that one can trade in the underlying asset but that trading is not continuous. They apply stochastic dynamic programming to derive optimal strategies to minimize mean-squared tracking error. These strategies are then employed in simulations to estimate quantitatively how close one can get to dynamic completeness.

Determine the optimal hedging portfolio in two steps: first, find the portfolio strategy constructed from all continuously traded assets that has the smallest "tracking error" in replicating the returns on the underlying asset. For the underlying asset with price V, call this portfolio, the "V-Fund." In the second step, derive the hedging portfolio for the derivative security as a dynamic portfolio strategy mixing the V-Fund with the riskless asset.

Let $S_i(t)$ denote the price of continuously traded asset i at time t. There are n such risky assets plus the riskless asset which are traded continuously. The dynamics for S_i are assumed to follow a continuous-sample-path Itô process given by

(3)
$$dS_i = \alpha_i S_i\, dt + \sigma_i\, S_i\, dZ_i,\ i = 1, \ldots, n$$

where α_i is the instantaneous expected rate of return on asset i; dZ_i is a Wiener process; σ_{ij} is the instantaneous covariance between the returns on i and j [that is, $(dS_i/S_i)(dS_j/S_j) = \sigma_{ij}\, dt$ and $\sigma_{ii} = \sigma_i{}^2$]; let η_i be defined as the instantaneous correlation between dZ_i and dZ in Assumption II such that $dZ_i\,dZ = \eta_i\,dt$. Let $S(t)$ denote the value of the V-Fund portfolio and let $w_i(t)$ denote the fraction of that portfolio allocated to asset i, $i=1,\ldots,n$, at time t. The balance of the portfolio's assets are invested in the riskless asset. The dynamics for S can be written as

$$(4) \qquad\qquad dS = [\mu\,S - D_1\,(V\!,t)]\,dt + \delta\,S\,dq$$

where $\mu = r + \sum_{i=1}^{n} w_i(t)[\alpha_i - r]$, $\delta^2 = \sum_{i=1}^{n}\sum_{j=1}^{n} w_i(t)w_j(t)\sigma_{ij}$, and $dq = [\sum_{i=1}^{n} w_i(t)\sigma_i dZ_i]/\delta$.

To create the V-Fund, the w_i are chosen so as to minimize the unanticipated part of the difference between the return on the underlying asset and the traded portfolio's return. That is, at each point in time, the portfolio allocation is chosen so as to minimize the instantaneous variance of $[dS/S - dV/V]$. As shown in Merton (1992, Theorem 15.3, p.501), the portfolio rule that does this is given by

$$(5) \qquad\qquad w_i(t) = \sigma\sum_{k=1}^{n} v_{ki}\,\sigma_k\,\eta_k \ , \ i = 1,\ldots,n.$$

where v_{ki} is the kth-ith element of the inverse of the variance-covariance matrix of the returns on the n risky continuously traded assets. From Merton (1992, p.502), the instantaneous correlation between the returns on the V-Fund and the underlying asset, $\rho\,dt = dZ\,dq$, can be written as

$$(6) \qquad\qquad \rho = (\sum_{k=1}^{n}\sum_{i=1}^{n} v_{ki}\,\sigma_k\,\sigma_i\,\eta_k\,\eta_i)^{\frac{1}{2}}$$

and

$$(7) \qquad\qquad \delta = \rho\sigma.$$

The dynamics of the tracking error can thus be written as

$$(8) \qquad\qquad dS/S - dV/V = (\mu - \alpha)\,dt + \theta db$$

where $\theta^2 = (1 - \rho^2)\,\sigma^2$ and the Wiener process $db = (\rho\,dq - dZ)/\sqrt{1 - \rho^2}$. As shown in Merton (1992, eq. 15.51), it follows that

$$(9) \qquad\qquad dS_i/S_i\,db = 0 , \ i = 1,\ldots,n.$$

That is, the tracking error in (8) is uncorrelated with the returns on all traded assets, which is a consequence of picking the portfolio strategy that minimizes that error.

With this, we now proceed with a "cookbook-like" derivation of the production process for our hypothetical financial intermediary to best hedge the cash flows of the derivative securities it issues. The derivation begins with a description of the activities for the intermediary's quantitative-analysis ("quant") department which is responsible for gathering the variance-covariance information necessary to use (5) to construct and maintain the V-Fund portfolio. It is also assigned the responsibility to solve the following linear parabolic partial differential equation for $F[V\!, t]$

(10) $\quad 0 = \frac{1}{2}\sigma^2(V,t)V^2F_{11}[V,t]+[rV-D_1(V,t)]F_1[V,t]-rF[V,t]+F_2[V,t]+D_2(V,t)$

subject to the boundary conditions: for $\underline{V}(t) \leq V \leq \overline{V}(t)$ and $t < T$,

(11) $\qquad\qquad\qquad F[\overline{V}(t),t] = f[\overline{V}(t),t] \geq 0$

(12) $\qquad\qquad\qquad F[\underline{V}(t),t] = g[\underline{V}(t),t] \geq 0$

(13) $\qquad\qquad\qquad F[V,T] = h[V] \geq 0$

where $F_{11} \equiv \partial^2 F/\partial V^2$, $F_1 \equiv \partial F/\partial V$; and $F_2 \equiv \partial F/\partial t$. Note that the non-negativity conditions in (11)–(13) together with $D_2(0, t) = 0$ implies that the derivative security has limited liability. As a mathematical question, this is a well-posed problem, and a solution to (10)–(13) exists and is unique.

Having solved for the function $F[V,t]$, the quant department has the pre-scribed ongoing tasks at each time t $(0 \leq t \leq T)$ to:

(i)   ask the trading desk for the prices of all traded assets necessary to determine the price $S(t)$ of the V-Fund and the best estimate of the current price of the underlying asset, $V(t)$;

(ii)   compute from the solution to (10)-(13) compute

$$M(t) \equiv F_1[V(t), t]V(t);$$

(iii)   tell the trading desk that the strategy of portfolio (*) requires that $\$M(t)$ be invested in the V-Fund for the period t to $t + dt$;

(iv)   compute $Y(t) \equiv F[V(t), t]$ and store $Y(t)$ in the intermediary's data files for (later) analysis of the time series (i.e., stochastic process) $Y(t)$.

The prescription for the execution or trading-desk activities of the intermediary is as follows: At time $t = 0$, give the trading desk $\$P(0)$ as an initial funding (investment) for portfolio (*) which contains the V-Fund asset and the riskless asset. Let $P(t)$ denote the value of portfolio (*) at t, after having made any prescribed cash distribution (payment) from the portfolio. The trading desk has the job at each time t $(0 \leq t \leq T)$ to:

(a)   determine the current prices of the underlying asset, $V(t)$ and all individual traded assets held in the V-Fund, and send that price information to the quant department;

(b)   pay a cash distribution of $\$D_2[V(t), t]dt$ to the customer holding the derivative security; by selling securities in the portfolio (if necessary);

(c)   compute the value of the balance of the portfolio, $P(t)$;

(d)   receive instructions on $M(t)$ from the quant department;

(e)   readjust the portfolio allocation so that $\$M(t)$ is now invested in the V-Fund and $\$[P(t) - M(t)]$ is invested in the riskless asset.

It follows that the dynamics for the value of portfolio (*) are given by

$$(14) \qquad dP = M(t)\frac{dS}{S} + M(t)\frac{D_I(V,t)}{S}dt + [P - M(t)]rdt - D_2(V,t)dt$$

where

$$M(t)\frac{dS}{S} = \text{price appreciation}$$

$$M(t)\frac{D_I(V,t)}{S}dt = \text{dividend payments received into the portfolio}$$

$$[P - M(t)]rdt = \text{interest earned by the portfolio}$$

$$D_2(V,t)dt = \text{cash distribution to customer}$$

Noting that $M(t) = F_1[V,t]V$, one has by substitution from (4) into (14) that the dynamics of P satisfy

$$dP = F_I[V,t]VdS/S + F_I[V,t]VD_I(V,t)/S + (P - F_I[V,t]V)rdt - D_2(V)dt$$

$$(15)$$
$$= [F_IV(\mu - r) + rP - D_2]dt + F_IV\delta dq$$

Return now to the quant department to derive the dynamics for $Y(t)$. From (iv), one has that $Y(t) = F[V, t]$ for $V(t) = V$. Because F is the solution to (10–13), F is a twice-continuously differentiable function of V and t. Therefore, we can apply Itô's lemma, so that for $V(t) = V$,

$$dY = F_I[V,t]dV + F_2[V,t]dt + \tfrac{1}{2}F_{11}[V,t](dV)^2$$

$$(16)$$
$$= [\tfrac{1}{2}\sigma^2V^2F_{11} + F_I(\alpha V - D_I) + F_2]dt + F_IV\sigma dZ$$

because $(dV)^2 = \sigma^2V^2dt$. Because $F[V,t]$ satisfies (10), one has that

$$(17) \qquad \tfrac{1}{2}\sigma^2V^2F_{11} - D_IF_I + F_2 = rF - rVF_I - D_2$$

Substituting (17) into (16), one can rewrite (16) as

$$(18) \qquad dY = [F_I(\alpha - r)V + rF - D_2]dt + F_IV\sigma dZ$$

Note that the calculation of $Y(t)$ and its dynamics by the quant department in no way requires knowledge of the time-series of values for portfolio (*), $\{P(t)\}$, that are calculated by the trading desk. Putting these two time series together, we define $Q(t) \equiv P(t) - Y(t)$. It follows that $dQ = dP - dY$. Substituting for dP from (15) and for dY from (18), rearranging terms using (8), one has that

$$(19) \qquad \begin{aligned} dQ &= rQ\,dt + F_I\,V(\,dS/S - dV/V) \\ &= (\,rQ + F_I\,V[\mu - \alpha]\,)dt + F_I\,V\,\theta\,db. \end{aligned}$$

At this point, we digress to examine the special case in which perfect replication of the return on the underlying asset obtains (i.e., $\rho = 1$ and there is no tracking error). In that case, equation (19) reduces to an ordinary differential equation ($\dot{Q}/Q = r$) with solution

(20) $$Q(t) = Q(0)exp(rt)$$

where $Q(0) = P(0) - Y(0) = P(0) - F[V(0),0]$. Therefore, if the initial funding provided to the trading desk for portfolio (*) is chosen so that $P(0) = F[V(0),0]$, then from (20), $Q(t) \equiv 0$ for all t and

(21) $$P(t) = F[V(t),t]$$

By comparison of (11)–(13) with (2), one has from (21) that the (*)-portfolio strategy generates the identical payment flows and terminal (and boundary) values as the derivative security described at the outset of this analysis. That is, for a one-time, initial investment of $\$F[V(0),0]$, a feasible portfolio strategy has been found that exactly replicates the payoffs to the derivative security. Thus, $\$F[V(0),0]$ is the cost to the intermediary for producing the derivative. *If the derivative security is traded,* then to avoid ("conditional") arbitrage (conditional on $\sigma,\ r,\ D_1$), its price must satisfy

(22) $$W(t) = P(t) = F[V(t),t].$$

Since the absence of arbitrage opportunities is a *necessary* condition for equilibrium, it follows that equilibrium prices for derivative securities on continuously tradable underlying assets must satisfy (22). This is, of course, the original Black-Scholes result and the V-Fund degenerates into a single asset, the underlying asset itself. However, note that (22) obtains without assuming that the derivative-pricing function is a twice-continuously differentiable function of V and t. The smoothness of the pricing function is instead a derived conclusion.

Note further that the development of the (*)-portfolio strategy did not require that the derivative security (defined by (2)) actually trades in the capital market. The (*)-portfolio strategy provides the technology for "manufacturing" or synthetically creating the cash flows and payoffs of the derivative security if it does not exist. That is, if one describes a state-contingent schedule of outcomes for a portfolio (i.e. specifies $f,\ g,\ h,\ D_2,\ T,\ \underline{V}(t),\ \overline{V}(t)$), then the (*)-portfolio strategy provides the trading rules to create this pattern of payouts and it specifies the cost of implementing those rules. The cost of creating the security at time t is thus $F[V(t),t]$. Moreover, if the financial-services industry is competitive, then price equals marginal cost, and (22) obtains as the formula for equilibrium prices of derivatives sold directly by intermediaries.

Returning from this digression to the case of imperfect replication, one has, by construction of the process for Y, that $Q=P-Y$ is the cumulative arithmetic tracking error for the hedging portfolio. By inspection of (19), the instantaneous tracking error for the derivative security is perfectly correlated with the tracking error of the V-Fund. Hence, from (9), it follows that the tracking error for the hedging portfolio is uncorrelated with the returns on

446

all continuously traded assets. Using this lack of correlation with any other traded asset, I now argue that in this case the replication-based valuation can be used for pricing the derivative security even though replication is not feasible.

As we know, in all equilibrium asset-pricing models, assets that have only non-systematic or diversifiable risk are priced to yield an expected return equal to the riskless rate of interest. The condition satisfied by the tracking-error component of the hedging portfolio satisfies an even stronger no-correlation condition than either a zero-beta asset in the CAPM, a zero multibeta asset of the Intertemporal CAPM, or a zero factor-risk asset of the Arbitrage Pricing Theory. Thus, by any of those theories, the equilibrium condition from either (8) or (19) is that

$$(23) \qquad\qquad \mu = \alpha.$$

If (23) obtains, it follows immediately that the equilibrium price for the derivative security is $F[V(t), t]$, the same formula "as if" the underlying asset is traded continuously. And as a consequence, the Black-Scholes formula would apply even in those applications in which the underlying asset is not traded.

As is well known from the literature on incomplete markets, (23) need not obtain if the creation of the new derivative security helps complete the market for a large enough subset of investors that the incremental dimension of risk spanned by this new instrument is "priced" as a systematic risk factor with an expected return different from the riskless interest rate. Markets tend to remain incomplete with respect to a particular risk either because the cost of creating the securities necessary to span that risk exceeds the benefits, or because non-verifiability, moral-hazard, or adverse-selection problems render the viability of such securities untenable. Generally, major macro risks for which significant pools of investors want to manage their exposures are not controllable by any group of investors, and it is unlikely that any group would have systematic access to materially better information about those risks. Hence, the usual asymmetric-information and incentive reasons given for market failure do not seem to be present. In systems with well-developed financial institutions and markets and with today's financial technology, it is thus not readily apparent what factors make the cost of developing standardized derivative markets (e.g., futures, swaps, options) prohibitive if, in large scale, there is a significant premium latently waiting to be paid by investors who currently participate in the markets. On a more prosaic empirical note, in most applications of the option-pricing model, the "residual" or tracking-error variations are likely to be specific to the underlying project, firm, institution, or person, and thereby they are unlikely candidates for macro-risk surrogates. These observations support the prospects for (23) to obtain.

However, the risk need not be macro in scope in order to be significant to one investor or a small group of investors. Obvious examples of such risks would be various firm- or person-specific components of human capital, including death and disability risks. To make a case for instruments with these types of exposures to be priced with a risk premium, incomplete-market models often focus on the "incipient-demand" (or "maximum reservation") price or risk premium that an investor would pay to eliminate a risk that is not covered in the market by the existing set of securities. In the abstract, that price, of course, can be quite substantial. However, arguments along these lines to explain financial product pricing implicitly assume a rather modest and static financial-services sector. A classic example is life insurance. Risk-averse individuals with families may, if necessary, be willing to pay a considerable premium for life insurance, well in excess of the actuarial mortality risk, even after taking into account moral-hazard and person-specific informational asymmetries. Moreover, if the analysis further postulates a financial sector so crude that bilateral contracts between risk-averse individuals are the only way to obtain such insurance, then the equilibrium price for such insurance in that model can be so large that few, if any, contracts are created. But, such models are a poor descriptor of the real world. If the institutions and markets were really that limited, the incentives for change and innovation would be enormous. Modern finance technology and experience in implementing it provide the means for such change. And if, instead, one admits into the model just the classic mechanism for organizing an "insurance" institution (whether government-run or private-sector) to take advantage of the enormous diversification benefits of pooling such risks and subdividing them among large numbers of participants, then the equilibrium price equals the "supply" price of such insurance contracts which approaches the actuarial rate.

As is typical in analyses of other industries, the equilibrium prices of financial products and services are more closely linked to the costs of the efficient producers than to the inefficient ones (except perhaps as a very crude upper bound to those prices). Furthermore, the institutional structure of the financial system is neither exogenous nor fixed. In theory and in practice, that structure changes in response to changing technology and to profit-opportunities for creating new products and existing products more efficiently. As discussed at length elsewhere (Merton 1992, pp. 457-467; 535-536), a financial sector with a rich and well-developed structure of institutions can justify a "quasi-dichotomy" modeling approach to the pricing of real and financial assets that employs "reduced-form" equilibrium models with a simple financial sector in which all agents are assumed to be minimum-cost information processors and transactors. However, distortions of insights into the real world can occur if significant costs for the agents are introduced into that model while the simple financial sector is retained as an unchanged assumption. Put simply, high transaction and information costs for most of the economy's agents to directly create their own financial products and services does not imply that equilibrium asset prices are influenced by those high costs, as long as there is an efficient financial-service industry with low-cost, reasonably competitive producers.

In considering the preceding technical analysis, one might wonder if there are relevant situations in which the price is observable but trade in the asset cannot take place? One common class of real-world instances is characterized as follows: consider an insurance company that has guaranteed the financial performance of the liabilities of a privately-held opaque institution with a mark-to-market portfolio of assets. The market value of that portfolio (corresponding to V in the analysis here) is provided to the guarantor on a continuous basis, but the portfolio itself cannot be traded by the guarantor to hedge its exposure because it does not know the assets held within the portfolio. Elsewhere (Merton, 1997a), I have developed a model using an alternative approach of incentive-contracting combined with the derivative-security technology to analyze the problem of contract guarantees for an opaque institution. It is nevertheless the case that discontinuous tradability of an asset is often accompanied by discontinuous observations of its price. And so, the combination of the two warrants attention. Hence, I complete this section with consideration of how to modify the valuation formula if the price of the underlying asset V is not continuously observable.

Suppose that in the example adopted in this section, the price of the underlying asset is observed at t=0 and then again at the maturity of the derivative contract, t=T. In between, there is neither direct observation nor inferential information from payouts on the asset. Hence, $D_1(V,t) = 0$, and the derivative security has no payouts or interim "stopping points" prior to maturity [as specified in (11) and (12)] contingent on $V(t)$. It is however known that the dynamics of V are as described in Assumption II with a covariance structure with available traded assets sufficiently well specified to construct the V-Fund according to (5). Define the random variable $X(t) \equiv V(t)/S(t)$, the cumulative *proportional* tracking error, with $X(0) = 1$. By applying Itô's lemma, one has from (8), (9), and (23) that the dynamics for X can be written as

(24) $$dX = \theta \, X \, db.$$

It follows from (24) that the distribution for $X(t)$, conditional on $X(0) = 1$, is lognormal with the expected value of $X(t)$ equal to 1 and the variance of $\ln[X(t)]$ equal to $\theta^2 t$. The partial differential equation for F, corresponding to (10), that determines the hedging strategy uses as its independent variable the best estimate of $V(t)$, which is $S(t)$, and it is written as

(25) $$0 = \tfrac{1}{2}\delta^2 S^2 F_{11}[S,t] + rS F_1[S,t] - rF[S,t] + F_2[S,t],$$

subject to the terminal-time boundary condition that for $S(T-) = S$,

(26) $$F[S, T] = E \{ h(SX) \}$$

where h is as defined in (13), X is a lognormally distributed random variable with $E\{ X \} = 1$ and variance of $\ln [X]$ equal to $\theta^2 T$ and $E\{ \}$ is the expectation operator over the distribution of X.

Condition (26) reflects the fact that for all $t < T$, the best estimate of $V(t)$ is $S(t)$. However, at $t = T$, $V(T)$ is revealed and the value of S "jumps" by the total cumulative tracking error of $X(T)$ from its value S at $t = T-$ to $S(T) = V(T)$. The effect of the underlying asset price not being observable is perhaps well-illustrated by comparing the solution for the European-type call option with the classic Black-Scholes solution given here in (1). The solution to (25) and (26) with $h(V) = max [0, V - L]$ is given by, for $0 < t < T$,

(27) $$F[S, t]) = S N(u) - L \exp(-r[T\text{-}t]) N(u - \sqrt{\gamma})$$

where $u = (ln[S/L] + r[T\text{-}t] + \gamma/2) /\sqrt{\gamma}$, $\gamma = \delta^2(T\text{-}t) + \theta^2 T$, and $N( )$ is the cumulative density function for the standard normal distribution.

By inspection of (1) and (27), the key difference in the option-pricing formula with and without continuous observation of the underlying asset price is that the variance over the remaining life of the option does not go to zero as t approaches T, because of the "jump" event at the expiration date corresponding to the cumulative effect of tracking error.

This section has explored conditions under which the Black-Scholes option-pricing model can be validly applied to the pricing of assets with derivative-security-like structures, even when the underlying asset-equivalent is neither continuously traded nor continuously observable. A fuller analysis of this question would certainly take account of the additional tracking error that obtains as a consequence of imperfect dynamic trading of the V-Fund portfolio, along the lines of Bertsimas, Kogan, and Lo (1997). However, a more accurate assessment of the real-world impact should also take into account other risk-management tools that intermediaries have to reduce tracking error. For instance, as developed in analytical detail in Merton (1992, pp. 450–457), intermediaries need only use dynamic trading to hedge their *net* derivative-security exposures to various underlying assets. For a real-world intermediary with a large book of various derivative products, netting, which in effect extends the capability for hedging to include trading in securities with "non-linear" pay-off structures, can vastly reduce the size and even the frequency of the hedging transactions necessary to achieve an acceptable level of tracking error. Beyond this, as part of their optimal risk management, intermediaries can "shade" their bid and offer prices among their various products to encourage more or less customer activity in different products to help manage their exposures. The limiting case when the net positions of customer exposures leaves the intermediary with no exposure is called a "matched book."

APPLICATIONS OF THE OPTION-PRICING TECHNOLOGY

Open the financial section of a major newspaper almost anywhere in the world and you will find pages devoted to reporting the prices of exchange-traded derivative securities, both futures and options. Along with the vast over-the-counter derivatives market, these exchange markets trade options and futures on individual stocks, stock-index and mutual-fund portfolios, on bonds and other fixed-income securities of every maturity, on currencies, and on commodities including agricultural products, metals, crude oil and refined products, natural gas, and even, electricity. The volume of transactions in these markets is often many times larger than the volume in the underlying cash-market assets. Options have traditionally been used in the purchase of real estate and the acquisition of publishing and movie rights. Employee stock options have long been granted to key employees and today represent a significantly growing proportion of total compensation, especially for the more highly paid workers in the United States. In all these markets, the same option-pricing methodology set forth in the preceding section is widely used both to price and to measure the risk exposure from these derivatives (cf. Jarrow and Rudd [1983] and Cox and Rubinstein [1985]). However, financial options represent only one of several categories of applications for the option-pricing technology.

In the late 1960s and early 1970s when the basic research leading to the Black-Scholes model was underway, options were seen as rather arcane and specialized financial instruments. However, both Black and Scholes (1972, 1973) and I (Merton, 1970,1974) recognized early on in the research effort that the same approach used to price options could be applied to a variety of other valuation problems. Perhaps the first major development of this sort was the pricing of corporate liabilities, the "right-hand side" of the firm's balance sheet. This approach to valuation treated the wide array of instruments used to finance firms such as debentures, convertible bonds, warrants, preferred stock, and common stock (as well as a variety of hybrid securities) as derivative securities with their contractual payouts ultimately dependent on the value of the overall firm. In contrast to the standard fragmented valuation methods of the time, it provided a unified theory for pricing these liabilities. Because application of the pricing methodology does not require a history of trading in the particular instrument to be evaluated, it was well-suited for pricing new types of financial securities issued by corporations in an innovating environment. Applications to corporate finance along this line developed rapidly.[10]

"Option-like" structures were soon seen to be lurking everywhere; thus there came an explosion of research in applying option-pricing theory which still continues. Indeed, I could not do full justice to the list of contributions accumulated over the past 25 years even if this entire paper were devoted to that endeavor. Fortunately, a major effort to do just that is underway and the results will soon be available (Jin, Kogan, Lim, Taylor, and Lo, forthcoming). The authors have generously shared their findings with me. And so, I can convey here some sense of the breadth of applications and be necessarily incomplete without harm.

The put option is a basic option which gives its owner the right to sell the underlying asset at a specified ("exercise") price on or before a given ("expiration") date. When purchased in conjunction with ownership of the underlying asset, it is functionally equivalent to an insurance policy that protects its owner against economic loss from a decline in the asset's value below the exercise price for any reason, where the term of the insurance policy corresponds to the expiration date. Hence, option-pricing theory can be applied to value insurance contracts. An early insurance application of the Black-Scholes

---

[10] See Merton (1992, pp. 423–427) for an extensive list of references. See also Gregory D. Hawkins (1982) and Michael J. Brennan and Eduardo S. Schwartz (1985a) and the early empirical testing by E. Philip Jones et al. (1984).

model was to the pricing of loan guarantees and deposit insurance (cf., Merton, 1977a). A contract that insures against losses in value caused by default on promised payments on a contract in effect is equivalent to a put option on the contract with an exercise price equal to the value of the contract if it were default-free. Loan and other contract guarantees, collectively called credit derivatives, are ubiquitous in the private sector. Indeed, whenever a debt instrument is purchased in which there is any chance that the promised payments will not be made, the purchaser is not only lending money but also in effect issuing a loan guarantee as a form of self-insurance. Another private-sector application of options analysis is in the valuation of catastrophic-insurance reinsurance contracts and bonds.[11] Dual funds and exotic options provide various financial insurance and minimum-return-guarantee products.[12]

Almost surely, the largest issuer of such guarantees are governments. In the United States, the Office of the Management of the Budget is required by law to value those guarantees. The option model has been applied to assess deposit insurance, pension insurance, guarantees of student loans and home mortgages, and loans to small businesses and some large ones as well.[13] The application to government activities goes beyond just providing guarantees. The model has been used to determine the cost of other subsidies including farm-price supports and through-put guarantees for pipelines.[14] It has been applied to value licenses issued with limiting quotas such as for taxis or fisheries or the right to pollute and to value the government's right to change those quotas.[15] Government sanctions patents. The decision whether to spend the resources to acquire a patent depends on the value of the patent which can be framed as an option-pricing problem. Indeed, even on something that is not currently commercial, one may acquire the patent for its "option value," should economic conditions change in an unexpected way.[16] Paddock, Siegel, and Smith (1988) show that option value can be a significant proportion of the total valuation of government-granted offshore drilling rights, especially when current and expected future economic conditions would not support development of the fields. Option-pricing analysis quantifies the government's economic decision whether to build roads in less-populated areas

[11] Cf. Alan Kraus and Ross (1982), Neil A. Doherty and James R. Garven (1986), J. David Cummins (1988), Cummins and Hélyette Geman (1995), and Scott E. Harrington et al. (1995).
[12] Brennan and Schwartz (1976), Jonathan J. Ingersoll, Jr. (1976), M. Barry Goldman et al. (1979), Mary Ann Gatto et al. (1980), and René Stulz (1982). In an early real-world application, Myron Scholes and I developed the first options-strategy mutual fund in the United States, Money Market/Options Investments, Inc., in February 1976. The strategy which invested 90 percent of its assets in money market instruments and ten percent in a diversified portfolio of stock call options provided equity exposure on the upside with a guaranteed "floor" on the value of the portfolio. The return patterns from this and similar "floor" strategies were later published in Merton, et al. (1978, 1982).
[13] Howard B. Sosin (1980), Carliss Baldwin, Donald Lessard, and Scott P. Mason (1983), Donald F. Cunningham and Patric H. Hendershott (1984), Alan J. Marcus (1987), Merton and Zvi Bodie (1992), Bodie (1996), Ashoka Mody (1996), and Robert S. Neal (1996).
[14] Scott P. Mason and Merton (1985), Calum G. Turvey and Vincent Amanor-Boadu (1989) and Taehoon Kang and B. Wade Brorsen (1995).
[15] James E. Anderson (1987) and Jonathan M. Karpoff (1989).
[16] Lenos Trigeorgis (1993).

452

depending on whether it has the policy option to abandon rural roads if they are not used enough.[17]

Various legal and tax issues involving policy and behavior have been addressed using the option model. Among them is the valuation of plaintiffs' litigation options, bankruptcy laws including limited-liability provisions, tax delinquency on real estate and other property as an option to abandon or recover the property by paying the arrears, tax evasion, and valuing the tax "timing" option for the capital-gains tax in a circumstance when only realization of losses and gains on investments triggers a taxable event.[18]

In a recent preliminary study, the options structure has been employed to help model the decision of whether the Social Security fund should invest in equities (Smetters 1997). As can be seen in the option formula of the preceding section, the value of an option depends on the volatility of the underlying asset. The Federal Reserve uses as one of its indicators of investor uncertainty about the future course of interest rates, the "implied" volatility derived from option prices on government bonds.[19] In his last paper, published after his death, Fischer Black (1995) applies options theory to model the process for the interest rates that govern the dynamics of government bond prices. In another area involving central-bank concerns, Perold (1995) shows how the introduction of various types of derivatives contracts has helped reducepotential systemic-risk problems in the payment system from settlement exposures. The Black-Scholes model can be used to value the "free credit option" implicitly offered to participants, in addition to "float," in markets with other than instantaneous settlement periods. See also Kupiec and White (1996). The prospective application of derivative-security technology to enhance central-bank stabilization policies in both interest rates and currencies is discussed in Merton (1995, 1997b).

In an application involving government activities far removed from sophisticated and relatively efficient financial markets, options analysis has been used to provide new insights into optimal government planning policies in developing countries. A view held by some in development economics about the optimal educational policy for less-developed countries is that once the expected future needs for labor-force composition are determined, the optimal education policy should be to pursue targeted training of the specific skills forecast and in the quantities needed. The alternative of providing either more general education and training in multiple skills or training in skills not expected to be used is seen as a "luxury" that poorer, developing countries could not afford. It, of course, was understood, that forecasts of future labor-training needs were not precise. Nevertheless, the basic prescription formally treated them as if they were. In S. J. Merton (1992), the question is revisited, this time with an explicit recognition of the uncertainty

---

[17] Cathy A. Hamlett and C. Phillip Baumel (1990).
[18] George M. Constantinides and Ingersoll (1984), Brendan O'Flaherty (1990), William J. Blanton (1995), Paul G. Mahoney (1995), and Charles T. Terry (1995).
[19] Sylvia Nasar (1992). See Bodie and Merton (1995) for an overview article on implied volatility as an example of the informational role of asset and option prices.

about future labor requirements embedded in the model. The analysis shows that the value of having the option to change the skill mix and skill type of the labor force over a relatively short period of time can exceed the increased cost in terms of longer education periods or less-deep training in any one skill. The Black-Scholes model is used to quantify that tradeoff. In a different context of the private-sector in a developed country, the same technique could be used to assess the cost-benefit tradeoff for a company to pay a higher wage for a labor force with additional skills not expected to be used in return for the flexibility to employ those skills if the unexpected happens.

The discussion of labor education and training decisions and litigation and taxes leads naturally into the subject of human capital and household decision-making. The individual decision as to how much vocational education to acquire can be formulated as an option-valuation problem in which the optimal exercise conditions reflect when to stop training and start working.[20] In the classic labor-leisure tradeoff, one whose job provides the flexibility to increase or decrease the number of hours worked, and hence his total compensation, on relatively short notice, has a valuable option relative to those whose available work hours are fixed.[21] Wage and pension-plan "floors" that provide for a minimum compensation, and even tenure for university professors (McDonald 1974), have an option-like structure. Other options commonly a part of household finance are: the commitment by an institution to provide a mortgage to the house buyer, if he chooses to get one; the pre-payment right, after he takes the mortgage, that gives the homeowner the right to renegotiate the interest rate paid to the lender if rates fall;[22] a car lease which gives the customer the right, but not the obligation, to purchase the car at a pre-specified price at the end of the lease.[23] Health-care insurance contains varying degrees of flexibility, a major one being whether the consumer agrees in advance to use only a pre-specified set of doctors and hospitals ("HMO plan") or he retains the right to choose an "out-of-plan" doctor or hospital ("point-of-service" plan). In the consumer making the decision on which to take and the health insurer assessing the relative cost of providing the two plans, each solves an option-pricing problem as to the value of that flexibility.[24] Much the same structure of valuation occurs in choosing between "pay-per-view" and "flat-fee" payment for cable-television services.

Many of the preceding option-pricing applications do not involve financial instruments. The family of such applications is called "real" options. The most developed area for real-option application is investment decisions by firms.[25] However, real-options analysis has also been applied to real-estate in-

---

[20] Uri Dothan and Joseph Williams (1981).

[21] Bodie et al. (1992).

[22] Kenneth B. Dunn and John J. McConnell (1981) and Brennan and Schwartz (1985b).

[23] Stephen E. Miller (1995).

[24] Hayes et al. (1993) and Magiera and McLean (1996).

[25] Mason and Merton (1985), Robert L. McDonald and Daniel R. Siegel (1985), Saman Majd and Robert S. Pindyck (1987), Alexander J. Triantis and James E. Hodder (1990), Avinash K. Dixit and Pindyck (1994), Nancy A. Nichols (1994), Trigeorgis (1996) and Keith J. Leslie and Max P. Michaels (1997).

vestment and development decisions.[26] The common element for using option-pricing here is the same as in the preceding examples: the future is uncertain (if it were not, there would be no need to create options because we know now what we will do later) and in an uncertain environment, having the flexibility to decide what to do after some of that uncertainty is resolved definitely has value. Option-pricing theory provides the means for assessing that value.

The major categories of options within project-investment valuations are: the option to initiate or expand, the option to abandon or contract, and the option to wait, slow-down, or speed-up development. There are "growth" options which involve creating excess capacity as an option to expand and research and development as creating the opportunity to produce new products and even new businesses, but not the obligation to do so if they are not economically viable.[27]

A few examples: For real-world application of the options technology in valuing product development in the pharmaceutical industry, see Nichols (1994). In the generation of electric power, the power plant can be constructed to use a single fuel such as oil or natural gas or it can be built to operate on either. The value of that option is the ability to use the least-cost, available fuel at each point in time and the cost of that optionality is manifest in both the higher cost of construction and less-efficient energy conversion than with the corresponding specialized equipment. A third example described in Luehrman (1992) comes from the entertainment industry and involves the decision about making a sequel to a movie: the choices are: either to produce both the original movie and its sequel at the same time, or wait and produce the sequel after the success or failure of the original is known. One does not have to be a movie-production expert to guess that the incremental cost of producing the sequel is going to be less if the first path is followed. While this is done, more typically the latter is chosen, especially with higher-budget films. The economic reason is that the second approach provides the option not to make the sequel (if, for example, the original is not a success). If the producer knew (almost certainly) that the sequel will be produced, then the option value of waiting for more information is small and the cost of doing the sequel separately is likely to exceed the benefit. Hence, once again, we see that the amount of uncertainty is critical to the decision, and the option-pricing model provides the means for quantifying the cost/benefit tradeoff. As a last example, Baldwin and Clark (1999) develop a model for designing complex production systems focused around the concept of modularity. They exemplify their central theme with several industrial examples which include computer and automobile production. Modularity in production provides options. In assessing the value of modularity for production, they em-

---

[26] V. Kerry Smith (1984), Raymond Chiang et al. (1986), David Geltner and William C. Wheaton (1989), Joseph T. Williams (1991), and F. Christian Zinkhan (1991).
[27] W. Carl Kester (1984), Robyn McLaughlin and Robert A. Taggart (1992) and Terrance W. Faulkner (1996).

ploy an option-pricing type of methodology, where complexity in the production system is comparable to uncertainty in the financial one.[28]

In each of these real-option examples as with a number of the other applications discussed in this section, the underlying "asset" is rarely traded in anything approximating a continuous market and its price is therefore not continuously observable either. For that reason, this paper, manifestly focused on applications, devotes so much space to the technical section on extending the Black-Scholes option-pricing framework to include non-tradability and non-observability.

FUTURE DIRECTIONS OF APPLICATIONS

As I suggested at the outset, innovation is a central force driving the financial system toward greater economic efficiency with considerable economic benefit having accrued from the changes since the time that the option-pricing papers were published. Indeed, much financial research and broad-based practitioner experience developed over that period have led to vast improvements in our understanding of how to apply the new financial technologies to manage risk. Moreover, we have seen how wide ranging are the applications of our technology for pricing and measuring the risk of derivatives. Nevertheless, there still remains an intense uneasiness among managers, regulators, politicians, the press, and the public over these new derivative-security activities and their perceived risks to financial institutions. And this seems to be the case even though the huge financial disruptions, such as the savings-and-loan debacle of the 1980s in the United States and the current financial crises in Asia and some emerging markets, appear to be the consequence of the more traditional risks taken by institutions such as commercial, real-estate, and less-developed-country lending, loan guarantees, and equity-share holdings.

One conjecture attributes this uneasiness to the frequently cited instances of individual costly events that are alleged to be associated with derivatives, such as the failure of Barings Bank, Proctor and Gamble's losses on complex interest-rate contracts, the financial distress of Orange County, and so forth. Perhaps.[29] But, as already noted, derivatives are ubiquitous in the financial world and thus, they are likely to be present in any financial circumstance, whether or not their use has anything causal to do with the resulting financial outcomes. However, even if all these allegations were valid, the sheer fact that we are able to associate individual names with these occurrences instead of mere numbers ("XYZ company" instead of "475–500 thrifts" as the relevant

---

[28] See also Hau He and Pindyck (1992). On an entirely different application, Kester's 1984 analysis of whether to develop products in parallel or sequentially could be applied to the evaluation of alternative strategies for funding basic scientific research: is it better to support N different research approaches simultaneously or just to support one or two and then use the resulting outcomes to sequence future research approaches? See also Merton (1992, p. 426).

[29] Merton H. Miller (1997) provides a cogent analysis refuting many of the specific-case allegations of derivatives misuse.

descriptor) would suggest that these are relatively isolated events–unfortunate pathologies rather than indicators of systemic flaws. In contrast, the physiology of this financial technology, that is, how it works when it works as it should, is not the subject of daily reports from around the globe but is essentially taken for granted.

An alternative or supplementary conjecture about the sources of the collective anxiety over derivatives holds that they are a part of a wider implementation of financial innovations which have required major changes in the basic institutional hierarchy and in the infrastructure to support it. As a result, the knowledge base now required to manage and oversee financial institutions differs greatly from the traditional training and experience of many financial managers and government regulators. Experiential changes of this sort are threatening. It is difficult to deal with change that is exogenous to our traditional knowledge base and framework and thus comes to seem beyond our control. Decreased understanding of the new environment can create a sense of greater risk even when the objective level of risk in the system remains unchanged or is actually reduced. If so, we should start to deal with the problem now since the knowledge gap may widen if the current pace of financial innovation, as some anticipate, accelerates into the 21st century. Moreover, greater complexity of products and the need for more rapid decision-making will probably increase the reliance on models, which in turn implies a growing place for elements of mathematical and computational maturity in the knowledge base of managers. Dealing with this knowledge gap offers considerable challenge to private institutions and government as well as considerable opportunity to schools of management and engineering and to university departments of economics and mathematics.

There are two essentially different frames of reference for trying to analyze and understand changes in the financial system. One perspective takes as given the existing institutional structure of financial service providers, whether governmental or private-sector, and examines what can be done to make those institutions perform their particular financial services more efficiently and profitably. An alternative to this traditional institutional perspective–and the one I favor–is the functional perspective, which takes as given the economic functions served by the financial system and examines what is the best institutional structure to perform those functions.[30] The basic functions of a financial system are essentially the same in all economies, which makes them far more stable, across time and across geopolitical borders, than the identity and structure of the institutions performing them. Thus, a functional perspective offers a more robust frame of reference than an institutional one, especially in a rapidly changing financial environment. It is difficult to use institutions as the conceptual "anchor" for analyzing the evolving financial system when the institutional structure is itself changing significantly, as has been the case for the past two decades and as appears likely to continue well

---

[30] For elaboration on the functional perspective, see Merton (1993, 1995), Crane et al. (1995), and Bodie and Merton (1998).

into the future. In contrast, in the functional perspective, institutional change is endogenous, and may therefore prove especially useful in predicting the future direction of financial innovation, changes in financial markets and intermediaries, and regulatory design.[31]

The successful private-sector and governmental financial service providers and overseers in the impending future will be those who can address the disruptive aspects of innovation in financial technology while still fully exploiting its efficiency benefits. What types of research and training will be needed to manage financial institutions? The view of the future here as elsewhere in the economic sphere is clouded with significant uncertainties. With this in mind, I nevertheless try my hand at a few thoughts on the direction of change for product and service demands by users of the financial system and the implications of those changes for applications of mathematical financial modeling.

The household sector of users in the more fully developed financial systems has experienced a secular trend of disaggregation in financial services. Some see this trend continuing with existing products such as mutual funds being transported into technologically less-developed systems. Perhaps so, especially in the more immediate future, with the widespread growth of relatively inexpensive Internet accessibility. However, deep and wide-ranging disaggregation has left households with the responsibility for making important and technically complex micro financial decisions involving risk (such as detailed asset allocation and estimates of the optimal level of life-cycle saving for retirement)—decisions that they had not had to make in the past, are not trained to make in the present, and are unlikely to execute efficiently even with attempts at education in the future. The low-cost availability of the Internet does not solve the "principal-agent" problem with respect to financial advice dispensed by an agent. That is why I believe that the trend will shift toward more integrated financial products and services, which are easier to understand and more tailored toward individual profiles. Those products and services will include not only the traditional attempt to achieve an efficient risk-return tradeoff for the tangible-wealth portfolio but will also integrate human-capital considerations, hedging, and income and estate tax planning into the asset-allocation decisions. Beyond the advisory role, financial service providers will undertake a role of principal to create financial instruments that eliminate "short-fall" or "basis" risk for households with respect to target-

[31] During the last 25 years, finance theory has been a good predictor of future changes in finance practice. That is, when theory seems to suggest that something "should be there" and it isn't, practice has evolved so that it is. The "pure" securities developed by Kenneth J. Arrow (1953) that so clearly explain the theoretical function of financial instruments in risk bearing were nowhere to be found in the real world until the broad development of the options and derivative-security markets. It is now routine for financial engineers to disaggregate the cash flows of various securities into their elemental Arrow-security component parts and then to reaggregate them to create securities with new patterns of cash flows. For the relation between options and Arrow securities and the application of the Black-Scholes model to the synthesis and pricing of Arrow securities, see Ross (1976b), Rolf W. Banz and Miller (1978), Breeden and Robert Litzenberger (1978), Darrell J. Duffie and Chi-fu Huang (1986), and Merton (1992, pp. 443–450).

458

ed financial goals such as tuition for children's higher education and desired consumption-smoothing throughout the life-cycle (e.g., preserving the household's standard of living in retirement, cf., Franco Modigliani, 1986). The creation of such customized financial instruments will be made economically feasible by the derivative-security pricing technology that permits the construction of custom products at "assembly-line"-levels of cost. Paradoxically, making the products more user-friendly and simpler to understand for customers will create considerably more complexity for the producers of those products. Hence, financial-engineering creativity and the technological and transactional bases to implement that creativity, reliably and cost-effectively, are likely to become a central competitive element in the industry. The resulting complexity will require more elaborate and highly quantitative risk-management systems within financial service firms and a parallel need for more sophisticated approaches to government oversight. Neither of these can be achieved without greater reliance on mathematical financial modeling, which in turn will be feasible only with continued improvements in the sophistication and accuracy of financial models.

Non-financial firms currently use derivative securities and other contractual agreements to hedge interest rate, currency, commodity, and even equity price risks. With improved lower-cost technology and learning-curve experience, this practice is likely to expand. Eventually, this alternative to equity capital as a cushion for risk could lead to a major change of corporate structures as more firms use hedging to substitute for equity capital; thereby moving from publicly traded shares to closely-held private shares.

The preceding section provides examples of current applications of the options technology to corporate project evaluation: the evaluation of research-and-development projects in pharmaceuticals and the value of flexibility in the decision about sequel production in the movie industry. The big potential shift in the future, however, is from tactical applications of derivatives to strategic ones.[32] For example, a hypothetical oil company with crude oil reserves and gasoline and heating-oil distribution but no refining capability could complete the vertical integration of the firm by using contractual agreements instead of physical acquisition of a refinery. Thus, by entering into contracts that call for the delivery of crude oil by the firm on one date in return for receiving a mix of refined petroleum products at a pre-specified later date, the firm in effect creates a synthetic refinery. Real-world strategic examples in natural gas and electricity are described in Harvard Business School case studies, "Enron Gas Services" (1994) and "Tennessee Valley Authority: Option Purchase Agreements" (1996), by Peter Tufano. There is some evidence that these new financial technologies may even lead to a revisiting of the industrial-organization model for these industries.

It is no coincidence that the early strategic applications are in energy- and power-generation industries that need long-term planning horizons and have

---

[32] See Kester (1984), Stewart C. Myers (1984), and Edward H. Bowman and Dileep Hurry (1993) on the application of option-pricing theory to the evaluation of strategic decisions.

major fixed-cost components on a large scale with considerable uncertainty. Since energy and power generation are fundamental in every economy, this use for derivatives offers mainline applications in both developed and developing countries. Eventually, such use of derivatives may become standard tools for implementing strategic objectives.

A major requirement for the efficient broad-based application of these contracting technologies in both the household and non-financial-firm sectors will be to find effective organizational structures for ensuring contract performance, which includes global clarification and revisions of the treatment of such contractual agreements in bankruptcy. The need for assurances on contract performance is likely to stimulate further development of the financial-guarantee business for financial institutions. Such institutions will have to improve the efficiency of collateral management further as assurance for performance. As we have seen, one early application of the option-pricing model focuses directly on the valuation and risk-exposure measurement of financial guarantees.

A consequence of all this prospective technological change will be the need for greater analytical understanding of valuation and risk management by users, producers, and regulators of derivative securities. Furthermore, improvements in efficiency from derivative products will not be effectively realized without concurrent changes in the financial "infrastructure"–the institutional interfaces between intermediaries and financial markets, regulatory practices, organization of trading, clearing, settlement, other back-office facilities, and management-information systems. To perform its functions as both user and overseer of the financial system, government will need to innovate and make use of derivative-security technology in the provision of risk-accounting standards, designing monetary and fiscal policies, implementing stabilization programs, and overseeing financial-system regulation.

In summary, in the distant past, applications of mathematical models had only limited and sidestream effects on finance practice. But in the last quarter century since the publication of the Black-Scholes option-pricing theory, such models have become mainstream to practitioners in financial institutions and markets around the world. The option-pricing model has played an active role in that transformation. It is safe to say that mathematical models will play an indispensable role in the functioning of the global financial system.

Even this brief discourse on the application to finance practice of mathematical models in general and the option-pricing model in particular would be negligently incomplete without a strong word of caution about their use. At times we can lose sight of the ultimate purpose of the models when their mathematics become too interesting. The mathematics of financial models can be applied precisely, but the models are not at all precise in their application to the complex real world. Their accuracy as a useful approximation to that world varies significantly across time and place. The models should be applied in practice only tentatively, with careful assessment of their limitations in each application.

BIBLIOGRAPHY

Anderson, James E. "Quotas as Options: Optimality and Quota License Pricing Under Uncertainty," *Journal of International Economics,* August 1987, *23* (1–2), pp. 21–39.

Arrow, Kenneth J. "Le rôle des valeurs boursières pour la répartition la meilleure des risques," *Econometrie,* Colloques Internationaux du Centre National de la Recherche Scientifique, 1953, Vol. XI, Paris, pp. 41–7.

Bachelier, Louis. "Théorie de la Spéculation," *Annales Science de l'Ecole Normale Supérieure,* Paris: Gauthier-Villars, 1900 (3) No. 1018. (English translation in Cootner, P.H., ed. *The Random Character of Stock Market Prices,* Cambridge, MA: MIT Press, 1964, pp. 17–78.)

Baldwin, Carliss. "Pricing Convertible Preferred Stock According to the Rational Option Pricing Theory," B.S. dissertation, Massachusetts Institute of Technology, Cambridge, MA, 1972.

Baldwin, Carliss and Clark, Kim. *Design Rules: The Power of Modularity,* forthcoming, Cambridge, MA: MIT Press, 1999 (forthcoming).

Baldwin, Carliss, Lessard, Donald and Mason, Scott P. "Budgetary Time Bombs: Controlling Government Loan Guarantees," *Canadian Public Policy,* 1983, *9,* pp. 338–346.

Banz, Rolf W. and Miller, Merton H. "Prices for State-Contingent Claims: Some Estimates and Applications," *Journal of Business,* October 1978, *51* (4), pp. 653–72.

Bernstein, Peter L. *Capital Ideas: The Improbable Origins of Modern Wall Street,* New York: Free Press, 1992.

Bertsimas, Dimitris, Kogan, Leonid and Lo, Andrew W. "Pricing and Hedging Derivative Securities in Incomplete Markets: An e–Arbitrage Approach," Sloan School of Management, Massachusetts Institute of Technology Working Paper #LFE-1027–97, June 1997.

Black, Fischer. "How We Came Up With the Option Formula," *Journal of Portfolio Management,* Winter 1989, *15* (2), pp. 4–8. Originally, distributed in two parts by Fischer Black's pricing and commentary service on options, *Options,* Vol. 1, No. 10, June 21, 1976; Vol. 1, No. 11, July 5, 1976.

–. "Interest Rates as Options," *Journal of Finance,* December 1995,: *50* (5), pp. 1371–1376.

Black, Fischer and Scholes, Myron S. "The Valuation of Option Contracts and a Test of Market Efficiency," *Journal of Finance,* May 1972, *27* (2), pp. 399–418.

–. "The Pricing of Options and Corporate Liabilities," *Journal of Political Economy,* May–June 1973, *81* (3), pp. 637–54.

Blanton, William J. "Reducing the Value of Plaintiff's Litigation Option in Federal Court: Daubert v. Merrell Dow Pharmaceuticals, Inc.," *George Mason University Law Review,* Spring 1995, *2,* pp. 159–222.

Bodie, Zvi. "What the Pension Benefit Guaranty Corporation Can Learn from the Federal Savings-and-Loan Insurance Corporation," *Journal of Financial Services Research,* January 1996, *10* (1), pp. 83–100.

Bodie, Zvi and Merton, Robert C. "The Informational Role of Asset Prices: The Case of Implied Volatility," Chapter 6 in Dwight B. Crane et al, 1995, pp. 197–224.

–. *Finance,* Upper Saddle River, NJ: Prentice Hall, 1998.

Bodie, Zvi, Merton, Robert C. and Samuelson, William F. "Labor Supply Flexibility and Portfolio Choice in a Life-Cycle Model," *Journal of Economic Dynamics and Control,* July–October 1992, *16* (3,4), pp. 427–449.

Bowman, Edward H. and Hurry, Dileep. "Strategy Through the Option Lens: An Integrated View of Resource Investments and the Incremental-Choice Process," *Academy of Management Review,* October 1993, *18* (4), pp. 760–82.

Breeden, Douglas T. "An Intertemporal Asset Pricing Model with Stochastic Consumption and Investment Opportunities," *Journal of Financial Economics,* September 1979, *7* (3) pp. 265–96.

–. "Futures Markets and Commodity Options: Hedging and Optimality in Incomplete Markets," *Journal of Economic Theory,* April 1984, *32* (2), pp. 275–300.

Breeden, Douglas T. and Litzenberger, Robert. "Prices of State-Contingent Claims Implicit in Option Prices," *Journal of Business*, October 1978, *51* (4), pp. 621–51.

Brennan, Michael J. and Schwartz, Eduardo S. "The Pricing of Equity–Linked Life Insurance Policies with an Asset Value Guarantee," *Journal of Financial Economics*, June 1976 *3* (3) pp. 195–213.

–. "Evaluating Natural Resource Investments," *Journal of Business*, April 1985a, *58* (2), pp. 135–57.

–, "Determinants of GNMA Mortgage Prices," *Journal of the American Real Estate & Urban Economics Association*, Fall 1985b, *13* (3), pp. 209–28.

Chiang, Raymond, Lai, Tsong-Yue and Ling, David C. "Retail Leasehold Interests: A Contingent Claim Analysis," *Journal of the American Real Estate & Urban Economics Association*, Summer 1986, *14* (2), pp. 216–29.

Constantinides, George M. and Ingersoll, Jonathan E., Jr. "Optimal Bond Trading with Personal Taxes," *Journal of Financial Economics*, September, 1984, *13* (3), pp. 299–336.

Cox, John C. and Ross, Stephen A. "The Valuation of Options for Alternative Stochastic Processes," *Journal of Financial Economics*, January-March 1976, *3* (1/2), pp. 145–66.

Cox, John C. and Rubinstein, Mark. *Options Markets*. Upper Saddle River, NJ: Prentice Hall, 1985.

Crane, Dwight B., Froot, Kenneth A., Mason, Scott P., Perold, André F., Merton, Robert C., Bodie, Zvi, Sirri, Erik R. and Tufano, Peter. *The Global Financial System: A Functional Perspective*, Boston: Harvard Business School Press, 1995.

Cummins, J. David. "Risk-Based Premiums for Insurance Guarantee Funds," *Journal of Finance*, September 1988, *43* (4), pp. 823–89.

Cummins, J. David and Geman, Hélyette. "Pricing Catastrophe Insurance Futures and Call Spreads: An Arbitrage Approach," *Journal of Fixed Income*, March 1995, *4* (4) pp. 46–57.

Cunningham, Donald F, and Hendershott, Patric H. "Pricing FHA Mortgage Default Insurance," *Housing Finance Review*, December 1984, *3* (4), pp. 373–92.

Davis, Mark H.A. "Option Pricing in Incomplete Markets," in M.A.H. Dempster and S. Pliska, eds., *Mathematics of Derivative Securities*, Cambridge: Cambridge University Press: 1997, pp. 216–226.

Dixit, Avinash K. and Pindyck, Robert S. *Investment Under Uncertainty*, Princeton: Princeton University Press, 1994.

Doherty, Neil A. and Garven, James R. "Price Regulation in Property-Liability Insurance: A Contingent-Claims Approach," *Journal of Finance*, December 1986, *41* (5), pp. 1031–50.

Dothan, Uri and Williams, Joseph. "Education as an Option," *Journal of Business*, January 1981, *54* (1), pp. 117–39.

Duffie, Darrell J. and Huang, Chi-fu. "Implementing Arrow-Debreu Equilibria by Continuous Trading of a Few Long-Lived Securities," *Econometria*, November 1986, *53* (6), pp. 1337–56.

Dunn, Kenneth B. and McConnell, John J. "Valuation of GNMA Mortgage-Backed Securities," *Journal of Finance*, June 1981, *36* (3), pp. 599–616.

Faulkner, Terrance W. "Applying 'Options Thinking' to R & D Valuation," *Research-Technology Management*, May–June 1996, *39* (3), pp. 50–56.

Figlewski, Stephen. "Options Arbitrage in Imperfect Markets," *Journal of Finance*, December 1989, *44* (5), pp. 1289–1311.

Föllmer, Hans and Sondermann, Dieter. "Hedging of Non-Redundant Contingent-Claims," in Werner Hildenbrand and Andreau Mas-Colell, eds., *Contributions to Mathematical Economics, in Honor of Gérard Debreu*, Amsterdam: North Holland, 1986, pp. 205–223.

Gatto, Mary Ann, Geske, Robert, Litzenberger, Robert and Sosin, Howard B. "Mutual Fund Insurance," *Journal of Financial Economics*, September 1980, *8* (3), pp. 283–317.

Geltner, David and Wheaton, William C. "On the Use of the Financial Option Price Model to Value and Explain Vacant Urban Land," *Journal of the American Real Estate & Urban Economics Association*, Summer 1989, *17* (2), pp. 142–58.

Goldman, M. Barry, Sosin, Howard B. and Shepp, Lawrence A. "On Contingent Claims that

Insure Ex-Post Optimal Stock Market Timing," *Journal of Finance*, (May 1979, *34* (2), pp. 401–13.

Hamlett, Cathy A. and Baumel, C. Phillip. "Rural Road Abandonment: Policy Criteria and Empirical Analysis," *American Journal of Agricultural Economics*, February 1990, *72* (1) pp. 114–20.

Harrington, Scott E., Mann, Steven V. and Niehaus, Greg. "Insurer Capital Structure Decisions and the Viability of Insurance Derivatives," *Journal of Risk and Insurance*, September 1995, *62* (3), pp. 483–508.

Hawkins, Gregory D. "An Analysis of Revolving Credit Agreements," *Journal of Financial Economics*, March 1982, *10* (1), pp. 59–82.

Hayes, James A., Cole, Joseph B. and Meiselman, David I. "Health Insurance Derivatives: The Newest Application of Modern Financial Risk Management," *Business Economics*, April 1993, *28* (2), pp. 36–40.

He, Hua and Pindyck, Robert, S. "Investments in Flexible Production Capacity," *Journal of Economic Dynamics and Control*, July–October 1992, *16* (3.4), pp. 575–99.

Ingersoll, Jonathan E., Jr. "A Theoretical Model and Empirical Investigation of the Dual Purpose Funds: An Application of Contingent-Claims Analysis," *Journal of Financial Economics*, January–March 1976, *3* (1/2), pp. 82–123.

Itô, Kiyoshi. *Kiyoshi Itô Selected Papers*, New York: Springer-Verlag, 1987.

Jarrow, Robert A. and Rudd, Andrew T. *Option Pricing*, Homewood, IL: Richard D. Irwin 1983.

Jin, Li, Kogan, Leonid, Lim, Terence, Taylor, Jonathan and Lo, Andrew W. "The Derivatives Sourcebook: A Bibliography of Applications of the Black-Scholes/Merton Option-Pricing Model," Sloan School of Management, Massachusetts Institute of Technology Working Paper, (forthcoming).

Jones, E. Philip, Mason, Scott P., Rosenfeld, Eric E. and Fisher, Lawrence. "Contingent Claims Analysis of Corporate Capital Structures: An Empirical Investigation," *Journal of Finance*, July 1984 *39* (3), pp. 611–625.

Kang, Taehoon and Brorsen, B. Wade. "Valuing Target Price Support Programs with Average Option Pricing," *American Journal of Agricultural Economics*, February 1995, *77* (1), pp. 106–118.

Karpoff, Jonathan M. "Characteristics of Limited Entry Fisheries and the Option Component of Entry Licenses," *Land Economics*, November 1989, *65* (4), pp. 386–393.

Kester, W. Carl. "Today's Options for Tomorrow's Growth," *Harvard Business Review*, March–April 1984, *62* (2), pp. 153–60.

Kraus, Alan and Ross, Stephen A. "The Determination of Fair Profits for the Property-Liability Insurance Firm," *Journal of Finance*, September 1982, *37* (4), pp. 1015–28.

Kupiec, Paul H. and White, A. Patricia. "Regulatory Competition and the Efficiency of Alternative Derivative Product Margining Systems," *Finance and Economics Discussion Series*, Board of Governors of the Federal Reserve System, Washington, DC, February 1996, 96/11.

Leonard, Roger J. "An Empirical Examination of a New General Equilibrium Model for Warrant Pricing," M.S. thesis, Massachusetts Institute of Technology, September 1971.

Leslie, Keith J. and Michaels, Max P. "The Real Power of Real Options," *McKinsey Quarterly*, 1997, *2* (3), pp. 4–22.

Long, John B. "Discussion," *Journal of Finance*, May 1974, *29* (2), pp. 485–8.

Luehrman, Timothy A. "Arundel Partners: The Sequel Project," Harvard Business School Case #9-292-140, 1992.

Magiera, Frank T. and McLean, Robert A. "Strategic Options in Capital Budgeting and Program Selection under Fee-for-Service and Managed Care," *Health Care Management Review*, Fall 1996, *21* (4), pp. 7–17.

Mahoney, Paul G. "Contract Remedies and Options Pricing," *Journal of Legal Studies*, January 1995, *24* (1), pp. 139–63.

Majd, Saman and Pindyck, Robert S. "Time to Build, Option Value, and Investment Decisions," *Journal of Financial Economics*, March 1987, *18* (1), pp. 7–28.

Marcus, Alan J. "Corporate Pension Policy and the Value of PBGC Insurance," in Zvi Bodie, John B. Shoven, and David A. Wise, eds., *Issues in Pension Economics,* Chicago, IL: University of Chicago Press, 1987, pp. 49–76.

Mason, Scott P. and Merton, Robert C. "The Role of Contingent Claims Analysis in Corporate Finance," in Edward Altman and Marti Subrahmanyan, eds., *Recent Advances in Corporate Finance,* Homewood, IL: Richard D. Irwin, 1985, pp. 7–54.

McLaughlin, Robyn and Taggart, Robert A. "The Opportunity Cost of Using Excess Capacity," *Financial Management,* Summer 1992, *21* (2), pp. 12–23.

McDonald, John G. "Faculty Tenure as a Put Option: An Economic Interpretation," *Social Science Quarterly,* September 1974, *55* (2), pp. 362–71.

McDonald, Robert L. and Siegel, Daniel R. "Investment and the Valuation of Firms When There is an Option to Shut Down," *International Economic Review,* June 1985, *26* (2), pp. 331–49.

Merton, Robert C. "Lifetime Portfolio Selection Under Uncertainty: The Continuous-Time Case," *Review of Economics and Statistics,* August 1969, *51* (3), pp. 247–57. Reprinted in Merton (1992, Ch. 4).

–. "A Dynamic General Equilibrium Model of the Asset Market and its Application to the Pricing of the Capital Structure of the Firm." Massachusetts Institute of Technology Working Paper No. 497-70, 1970. Reprinted in Merton (1992, Ch. 11).

–. "Optimum Consumption and Portfolio Rules in a Continuous-Time Model," *Journal of Economic Theory,* December 1971, *3* (4), pp. 373–413. Reprinted in Merton (1992, Ch. 5).

–. "Appendix: Continuous-Time Speculative Processes," in R.H. Day and S.M. Robinson, eds., *Mathematical Topics in Economic Theory and Computation,* Philadelphia, PA: Society for Industrial and Applied Mathematics, 1972. Reprinted in SIAM Review, January 1973, *15* (1), pp. 34–38.

–. "Theory of Rational Option Pricing," *Bell Journal of Economics and Management Science,* Spring 1973a, *4* (1), pp. 141–83. Reprinted in Merton (1992, Ch. 8). Original Working Paper #574-71, Sloan School of Management, Massachusetts Institute of Technology, Cambridge, MA (October 1971).

–. "An Intertemporal Capital Asset Pricing Model," *Econometrica,* September 1973b, *41* (5), pp. 867–87. Reprinted in Merton (1992, Ch. 15).

–. "On the Pricing of Corporate Debt: The Risk Structure of Interest Rates," *Journal of Finance,* May 1974, *29* (2), pp. 449–70. Reprinted in Merton (1992, Ch. 12).

–. "Option Pricing When Underlying Stock Returns are Discontinuous," *Journal of Financial Economics,* January–March 1976a, *3* (1/2), pp. 125–44. Reprinted in Merton (1992, Ch. 9).

–. "The Impact on Option Pricing of Specification Error in the Underlying Stock Price Returns," *Journal of Finance,* May 1976b, *31* (2), pp. 333–50.

–. "An Analytic Derivation of the Cost of Deposit Insurance and Loan Guarantees: An Application of Modern Option Pricing Theory," *Journal of Banking and Finance,* June 1977a, *1* (1), pp. 3–11. Reprinted in Merton (1992, Ch. 19).

–. "On the Pricing of Contingent Claims and the Modigliani-Miller Theorem," *Journal of Financial Economics,* November 1977b, *5* (3), pp. 241–9. Reprinted in Merton (1992, Ch. 13).

–. "Financial Economics," in E.C. Brown and R.M. Solow, eds., *Paul Samuelson and Modern Economic Theory,* New York: McGraw-Hill, 1983, pp. 105–140.

–.*Continuous-Time Finance,* Revised Edition, Cambridge, MA: Basil Blackwell, 1992.

–. "Operation and Regulation in Financial Intermediation: A Functional Perspective," in Peter Englund, ed., *Operation and Regulation of Financial Markets,* Stockholm: The Economic Council, 1993, pp. 17–67.

–. "Influence of Mathematical Models in Finance on Practice: Past, Present and Future," *Philosophical Transactions of the Royal Society of London,* June 1994, *347* (1684), pp. 451–463.

–. "Financial Innovation and the Management and Regulation of Financial Institutions," *Journal of Banking and Finance,* June 1995, *19* (3,4), pp. 461–481.

–. "A Model of Contract Guarantees for Credit-Sensitive, Opaque Financial Intermediaries," *European Finance Review,* 1997a, *1* (1), pp. 1–13.

464

–. "On the Role of the Wiener Process in Finance Theory and Practice: The Case of Replicating Portfolios," in David Jerison, I.M. Singer, and Daniel W. Stroock, eds., *The Legacy of Norbert Wiener: A Centennial Symposium*, PSPM Series, Vol. 60, Providence, RI: American Mathematical Society, 1997b, pp. 209–221.

Merton, Robert C. and Bodie, Zvi. "On the Management of Financial Guarantees," *Financial Management,* Winter 1992, *21* (4), pp. 87–109.

Merton, Robert C. and Scholes, Myron S. "Fischer Black," *Journal of Finance,* December 1995, *50* (5), pp. 1359–1370.

Merton, Robert C., Scholes, Myron S. and Gladstein, Mathew L. "The Returns and Risk of Alternative Call Option Portfolio Investment Strategies," *Journal of Business,* April 1978, *51* (2), pp. 183–242.

–. "The Returns and Risks of Alternative Put-Option Portfolio Investment Strategies," *Journal of Business,* January 1982, *55* (1), pp. 1–55.

Merton, Samantha J. "Options Pricing in the Real World of Uncertainties: Educating Towards a Flexible Labor Force," B.A. thesis, Department of Economics, Harvard University, March 18, 1992.

Miller, Merton H. *Merton Miller on Derivatives,* New York: John Wiley & Sons, Inc., 1997.

Miller, Stephen E. "Economics of Automobile Leasing: The Call Option Value," *Journal of Consumer Affairs,* Summer 1995, *29* (1), pp. 199–218.

Modigliani, Franco. "Life Cycle, Individual Thrift and the Wealth of Nations," *Les Prix Nobel 1985,* Stockholm: Nobel Foundation, 1986.

Mody, Ashoka. "Valuing and Accounting for Loan Guarantees," *World Bank Research Observer,* 1996, *11* (1), pp.119–42.

Myers, Stewart C. "Finance Theory and Financial Strategy," *Interfaces,* January–February 1984, *14* (1), pp. 126–37.

Nasar, Sylvia. "For Fed, a New Set of Tea Leaves," *New York Times,* 5 July 1992, sec. D:1.

Neal, Robert S. "Credit Derivatives: New Financial Instruments for Controlling Credit Risk," *Economic Review,* (Federal Reserve Bank of Kansas City), Second Quarter 1996, *81* (2), pp.15–27.

Nichols, Nancy A. "Scientific Management at Merck: An Interview with CFO Judy Lewent," *Harvard Business Review,* January–February 1994, *72* (1), pp. 89–99.

O'Flaherty, Brendan. "The Option Value of Tax Delinquency: Theory," *Journal of Urban Economics,* November 1990, *28* (3), pp. 287–317.

Paddock, James L., Siegel, Daniel R. and Smith, James L. "Option Valuation of Claims on Real Assets: The Case of Offshore Petroleum Leases," *Quarterly Journal of Economics,* August 1988, *103* (3), pp. 479–508.

Perold, André F. "BEA Associates: Enhanced Equity Index Funds," Harvard Business School Case #293–024, 1992.

–. "The Payment System and Derivative Instruments," Chapter 2 in Crane et al. 1995, pp. 33–79.

Romano, Marc and Touzi, Nizar. "Contingent Claims and Market Completeness in a Stochastic Volatility Model," *Mathematical Finance,* October 1997, *7* (4), pp. 399–412.

Rosenfeld, Eric. *Stochastic Processes of Common Stock Returns: An Empirical Examination,* Ph.D. dissertation, Sloan School of Management, Massachusetts Institute of Technology, Cambridge, MA, 1980.

Ross, Stephen A. "Arbitrage Theory of Capital Asset Pricing," *Journal of Economic Theory,* December 1976a, *13* (3), pp. 341–60.

–. "Options and Efficiency," *Quarterly Journal of Economics,* February 1976b, *90* (1), pp. 75–89.

Samuelson, Paul A. "Rational Theory of Warrant Pricing," *Industrial Management Review,* Spring 1965, *6* (2), pp. 13–31.

–. "Mathematics of Speculative Price," in R.H. Day and S.M. Robinson, eds., *Mathematical Topics in Economic Theory and Computation,* Philadelphia, PA: Society for Industrial and Applied Mathematics, 1972. Reprinted in *SIAM Review,* January 1973, *15* (1), pp. 1–42.

Samuelson, Paul A. and Merton Robert C. "A Complete Model of Warrant Pricing that

Maximizes Utility," *Industrial Management Review,* Winter 1969. *10* (2), pp. 17–46. Reprinted in Merton (1992, Ch. 7).

Scholes, Myron S. "Taxes and the Pricing of Options," *Journal of Finance,* May 1976, *31* (2), pp. 319–32.

–. "Derivatives in a Dynamic Environment," *Les Prix Nobel 1997,* Stockholm: Nobel Foundation, 1998.

Scholes, Myron S. and Wolfson, Mark A. *Taxes and Business Strategy: A Planning Approach,* Upper Saddle River, NJ: Prentice-Hall, 1992.

Smetters, Kenneth. "Investing the Social Security Trust Fund in Equities: An Option Pricing Approach," *Technical Paper Series,* Macroeconomic Analysis and Tax Analysis Divisions, Washington, DC., 1997.

Smith, Clifford W., Jr. "Option Pricing: A Review," *Journal of Financial Economics,* January–March 1976, *3* (1/2), pp. 3–52.

Smith, V. Kerry. "A Bound for Option Value," *Land Economics,* August 1984, *60* (3), pp. 292–6.

Sosin, Howard B. "On the Valuation of Federal Loan Guarantees to Corporations," *Journal of Finance,* December 1980, *35* (5), pp. 1209–21.

Stratonovich, R.L. *Conditional Markov Processes and Their Application to the Theory of Optimal Control,* New York: American Elsevier, 1968.

Stulz, René M. "Options on the Minimum or the Maximum of Two Risky Assets: Analysis and Applications," *Journal of Financial Economics,* July 1982, *10* (2), pp. 161–85.

Terry, Charles T. "Option Pricing Theory and the Economic Incentive Analysis of Nonrecourse Acquisition Liabilities," *American Journal of Tax Policy,* Fall 1995, *12* (2), pp. 273–397.

Triantis, Alexander J. and Hodder, James E. "Valuing Flexibility as a Complex Option," Journal of Finance, June 1990, *45* (2), pp. 549–65.

Trigeorgis, Lenos. "Real Options and Interactions with Financial Flexibility," *Financial Management,* Autumn 1993, *22* (3), pp. 202–24.

–. *Real Options,* Cambridge, MA: The MIT Press, 1996.

Tufano, Peter. "Enron Gas Services," Harvard Business School Case #294–051, 1994.

–. "Tennessee Valley Authority: Option Purchase Agreements," Harvard Business School Case #296–038, 1996.

Turvey, Calum G. and Amanor-Boadu, Vincent. "Evaluating Premiums for a Farm Income Insurance Policy," *Canadian Journal of Agricultural Economics,* July 1989, *37* (2), pp. 233–47.

Wiggins, James B. "Option Values Under Stochastic Volatility: Theory and Empirical Estimates," *Journal of Financial Economics,* December 1987, *19* (2), pp. 351–72.

Williams, Joseph T. "Real Estate Development as an Option," *Journal of Real Estate Finance and Economics,* June 1991, *4* (2), pp. 191–208.

Zinkhan, F. Christian. "Option-Pricing and Timberland's Land-Use Conversion Option," *Land Economics,* August 1991, *67* (3), pp. 317–325.

Myron S Scholes

MYRON S. SCHOLES

I was born in Timmins, Ontario, Canada on July 1, 1941. My father had ventured to Timmins, a relatively prosperous gold-mining region, to practice dentistry during the depression. My mother and her uncle established a chain of small department stores in and around Timmins. The death of her uncle resulted in a family dispute, my first exposure to agency and contracting problems. To my benefit, my mother then devoted her time to raising her two sons. At the age of ten, we moved 500 miles south to Hamilton, Ontario.

I was a good student, ranking near the top of my class. Soon after we arrived in Hamilton, my life changed dramatically. My mother developed cancer. She died a few days after my sixteenth birthday. Another shock awaited me. I developed scar tissue on each of my corneas that impaired my eyesight. It was difficult to read for extended periods of time. I learned to think abstractly and to conceptualize the solution to problems. Out of necessity, I became a good listener–a quality appreciated by subsequent associates and students. Luckily, at age twenty-six, a successful cornea transplant greatly improved my vision.

Through my parents and relatives I became interested in economics and, in particular, finance. My mother loved business and wanted me to work with her brother in his book publishing and promotion business. During my teenage years, I was always treasurer of my various clubs; I traded extensively among my friends; I gambled to understand probabilities and risks; and worked with my uncles to understand their business activities. I invested in the stock market while in high school and university through accounts set up first by my mother and then by my father. I was fascinated with the determinants of the level of stock prices. I spent long hours reading reports and books to gleam the secrets of successful investing, but, alas, to no avail.

Because of my mother's death, I decided to remain in Hamilton attending McMaster University for my undergraduate studies. Although the McMaster University entrance committee thought that I would concentrate in Physics or Engineering, I stuck mostly to the liberal arts, majoring in Economics. At McMaster, Professor McIver, a University of Chicago graduate in economics, worked closely with me and directed me to read and understand the works of George Stigler and Milton Friedman, two subsequent Nobel Prize winners in Economics. I was impressed. Upon graduation in 1962, I had considered attending law school but instead, I decided to follow my mother's wishes and join my uncle in his publishing business. I would do so, however, if I could first attend graduate school at the University of Chicago.

Intuitively, I knew that if I wanted to grow and achieve my potential, I should attend a school where I could learn from and work with those who were the best and who could bring out the best in me. And that has become a cornerstone of my career. During that first year in Chicago, I met a few classmates, who would become life-long friends, and from whom I have learned a tremendous amount over the years. Michael Jensen and Richard Roll, both in the Ph.D. program in Finance, who have become world-renowned scholars in their own right, were significant contributors to my growth in understanding of finance and economics. Also, I credit Jack Gould for helping me clarify many of the finer points of economic reasoning.

The summer after my first year at Chicago changed the direction of my life forever. I decided that I would not return to my uncle's firm. Instead, although I had never programmed before, I secured a junior computer-programming position at the school through the kindness of Dean Robert Graves. During my first few days on the job, several professors asked for computer-programming assistance on their research projects. I was able to fend them off by arguing that the senior programmers would soon be on scene to assist them. They never did show up. By the third day, I could no longer fend off the aggressive professors seeking programming assistance. On confronting Dean Graves, he informed me that I, a novice, was the only "programmer" left. He pointed me to the computer facility some six blocks from the school, and I was on my way. I spent the next four and one-half months falling in love with computers and with the researchers that I met that summer. I must have been one of the first computer nerds; I worked all hours of the day and night. But by the end of that summer, I was becoming a computer wizard, a skill that I would continue to develop over many years. If Chicago had had a computer science school or if computer science had been a more developed field, I might have become a computer scientist.

A more powerful force, however, had taken hold of me that summer: the love of economics and economic research. I absorbed how my professors created and addressed their own research. This was empowering. They enjoyed the process. From time to time I ventured to ask them to explain their research, and occasionally I made suggestions to improve the research design. Lester Telser and Peter Pashigian were two of my clients. Merton Miller and Gene Fama, two financial-economics professors, were clients as well. Either because of my scholastic qualities or because he did not want to lose me as a programmer, Merton Miller suggested that I enter the Ph.D. program. I did and I came to love economics and its young new branch, which has come to be called Financial Economics. Chicago provided me with a wonderful learning environment. Miller and Fama were blazing ahead in financial economics. Stigler was leading the way in information economics. Friedman was fighting on in the macro-economic front.

I became interested in relative asset prices and the degree to which arbitrage prevented economic agents from earning abnormal profits in security markets. My Ph.D. dissertation attempted to determine the shape of the demand curve for traded securities. Since risk and return characteristics distinguish one security from another, the extent of the market was far greater than that of the individual stock. It was new information that would cause a change in the price of the security, information that was signaled by a large sale by an informed trader.

In addition, I worked on measures of risk and the effect of differential risk on security returns in a paper with Merton Miller. I studied the relation between accounting and market-determined measures of risk in another paper with William Beaver and Paul Kettler.

After essentially finishing my Ph.D. dissertation in the fall of 1968, I became an Assistant Professor of Finance at the Sloan School of Management at MIT. Paul Cootner, Franco Modigliani, and Stewart Myers became my colleagues. During my first year at the Sloan School I met Fischer Black, then a consultant working for Arthur D. Little, in Cambridge. We started collaborating on many research projects. It was an extremely productive relationship.

Although Paul Cootner unfortunately left the Sloan School in 1969, Robert Merton joined our group at that time. Essentially, because Franco Modigliani was involved in large macro projects, the young assistant professors controlled the development of the financial economics program at the Sloan school. Stewart Myers greatly influenced my thinking in the area of corporate finance, and Franco Modigliani on macro and asset-pricing models.

Robert Merton, Fischer Black and I were interested in asset pricing and derivative pricing models. It was through many interactions that we developed and extended the field of contingent-claims pricing. During my years at the Sloan school, I worked on testing the capital asset pricing model with Fischer Black and Michael Jensen, and developing the option pricing technology with Fischer Black, while continuing to work with Merton Miller.

Although I knew that I would miss working on a day-to-day basis with Robert Merton, I returned permanently to the Graduate School of Business at the University of Chicago after visiting for the 1973-74 academic year. Fischer Black took his first position in academics as a Professor at the University of Chicago in 1972. I wanted to return to Chicago and, in particular, work with Fischer Black, Gene Fama and Merton Miller. It was an important period in the life of the school and I had the opportunity to interact with many interesting colleagues. Although Robert Merton was successful in luring Fischer back to Boston in 1974, I resisted and remained at Chicago. During my Chicago years, I started to work on the effects of taxation on asset prices and incentives. For example, I studied the effects of the taxation of dividends on the prices of securities in three papers, one with Fischer Black and two others with Merton Miller. Merton Miller and I studied the interaction of incentives and taxes in executive compensation. Robert Hamada and I addressed capital structure issues with taxation, and George Constantinides and I studied the effects of taxes on the optimal liquidation of assets.

I became heavily involved with the Center for Research in Security Prices at the University of Chicago between 1973 – 1980. This led to the development of large research data files of daily security prices. Joe Williams and I wrote a paper on the estimation of risk parameters employing nonsynchronous data.

In 1981, I visited Stanford University and became a permanent faculty member in the Business School and the Law School in 1983. The period at Stanford was a time of significant learning for me. My close colleagues in the Business School included William Sharpe, James Van Horne, and a host of up and coming younger professors most notably Jeremy Bulow, Anat Admati, Paul Pfleiderer and Michael Gibbons. My close colleagues in the Law School included Ronald Gilson and Kenneth Scott. With Jeremy Bulow, I wrote several papers on pension planning. Most important, I was fortunate to work with and become a close friend of Mark Wolfson. We wrote several articles together on investment banking and incentives. We developed a new theory of tax planning under uncertainty and information asymmetry. Many of our published articles on these topics were rewritten and incorporated into our book, *Taxes and Business Strategy: A Planning Approach* that was published in 1992.

In 1990 my interests shifted back to the role of derivatives in financial intermediation. I became a special consultant to Salomon Brothers, Inc. and continued on as a managing director and co-head of its fixed-income-derivative sales and trading group, while still conducting research and teaching at Stanford University. In 1994, I joined with several colleagues, many from Salomon Brothers, to become a principal and co-founder of a firm called Long-Term Capital Management. By applying financial technology to practice, I have achieved a better understanding of the evolution of financial institutions and markets, and the forces shaping this evolution on a global basis. My research papers in the last few years have focused on the interaction and evolution of markets and financial institutions.

I have received honorary doctorate degrees from three universities. University of Paris-Dauphine awarded one to me in 1989. McMaster University awarded me another in 1990, and Katholieke Universiteit Leuven awarded me my third in 1998.

I am fortunate to have two wonderful daughters, Anne and Sara, and a son-in-law, Anne's husband Seth. They have added tremendous joy to my life. My fortunes have also risen in the last few years for I have found Jan. She completes my life. We plan to be married on October 4th 1998 and enjoy each other's company and insights for many years to come. Although I do not have time for many hobbies, I do enjoy skiing and golf, two sports that allow me to be outdoors in both winter and summer.

Selected Publications:

"The Association Between Market Determined and Accounting Determined Risk Measures," *Accounting Review*, Vol. XLV, No. 4, October 1970 (with W. Beaver and P. Kettler).

"The Capital Asset Pricing Model: Some Empirical Tests," in *Studies in the Theory of Capital Markets*, Michael C. Jensen ed., Praeger, Inc., 1972 (with Fischer Black and Michael Jensen).

"The Market for Securities: Substitution Versus Price Pressure and the Effects of Information on Share Prices," *Journal of Business*, Vol. 45, No. 2, April 1972.

"Rates of Return in Relation to Risk: A Re-examination of Some Recent

Findings," in *Studies in the Theory of Capital Markets*, Michael C. Jensen, ed., Praeger, Inc., 1972 (with Merton Miller).

"The Valuation of Options Contracts and a Test of Market Efficiency," *Journal of Finance*, Vol. 27, No. 2 May 1972 (with Fischer Black).

"The Pricing of Options and Corporate Liabilities," *Journal of Political Economy*, Vol. 81, No. 3, May/June 1973 (with Fischer Black).

"The Effects of Dividend Yield and Dividend Policy on Common Stock Prices and Returns," *Journal of Financial Economics*, May 1974 (with Fischer Black).

"Taxes and the Pricing of Options," *Journal of Finance*, Vol. XXI, May 1976.

"Estimating Betas from Nonsynchronous Data," *Journal of Financial Economics*, Vol. 5, No. 3, February 1978 (with Joseph Williams).

"Dividends and Taxes," *Journal of Financial Economics*, Vol. 6, No. 4, 1978 (with Merton Miller).

"Optimal Liquidation of Assets in the Presence of Personal Taxes: Implications for Asset Pricing," *Journal of Finance*, Nov. 35, No. 2, 1980 (with George Constantinides).

"Executive Compensation Taxes and Incentives," *Financial Economics: Essays in Honor of Paul Cootner*, edited by Katherine Cootner and William Sharpe, Prentice-Hall, 1981 (with Merton Miller).

"Dividends and Taxes: Some Empirical Results," *Journal of Political Economy*, Vol. 90, No. 6, December 1982 (with Merton Miller).

"Economic Implications of ERISA," *Financial Aspects of the U.S. Pension System*, University of Chicago Press, 1983 (with Jeremy Bulow and Peter Menell).

"Who Owns the Assets in a Defined Benefit Pension Plan," *Financial Aspects of the U.S. Pension System*, University of Chicago Press, 1983 (with Jeremy Bulow).

"Taxes and Corporate Financial Management," *Recent Advances in Corporate Finance*, edited by E. Altman and M. Subrahmanyan, Richard D. Irwin, 1985 (with Robert S. Hamada).

"Taxation and the Dynamics of Corporate Control: The Uneasy Case for Tax-Motivated Acquisitions," *Knights, Raiders and Targets: The Impact of the Hostile Takeover*, edited by John C. Coffee, Jr., Louis Lowenstein and Susan Rose-Ackerman, Oxford University Press, 1987 (with Ronald J. Gilson and Mark A. Wolfson).

"Taxes and Compensation Planning," *Taxes*, December 1986 (with Mark Wolfson).

"Issues in the Theory of Optimal Capital Structure," *Frontiers in Modern Finance*, edited by S. Bhattacharya and G. Constantinides, Rowman and Littlefield, 1987 (with Mark A. Wolfson).

"The Cost of Capital and Changes in Tax Regimes," *Uneasy Compromise: Problems of a Hybrid Income-Consumption Tax*, edited by Joseph A. Pechman, The Brookings Institution, 1988 (with Mark Wolfson).

"Taxes, Trading and the Value of Real Estate," *Journal of Accounting, Auditing and Finance*, Vol. 4, No. 3, Summer 1989, pp. 317–40 (with Eric Terry and Mark Wolfson).

"Decentralized Investment Banking: The Case of Discount Dividend-

Reinvestment and Stock-Purchase Plans," *Journal of Financial Economics*, Vol. 24, No. 1, September 1989 (with Mark A. Wolfson).

"The Effects of Changes in Tax Laws on Corporate Reorganization Activity," *Journal of Business*, Vol. 63, No. 1, Pt. 2, January 1990 (with Mark A. Wolfson).

"Converting Corporations to Partnerships through Leverage: Theoretical and Practical Impediments," in *Debt, Taxes and Corporate Restructuring*, edited by John B. Shoven and Joel Waldfogel, Brookings Institution, 1990 (with Mark A. Wolfson).

"Tax Planning, Regulatory Capital Planning, and Financial Reporting Strategy for Commercial Banks," *Review of Financial Studies*, Vol. 3, No. 4, May 1990 (with Pete Wilson and Mark A. Wolfson).

"Employee Stock Ownership Plans and Corporate Restructuring: Myths and Realities," *The Battle for Corporate Control*, edited by Arnold W. Sametz, Business One, Irwin, 1991 (with Mark A. Wolfson).

"The Roles of Tax Rules in the Recent Restructuring of U.S. Corporations," *Tax Policy and the Economy*, edited by David F. Bradford, NBER/MIT Press, Vol. 5, 1991 (with Mark A. Wolfson).

"Stock and Compensation," *Journal of Finance*, July 1991.

"Firms' Responses to Anticipated Reductions in Tax Rates: The Tax Reform Act of 1986," *Journal of Accounting Research*, 1992 supplement (joint with Mark A. Wolfson).

"The Future of Futures," *Risk Management Problems & Solutions*, edited by William H. Beaver and George Parker, McGraw-Hill., 1995.

"Financial Infrastructure and Economic Growth," *The Mosaic of Economic Growth*, edited by Ralph Landau, Stanford University Press, 1996.

"Global Financial Markets, Derivative Securities and Systemic Risks," *Journal of Risk and Uncertainty*, March 1996, edited by Kip Viscuzi.

Books:

Taxes and Business Strategy: A Planning Approach, Prentice Hall, 1991 (with Mark A. Wolfson).

DERIVATIVES IN A DYNAMIC ENVIRONMENT

Nobel Lecture, December 9, 1997

by

MYRON S. SCHOLES

Graduate School of Business, Stanford University, Stanford, CA, USA and Long-Term Capital Management, L.P., One East Weaver Street, Greenwich, CT 06831-5146, USA

1. INTRODUCTION*

The trading of financial derivatives on organized exchanges has exploded since the early 1970s. The trading of off-exchange financial derivatives on the so-called "Over-the-Counter" or "OTC" market has exploded since the mid-1980s. Academic and applied research on financial derivatives, which was initiated by the Black-Scholes and Merton option-pricing research in the late 1960s and early 1970s, also has exploded. As a result, three industries have blossomed: an exchange industry in derivatives, an OTC industry in synthetic products, and an academic industry in derivative research, populated by scientists in and out of academic institutions. The academic industry has seen a growth of research and course offerings in economics and business schools in the areas of options, futures, risk management, financial engineering, and by marrying institutional and derivative modeling, a richer approach to financial intermediation and innovation under uncertainty. In addition, business schools and economics departments have competition from new research and courses in mathematics departments and engineering schools in the mathematics of derivative pricing and alternative stochastic processes, and in law schools in understanding contracting under uncertainty.

The academic industry has produced myriad innovative research papers following the fundamental insights of Black and Scholes (1973) and Merton (1973). The Chicago Board of Trade and Chicago Mercantile Exchange initiated the exchange industry by developing financial options and futures contracts on securities; they have spawned the growth of many new derivative exchanges around the world. The first was the Chicago Board of Trade's sponsorship of the Chicago Board Options Exchange in 1973. Moreover, some exchanges such as the Options Market in Stockholm have transported the technology used to trade derivatives to other markets in Europe and Asia.

---

* I would like to thank Robert C. Merton for many years of fruitful and exciting discussions on these topics. In addition, I would like to thank my many colleagues at the University of Chicago, MIT, and Stanford University, for their ideas and stimulating discussions. Most important has been the support and involvement of Merton H. Miller in my career: I owe him a tremendous debt and cherish his friendship. I miss Fischer Black; I miss his friendship, his insights, and his good humor.

These exchanges succeed by producing the derivative contracts that add value for individuals and institutions around the world. The OTC industry, which has grown to prominence since the mid-1980s, first in the United States and now in every corner of the globe, is now larger in size than the exchange industry. Financial institutions in the OTC industry offer customized derivative products to meet the specific needs of each of their clients; the exchange industry offers standardized products to reach a richer cross-section of demand.

Each industry requires original research to understand the pricing and production costs of the products and financial services that they bring to their clients. Derivative research is quickly transferred to practice; moreover, practice stimulates both academic and applied research. Some of the best research is conducted outside of academic institutions and academics have found a home in each of the three industries. Graduates from mathematics, computer sciences, engineering and physics compete and cooperate with those trained in financial economics for research and structuring positions in both the exchange and OTC industry.

It is difficult to define financial derivatives in a dynamic environment. The purest among us might argue that any security is a derivative if its price dynamics depend on the dynamics of some other underlying asset or assets and time. This broad definition allows not only for what currently exists but also what new derivative instruments will be developed in the future with enhanced understanding and changing production costs. The popular press, however, tends to limit the definition to include financial options, futures and forward contracts either traded on an exchange or issued in the OTC industry. In the future they may come to be called financial products.

The will of Alfred Nobel states, in part, that the Nobel Prize shall be awarded for an "important discovery or invention." Fischer Black's and my discovery was how to price options and to provide a way to manage risk. Robert Merton developed an important alternative proof of the pricing technology and extended the approach in many directions including how to price options with dividends, how to price options when the interest rate is not constant, and how to apply a more general structure to price many other contingent contracts.

Black and Scholes have over the years been accused of inventing derivatives, at least those derivative products that have been claimed to have had bad economic consequences for their users. It is seldom remembered that these contracts have two sides: if a buyer loses, the ultimate seller might gain. Only if losses cause dead-weight costs is there a net loss to society. It is said that "every successful idea has a thousand fathers, and every failure is an orphan." Over the years we have been granted both distinctions. We did not, however, invent derivatives. Options existed in many financial contracts prior to the Black-Scholes and Merton pricing technologies. Options were noted to have been traded on the Amsterdam Stock Exchange in the late 17th century and traded on the Chicago Board of Trade into the early 1930s. As described in Cootner (1964), research in option pricing goes back as far as Bachelier's

476

Ph.D. thesis in 1900. Although they are not generally thought of as options, myriad securities and investment decisions have been made in the past and are being made currently that could be evaluated using the Black-Scholes technology. The technology was an invention that facilitated multiple inventions in each of the three industries. What I did not realize at the time of the invention was how the technology would evolve and how it would be used to produce new types of securities with imbedded options at lower cost than could be accomplished prior to the development of the technology. This enhanced the efficiency set of demanders and suppliers of capital, not only in the United States but also around the world.

With the Christmas season approaching at these Nobel award ceremonies in Stockholm, I will invoke the "Past," the "Present" and the "Future," as Charles Dickens did in "A Christmas Carol," to describe the evolution of derivatives in a dynamic environment. I do not mean to draw too fine a parallel, however. That is, I am not implying that through the eyes of Mr. Scrooge the past for derivatives was bright with hope and innocence, and the present is dark and foreboding and the future, without changing our ways, presents a bleak picture. On the contrary, many in academics and those in practice have often asked for a glimpse of the past; that is, how we developed the technology and the model, and the past gives insights into the present. It was a time of innocence. It was a time of discovery. It is a tradition at these Nobel award ceremony lectures to describe the age of innocence. I am honored and thank the Nobel Prize Committee for this wonderful opportunity do so. I wish that Fischer Black were alive today to share this honor with us.

Twenty-five years is a tender age for the new academic and the new exchange industry. Fifteen years is still a young age for the new OTC industry. The Present, which I date from the late 1980s to current time, shows an industry that has experienced growing pains, and many, including regulators, are worried that it still has not come of age. And, will the Future be bleak? No, there will be failures, but the industries will thrive because derivative instruments will provide progressively lower-cost solutions to investor and entity problems than will competing alternatives. These lower-cost solutions will involve the unbundling and repackaging of coarse financial products into their constituent parts to satisfy client demands. The process will continue to evolve as advances in information technology drive down the cost of providing alternative and more productive solutions.

2. THE PAST

Although Black (1989) and Bernstein (1992) described their versions of the development of the option-pricing technology, this lecture, however, gives me an opportunity to add to their description through my recollection of things past. My formal training at the University of Chicago was in financial economics, statistics and economics. At Chicago, Merton Miller, the 1990 Nobel laureate, and Eugene Fama, a prolific scholar, stimulated my excitement in economics and a new branch of economics, which has come to be called financial economics. I also owe a similar and considerable debt to my fellow classmates at Chicago, most notably, Jack Gould, Michael Jensen and Richard Roll.

The three strands of financial economics that most set the tone for my future research were arbitrage and the notion of substitutes; the efficient markets hypothesis; and the capital asset pricing model.[1] These strands gave a mathematical basis to the models of finance, in a general equilibrium framework. Modigliani and Miller (see Miller (1988) for a retrospective) were making profound breakthroughs that provided a general equilibrium model for corporate finance. Their arbitrage arguments, which demonstrated how a firm's value was independent of how it financed its activities, had a profound effect on the way I analyze and model many problems in economics. The Fama (1965) and Samuelson (1965b) efficient-markets hypothesis that states that, in a well-functioning capital market, the dynamics of asset prices are described by a submartingale and that the best estimate of the value of a security is today's price, was revolutionary to economics. Their insights gave me an important framework to think about the dynamics of asset prices and how markets adjust to "news." It set the stage for empirical testing of how information was incorporated into security prices and gave me a vehicle to apply my statistics and computer skills in a financial economics context. For example, Jensen (1968) had used the concepts of the efficient-markets hypothesis to test whether mutual funds, which were professionally managed and spent considerable sums of money to discover undervalued assets, could outperform randomly-selected investments on a risk-adjusted basis. Roll (1970) had tested the efficiency of the bond market controlling for changes in expected returns impounded in bond prices. In my own work, Scholes (1972), I used the concepts of efficient markets and substitutes (arbitrage) to test the extent to which security prices were influenced by the size of the sales of large blocks of securities or by changes in the information set. Following on the work of Markowitz (1952, 1959), the Sharpe (1964), and Lintner (1965) the capital asset pricing model provided a general equilibrium model of asset prices under uncertainty. This became the fundamental model for measuring the risk of a security. It was elegant to condense the required relative rates of return on securities into a simple reduced-form equation that depended only on their "betas," a measure of their relative contribution to the risk of the optimal portfolio.

The capital structure models, the efficient-markets hypothesis, and the capital asset pricing model had the common central themes of arbitrage and market equilibrium: securities with similar economic risk had to exhibit similar returns to prevent arbitrage profits. This principle applies to all securities, whether they are common stock, bonds, or hybrid instruments. Through participation in seminar presentations at the University of Chicago, I became

---

[1] I am sure that Fischer Black would pick at least the efficient-markets hypothesis and the capital asset pricing model as most influential in the development of his thinking in financial economics.

generally aware of the nature of warrants and convertible bonds. I was unaware, however, of the interest in warrant pricing and the research that had been conducted at MIT on this topic in the 1960s even though I became an Assistant Professor at the Sloan School of Management at MIT in 1968.

I did not meet Robert Merton until the spring of 1969, when he was interviewing for a position at the Sloan School. We began interacting in the fall of 1969. We talked then about his current research on dynamic applications of the capital asset pricing model with changing opportunity sets and my work, at the time, including tests of the capital asset pricing model. We did not talk about warrant pricing even though Fischer Black and I were working on the problem. I guess we did not appreciate that each of us had an interest in this research area.

In the summer of 1968, a research project at Wells Fargo Bank in San Francisco convinced me that the passive management of assets could be a viable contender to actively managed portfolios. In my report to Wells Fargo Bank, I recommended that they initiate passive investment strategies and offer them to their clients, the forerunner to so-called "index funds." That fall, on the suggestion of Michael Jensen, I had lunch with Fischer Black, who he had met because of Jensen's research on mutual funds. Fischer was employed at Arthur D. Little, a consulting firm in Cambridge, Mass. We had several other lunches that fall and Fischer suggested that he was thinking of leaving Arthur D. Little to start his own consulting firm. At about the same time, John McQuown at Wells Fargo Bank asked whether I wanted to conduct research that would describe the tradeoff of risk and return in the market as a forerunner to introducing passive investment strategies to their clients. Without research, they were not willing to offer index-fund-like products to clients. Being an Assistant Professor, I was restricted as to the number of days I could consult. I asked Fischer whether he wanted to join forces on the project. It was obvious from our lunch discussions that he had very similar ideas, and was starting a research project with Jensen on measuring risk and return. We joined forces and worked together to test the capital asset pricing model (see Black, Jensen and Scholes (1972)). We developed the concept of the zero-beta portfolio to test the model. If we could create a zero beta-minimum variance portfolio by buying low beta stocks and selling high beta stocks and achieve realized returns on this portfolio that were significantly different from the interest rate this would violate the predictions of the original capital asset pricing model.

In the winter of 1969, I agreed to direct the Masters thesis of an MIT graduate student who had garnered a time series of warrant and underlying stock prices and wanted to apply the capital asset pricing model to value the warrants. I read all of the articles relating to warrant pricing in Paul Cootners' book of readings on The Random Character of Stock Prices (1964). One included paper, by Case Sprenkle and dated 1960, seemed the most relevant to me, but Sprenkle used an exogenously determined discount rate to discount the expected terminal value of the warrant to its present value.

What seemed apparent was that the expected return of the warrant could not be constant for each time period because the risk of the warrant changed with changes in the stock price and with changes in time to maturity. For example, if the warrant was far "in-the-money," that is, the underlying stock price was far above the exercise price, and the warrant was almost sure to be exercised, its price would change almost dollar for dollar with a change in the underlying stock price. The percentage change in the value of the warrant, however, would be greater than the percentage change in the value of the common stock because the warrant was a leveraged instrument. On the other hand, if the warrant was "out-of-the-money," that is, the underlying stock price was less than the exercise price, the warrant price would move far less than dollar for dollar with the price of the common stock (for example, $.5 for $1 move in the common). The percentage change in the price of the warrant, however, would be even greater than that of the in-the-money warrant.

As a result, the expected return on the warrant could not be constant each period if the beta of the stock was constant each period. I thought about using the capital asset pricing model to establish a zero-beta portfolio of common stock and warrants by selling enough shares of common stock per each warrant held each period to create a zero-beta portfolio. Given I could create a zero-beta portfolio, the expected return on the net investment in this portfolio would be equal to the riskless rate of interest. I knew that I would have to change the number of shares of stock each period to retain my zero-beta portfolio. But, after working on this concept, off and on, I still couldn't figure out analytically how many shares of stock to sell short to create a zero-beta portfolio.

Fischer and I continued working on tests of the capital asset pricing model and the development of investment products based on the implications of our research throughout 1969. In the summer or early fall of 1969, I discussed with Fischer my earlier experience with warrants, my attempt at creating the zero-beta portfolio, and my inability to determine the changing number of shares needed each period to create the zero-beta portfolio. He described to me his research on warrants and that he was frustrated in his inability to progress further than he had to that time. He showed me a sheet of paper, which described the relation between the return on the warrant and the underlying stock. Following on earlier work by Jack Treynor, Fischer had used a Taylor Series expansion of w(x,t), where "w" is the warrant price, "x" is the current stock price and "t" is time to maturity to show the relation between the change in the warrant price as a function of the change in the price of the common stock and a decrease in the time to maturity of the option. Ignoring terms of second order with regard to time, over a short period of time, this expansion was:

$$\Delta w(x, t) = w_1 \, \Delta x + w_2 \, \Delta t + \tfrac{1}{2} \, w_{11} \, \Delta x^2 \Delta t$$

where Δ is the change symbol, and the subscripts refer to partial derivatives with respect to the first or second arguments.

Not surprisingly, Fischer had used the capital asset pricing model to describe the relation between the expected return on the warrant and the market and the expected return on the common stock and the market. By substituting for the change in the warrant price as a function of changes in the stock price and time in the capital asset pricing relation, it became obvious on how to create a zero-beta portfolio that would have an expected rate of return equal to the interest rate (for we assumed a constant interest rate).

Consider the returns over a very short period of time on two alternative investment strategies: under (1), we acquire the warrant, and enough bonds earning at interest, r, per period, such that our investment in strategy (1) is the same as in alternative strategy (2), in which we buy w_1 of stock. The following is the investment and the return on these two alternative strategies:

Investment		Return
(1) Buy warrant	w	$w_1 \Delta x + w_2 \Delta t + \frac{1}{2} w_{11} \Delta x^2 \Delta t$
Bonds	$w_1 x - w$	$r \Delta t (w_1 x - w)$
(2) Buy Stock	$w_1 x$	$w_1 \Delta x$

The investment was constructed to be the same in strategy (1) and strategy (2). The risk appears to be the same in both strategies. The only uncertain term is Δx, the change in the stock price, and the total uncertainty due to changes in the stock price is the same in both strategies. Δx^2 involves the change in the stock price squared, a form of variance, which as Δt becomes small approaches $x^2 \sigma^2$, the stock price squared times the instantaneous variance of the underlying returns on the common stock, which is assumed to be constant.

Since the risk is the same and the investment is the same under both strategies, to prevent arbitrage, the returns must be the same over a short period of time. After equating the returns on strategy (1) with the returns on strategy (2), and substituting for Δx^2, we find:

$$-r w + w_1 x r + w_2 + \frac{1}{2} w_{11} x^2 \sigma^2 = 0$$

This is the Black-Scholes differential equation. The initial condition for a warrant or call option is that $w(x,t^*) = \text{Max}(x - c, 0)$, where t^* is the maturity date of the option, and c is the exercise price of the option. The only required inputs to value the option, other than its initial conditions, are r, the interest rate, and σ^2, the variance rate per unit time on the returns on the underlying stock. We were both amazed that the expected rate of return on the underlying stock did not appear in the differential equation.

Although the number of shares needed to create a zero-beta portfolio each period was w_1 it was not obvious to us how to find w_1. The next step in solving the problem was to realize that since the warrant valuation depended only on the variability of returns and not the expected return on the underlying common stock, it was arbitrary what expected return was assumed for the underlying common stock. The same warrant valuation equation would result because we had hedged out the risk of the common stock in establishing the zero-beta portfolio or the alternative replicating portfolio, as above. We assumed that the expected return on the common stock was equal to the interest rate over the next short period of time, or in terms of the capital-asset pricing model that the common stock had a zero beta.

With the assumption of constant return and variance of return, the distribution of returns on the underlying stock at expiration of the warrant would be lognormally distributed. We used the Sprenkle formulation to find the terminal value of the warrant using a constant interest rate as the expected rate of return on the stock. But, we wanted the present value of the warrant. The key here was to realize that although the warrant would have greater price variability than the underlying stock, if we assume that the stock had a zero beta, the warrant would have a zero beta. If the warrant had a zero beta each period of time, the warrant had also to return the interest rate, r, each period of time.

If we had decided to value the warrant using the actual expected return on the common stock or, for that matter, any other appreciation rate, the discount rate to value the warrant would depend on time and changes in the stock price. It does not for the zero-beta case. Using Sprenkle's formula with the assumption that the expected return on common stock and the discount rate for the warrant was equal to a constant interest rate, we obtained the Black-Scholes option-pricing formula.

$$w(x,t) = x \, N(d_1) - c \, e^{\, r(t-t^*)} \, N(d_2)$$

where $N(d)$ is the cumulative normal density function, c is the exercise price, t^* is the expiration date, and t is the current date, t^*-t is the remaining number of periods in the life of the option, and "e" is the exponential operator. Lastly,

$$d_1 = [\ln x/c + (r + 1/2\sigma^2)\,(t^* - t)] \,/\, \sigma \sqrt{t^* - t}$$

$$d_2 = d_1 - \sigma \sqrt{t^* - t}$$

We checked the formula against the differential equation and, as we expected, it fit. We were sure that we had the correct formula for valuing call options or warrants, the right to buy an asset at a fixed price, the exercise price, at maturity of the right, its expiration date. With minor adjustments we could value a put option, the right to sell an asset under similar terms.

From the formula, we were finally able to compute w_1, which was equal to $N(d_1)$, the required number of shares to hedge the option. The number of shares will change over time and as the price of the underlying security changes with respect to the exercise price. But, given the assumptions it is a known quantity each time period.

The formulation also suggests the technology necessary to price any contingent claim that depends on an underlying asset's price (or even other state variables) and time. This is so even with differential known pay-outs, such as dividends on a stock or coupons on a bond, that are not received by the option holder. The technology suggests that what is necessary is to hedge the stochastic term, Δx, to create an alternative investment that is riskless. Merton (1973) formalized these relations.

We had spent a considerable amount of time working to finish up several other papers including our paper on testing the capital asset pricing model. As a result, we finished a draft of the paper sometime in the winter of 1970. We did not know whether our formulation was exact, but intuitively we thought investors could diversify away any residual risk that was left. For larger price changes in the common stock, the hedge position of being long the option and short the appropriate number of shares of stock would tend to make money whether the market went up or down, and would lose money on small changes in the market portfolio. The risk of the position appeared to be independent of market risk. We programmed the model and tried to understand the sensitivity of the price of the option to changes in the stock price, time to maturity, volatility, and the interest rate.

We presented a draft of the paper at a conference on capital market theory sponsored by Wells Fargo Bank in July of 1970. Later that summer, on vacation together, Fischer and I worked out the applications of the option-pricing framework to the pricing of risky debt and other capital structure issues. We viewed the common stock of a company with debt in its capital structure as a call option. The equity holders have an option to buy back the firm from the debt holders by paying off the face amount of the debt at its maturity. The equity holders will not buy back the firm from the debt holders at the maturity of the debt if the face amount of the debt is less than the value of the firm's assets; they will turn the remaining assets of the firm over to the debt holders. For us, it was exciting to realize that the equity of a corporation was an option, and that our framework applied far more broadly than the valuation of warrants or put and call options. The methodology provided a systematic approach that relied on arbitrage to value the capital structures of firms, and to understand how management decisions affect the relative values of debt and equity in the firm's capital structure.

As it turned out, Robert Merton, who had written an earlier paper on the valuation of warrants with Paul Samuelson (see Samuelson and Merton, 1969) following on Samuelson (1965a) early work on warrent valuation, had expected to attend our session at the Wells Fargo conference, but he overslept and missed the session. In the winter and spring of 1970, Fischer and I searched the academic literature to determine how close others were to our invention. Fischer and I realized that the Samuelson and Merton paper contained an equilibrium model to value warrants but they did not value the warrant continuously. Given that there was friendly rivalry between the two teams, Fischer and I wanted to progress, on our own, as far as we could prior to the conference.

After the conference, in the early fall, Robert Merton and I discussed the Black-Scholes valuation methodology and option-valuation formula. He was not convinced that using the capital asset pricing model framework was sufficient. It seemed to him that, as the interval of adjustment of the hedge became closer to continuous time, there might still be covariance between the hedged position and the market return. Merton and I speculated that one way that there would be no such covariance would be if the return on the option was perfectly correlated with the return on the stock in continuous time, and therefore the hedge was exact. Merton later proved that the hedged position in continuous time was riskless, and that the replicating portfolio argument was exact. Fischer and I used this derivation in the final version of the paper because it relied on arbitrage and not on any underlying model of capital market equilibrium. However, we still presented the capital asset pricing model derivation of the model, as it provided us with the many insights we used to unlock the puzzles of option pricing.

Merton (1973) then started working on his paper on various aspects of the option formula. He incorporated his alternative proof of the option-pricing model. He also showed that the right to exercise a call option prior to maturity is not valuable for a non-dividend paying stock, but valuable for a put option on a similar stock. He also showed how to incorporate changes in interest rates into the valuation methodology, and generalized the formula to handle other state variables.

To our dismay, when we submitted a version of our paper entitled "A Theoretical Valuation Formula for Options, Warrants, and Other Securities" (October, 1970) to the *Journal of Political Economy*, it was rejected without review. The *Review of Economics and Statistics* also rejected the paper. Fischer felt that the paper was rejected because he was not an academic; I felt that I was an unknown Assistant Professor and the paper would not be considered to be broad enough for those academic journals. With the help of Merton Miller and Eugene Fama, who took an interest in the paper and stepped in on our behalf, the *Journal of Political Economy* agreed to consider the paper if we revised it and broadened its applicability. We had planned to publish the corporate-finance-capital structure applications in a subsequent paper but we broadened the original paper and showed how corporate liabilities could be viewed as options.. The final version of the paper was published in 1973 in the *Journal of Political Economy* under the title "The Pricing of Options and Corporate Liabilities."

2.1 *The Aftermath*

In Black and Scholes (1972), we tested the option pricing model using data recorded in a transactions diary of a broker in the over-the-counter option's market provided to us by another Master's student at MIT. The diary listed the prices at which he sold options to his clients. Using simple estimates of the volatility, the model generally performed well. It produced profits if one could buy options at diary-market prices if the model indicated a higher value than the market and sell options at diary-market prices if the model indicated a lower value than the market. Each trading day, we assumed that the model could be used to determine the hedge ratio, the delta, and undertook these hedges (assuming that transaction costs were zero). We regressed the daily returns on our hedged portfolio on the market returns. As expected, the portfolio returns were uncorrelated with the market returns, but the model produced substantial and significant abnormal profits. The market appeared to ignore information available in the historical data on estimating volatility.

When we assumed that we could buy the undervalued and sell the overvalued options at model prices and hedge out the underlying stock risk, we incurred significant losses. These losses were incurred because using simple estimates of the volatility ignored information on future volatility that the market was using to price the options. When actual realized volatility over the life of the option was used to compute the model prices, buying undervalued and selling overvalued options at model prices generated returns that were insignificantly different from zero.

It became apparent to us that the transaction costs of dealing in the over-the-counter market were quite large. The dealers would only sell options. As a result, the market in put and call options was quite small. The world was about to change. In the early 1970s, various studies were commissioned to provide an economic justification for a new options exchange. As a result, The Chicago Board Options Exchange (CBOE) was born in 1973 almost simultaneously with the publication of the Black-Scholes and Merton option-pricing papers. The reduction in transaction costs and the transparency of the market were justifications enough for the subsequent success of the options market.

It is ironic that these empirical tests of the Black-Scholes model were published in the *Journal of Finance* in the proceedings volume of the *American Finance Association Meetings*, in May of 1972, a full year prior to the publication of the model itself. Although we did not present it as such, it is ironic that the methodology in the paper is generally the same as that used today by financial entities to manage the risks of their trading positions and to measure the performance of their traders.

2.2 *Historical Notes: From Theory to Practice*

Both the derivative exchange industry and the derivative academic industry grew significantly from 1973 to 1985. Financial economists started to interact with a broad set of practitioners and this led to a cross-fertilization of ideas among the participants in both industries.

The option-pricing technology was adopted simply because it reduced transaction costs. For without a model, traders could neither price securities with imbedded options with sufficient accuracy to compete against other traders with models, nor could they reduce the risk of their positions to employ their capital efficiently at a low enough cost to compete with other traders. Although it is hard to prove, I do think that the success of the CBOE and other exchanges, in part, can be attributable to option-pricing models. As traders became familiar with these models, bid-offer spreads narrowed. As traders became more familiar with risk-management techniques they could take on larger position sizes to support the market. With a deeper and more

efficient market, investors began to use options to facilitate their own investment strategies.

In those formative years, notable extensions and additions to the basic
framework include important contributions by Black (1975, 1976), Banz and
Miller (1978), Breeden and Litzenberger (1978), Brennan and Schwartz
(1979), Cox and Ross (1976), Cox, Ross and Rubinstein (1979), Geske
(1979), Harrison and Kreps (1979), Magrabe (1978), Merton (see Merton,
1992a), Parkinson (1977), Richard (1978), Ross (1976), Rubinstein (1976),
Scholes (1976), Sharpe (1978), and Vasicek (1977).

In 1971, Fischer Black left Boston to become a Professor at the University
of Chicago. In 1972, Robert Merton and I became consultants to Donaldson,
Lufkin and Jenrette (DLJ) to build mathematical models to price so-called
"Down-and-Out Options" and to build their options technology to price call
options in the event of a launch of the CBOE. Leo Pomerance, the head of
the DLJ options group, was an options trader from the old school; he traded
OTC options using intuition and experience without regard to a formal
model. He later became the first chairman of the CBOE. At DLJ we forged a
marriage of the old-time trader types, with their mental set, with young
mathematical modeling types, with their model assumptions, to add value for
the firm.

The spread of the option-valuation technology was rapid once the CBOE
launched its first contracts on listed securities. Initially, many of the older-
market-wise traders rejected using a model to price options. And, initially
prices were not in line with prices predicted from using the Black-Scholes
model adjusting for dividends and using relatively simple estimates of volatility to price the options. This left an opportunity for younger model-based
traders to step in and profit from price discrepancies in the market. They
used the model to price options and to determine the appropriate hedge
ratios to reduce the risk of their positions. Generally, retaining these risks had
zero present value because traders had little expertise in forecasting stock
returns. By so doing they could undertake larger positions and enhance their
profits by concentrating on risks that could add to their profits.

In Galai (1975), Dan Galai, one of my Ph.D. students as the University of
Chicago, where I had returned in 1973, tested the pricing of options on the
CBOE in the first year of its existence using the model with simple historical
estimates of the volatility. He found that the profits on trading options; that is,
buying undervalued contracts and selling overvalued contracts each day to
maintain a neutral risk position, were even greater than those found in our
original tests. His strategies could achieve greater profits by reducing positions if the prices of options return to model values prior to the expiration of
the contract. Transaction costs could have reduced actual trading profits for
other than the option dealers.

By the end of the first year of trading options, it was no longer possible to
use simple estimates of the historical volatility to spot opportunities in the
market. Many of the clearing firms, who financed the positions of the option
traders, used the model and the hedge ratios to determine the net risk of

each of these traders. Fischer had started a service to provide option prices and the share-equivalent positions (hedge ratios) on each of the options traded on the various exchanges. He used a more sophisticated estimate of volatility to price the options. He combined historical estimates adjusted for changes in stock-market levels, with the volatility implied by the prices of options. As is true even to this day, as the market-price level of securities increases relative to a previous level over a relatively short period of time, the volatility of stocks tends to fall. This result is due, in part, to a reduction in the leverage of the underlying equities. Given the rate of interest, the price of the common stock, the dividend yields, the exercise price, and the maturity date of the option, the model can be used to infer the implied volatility that the market is using to price the option. In fact, even today, options are described in terms of implied volatility. Traders are asked whether they want to buy or sell volatility. Although his volatility estimates held some cache for a while, advanced computer technology made Fischer's pricing sheets obsolete after a few years.

In fact, Texas Instruments marketed a hand-held calculator in 1977 that gave the Black-Scholes model values and hedge ratios. When I asked them for royalties, they replied that our work was in the public domain; when I asked, at least, for a calculator, they suggested that I buy one. I never did. Robert Merton and I continued to consult for DLJ. Working with Mathew Gladstein, we decided that the time might be appropriate to provide investors with a fund that protected their downside risk but allowed for some upside participation in the performance of the stock market. To achieve this goal, we decided that the assets of the fund would be held in two parts: in any six-month period, 90% of the assets would be held in U.S. Treasury bills and 10% of the assets would be used to buy a diversified portfolio of call options. In several papers, Merton, Scholes and Gladstein (1978, 1982) simulated the performance characteristics of such a strategy using the underlying stocks of the options that were traded in the various markets. The return characteristics were as predicted by the theory: losses were truncated and gains were less than a direct investment in the underlying stocks. The returns on the strategy were non-linearly related to the market. We always stressed the role of options as insurance. In early 1976, we attempted to launch Money Market/ Options Investments under the auspices of Phoenix Investment Counsel of Boston. Unfortunately, the fund raised only a small amount of money. Our simulation results indicated that fully-covered investment strategies; that is, a sale of an option on a position in the underlying stock (for example, long 100 shares of IBM and short a call option to buy 100 shares of IBM), would provide returns of only the premium received on the option approximately 60% of the time. Call-option holders would call their stock away if the stock price were above the exercise price on expiration of the contract and would not exercise call options if the stock price were below the exercise price at expiration. This strategy produces higher current income but with the possibility of capital losses just like a high-yield bond. The expected return, however, was less than the expected return on the money market-options strategy. At about this time other investment companies marketed the fully-covered strategy, which we thought exhibited inferior return characteristics for most investors, and naturally, to our dismay, were quite successful because of the promises of higher income (but at the unadvertised expense of expected capital losses.)

3. THE PRESENT

The past twenty years has seen a transformation of the entire financial services industry, first in the United States, and now around the world. During the 1970s and 1980s, regulations divided the activities of financial institutions into separate market segments. In the U.S., commercial banks handled deposits and made commercial loans; investment banks were involved in mergers, acquisitions and underwriting; brokerage companies sold stocks and bonds; savings and loans, along with banks, initiated and held mortgages; and, insurance companies sold life, and property and casualty insurance products. Many of the regulations were directed at preserving the profitability of these institutions by restricting competition, mainly at the expense of the users of these services. Each institution had a product focus; for example, deposits, or life insurance, or commercial loans. No financial company served a broad range of its clients' financial needs.

As happens at times, it is not possible for regulators to protect the profitability of the industries they regulate. In the U.S., mutual funds competed with banks in providing deposit services after banks were not permitted to pay market interest rates on deposits in the early 1970s. The growth of institutional investors managing pension funds and mutual funds forced the abolition of fixed commission rates to trade securities in the U.S. and around the world. The larger brokerage firms evolved to compete against the banks and the savings and loan associations in packaging and repackaging mortgages to broaden the extent of the market. Banks started to compete with brokerage, investment banks, and insurance companies in financing commercial real estate and financing highly-leveraged mergers and acquisitions, so-called "Leveraged Buyouts." It is nearly impossible to maintain regulations that restrict activities in one industry when new competitors not subject to costly regulations are attacking the profitable businesses of that industry.

The driving force behind today's tidal wave of financial innovation has been the reduction in the cost of computer and communications technology. This lower-cost technology has led to a globalization of the product and financial markets. Corporate and institutional needs have become more complex. Investors are demanding more services. Technology brings new competitors to the market who can offer similar and expanded services at lower cost than existing competitors can. The growth of lower cost providers of brokerage services such as Schwab, Fidelity, and Internet brokers are examples.

Financial service firms today must decide which clients to serve, determine those clients' needs and then decide which products and services add value for their clients as well as their own shareholders. Firms that were quite similar fifteen years ago have become very different today. For instance, J.P.

Morgan, a wholesale bank, today differs far more from Citicorp, a retail bank than it did in the early 1980s. Conversely, firms that were quite different from each other fifteen years ago have become quite similar today. It is hard to distinguish the activities of today's J.P. Morgan from UBS, from Goldman Sachs or Merrill Lynch. Meanwhile, A.I.G. and Travelers, both insurance companies, these days offer a number of services that are similar to those offered by Goldman Sachs or UBS. Investment banks no longer merely structure and advise in transactions but instead have moved to a more packaged, integrated, convenient financial-solutions approach, directed at solving the complex problems of their clients around the world.

The many advances in financial theory have enabled financial services firms to meet those complex needs more effectively and at lower cost than was possible previously. The marriage of business school and economics department graduates with engineers, mathematicians, physicists and computer scientists has led to more efficient and lower-cost financial engineering solutions to client problems.

To date, the major growth in the use of derivatives has been fueled by trends toward securitization and the increased understanding of the role that derivatives can play in the unbundling, packaging, and transferring of risks. No longer do financial service firms only sell the same products they buy from clients. Instead, they break the products down into their component parts and either sell the parts or recombine them into new and hybrid custom-tailored financial instruments. And, this unbundling and repackaging is only in the beginning stages of evolution.

With information asymmetries between clients and their financial service providers, it would be prohibitively expensive for a client to develop close relations with many financial service firms. To be productive, the financial service firm must learn the needs of its clients and understand their businesses. As a result, it can be expert to only a select client list. Clients find it inefficient to "shop" widely for new financial service firms. Creating custom-tailored solutions strengthens relations between the financial services firm and its clients. It would be too costly for each client to replicate the specialized expertise required to engineer financial theory solutions; such talent would be underutilized most of the time. It would be analogous to every corporation maintaining an entire full-service law firm on its premises. Notwithstanding many regulators' fears, it is not likely that all financial service firms will disappear if left to compete in the global arena. Product standardization will erode profits more quickly than in the past because more diverse entities, such as General Electric or Enron or accounting firms can compete in providing financial services using financial technology. New competition will enter various markets from global competitors. Although inefficient financial service firms will disappear more quickly than in the past, their clients will obtain more value-enhancing and less costly services from the remaining financial service firms. Financial products are becoming so specialized that, for the most part, it would be prohibitively expensive to trade them in organized markets.

Financial service firms have become the leaders in using derivatives in their risk-management programs. Using information and option-pricing technology, financial services firms can not only value their commitments, such as guarantees and other derivative contracts, but also are moving to understand the sensitivities of their holdings to various market factors. They can decide what risks to transfer and what risks to retain.

Tables 1 and 2 show the growth of derivative contracts trading since 1986 in both the exchange industry and in the OTC industry. The cells of the tables contain the "notional principal amounts outstanding" for various categories of derivative contracts. For example, the face amount of stock market index options (including call and put options) at the end of 1986 stood at $37.8 billion and by the end of 1996 grew to $380.2 billion.[2]

These tables indicate that the OTC market in derivatives has grown much faster than the exchange market in the last 10 years. In 1995, turnover on the major derivative exchanges around the world actually declined while OTC activity rose by 40 percent. The Bank for International Settlements estimated that outstanding OTC contracts exceeded $47.5 trillion in early 1995, much greater than the numbers reported in Table 2. To put these values into perspective, the value of all outstanding debt in Europe, Japan and North America totaled $25.8 trillion in 1995.

The growth of the OTC market will continue to outstrip the growth of the exchange market because the clients of the financial service firms need assistance to structure their financial programs. The current growth path is to provide more client-focused structured solutions to problems. Clients likely would find it less expensive to execute a program through their financial service firm than to execute it themselves in the exchange market. This is even more likely if the positions must be adjusted frequently to hedge risks.

Moreover, the relative growth of the OTC market is overstated because the exchange markets require that entities post margin on contracts each day. Futures contracts are settled at the end of each day. Forward contracts, such as swaps and options written by OTC firms such as caps and floors, are not settled each day. The product offerings are different. The financial service firms and their counterparts rely on each other's credit. Most financial service firms can post collateral on OTC contracts, which is very similar to settling the contracts as in the case of posting margin on an exchange. These entities will use either the financial futures and options markets or the OTC markets. They will use the industry that provides services at lower cost. Many entities, however, are not indifferent to posting collateral. In particular, many

---

[2] See "International Capital Markets, Developments, Prospects and Key Policy Issues," **International Monetary Fund** (September 1997) for the source of these statistics. The notional amount outstanding is not an economic measure of the size of the market. The notional amount of a swap or an option is the amount on which the contract is based. It is not the value that the security would trade at in the market. For example, if a call option to buy $100,000 of a major-market index trades at $5,000, the notional amount is recorded as $100,000 while the economic value is only $5,000. The economic value of swaps and options might be as low as 2% and 5% of the notional outstanding amounts of the contracts. These statistics provide estimates of the growth of the derivative market.

Table 1. Markets for Selected Derivative Financial Instruments: Notional Principal Amounts Outstanding: 1986-96 (In billions of U.S. dollars)

	1986	1987	1988	1989	1990	1991	1992	1993	1994	1995	1996
Interest rate futures	370.0	487.7	895.4	1,200.8	1,454.5	2,156.7	2,913.0	4,958.7	5,777.6	5,863.4	5,931.1
Interest rate options[1]	146.5	122.6	279.2	387.9	599.5	1,072.6	1,385.4	2,362.4	2,623.6	2,741.8	3,277.8
Currency futures	10.2	14.6	12.1	16.0	17.0	18.3	26.5	34.7	40.1	38.3	50.3
Currency options[1]	39.2	59.5	48.0	50.2	56.5	62.9	71.1	75.6	55.6	43.2	46.5
Stock market index futures	14.5	17.8	27.1	41.3	69.1	76.0	79.8	110.0	127.3	172.2	198.6
Stock market index options[1]	37.8	27.7	42.9	70.7	93.7	132.8	158.6	229.7	238.3	329.3	380.2
Total	618.3	729.9	1,304.8	1,766.9	2,290.4	3,519.3	4,634.4	7,771.1	8,862.5	9,188.2	9,884.6
North America	518.1	578.1	951.7	1,155.8	1,268.5	2,151.7	2,694.7	4,358.6	4,819.5	4,849.6	4,839.7
Europe	13.1	13.3	177.7	251.0	461.2	710.1	1,114.3	1,777.9	1,831.7	2,241.6	2,831.7
Asia-Pacific	87.0	138.5	175.4	360.0	560.5	657.0	823.5	1,606.0	2,171.8	1,990.1	2,154.0
Other	0.0	0.0	0.0	0.1	0.2	0.5	1.8	28.7	39.5	106.8	59.3

[1] Calls plus puts.

Table 2. Notional Principal Value of Outstanding Interest Rate and Currency Swaps of the Members of the International Swaps and Derivatives Association, 1987-June 1996 (In billions of U.S. dollars)

	1987	1988	1989	1990	1991	1992	1993	1994	1995	June 1996
Interest rate swaps										
All counterparties	682.9	1,101.2	1,502.6	2,311.5	3,065.1	3,850.8	6,177.3	8,815.6	12,810.7	15,584.2
Interbank (ISDA member)	206.6	341.3	547.1	909.5	1,342.3	1,880.8	2,967.9	4,533.9	7,100.6	—
Financial Institutions	300.0	421.3	579.2	817.1	985.7	1,061.1	1,715.7	2,144.4	3,435.0	—
Governments[1]	47.6	63.2	76.2	136.9	165.5	242.8	327.1	307.6	500.9	—
Corporations[2]	128.6	168.9	295.2	447.9	571.7	666.2	1,166.6	1,829.8	1,774.2	—
Currency swaps										
All counterparties (adjusted for reporting of both sides)	182.8	319.6	449.1	577.5	807.2	860.4	899.6	914.8	1,197.4	1,294.7
Interest rate options[3]	0.0	327.3	537.3	561.3	577.2	634.5	1,397.6	1,572.8	3,704.5	4,190.1
Total	865.6	1,657.1	2,489.0	3,450.3	4,449.5	5,345.7	8,474.5	11,303.2	17,712.6	21,068.9

[1] Including international institutions.
[2] Including others.
[3] Including caps, collars, floors, and swaptions.

491

OTC swap and option contracts have a financial entity and a corporation as counterparts because the corporation is willing to pay the financial entity to post margin for it in the futures or options market. That is, the financial services firm enters into a swap with a corporate entity, which does not post collateral, and the financial service firm hedges its market risk by entering into an offsetting swap with another financial service firm or by using the exchange-derivatives industry. In either case, the financial service firm posts collateral or margin on its transactions. It is the lower cost producer of margin services. Financial service firms have the capacity and the personnel to undertake the pricing of credit risk and can handle these transactions; many corporate entities currently do not.

To the extent that collateral is not posted on the obligation, one consequence of the these transactions is that the financial service firm and the corporation are exposed to each other's credit risk. The corporation buying a call option on an underlying debt instrument from the financial service firm has credit risk to the extent of the value of the call option. The financial service firm can fail to honor its obligation to deliver the underlying debt instrument. The financial service firm holding a put option, issued by the corporation, on the same debt instrument is a creditor of the corporation to the extent of the value of the put option. A swap contract, which states that the corporation will receive a fixed rate of interest on an underlying debt instrument and pay a floating rate of interest, is equivalent to the corporation being long a call option and short a put option.

The other major reason that the OTC industry will continue to grow faster than the exchange industry is that financial service firms and others need only to hedge the remaining factor risks of their portfolio positions, which is a far smaller amount than their gross contracting with their clients. Moreover, depending on the costs, they can hedge either with another financial service firm or in the exchange industry. The financial service firm that hedges factor risks retains the remaining risk, the so-called "basis risk," of its net positions.

Another reason for the growth of the OTC market has been that the outstanding amounts in Table 2 do not necessarily represent net exposures. It might be less expensive for a corporation or a financial service firm to enter into an offsetting derivative contract with another counterparty than it would be to unwind the initial contract. If it does, the contract volume increases but the net exposure falls.

3.1 *The Present: The Pathologies*

From the perspective of market commentators, many regulators, and the public, derivatives tend to top the list of suspects when the stock market turns downward or when entities announce unanticipated financial losses. The press, the public and regulators fear derivatives, in part, because they are new and, in part, because their growth has appeared to be so explosive over the last ten years. Although they vastly overstate the economic exposure, notional amounts as high as $45 trillion cause worry. The press and others credit the market crash of 1987 to portfolio insurance, an attempt to dynamically replicate the returns on options. Even in this time, market pundits warn that forms of dynamic hedging could foster a severe market downturn. Widely publicized losses attributed to derivative trading in the 1990s include: the leveraged-derivative contracts issued by Bankers Trust to firms such as Proctor and Gamble and Gibson Greeting (over $150 million in losses); the loss of $1.5 billion by Shell Sekiyu, the losses incurred by Orange County investing in inverse floaters; the bankruptcy of Metallgesellschaft and Barings Corporation (both over $1 billion in losses) and many other losses by financial service firms such as UBS, Salomon Brothers, etc. Obviously, many of these losses are overstated because there were gains made by the other side to these contracts: It is only the dead-weight costs to society that result in actual loss. For excellent discussions of the entire range of purported pathologies and an excellent review of the literature addressing these issues see Miller (1997), who argues that most, if not all, of the "diagnoses" of severe pathologies are misdiagnosed.

Yet, the growth of these industries depicted in Tables 1 and 2 clearly suggests that these instruments have added net value. It is hard to believe such growth could continue for so many years without value being realized by the clients of financial service firms, the shareholders of these firms and the exchanges. I have argued in Scholes (1995, 1996a) that the development of financial infrastructure might lag financial innovation. It is costly to develop controls and firm-wide understanding of new products that are in the prototype phase of their development. Prototypes are built using existing infrastructure. For an innovation as long lasting and profitable as derivatives, the OTC industry, the exchange industry and the academic industry find it profitable to build the infrastructure necessary to support them. Each of these industries has a vested interest in profiting from adding value that is sustainable, so each will attempt to invest in the cost-effective infrastructure necessary to preserve this value.

This is not to argue that we have seen the end of derivative failures. There will be losses sustained as in many other business activities. In 1997, the Governments of many countries in Asia could no longer support the losses of their financial institutions resulting from defaulted commercial and real estate loans. Although many banks had been economically bankrupt without the support of their Governments (that is; the value of their equity would have been effectively zero without Government implicit guarantees), the Governments allowed these banks to participate in any potential gains and sheltered them against bank runs by promising to pay off their depositors. These options were costly to society, and it will be difficult to prove that they were value enhancing. In part, other countries, through the grants made by the International Monetary Fund, as the lenders of last resort to these and other countries, may have written the put options that supported the activities of the financial institutions of the region and granting these options might have encouraged risk taking and even unprofitable activities.

Moreover, absent government guarantees, some brokerage houses and banks in Japan probably would be bankrupt, because while these entities had promised clients protection against loss on any decline in value of Japanese stocks, they did not hedge their commitments. Clients might have paid for these put options through higher commission rates in Japan. These Japanese financial service entities, however, suffered severe losses when their clients exercised these put rights during the decline in the value of Japanese stocks in the 1990s. The entities currently are not required to value their commitments on a mark-to-the-market basis. As a result, neither regulators, nor investors nor even senior management could deduce the financial condition of the entities. In all probability, the extent of these losses could have been mitigated if risk management policies had been put in place.

4. THE FUTURE

The future will be a continuation of the present. Financial innovation will continue at the same or at even an accelerating pace because of the insatiable demand for lower-cost, more efficient solutions to client problems. Information and financial technology will continue to expand and so will the circle of understanding of how to use this technology. There is value to investing in education. Financial service firms will expand the use of this technology to manage their own activities. Otherwise, they will have to face mergers with other financial service entities. Although some would like to see derivatives wither in importance, they will not, for they have become essential mechanisms in the tool kit of financial innovation.

Scholes and Wolfson (1992) used the concepts of frictions and restrictions to illustrate how tax rules and other regulations affect investor and corporate behavior. As Merton (1992) argues, the functions of a financial system change far less than institutions. Institutions change because lower-cost solutions that reduce information asymmetries are found to facilitate transactions, to provide funding for large-scale investment projects, to transfer savings across borders and into the future, and provide more efficient risk-sharing and diversification mechanisms.

Most financial instruments are derivative contracts in one form or another. Black and Scholes (1973) pointed out that the equity holders of a firm with debt in its capital structure have an option to buy back the firm from its debtholders at maturity of the debt. The high-yield bond (the so-called "junk bond") is a riskier debt-option contract than more-highly rated corporate debt. Corporate debt and equity contracts are derivative to underlying investments. Other lines of research on so-called "real options" indicate that even the investment decisions of firms are better understood by using an option framework rather than a more conventional present-value-analysis framework.

Standard debt and equity contracts are institutional arrangements or boxes. They provide particular cash flows to investors with their own particular risk and return characteristics. These institutional arrangements survive only because they provide lower cost solutions than competing alternative ar-

494

rangements. Competitive opportunities evolve over time with changing frictions and restrictions. Because of information asymmetries and regulatory restrictions, investors might require a higher rate of return to hold these standard-form contracts than contracts (now and in the future) of alternative design but of similar risk. Time will continue to blur the distinctions between debt and equity.

The firm's investment set is generally the composite of coarse bundles of payoffs. Firms issue claims to finance these activities, claims that themselves represent bundles of coarse cash flows. It will become more efficient for financial service firms to offer new derivative securities in various forms to break cash flows into finer gradients that can be tailored to the specific needs of demanders and suppliers of capital. In the process, dead-weight costs are mitigated, thereby reducing the cost of capital. The financial service firm can sell the newly created securities or retain them in whole or in part for its own account. It can create new products on its own name or use the OTC or exchange markets to hedge its risks. Given information asymmetries, it will use the lower-cost solution.

4.1 *Investor Demands*
In recent years, we have witnessed a movement from a limited number of investors holding an undiversified portfolio of their own home-country securities to many more investors holding diversified portfolios domestically and internationally. More and more investors around the world, who have never invested in financial products other than through social promises made by their governments, will become more willing to select from a broad class of "mutual-fund" type offerings. Although the diversity of products has grown, few tools are in place other than in academic circles that allow investors to make informed portfolio allocation decisions. As Franco Modigliani, the 1985 Nobel laureate, has argued, individuals want to smooth consumption over the life cycle. If it were more cost efficient, investors would want to insure against contingencies, control risks more efficiently, and plan their investments efficiently to meet life-cycle needs. As information and financial technology become more easily available, financial service firms will repackage investments to meet these investor demands, and this will spur financial innovation. The financial service firm will offer products in its own name that promise specific risk and return patterns; these firms will also offer products in the form of mutual funds. The classifications of investment products into stock funds, bond funds, growth, income, etc. will diminish in importance with reduced costs to understand risk, return, and contingent payoffs.

Even today, the boxes that define institutional-fund arrangements have blurred. For example, if a pension fund manager wants to achieve a stock-index fund return, she can invest with an index-fund provider that buys a diversified portfolio of the index-fund stocks. She can achieve the same result, however, in myriad other ways including using another manager who might claim to have expertise in the bond market and can provide an enhanced return over the index-fund return. To achieve this, the enhanced manager might undertake a complicated strategy. He might hold a portfolio of under-valued corporate and government bonds, hedge the credit risk of the corpo-rate bonds by selling stock short, and hedge the price risk of interest rate movements by using futures or options. He might buy stock-index futures to achieve the systematic risk exposure of the stock-index fund. Given costs, the manager might be able to produce a return in excess of that achieved by holding the index fund directly while the systematic risks of the two offerings would be exactly the same.

The exchange industry will compete with the OTC industry to provide in-vestment products. If the exchange industry can provide efficient margining systems for those investors who can not post collateral in a cost efficient man-ner, those products that become standardized will most likely be ideally suited for the exchange industry: it can address a larger set of participants in a lower-cost marketplace. The exchange industry complements the OTC in-dustry; they will grow together.

4.2 *Corporate Demands for Derivatives*

Finance specialists have puzzled over the reasons why corporations hedge the risks of their cash flows. Under classical finance theory, it is often asked why shareholders of a firm pay it to incur costs to reduce risk when they can diversify on their own account. The firm's managers should act as if the firm is risk neutral. Smith and Stulz (1985) provide three reasons, all tied to the cost of financial distress, why a firm might hedge its cash flows. Because of the convexity of the tax schedule, a firm might issue more debt only after hedg-ing its cash flows to reduce its expected operating losses and the resultant loss of tax benefits. Because of bankruptcy costs associated with high levels of debt, the firm that hedges can use more debt to finance its activities. As in Froot, Scharfstein, and Stein (1993), if the firm can hedge its cash flows, a reduction in the probability of financial distress reduces the expected costs of financial distress and, as a result, encourages investment in profitable projects that might have been foregone without such hedging. This argument is based on the observation that firms are reluctant to issue equity, and, instead, use retained earnings to finance investments before using the debt markets. Also, if a high-debt-to-equity firm were to become financially distressed it would not be possible to issue equity to finance business activities. Because owner-managers in smaller firms might not be able to diversify their holdings, hedg-ing the cash flows of the firm might be a lower-cost alternative than selling off pieces of the firm to outsiders and using the proceeds to diversify. If corpora-tions face these problems there are financial engineering solutions that might reduce their import.

The corporate use of derivatives is not limited to hedging. Some corporate financial strategists believe that they can outperform other market partici-pants in forecasting the direction of interest rates or commodity prices. Stulz (1996) argues that firms that have such financial acumen can hedge their downside exposures by buying put options. This allows the financial officers of the firm to become more active managers. By buying put options or by reducing systematic risks, they can use more leverage and increase their personal stakes by reducing the costs of financial distress. This tactical use of derivatives probably explains a significant part of the growth of the use of derivatives attributable to financial service firms and corporations, as shown in Tables 1 and 2.

As reported in Stulz (1996), empirical evidence gathered from surveys of corporations indicates that large corporations without debt in their capital structures hedge cash flows more so than smaller corporations. And, those corporations that do hedge lift their hedges from time to time or do not fully hedge their exposures. It is these tactical uses of derivatives, an attempt to "beat" the market using highly leveraged strategies, that have been the cause of most of the reported financial losses. Obviously, the successful tactical users of derivatives are most often absent in press reports. It is unlikely, however, that corporate officials, on average, can outperform other market participants.

Large firms hedge cash flows, in part, to smooth reported financial earnings with the hope those smoother earnings will boost their price-to-earnings ratios. This might be a value-enhancing strategy if market participants can not discern whether the variability in earnings is caused by the firm's taking systematic exposures to market factors or by firm-specific risks.

The Present is still young. The Future will bring many new solutions to solve corporate problems. Many corporations and financial entities still need to learn and evaluate to what extent hedging and risk control can be beneficial to their activities. Smaller firms and product markets are just now becoming familiar with the risk control aspects of these financial instruments. It may be surprising that in the United States the top 8 banks account for 94% (almost $19 trillion) of the total outstanding notional amount in the OTC market as of the end of 1996.[3] As of this date, the knowledge base or the financial acumen needed to financial engineer solutions to client problems is highly concentrated.

As in Scholes (1995, 1996a), I argue that corporations will use risk management techniques to reduce their level of equity capital, and, as a result of risk management techniques, some firms that would have gone public will remain private. Equity capital is an expensive form of financing. There are large differences between the knowledge base of insiders and outsiders. Insiders can not fully divulge their plans to outsiders for the fear that competitors will profit from this knowledge, and generally must sell shares at a discount. Moreover, tax and other considerations make the corporate form of undertaking activities in the U.S. and in other countries very expensive.

Equity is a risk-management device. It is an "all purpose" risk cushion. The more equity a firm has, the more it cushions itself against outcomes that require it to go the capital markets in adverse times or when it might have to divulge its confidential operating plans to outside parties. Hedging, on the other hand, is targeted risk control. Hedging requires more refined knowl-

---

[3] See **International Monetary Fund, op. cit.**

497

edge of the firm, and an understanding of the interaction of investment returns and financing alternatives. Moreover, it requires that the firm be able to warrant to others that it will maintain a strategy of hedging its activities to support higher levels of debt. But as the costs to hedge fall relative to the costs of equity, firms will substitute hedging for equity.

Moreover, hedging provides ancillary benefits as a measurement tool to help calibrate how the firm is making money. In a diverse, decentralized organization, management information systems might not divulge the true source of profits within the organization; that is, did profits arise because systematic risk exposures produced positive returns, or because the entity possessed superior skills? Standard accounting neither provides risk management reports which decompose profitability into profits from market forces and profits from managerial efforts, whether the firm is a manufacturing or a financial firm, nor does it describe the sensitivities of the firm's profit and loss to market factors. As more entities use financial engineering skills, the current accounting system will be under considerable pressure for change, as will many of the current forms of regulations and restrictions.

Because of differences in the required knowledge of insiders and outsiders, the growth of the private equities market has reduced the disclosure costs of becoming a public corporation. Private equity allows expert management teams to leverage their activities. Private equity, however, is still an inefficient form of financing compared with potential lower-cost solutions. Ways will be found through financial engineering to provide private entities with the advantages of the public market–risk sharing, liquidity, and pricing signals–while retaining the advantages of the private market–lower disclosure and agency costs. Financial engineering will foster the growth of the private corporation, and convert entities into alternative forms.

Many firms hedge interest rate movements, foreign currency exposures, or commodity price exposures. Firms will learn to use stock-index options or futures to reduce their risk exposures. The firm can reduce the beta of its own stock by hedging stock-market risks. Moreover, with this approach, the firm does not have to target risks. It can just hedge its own market risks or other factor risks, or the general stock-market risk that affect its stock price. This reduces the economic risks of the firm to firm-specific risks, or residual risks, and reduces the need for equity to cushion adverse outcomes.

I believe that the corporate form we know today will not be long-lived. With more knowledge and a better understanding of the power of financial engineering and of how to reduce asymmetric information costs, the costs of using financial engineering solutions will continue to fall. As more firms learn how to use these solutions, their profits will be enhanced and more investment will follow the increase in demand. Risk management is only a step in the direction of producing synthetic entities.

The firm of the future might be an organizational form far different from those used today. Some entities, such as electricity producers, aircraft manufactures and users, natural resource producers and users, and financial service firms already are deciding what services to produce and what risks to retain; what services to rent and what risks to shed, based on their perceived competitive advantage.

Financial service firms are building large capital bases to make markets around the world, and to put into practice specific knowledge to engineer solutions for their clients on a global basis and to create long-lived derivative products for issue in their own names. Their profits are made from modeling and understanding markets and providing value-added solutions for clients. A risk-management system provides information on what risks to keep and what risks to hedge. In addition, it provides a way to reduce information asymmetries between senior management and employees, and to provide the incentive system necessary to align the interests of the employees and the firm's shareholders.

A risk-management system must also address how a financial service firm handles crisis situations. To preserve its franchise, a financial service firm can insure against adverse price movements or unforeseen contingencies by holding working capital as a reserve against adverse liquidity needs. Alternatively, the financial service firm might be able to buy options from the exchange markets or from the OTC markets (for example, lines of credit) at a lower dead-weight cost to insure against extreme price movements that could adversely affect its business. Maybe regulatory bodies, in effect, provide lower cost insurance.

Because of tax and regulatory costs, financial-service firms might find that working capital held in corporate form is too expensive relative to other alternatives. For example, clients of financial service firms hold large quantities of passive wealth in mutual funds, insurance companies, pension funds, and various trusts as investment vehicles for individual savings. Financial-service firms and other entities must hold working capital to insure against adverse contingencies. With options and other forms of contingent capital arrangements, it will become possible to mobilize the capital in these client passive investment vehicles and reduce the dead-weight costs of the current system. This could lower the cost of capital of financial service firms and the cost of providing financial services to their client base.

Once again, information and financial technology will expand to reduce the costs of information asymmetries. Understanding and developing markets for credit derivatives, understanding the implications of contingent capital options under asymmetric information, and understanding what is the most efficient mechanisms to hold capital will change organizational forms, the boxes, and blur the distinctions between debt and equity, corporations and partnerships, and the demanders and suppliers of capital. The evolution of option technology will open up entire new institutional structures.

5. CONCLUSION

We started in the Past, the age of innocence, and we progressed to the Present, the age of understanding, growth, and maturation. The growth has not been without pains. A considerable amount of additional understanding and development awaits the users of the derivative technology in the Future–the age of excitement. Advances in communications and computing technology will allow for greater reduction in asymmetric information costs. The future growth of innovation using the option-pricing technology will be as great or greater than in the past. Organizational forms will change dramatically in a global environment. The exchange industry will continue to grow; the OTC industry will continue to grow, and the research necessary by academics and practitioners to understand and to foster the evolution will be so great that the academic industry will become more important than in the past. The need for highly trained and skilled practitioners that understand the technology will continue to increase on a global basis. None of these three industries has retained its past form and none will retain its present form. These economic organizational forms always will evolve and respond to the demands of economic agents.

The capital asset pricing model, arbitrage and capital structure models, and the efficient markets hypothesis introduced me to key finance concepts that were the genesis of our development of the option-pricing technology. In a world of information asymmetries, derivative instruments provide lower cost solutions to financial contracting problems in a dynamic environment and these lower-cost solutions enhance economic efficiency.

REFERENCES

Bachelier, L., 1900, "Théorie de la Spéculation", *Annales de l'Ecole Normale Supérieure,* 3, Paris: Gauthier-Villers. (English translation in Cootner, P. H., ed. The Random Character of Stock Market Prices, Cambridge, MA: MIT Press, 1964).

Banz, R.W., and M. H. Miller, 1978, "Prices for State-Contingent Claims: Some Estimates and Applications," *Journal of Business* 51, pp. 653–672.

Bernstein, P. L., 1992, *Capital Ideas: The Improbable Origins of Modern Wall Street,* New York: Free Press.

Black, F. and M. Scholes, 1973, "The Pricing of Options and Corporate Liabilities," *Journal of Political Economy,* 81, 637–654.

Black, F., and M. Scholes, 1972, "The Valuation of Option Contracts and a Test of Market Efficiency," *Journal of Finance,* May, pp. 399–417.

Black, F., M. Jensen and M. S. Scholes, 1972, "The Capital Asset Pricing Model: Some Empirical Tests," *Studies in the Theory of Capital Markets,* Edited by M. Jensen, Praeger, Inc.

Black, F., 1975, "Fact and Fantasy in the Use of Options," *Financial Analysts Journal* 31, pp. 36–41, 61–72.

Black, F., 1976, "The Pricing of Commodity Contracts." *The Journal of Financial Economics* 3, pp.167–179.

Black, F., 1989, "How We Came Up with the Option Formula." *The Journal of Portfolio Management,* Winter, pp. 4–8.

Breeden, D.T., and R. H. Litzenbeger, 1978, "Prices of State-Contingent Claims Implicit in Option Prices," *Journal of Business* 51, pp. 621–651.

Brennan, M. J., and E. S. Schwartz, 1979, "A Continuous Time Approach to the Pricing of Bonds," *Journal of Banking and Finance* 3, pp. 133–155.

Cootner, P. H. (ed.) 1964, *The Random Character of Stock Market Prices.* MIT Press.

Cox, J.C. and S.A. Ross, 1976, "The Valuation of Options for Alternative Stochastic Processes," *Journal of Financial Economics* 3, pp. 145–166.

Cox, J. C., S. A. Ross and M. Rubinstein, 1979, "Option Pricing: A Simplified Approach," *Journal of Financial Economics* 7, pp. 229–263.

Fama, E., 1965, "The Behavior of Stock Prices," *Journal of Business* 37, pp. 34–105.

Froot, K., D. Scharfstein, and J. Stein, 1993, "Risk Management: Coordinating Corporate Investment and Financing Policies," *The Journal of Finance* 48, pp. 1629–1658.

Galai, D., 1975, "Pricing of Options and the Efficiency of the Chicago Board Options Exchange, Ph.D. dissertation, University of Chicago.

Geske, R., 1979, "The Valuation of Compound Options," Journal of Financial Economics 7, pp. 63–81.

Harrison, J. M., and D. Kreps, 1979, "Martingales and Arbitrage in Multiperiod Securities Markets," *Journal of Economic Theory* 2, pp. 381–408.

Jensen, M. C. 1968, "The Performance of Mutual Funds in the Period 1945–64," *Journal of Finance* 23, pp. 389–419.

Lintner, J., 1965, "The Valuation of Risk Assets and the Selection of Risky Investments in Stock Portfolios and Capital Budgets," *Review of Economics and Statistics* 47, pp. 768–83.

Magrabe, W., 1978, "The Value of an Option to Exchange One Asset for Another," *Journal of Finance* 33, pp. 177–186.

Markowitz, H., 1952, "Portfolio Selection," *Journal of Finance* 7, pp. 77–91.

Markowitz, H., 1959, "Portfolio Selection: Efficient Diversification of Investment," New York: Wiley.

Merton, R. C., 1973, "Theory of Rational Option Pricing," *Bell Journal of Economic and Management Sciences* 4, pp. 141–83.

Merton, R.C., 1974, "On the Pricing of Corporate Debt: The Risk Structure of Interest Rates," *Journal of Finance*, 29, pp. 449–470.

Merton R.C., M. S. Scholes and M. L. Gladstein, 1978, "The Returns and Risk of Alternative Call Option Portfolio Strategies," *Journal of Business* 51, pp. 183–242.

Merton R.C., M. S. Scholes and M. L. Gladstein, 1982, "A Simulation of the Returns and Risk of Alternative Put Options Investment Strategies," *Journal of Business* 55, pp. 1–55.

Merton, R. C., 1992, "Financial Innovation and Economic Performance," *Journal of Applied Corporate Finance* 4, pp. 12–22.

Merton, R. C., 1992a, "Continuous-Time Finance," (revised edition), Cambridge, MA: Basil Blackwell.

Miller, M. H., 1988, "The Modigliani-Miller Propositions after Thirty Years," *Journal of Economic Perspectives* 2, pp. 99–120

Miller, M.H., 1997, *Merton Miller on Derivatives*, New York, N.Y.: John Wiley & Sons, Inc.

Parkinson, M., 1977, "Option Pricing: The American Put," *Journal of Business* 50, pp. 21–36.

Richard, S., 1978, "An Arbitrage Model of the Term Structure of Interest Rates," *Journal of Financial Economics* 6, pp. 33–57.

Roll, R., 1970, *The Behavior of Interest Rates: The Application of the Efficient Market Model to U.S. Treasury Bills*, Basic Books, NY.

Ross, S. A., 1976, "Options and efficiency," *Quarterly Journal of Economics* 90, pp. 75–89.

Rubinstein, M. E., 1976, "The Valuation of Uncertain Income Streams and the Pricing of Options," *Bell Journal of Economics* 7, pp. 407–425.

Samuelson, P. A. and R. C. Merton, 1969, "A Complete Model of Warrant Pricing that Maximizes Utility," *Industrial Management Review* 10, pp. 17–46.

Samuelson, P. A., 1965a, "Rational Theory of Warrant Pricing," *Industrial Management Review* 6, pp. 13–31.

Samuelson, P. A., 1965b, "Proof that Properly Anticipated Prices Fluctuate Randomly," *Industrial Management Review* 6, pp. 41–49.

Scholes, M. S., 1972, "The Market for Securities: Substitution Versus Price Pressure and the Effects of Information on Share Prices," *Journal of Business* 45, pp. 179–211.

Scholes, M. S., 1976, "Taxes and the Pricing of Options," *Journal of Finance* 31, pp. 319–32.

Scholes, M. S., and M. A. Wolfson, 1992, *Taxes and Business Strategy: A Planning Approach*, Englewood Cliffs, NJ: Prentice Hall.

Scholes, M. S., 1995, "The Future of Futures," *Risk Management Problems & Solutions,* Edited by W. H. Beaver and G. Parker, McGraw-Hill. pp. 349–369.

Scholes, M. S. 1996, "Financial Infrastructure and Economic Growth," *The Mosaic of Economic Growth,* Edited by R. Landau, Stanford, CA: Stanford University Press.

Scholes, M. S., 1996a, "Global Financial Markets, Derivative Securities and Systemic Risks," *Journal of Risk and Uncertainty* 12, pp. 271 –286.

Sharpe, W. F., 1964, "Capital Asset Pricing: A Theory of Market Equilibrium Under Conditions of Risk," *Journal of Finance* 19, pp. 425–42.

Sharpe, W.F., 1978, *Investments,* Englewood Cliffs, NJ.: Prentice Hall.

Smith, C.W., and R.M. Stulz, 1985, "The Determinants of a Firm's Hedging Policies," *Journal of Financial and Quantitative Analysis* 20, pp. 391–405.

Stulz, R. M., 1996, "Rethinking Risk Management," *Journal of Applied Corporate Finance* 9, pp. 8–24.

Vasicek, O. A., 1977, "An Equilibrium Characterization of the Term Structure," *Journal of Financial Economics* 5, pp. 177–188.